INTRODUCTION TO
Physiological psychology

INTRODUCTION TO Physiological psychology

FRANCIS LEUKEL, Ph.D.

Professor of Psychology
San Diego State College
San Diego, Calif.

With 116 illustrations

Saint Louis
THE C. V. MOSBY COMPANY
1968

Preface

This book is a text for lower-division college students. It was written originally for a course required for psychology majors and developed from a syllabus that has been used and revised each semester for five years; therefore, the content has been tested extensively for comprehension by students at that level. The course assumes that students in many upper-division psychology classes need an elementary background in physiological psychology to benefit most from their upper-division classes.

Most psychologists would agree that physiological psychology has developed rapidly in recent years and that an expanded use of physiological ideas has spread to many areas of psychology in which they were not common before. In addition to fields classically grounded in physiological ideas such as sensation, emotion, motivation, and learning, physiological discoveries have contributed to our understanding of perception, intelligence, "psychosomatic" disorders, stress, neurosis, "functional" psychoses, personality, and psychotherapy. Readers sophisticated in these fields can readily supply examples from their own experience.

It is not the purpose of this text, however, to treat these newer topics in more than a passing manner. This text attempts to prepare the student to understand physiological concepts in other specialized fields that he will encounter in his upper-division courses. The practical objective of this book is to provide a "tool course" for upper-division study in psychology. This course may be the only exposure to either physiology or physiological psychology that most students will have. The biology department in many small colleges lacks a physiologist just as the psychology department often has no physiological psychologist. The student may not have the opportunity to study either area without a text that provides limited useful background at a lower-division level, a level that he and the nonspecialist instructor may find most comfortable. Such a course and text may also aid nursing students, students of speech pathology, premedical and predental students, and others whose crowded upper-division program would otherwise preclude study of the topic.

This book makes no attempt to replace upper-division or graduate texts in physiological psychology. If supplementary readings or assignments from the reference list in the appendix were used, the book could be used for an upper-division text, but the intent was a text for lower-division students. Unlike most upper-division texts, this book does not attempt to cover all the major literature of physiological psychology. The major current *ideas* in sensation, motivation, emotion, learning, and stress are covered but usually without direct reference to authors or primary sources. The lower-division student has enough to do to learn the principles of the field. At the end of the book, reference is made by chapter number to secondary sources where references to the original literature can be found. Professional level books and review articles are cited for the instructor or more advanced student, together with original references when secondary sources were not available.

This book is organized in four sections. The two chapters of the first section, entitled The Organization of Life, introduce the field of physiological psychology and present some concepts of general physiology. The second section, entitled Integrating and Response Systems, treats elementarily the anatomy and physiology of the endocrine glands, nerves, muscles, and the nervous system. The third section, entitled The Senses, covers the topics of somesthesis, proprioception, the chemical senses, audition, and vision. The fourth section, entitled Adaptive Behavior, introduces the topics of motor organization, brain dynamics, motivation, emotion, learning, and stress. The plan of the book shows a traditional orientation with more emphasis on physiology than is usually the case for texts in the area of physiological psychology. Few behavioral applications are mentioned in early chapters, in which a minimum background in physiology is presented. I have discovered through experience that students tend to learn and remember applications at the expense of learning the physiological principles on which they are based. The applications crop up in the third and fourth sections—about three fourths of the book— hopefully after the student has enough background to apply them.

For the instructor who prefers a different orientation or topic emphasis than the one presented here, a list of inexpensive readings has been included at the end of each chapter, which are understandable for the lower-division student. An instructor who wishes to emphasize some chapters more than others can use these readings to do so. The readings may also help to provide projects such as term papers. The readings include paperbound books of a supplementary nature, *Scientific American* articles that are available as reprints, and other commercially available reprint materials. An instructor could, for example, omit the chapters on the senses and use reprints to give a more extensive treatment to the other topics. There are, of course, other possibilities for changes in emphasis.

The illustrations are simple and are closely integrated with the text.

Two difficulties are foreseen for the student, and attempts have been made to remedy them. One of these problems is acquiring a new vocabulary. A glossary for words printed in bold-faced type in the text is provided at the end of the book. The other problem for the student is generalizing from the detailed ideas presented in each chapter —making sense out of each area covered. As an aid in orienting the student, each chapter begins with an "overview" of the ideas to be covered and how these ideas will be treated. To crystallize the student's knowledge, each chapter ends with a summary.

A sincere attempt has been made to create a readable textbook at a lower-division level with a minimum loss of validity. However, omissions and distortions are unavoidable in giving the lower-division student some of the major ideas in a very complex field at his own level. In this sense, I am writing to students rather than to colleagues. If the book succeeds in reaching this audience, the credit belongs to students, from whose "naive" questions I have learned so much.

Credit is also due two of my graduate students, Barry Burns and Leonard Bonelli, who developed previously unsuspected talents of illustration in the course of assisting with the manuscript. Help has been freely given by so many other colleagues and co-workers that it is impossible to list them all here. They know who they are and how grateful I am to them.

Francis Leukel, Ph.D.

Contents

Part III The senses

Part I

The organization of life

Chapter 1

Introduction

This chapter will define the topic of physiological psychology and show how it will be treated in succeeding chapters. It is an introduction to what a physiological psychologist does. As in succeeding chapters, this one will begin with an overview— to indicate what will be discussed before going into detail—and end with a summary of what has been discussed so that the main ideas are not lost in the specific points that have been made.

OVERVIEW

Physiological psychology is psychology because it attempts to explain and predict behavior. It is physiological because it uses knowledge of how the organs and systems of the body work to predict behavior. The physiologist uses knowledge of anatomy, (structural relationships of the body), physics, chemistry, and other related fields to study how the component cells, organs, and systems of the body work. The psychologist, on the other hand, is interested in any part of this knowledge that will help him understand and predict behavior. He uses many of the methods of the anatomist, biochemist, physiologist, and other specialists, as well as psychological techniques. His goal, however, is to understand behavior rather than the systems of the body as such.

In studying physiological mechanisms in behavior the physiological psychologist must use all the tools and methods that are available. Often he must experiment with animals rather than humans since his operations involve damaging or stimulating parts of the brain. Although done in a humane fashion, such procedures cannot be used with human subjects for ethical reasons. Further, an animal may be sacrificed and studied after the experiment to locate the effects of brain damage or the site of brain stimulation. When accidents that involve brain damage occur to humans, the exact extent of the damage is often unknown and it is difficult to know what causes changes in their behavior. On the other hand, it is often risky to draw conclusions about humans from the effects of brain operations on animal behavior. As a result, physiological experiments must be interpreted with care.

PHYSIOLOGICAL APPROACH TO BEHAVIOR

All psychologists study **behavior,** but they are not the only students of people's actions. Philosophers, lawyers, sociologists, among others, also concern themselves with behavior. All use observation as a basic technique—but what differentiates scientific from nonscientific approaches, one behavioral science from another, or physiological psychologists from other psychologists?

In the first place, scientists and nonscientists are trying to answer different questions. For example, philosophers concern themselves with questions of logic, ethics, epistemology—given a set of *assumptions,* what *consequences* follow—in argument or human life? Lawyers and social workers study the behavior of individuals as applied to the way society is organized and try to improve social organizations or apply them to a *purpose.* By contrast, behavioral scientists study behavior for its own sake in an attempt to understand and predict behavior. The only assumptions they make or consequences they follow are supplied by what they observe; their intent is only to relate one behavioral event to another. Unlike nonscientific fields, behavioral sciences are usually classified by their subject matter rather than by their intent. For example, anthropologists and sociologists study cultures and groups, and individual behavior interests them only as it influences the group they are observing. Psychologists, on the other hand, are concerned with individual behavior as such, but psychologists must compare the behavior of the subjects they study with one another. Individual differences are as important as the "typical case" because individual differences define how variable the behavior becomes.

Specialties in psychology form categories defined by the kind of behavior the specialists is interested in and by the methods he uses. The psychologist may study personality, abnormal behavior, child behavior, social behavior, learning, animal behavior, and so on. Some of the more complex kinds of behavior are too unpredictable or too variable—the individual differences are too great—for a knowledge of physiological psychology to be helpful. Nothing precise enough to be useful is known, for example, of the relations between the functioning of

parts of the brain and leadership in social groups, or the development of anxiety as a result of rejection and the individual's glandular makeup. The understanding of many complex kinds of behavior is aided, however, by a knowledge of how the body—particularly the nervous system—works. Studies that relate nervous and glandular function to the areas of motivation, learning, and stress have added much to our understanding of behavior in these and other important areas.

Physiological psychology, then, relates the methods and findings of **physiology** to behavior. In so doing many fields are drawn upon: **anatomy, biochemistry,** and even physics and engineering. The **anatomist** is interested in how **organisms,** or living things, are structured. He is concerned with the structure of the differently specialized **cells,** of which the complex organism is composed, how they are organized into **tissues** of similar cells, and how different tissues are organized into **organs** and **systems.** The **biochemist** is concerned with the chemical reactions involved in the functioning of these cells, tissues, organs, and systems—the chemical reactions of life. The physiologist wants to know how all the systems of the body work—not just anatomically and biochemically, but physically as well. He makes use of the techniques of electronics, chemistry, and physics, in investigating how the cells, tissues, organs, and systems of the body function. He is interested in these phenomena for their own sake. The physiological psychologist, on the other hand, is concerned with those findings and methods of the anatomist, biochemist, physiologist, and others that will enable him to understand the behavior of the organism.

What are the mechanisms of inheritance whereby individual differences in many human behaviors can be understood? What characteristics of the nervous system **govern** learning and intelligence? What activities in the sense organs determine what we see, hear, smell, taste, and touch? What mechanisms in the brain and the glands enter into determining reactions to stress? These are only sample questions and we are far from complete answers to any of them. They serve to illustrate the fact, however, that the physiological psychologist is interested in physiology and the fields that contribute to it, mainly as they aid his understanding of human and animal behavior.

PHYSIOLOGICAL METHODS

Some of the scientific methods and techniques used by the physiological psychologist come from physiology, anatomy, and biochemistry. Other methods are more or less unique to psychology as the study of behavior. The techniques borrowed from other fields include **stimulation** of nerve tissue, electronic recording, ablation (destruction) of nervous and glandular tissue, anatomical methods, and clinical methods.

Stimulation. In learning how the brain deals with information sent to it from the sense organs via the nerves, it is often useful to bypass the sense organs and stimulate the nerves themselves or even parts of the brain. Small electrical current pulses are used since they resemble most closely the impulses initiated by sense organs in nerves going to the brain. In this way any part of the nervous system may be stimulated at will. Sometimes this is done in an animal under anesthesia when much of the nervous system must be surgically exposed to trace where the nerve impulses go. In other experiments electrodes may be permanently implanted in parts of the nervous system. The electrodes do not disturb the animal after it recovers, and the subject may be "plugged in" to stimulate a part of the nervous system while the animal is behaving normally. In some cases small tubes are planted in the brain and chemical stimuli are used.

Electronic recording techniques. Electrodes may be implanted in the nerves or brain in either a temporary or permanent fashion to record the electrical activity of nerve impulses traveling from place to place in the nerves and brain. Excitation may be traced from one part of the nervous system to another in this manner, or the response of the brain to stimulation of the sense organs can be observed in animals either anesthetized or conscious.

Ablation. Destruction of a gland or a part of the brain may be performed, followed by systematic observation of the animal's behavior after he recovers from the operation. Any deficiencies in activity, learning, or other kinds of behavior may be due to the missing structure. There are many chances for error in this technique because of the interactions of different structures. The errors possible in ablation procedure will be described as the occasion arises.

Anatomical methods. To confirm precisely where electrodes were placed for stimulation or recording during an experiment, or to determine what part of the brain was destroyed in ablation experiments, the animal must be sacrificed after the experiment ends and studied anatomically. The brain may be cut into thin slices and studied with a microscope to show exactly where an electrode was placed, or to find the limits of parts of the brain that were removed for an experiment.

Clinical methods. The experimental techniques described above have provided much information about the role of the sense organs, parts of the brain, glands, and other structures that control the behavior of typical laboratory animals such as the rat, the cat, or the monkey. The behavior of man is more complex, however, and his sensory mechanisms and brain differ in many respects from other animals. Results obtained with laboratory animals can be applied only uncertainly to man. Occasional accidents occur that cause brain damage in man, and the effects of that brain damage on behavior may be studied with various types of tests. The brain may be exposed in a conscious subject, as during surgery for a tumor, and systematically stimulated—the subject can then report his sensations and any observable responses to brain stimulation may be studied. In neither case, however, is the exact site of the damage or stimulation known; the subject cannot be "sacrificed" for study by anatomical methods (see above). In brain-damaged cases the brain may be studied much later after death from natural causes. In such instances the lesions are never precisely where we would like them to be, and many changes may have occurred since the original injury.

SUMMARY

A physiological psychologist is a scientist whose aim is to understand and predict behavior as it is controlled and regulated by the physiological systems of the body. Physiological psychology is the body of information that results from the experimental work of the physiological psychologist. To understand physiological psychology, therefore, some knowledge of how the body's physiological systems function is necessary. This study, undertaken for its own sake by the physiologist, depends partly on information and methods from the anatomist, who studies the structure of the cells, organs, and systems of the body. To talk about how a system functions, a knowledge of its structure is necessary. The physiologist and physiological psychologist also depend on information and methods taken from biochemistry (the chemical reactions of life), physics, electronics, engineering, and many other fields.

In addition to his study of behavior, the physiological psychologist uses the more physiological techniques of nerve and brain stimulation and recording in both anesthetized and awake animals, as well as ablation of tissue, and anatomical and clinical methods. Because stimulation, recording, and ablation techniques require surgery with living organisms, experiments are largely confined to laboratory animals such as the rat, cat, and the monkey. This limits conclusions about man since man's behavior and nervous system are more complex. In these experiments, however, the physiological psychologist can be quite precise about placing his electrodes for stimulation or recording. He can be sure about the location and extent of tissue ablated, because he can sacrifice the animal after the experiment and confirm his operations by anatomical study. In cases of accidental brain damage to man or of brain surgery, clinical studies can be made by observing behavior changes that result. Nevertheless, the exact locations involved in the brain are not planned and are seldom confirmed later by anatomical study. As a result, most of the data of physiological psychology come from the study of laboratory animals.

Chapter 2

Internal environment

OVERVIEW

Nearly all living matter consists of protoplasm that is organized into a unit of life —the cell. Some of the simplest forms of life consist of only a single cell, but more complex forms of life, including man, are assemblies of specialized cells. In seeking to understand how the physiology of the organism determines behavior, a beginning can be made in understanding how single cells are organized, and how their functions, including behavior, demonstrate the characteristics and organization of life. Then varieties of cell specialization will be studied to learn how complex, many-celled organisms such as man are integrated by assembling specialized cells into tissues, organs, and systems.

When cells specialize for a single function important to life, they carry on that function more efficiently, but lose part of their ability to carry on other functions necessary to life, depending on other and differently specialized cells to fulfill these functions for them. The cells of a complex organism thus become dependent on each other, or *interdependent,* and the cells "support" one another in various ways. Specialization also reduces the ability of the cell to adapt to a changing environment so that the internal environment surrounding the cells inside the body must be kept more

constant than the external environment outside the body. All the processes of the body, including behavior, are modified to that end.

Life in all cells is carried on by series of chemical reactions called metabolism. The reactions involve a class of chemical compounds called organic compounds. The reactions of metabolism either require or release energy in a balance that is maintained by automatic mechanisms in the body and by external behavior. Those chemical reactions that go on inside the cells are called cell metabolism, but the reactions that occur in the internal environment surrounding the cells are called intermediary metabolism—they are intermediary events between outside events and events in the cells. Energy exchanges between the outside world and the specialized cells are complex, but they form the basis for all behavior.

The chemical reactions of metabolism are controlled in various ways. Enzymes are compounds that control metabolism by determining the rate at which many chemical reactions occur, both inside and outside the cells. Enzymes selectively determine which needed chemical events occur in the body and when. They also determine the unique characteristics of specialized cells. In a similar way enzyme-manufacturing

7

arrangements in the cells determine hered-ity—whether the offspring is to be a man or a pig or have brown hair or blue eyes. The circulatory system has much to do with controlling intermediary metabolism since it is the major transportation system for energy exchanges between the cells and the outside world. Its most basic characteris-tics must be known before such energy exchanges can be understood. Finally, all the reactions of intermediary metabolism are directed toward maintaining a constant internal environment, an environment that must remain within narrow chemical and physical limits to support life in the spe-cialized cells. The organization of the spe-cialized cells into systems and the integrat-ing effects of the endocrine glands and nervous system are critical to maintaining homeostasis, a changing balance of events that protects the constancy of the internal environment. Organized reactions of the body to events in the external and internal

environment range from simple reflex re-actions, through inherited patterns of be-havior called instincts in lower animals, to complex learned behavior in higher animals and man—all serving to maintain life by maintaining homeostasis and a constant internal environment.

PROPERTIES OR FUNCTIONS OF CELLS

Living **protoplasm** is organized into cells, which show certain functions and charac-teristics not common to nonliving matter. The characteristics can be seen in their simplest form in organisms that consist of a single cell. Single-celled organisms are usually found in a water environment. They are one of the least specialized forms of "animal" life. Despite this, various *parts* of the single cell are specialized to carry on specific functions of life. Further spe-cialization of various parts of each cell occurs when groups of differently spe-

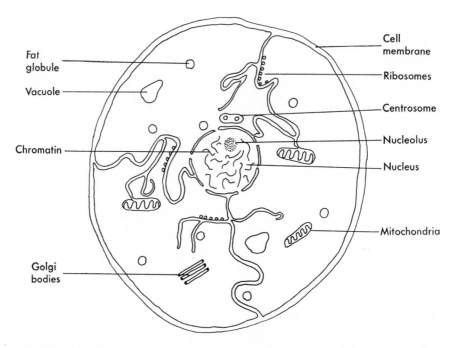

Fig. 2-1. Single cell. A semidiagrammatic sketch of a single-celled organism, showing some of its major features,

cialized cells are gathered together as many-celled organisms.

The single cell (Fig. 2-1)

To oversimplify, the cell consists of a **nucleus** surrounded by liquid **cytoplasm** that contains many **inclusions.** The **cell membrane** separates the cytoplasm of a cell from its environment. The properties of these parts of the cell enable it to carry on the activities necessary to life.

Functions or characteristics of cells

The diverse activities carried on by the single cell, including its reaction to stimulation, demonstrate the basic characteristics of life and show what part or parts of the cell are most important in carrying out each cell function.

Irritability (Fig. 2-2). When the cell is stimulated by a drop of acid, it reacts by changing shape to avoid the stimulus, thrusting out a **pseudopod** (false foot) and moving away. Among other things this demonstrates that the cell is sensitive to the acid, or is irritable to this form of **stimulus.** The cells in man that are specialized for **irritability** are found in the **sense organs.** Specialization for irritability has gone so far in man that some cells are most irritable or sensitive to **photic** stimuli (vision), **chemical** stimuli (taste, smell), **temperature** (warmth, cold), or **mechanical** stimuli (touch or pressure, hearing). From the independent cell to the most specialized cell, irritability persists as a property of the cell membrane. Such irritability is based on a property of the cell membrane called **selective permeability.** This means that the cell membrane passes some substances into the interior of the cell and excludes others. Stimulation alters this

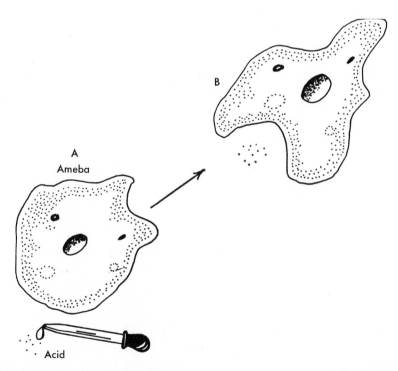

A
Ameba

B

Acid

Fig. 2-2. Reaction of a single-celled organism to an irritating stimulus. See text for explanation.

state of affairs and results in an electrical change in the membrane (Chapter 4), which signals the effect of the stimulus on the cell.

Conduction. As Fig. 2-2 demonstrates, stimulation initiated a change in the shape of the cell; the excitation must have been conducted from one part of the cell to the other. **Conduction** is also a property of the cell membrane. It is a continuation of the electrical change noted previously, a change that sweeps over the entire membrane of the cell. Conduction is most highly developed in the cells of man's nervous system, probably the most specialized cells of the human body. Nerve cells conduct excitation from one part of the body to another so that more widespread responses to a local stimulus may occur.

Contraction. The ability of the cell to change shape is **contraction,** as shown by the movement of the single cell away from the drop of acid. Contraction is a property of the cytoplasm of the cell and certain of its inclusions. It is most highly developed in the muscle cells of man. Threadlike inclusions running the length of each muscle cell shorten to reduce the length of muscles and move the bony levers of the body to which they are attached.

Secretion. The property of other types of cell inclusions is called **secretion.** It is carried on to provide substances manufactured in the cell from raw materials provided by the environment, substances necessary to the chemistry of life. Secretion is most highly developed by the cells that form **glands** in man. The glands secrete substances that aid in digesting food or organizing bodily changes. Glands are of two types in man: (1) **duct glands,** mostly digestive, which have tubes to carry the secretion to its site of action, and (2) **ductless glands,** or **endocrine glands,** which secrete substances into the bloodstream for more widespread effects over the body. Together with the conducting cells of the nervous system, the secretions of ductless glands aid in coordinating cell activity all over the body. For example, the adrenal glands secrete a substance into the bloodstream in emergencies, which increases heart rate and blood pressure, and performs other functions that organize the body for physical exertion. Ductless glands are therefore both an integrating system and a response system.

Elimination. The process by which the cell rids itself of waste products is **elimination.** It is a joint property of cell inclusions that filter out the waste material and the cell membrane that passes it to the environment. Cells specialized in this function are found in the kidney in man, where they form urine. Although all cells rid themselves of waste products, kidney cells are specialized in clearing the blood of the accumulated wastes from other cells.

Growth. **Growth** may be viewed either as an increase in the size of a single-celled organism or as an increase in the number of cells in a many-celled (multicellular) organism. When a single cell reaches a limiting size, it divides into two cells, a process called cell **mitosis,** an "unspecialized" form of cell **reproduction.** The cells in a multicellular organism likewise reproduce themselves to increase the size of each specialized part of the body during growth and to replace worn-out cells throughout life. However, reproduction of a whole new multicellular organism is a specialized function carried on by specialized cells. In either case the controlling mechanisms for reproduction are found in the cell nucleus.

Reproduction. Cell mitosis, as controlled by the nucleus, is the mechanism for cell reproduction after the single independent cell reaches a limiting size (Fig. 2-3). The cell nucleus divides along with the rest of the cell and so do specialized structures in the nucleus, the **genes.** The genes are DNA molecules contained in the chromosomes (colored bodies) of the cell nucleus. These molecules are "patterns" for manufacturing

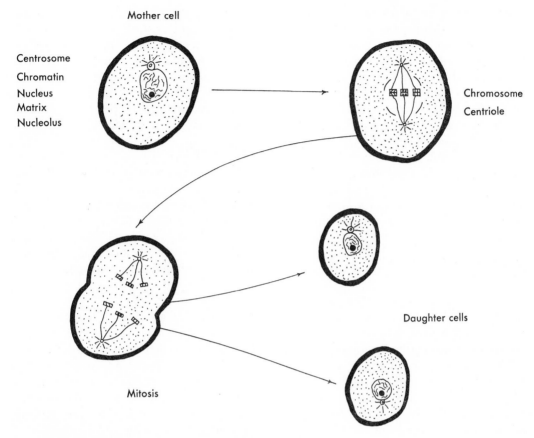

Mother cell

Centrosome
Chromatin
Nucleus
Matrix
Nucleolus

Chromosome
Centriole

Daughter cells

Mitosis

Fig. 2-3. Cell division, or mitosis. For details, see text.

each part of the two new cells. In man each specialized cell reproduces in a similar way, and the two new cells show the same specialized characteristics as the old cell. More complex sexual reproduction of a completely new multiple-celled organism is a still more specialized function of reproductive structures, the gonads. Each reproductive cell carries a "code" for the complete organism. One cell is contributed by the female and the other by the male, and they unite to form a single new cell in a manner so that each contributes some unique characteristics to the new organism. As this single cell multiplies, the "code" in the genes of its nucleus determines whether the resulting organism will be a pig or a man, have blue or brown eyes, etc.

Metabolism. All the functions of the cell require energy. This energy is supplied by a complex series of chemical processes called **metabolism.** Basically, metabolism involves breaking down foodstuffs (fat, proteins, and carbohydrates) into forms that the cell can utilize for energy or for part of its chemical structure. Energy for the chemical reactions of life is derived from processes such as **oxidation,** a chemical reaction similar to a fire. In this reaction oxygen combines with food to release energy and heat. The reactions of the body are like burning food since they require the same raw materials and release similar waste products. Burning a food gives a measure of heat released, the **calorie,** and indirectly gives a measure of the energy value of that food to the body. (Those on diets know if this energy is not utilized in exercise, the body utilizes it in building up fat deposits!) In a complex organism such as man, food is converted into blood sugar (**glucose**), which the specialized cells use as a foodstuff. To oversimplify, glucose combines with the oxygen we breathe to form carbon dioxide (released from the blood to the lungs before we exhale), heat to keep our body temperature up, waste, and water that is eliminated by the kidney and through perspiration, and, finally, about 20% useful energy to "power" the chemical reactions of life.

VARIETIES OF CELL SPECIALIZATION

The increased specialization and complexity of multicellular organisms resulted from **evolution** according to the principles of **random variation** and **natural selection.**

The characteristics of organisms are determined by genes in the reproductive cells of the sexual apparatus. Ordinarily immune to change by the environment, these genes are altered by natural and artificial radioactivity from cosmic rays of the sun, atomic explosions, x-rays, and other "natural" causes. This results in occasional organisms with novel characteristics, or **mutations.** In addition, a common physical characteristic (such as the length of a giraffe's neck) will vary randomly in the population. Both sets of events result in random variation in the physical characteristics of a species of animal.

Usually, new or extreme characteristics are unrelated to, or impair, survival, in the competition between species for food supplies, space, and other necessities. Occasionally a new characteristic may aid survival—early giraffes with long necks could perhaps reach more tree leaves and therefore more food. The animal with the new or extreme characteristic may survive better and produce more offspring than his fellows. Natural selection thus prevails and

the animals with the new characteristic are "selected" for survival. The new characteristic becomes more and more common among offspring as it is inherited from the larger number of surviving animals—those with the new and useful trait. Cell specialization and interdependence have resulted from just such influences.

Cell colonies

Cell colonies were probably the first step toward cell specialization. Clumping together of otherwise independent cells must have had survival value among some cell species. This was a necessary first step toward cell specialization and interdependence in **multicellular organisms.**

Tissue specialization

A tissue is a group of cells similarly specialized to perform a common function. Thus all the cells of muscle tissue are specialized alike for contraction, receptor tissue cells for irritability, nerve tissue for conduction, glandular tissue for secretion, etc. Specialized muscle cells were probably evolved first in multicellular organisms to improve mobility through efficient contracting cells. Then receptor tissue specialized to make organisms more sensitive to events in the environment. Receptor cells connected directly with muscle cells so that rapid response to such events could occur. Then nerve tissue evolved to connect receptor and **effector** (muscle and gland) cells, permitting more widespread and coordinated responses to stimuli. In man, many other types of specialized tissue are found, such as bone, cartilage, connective tissue, and vascular (blood vessel) tissue.

Organ specialization

An organ is a collection of differently specialized tissues, organized for the performance of common general function. It represents a further step in specialization and a new level of dependence of differently specialized tissues on each other.

Each tissue has a different role in the overall function of the organ. For example, the stomach is a digestive organ. It is made up of connective tissue that holds it together, vascular (blood vessel) tissue to nourish it, glandular tissue to provide digestive secretions, muscle tissue to mix the food and move it into the rest of the digestive tract, etc. Other examples of organs in the body include the brain (nervous), heart (circulatory), kidney (elimination), eye (receptor), pituitary gland (endocrine), and gonads (reproductive). In each case differently specialized tissues are integrated to perform a function that a single kind of tissue would perform less efficiently.

System specialization

The highest level of integration in the body for performance of still more general functions is a system. A system consists of several organs, each of which has a limited role in the overall performance of the system. For example, the digestive system consists largely of the following organs: oral apparatus, esophagus, stomach, small and large intestines, liver, and kidneys. The general function of the system is to assimilate food, transform it into a state the body can use, store it, and eliminate that which the body cannot use. Each organ has a role in that general function; for example, the oral appartus and esophagus specialize in ingestion, the stomach and intestines in digestion, the liver in storage, and the kidneys in elimination. The nervous system has nerves to carry excitation to and from the receptors and effectors, brain centers to make connections between incoming and outgoing excitation, etc. All serve the general function of carrying excitation from one part of the body to another so that response to internal and external events can occur. The circulatory system carries nourishment and removes waste with the heart as a pumping organ, the arteries, veins, capillaries, and lymph vessels as pipelines, and so on.

INTEGRATION OF THE COMPLEX ORGANISM: HOMEOSTASIS

As cells are organized into tissues, organs, and systems, they become more specialized to perform certain functions. At the same time they lose part of their ability to carry on other functions necessary for life and depend on other tissues, organs, and systems to carry on these functions for them. Increased interdependence among cells results. Specialized cells are also less able to adapt to changes in their environment than are independent cells. The internal environment that surrounds the cells inside the body must be more constant than that of independent cells. An independent cell, living in seawater, can tolerate wider variations in salinity (saltiness), temperature, sugar of food content, and fluid pressure of the environment compared to a specialized cell in the body. The physical and chemical conditions that surround a specialized cell in the human body must be more constant because the cell has lost its ability to cope with environmental changes. Many conditions must be kept within narrow limits inside the body to ensure the survival of its cells. The internal environment therefore is much more constant than is the external environment. Organization of the varied activities of the body becomes essential so that (1) the needs of functionally specialized tissues may be met by other tissues specialized in meeting such needs and (2) conditions inside the body are relatively constant in the face of varied cell activities inside the body and fluctuations in the external environment.

Integration

Activities in one part of the body are coordinated with activities in other parts of the body. A high degree of organization is necessary to permit the degree of interdependence shown by the many diverse cells, tissues, and organs. Organization is also necessary to maintain a constant internal environment in the face of an external environment that varies widely in temperature, food supply, and other factors. The integration of bodily activity required is carried out in three major ways: (1) the organization of tissues and organs into systems provides some coordination for a single general function such as digestion or circulation; (2) some coordination is supplied by the endocrine glands, whose secretions are carried all over the body in the bloodstream to affect widely scattered tissues in a consistent fashion; and (3) the nervous system is completely devoted to coordinating the many diverse functions of the other organs and systems of the body. Potentially, activity in nearly any part of the body can stimulate changed activity in any other part of the body since they are linked by conduction via the nervous system.

When tissues and organs are organized into systems, the many steps in carrying out a complex activity take place in proper sequence. For example, in the digestive system salivary glands in the mouth begin the process of food breakdown, the stomach mixes the result and stores it, the small intestine secretes substances to complete digestion, the liver manufactures and stores blood sugar, and the kidneys and large intestine store and eliminate the waste. The circulatory system includes a pump (the heart), pipelines (arteries) to the lungs (for air), arteries running all over the body, capillaries with thin walls to release nutrition and oxygen and recover carbon dioxide and waste in exchange with the fluid environment of the cells, and veins to return the blood to the heart.

The systems of the body are coordinated in part by the endocrine glands. Under conditions of stress, for example, the adrenal glands release a secretion into the bloodstream. This secretion increases the heart rate, breathing rate, muscle tension, and blood sugar to prepare the body for vigorous activity in the face of an emergency. The sequence of body changes in

pregnancy and childbirth are controlled by other endocrine glands. The changes that occur in puberty, or sexual maturity, are also largely under the control of the endocrine system.

The nervous system, however, is the most important integrating factor in a complex organism. Every stimulus in the external environment initiates changes in the internal environment. A drop in external temperature starts a drop in internal temperature, sudden physical exertion depletes the food (glucose) and oxygen (air) content within the body. Diverse cells, tissues, organs, and systems must react all over the body to keep the internal environment relatively constant so that the specialized cells can survive. Each change in the external and/or internal environment makes rapid reactions all over the body necessary so that the internal environment may be held within the limits that permit life. External and internal changes are detected by sense organs reacting to conditions outside and inside the body. The nervous system conducts impulses from sense organs all over the body to effectors (muscles and glands) so that the proper tissue, organ, or system reactions will occur to maintain the constancy of the internal environment.

Every change in the external and/or internal environment tends to alter internal conditions from those needed by the specialized cells for adequate functioning and survival, that is **functional integrity**. The organized reactions of the body to change maintain a *balance* among the often conflicting requirements posed by the needs of the varied cells. Such reactions are classed as homeostatic reactions and their end result is homeostasis, a dynamic equilibrium (changing balance) that maintains conditions in the internal environment within the limits that each cell requires for functional integrity.

Homeostatic responses to environmental change involve relatively simple reflex responses, **instinctive reactions** (in lower animals), and complex **learned reactions** (in higher animals or man). For example, a drop in the external temperature sets off a variety of reflex responses: (1) the heart will beat faster to provide food and oxygen and remove wastes, sustaining a higher level of metabolism throughout the body that produces heat; (2) muscle cells will contract in bursts (shivering) to produce heat while breathing will be faster to supply more oxygen; and (3) blood will be diverted from blood vessels near the surface of the body to keep it from being chilled.

Lower animals inherit complex response patterns that react to cold stresses; for example, a rat will build a nest for insulation from the cold, or a bear will reduce its body requirements and sleep (hibernation) in reaction to seasonal cold. Complex adaptive homeostatic responses of this kind are called instincts and may occur without prior learning. Man, however, acquires the complex adaptive responses called for—he *learns* to put on a coat, light a fire, and otherwise adapt to changed conditions.

The stresses imposed by a changing environment are often conflicting—to react to one stress imposes another; to adapt to one internal **need** imbalances homeostasis in another fashion. If an animal reflexly reacts to a low water supply by reducing its output of urine and perspiration, the needs of the body for removing wastes and keeping cool may be imperiled. In instances of this kind the more pressing homeostatic demands of the body are given precedence; minimum water is provided to remove waste and cool the body since death would result from a large change in these conditions more rapidly than from thirst. Homeostasis is thus a compromise among constantly changing and often conflicting stresses imposed by the environment. Homeostatic reactions are organized responses of the organism, ranging from simple reflexes to complex learned reactions; these responses tend to keep the internal environment constant enough to maintain the functional integrity of the cells of the body.

METABOLISM OF CELLS
Cell metabolism versus intermediary metabolism

Despite their specialization, the cells of the body must obtain the food and oxygen necessary for life from their environment inside the body (the internal environment). They must also eliminate their accumulated wastes via this environment. The activities of the individual cell that are involved in transforming food and oxygen into cellular structure and eliminating waste from the cell are called **cell metabolism.** These activities are complex chemical reactions that go on inside the cells. The chemical reactions involve simple chemical "food" compounds—glucose or blood sugar, amino acids, fatty acids, minerals, and oxygen—that have been broken down from more complex compounds in **intermediary metabolism.** Intermediary metabolism refers to the chemical reactions that go on outside the cells, where the fats, proteins, and carbohydrates used by the body as food are broken down into the simple compounds specialized cells can use, and where cellular waste is transformed for removal from the bloodstream.

Chemical reaction in cells

The individual specialized cells of the body obtain predigested food material and oxygen from the internal environment of **extracellular fluid** (the fluid that surrounds all cells). These raw materials are utilized in rebuilding the structure of the cell and in supplying the chemical energy to power the reactions necessary, including waste elimination from the cell.

Organic compounds. The raw materials used by the cell come from a class of chemical compounds called **organic compounds.** These compounds have in common a chemical structure built of long "chains" of carbon (C) atoms that form a "skeleton" to which other atoms and molecules are attached as a "superstructure." The attached atoms and molecules include hydrogen (H) and oxygen (O) atoms and hydroxyl (OH) and amino (NH$_2$) molecules (N is nitrogen). For example, the structure of the amino acid glycine could be diagrammed as follows:

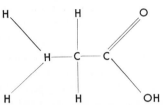

The raw materials used by the cell, the complex compounds from which they are derived in intermediary metabolism, and the structure of the cell itself are all organic compounds. The cell, in the reactions of cell metabolism, uses (1) **fatty acids** derived by intermediary metabolism from **fats,** (2) **amino acids** derived from **proteins,** and (3) glucose derived from these and from **carbohydrates.** Small amounts of **minerals** (potassium, calcium, and sodium) and **vitamins** are likewise needed. Fats, proteins, and minerals need no introduction. Carbohydrates are sugars and starches, and vitamins will be discussed later.

Anabolism and catabolism. The chemical reactions necessary to rebuild cellular structure and eliminate cellular waste require energy. Metabolic reactions that require energy input to proceed are collectively known as **anabolism.** The necessary energy is supplied by other chemical reactions that release energy, collectively known as **catabolism.** All organic chemical reactions either require or give off energy, that is, they are either catabolic or anabolic. Together they include all the chemical reactions of the body as metabolism.

The cell as a chemical factory. Thus considered, the cell is a "chemical factory" in which the energy for each anabolic reaction is obtained from catabolic reactions. Each time a complex compound is broken down into a simpler one, energy is released and used to rebuild other complex compounds needed by the cell. The complex compounds are made from building blocks such as amino acids and fatty acids; glucose is the basic energy source used. Although most of the twenty-two amino acids that the body uses are broken down from proteins in intermediary metabolism, there are ten **essential amino acids** that must be part of the diet because the body cannot manufacture them. There are likewise three **essential fatty acids** that cannot be made from fats in the diet. Small amounts of minerals—sodium, potassium, and calcium— are supplied by the diet in the form of salts. Vitamins are required to speed certain chemical reactions of life, and glucose is supplied from the carbohydrate of the diet. The cell assembles amino acids into the proteins that form the building blocks of its structure and constructs its fats from fatty acids. Glucose provides the basic energy source by catabolic reaction as it is broken down into lactic acid, which is eliminated from the body.

INTERMEDIARY METABOLISM

The food intake of the body consists of the fats, proteins, carbohydrates, essential amino and fatty acids, minerals, and vitamins. Taken in through the alimentary canal and combined with oxygen carried by the blood vessels from the lungs, these substances undergo the many chemical reactions of life referred to, collectively, as metabolism. Before the cell can utilize such raw materials, they must be broken down in a series of discrete steps into forms usable by the cells. The chemical reactions necessary to prepare raw materials for the cells are referred to as intermediary metabolism.

Oxidation

The many complex chemical reactions of intermediary and cell metabolism utilize the same raw material and liberate the same kind of wastes that would be involved in burning the raw material in a fire, a form of oxidation. The potential energy of a fat, protein, or carbohydrate can thus be expressed as a fraction of the energy released as heat by burning that food. The food is provided by the alimentary canal and the oxygen by the lungs. The kidneys dispose of wastes, and, together with the sweat glands and respiration, eliminate water and carbon dioxide. A simplified form of the basic equation would be as follows:

$$\text{Food} + \text{Oxygen} \longrightarrow \text{Energy} + \text{Heat}$$
$$+ \text{Waste} + \text{Carbon dioxide} + \text{Water}$$

The arrow includes hundreds of chemical reactions involved in the intermediary and cell metabolism of the body. Nevertheless, the input raw materials and output results are the same. The body is able to utilize about 20% of the potential energy of food, and the rest is given off as heat. A portion of the heat is used to keep the temperature of the body (internal environment) constant in the face of fluctuations in the (usually) colder external environment. The 20% efficiency of the body may be compared to that of a heat-operated steam engine (15%) or a gasoline motor (10%). The energy value of a food can thus be measured as a fraction of the heat that would be released by burning the food. The unit involved is the calorie—the amount of heat required to raise the temperature of one gram of water one degree centigrade. The more work done by the body, the greater the number of calories of food and volumes of oxygen required, so that one needs to eat more before or after exercise, as well as breathe harder to obtain more oxygen during strenuous activity.

The basic food that is "burned" by cells is glucose, which may be formed in intermediary metabolism from either fats, proteins, or carbohydrates. Fatty acids and amino acids are needed for cellular structure, but they cannot be derived from carbohydrates. Fatty acids are derived from fats and amino acids from proteins, but carbohydrates lack the essential NH_2 molecule to form amino acids and oxygen (O) and carboxyl (COOH) molecules to form fatty acids. These facts have important consequences for metabolism. The Japanese have plenty of carbohydrates, but were stunted for many generations from lack of amino acids and vitamins for cell building in their diet. The Eskimos, on the other hand, remained vigorous in the face of a hostile environment, living on fats and proteins from which they obtained cell-building amino and fatty acids as well as breaking these substances down into glucose to power the reactions of the body.

Respiratory quotient

The great majority of the metabolic reactions of the body depend upon glucose, and glucose is more readily made from carbohydrate than from fats or proteins. This difference in efficiency is mirrored in the **respiratory quotient (RQ)**, a measure of how completely fat, protein, and carbohydrate are **oxidized** in the body (see previous equation). The RQ is the ratio of the volume of carbon dioxide (CO_2) given off by the lungs to the volume of oxygen (O_2) taken up by the lungs in normal respiration and is expressed as CO_2/O_2. The larger the respiratory quotient, the more complete the oxidation of the foodstuff. For example, on a pure fat diet the ratio is 0.7; on a protein diet, 0.8; and on a carbohydrate diet, 1.0 ("complete" oxidation). The difference lies in the extra carboxyl molecule of fat and amino molecule of protein that are not completely utilized.

Basal metabolism

Refer again to the basic oxidation equation of metabolism given previously. It should be evident that when energy is required at a greater rate by the body, more oxygen is utilized and more carbon dioxide is given off by the body. The overall rate at which metabolism is going on in the body can therefore be measured by the oxygen intake or carbon dioxide given off in breathing. Usually oxygen intake is measured with the subject breathing air (20% oxygen) from a measured container. When the subject exercises, he breathes harder— his metabolic rate and oxygen intake are higher because the reactions of metabolism are proceeding faster. When the subject is resting and not digesting food (a process requiring energy), an estimate of his minimum waking rate of metabolism is obtained, the **basal metabolic rate,** or BMR (the metabolic rate is lower during sleep). The BMR is an important measure of the functioning of the body. It is used to test the activity of the thyroid gland (Chapter 3), whose secretions regulate the metabolic rate of the body.

Energy exchange

The digestive system must break down fat, protein, and carbohydrate into glucose to be used by the cells and must store any excess glucose in a different form to be released into the bloodstream as the cells require it. In addition, cells must store energy by "packaging" it, by building complex compounds of simpler ones (anabolism). Energy is thus readily available; the complex "packages" may be broken down into simpler ones (catabolism), releasing energy for the cells to utilize in building the proteins and fats they require.

Glucose is stored by the liver and muscles in the form of **glycogen** and released

as required to keep the concentration of blood glucose for the cells within narrow limits so that food for the cells is always available. This set of reactions occurs in intermediary metabolism. In cell metabolism the **energy-rich phosphate bond** is the chief source of energy-releasing chemical reactions that "drive" other reactions inside the cell. Such bonds hold the parts of an increasingly complex compound together. Glucose is broken down into lactic acid as it is oxidized to "power" the transformation of **adenylic acid (AA)** into **adenosine diphosphate (ADP)** and thence to **adenosine triphosphate (ATP).** This series of reactions stores great amounts of energy with the addition of each phosphate bond, energy which can be bound as **creatine phosphate (CP).** Reversing these steps releases energy for use by the cell in anabolic reactions.

Carbohydrate metabolism

The basic oxidation equation given previously may now be combined with the notions of glycogen storage in the liver and energy storage in phosphate bonds to show an oversimplified picture of *carbohydrate metabolism*—how carbohydrates, fats, and proteins are broken down into glucose. The glucose is then used for (1) energy storage inside the cell in phosphate bonds, (2) food storage in the liver and muscles as glycogen, and (3) energy release in catabolism during cellular activity. The reactions given are descriptive rather than exact—many energy exchanges are "telescoped," omitted, or distorted. All the reactions are reversible as shown by the double arrows in the following equation:

$$AA \rightleftharpoons ADP \rightleftharpoons ATP \rightleftharpoons CP \text{ (energy storage—cells)}$$
$$\big\Updownarrow$$
$$O_2 + \text{Carbohydrate} \rightleftharpoons \text{Glucose} \rightleftharpoons \text{Glycogen (food storage—liver)}$$
$$\left. \begin{array}{l} O_2 + \text{Fat} \rightleftharpoons \text{Fatty acid} \\ O_2 + \text{Protein} \rightleftharpoons \text{Amino acid} \end{array} \right\} \rightleftharpoons \text{Pyruvic acid} \rightleftharpoons \text{Lactic acid} + CO_2 + H_2O \text{ (oxidation)}$$

Although glucose is directly formed from carbohydrate, fats and proteins must be broken down first into pyruvic acid before they can be made into glucose. Glucose breakdown can be used for the energy needed to form energy-rich creatine phosphate, which is later broken down by the cells, releasing new energy to power other reactions. Excess glucose is stored as glycogen in the liver. Anabolic reactions are powered by the catabolic oxidation of glucose into pyruvic acid and thence to lactic acid for elimination by the kidneys, CO_2 eliminated by the lungs, and water eliminated by the lungs, kidney, and sweat glands.

CONTROL OF METABOLISM BY ENZYMES

Every needed chemical reaction in the body must go on at a minimum rate to provide the necessary energy, structure, and food for the cells. The rate at which chemical reactions can proceed often depends on **enzymes.** Many reactions are reversible; which way the reaction goes depends upon enzymes. The presence of enzymes may determine which of several alternate reactions occur. Enzymes are organic **catalysts** for the chemical reactions involved in metabolism. Catalysts are chemicals that speed up the rate at which chemical reactions go on without being used up in the reactions. Only minute amounts are needed, and since they are not consumed by the reactions they speed, catalysts can be utilized over and over again to catalyze (speed up) the same reaction. The presence or absence of given catalysts, then, may decide the *direction* (anabolic or catabolic) of a reaction or which of several *alternate* reactions may occur or *selectively* speed up various metabolic reactions, according to which enzymes are present.

"Pattern theory" of enzyme action

An **enzyme system** is a complicated molecule made of a large protein **apoenzyme** and a smaller nonprotein **coenzyme** (or "prosthetic group"). The enzyme acts as a catalyst only when the two molecules are combined into an enzyme system. The complex "shape" of the enzyme system molecule then "fits" the shape of the **substrate** compound molecule whose reactions it catalyzes, just as one piece in a jigsaw puzzle piece fits another. If a compound is to be broken down, it fits the enzyme system in a way that places a "strain" on the molecular bonds to be broken in, making two simpler compounds out of a complex compound. If two molecules are to be put together, they both fit on the enzyme molecule, so aligned as to make the proper connections. **Enzyme inhibitors,** or **antienzymes,** are also involved in the reactions of the body. These are substances whose molecular shape is similar enough to the substrate to "take over" the enzyme molecules by fitting onto them so that the substrate molecules cannot do so. Enzyme inhibitors prevent the reactions that enzymes would otherwise catalyze from occurring at a useful rate.

Vitamins

Some vitamins appear to be coenzymes that cannot be manufactured by the cells of the body. They must be supplied in minute amounts in the diet to form part of essential enzyme systems. Before the discovery of their role, deficiency symptoms from lack of vitamins were common in certain areas or under diet conditions. Beriberi with lassitude, paralysis, and convulsive reactions was once common in the Far East because of the lack of vitamin B_1— the native ate polished rice and the B_1 was lost with the shell of the rice. Scurvy was once common in the British navy from lack of fresh fruit, which did not keep on ships, until the "limeys" learned to carry lime juice to prevent it. Vitamins are classified as water-soluble or fat-soluble for lack of a better basis. Table 2-1 lists the more important vitamins, together with their

Table 2-1. Summary of the major facts about vitamins, indicating their mode of action and the symptoms of vitamin deficiency*

Vitamins	Deficiency symptoms	Biochemical and physiological action
Fat-soluble		
Vitamin A (activated carotinoids)	"Night-blindness"; xerophthalmia, a dry condition and infection around the eyes; growth failure	Plays a role in photochemical processes; is stored in liver; other roles implied but not known
Vitamin D (calciferol or irradiated ergosterol, also irradiated cholesterol)	Rickets, a deficiency in bone calcification, leading to misshapen bones and defective teeth	Facilitates bone calcification and absorption of calcium and phosphorus from intestine; may be important in phosphorylating enzyme systems
Vitamin E	Sterility; degeneration of spermatogenic tissue in male; resorption of fetus in pregnant female	May play role in regulating biological oxidations
Vitamin K	Hemorrhages, caused by failure of blood to clot normally	Necessary for production of prothrombin, which is essential for blood clotting
Water-soluble		
Thiamine (B_1)	Beriberi in humans, polyneuritis in animals; both characterized by paralysis starting in hind limbs and slowed heart rate; hyperirritability and convulsions in severe cases	In phosphate form is coenzyme of pyruvate carboxylase, which is required in carbohydrate metabolism for catalysis of pyruvic acid breakdown; action inhibited by pyrithiamin and related compounds
Riboflavin (B_2)	Skin lesions around mouth, cataracts, blindness	Prosthetic group for different apoenzymes catalyzing oxidation-reduction reactions; inhibited by isoriboflavin; galactoflavin, and related compounds
Pyridoxine (B_6)	Rat dermatitis; fits in dogs, rats, and pigs	Important in several reactions concerned with amino acid metabolism, transamination, and decarboxylation, and other reactions; inhibited by deoxypyridoxine under some conditions
Niacin (nicotinic acid and nicotinamide) (B group)	Pellagra, characterized by one or all of following: dermatitis, gastrointestinal symptoms, and nervous symptoms such as anxiety, confusion, dementia	Required for synthesis of active component of coenzymes I and II, which function as hydrogen acceptors in some dehydrogenases in biological oxidations; inhibited by 3-acetylpyridine
Pantothenic acid (B group)	Graying of hair and dermatitis in rats	Important in general protein metabolism
Biotin (vitamin H; B group?)	Loss of appetite; muscle aches and fatigue in man	Concerned in carboxylation reactions
Inositol (B group)	Fatty liver	Unspecified role in fat metabolism
Para-aminobenzoic acid (B group)	Graying of hair in rats	Nature of action undetermined; probably concerned in synthesis of methionine, purines, and other compounds; sulfanilamide antagonizes its action

*From Mitchell, P. H.: A textbook of biochemistry, New York, 1946, McGraw-Hill Book Co., pp. 148-155.

Table 2-1. Summary of the major facts about vitamins, indicating their mode of action and the symptoms of vitamin deficiency—cont'd

Vitamins	Deficiency symptoms	Biochemical and physiological action
Water-soluble—cont'd		
Choline (vitamin?) (B group)	Fatty liver (under some circumstances)	Promotes phospholipid production; aids synthesis of creatine and methionine; important as methyl group donor in metabolism
Vitamin C (ascorbic acid)	Scurvy, hemorrhages of skin and mucous membranes; loss of rigidity of bones and elasticity of muscles	Affects enzymes in vitro; no conclusion on mechanism in vivo; promotes oxygen uptake and hydrogen transfer; inhibited by glucoascorbic acid
Vitamin P (citrin)	Capillary hemorrhages	Closely associated with vitamin C

sources and deficiency symptoms. It can readily be seen that the average diet includes them all, at least in the minute amounts necessary.

Hormones

Hormones are substances manufactured by the ductless or endocrine glands and secreted into the bloodstream, effecting metabolism all over the body. (The endocrine system is one of the most important integrating systems of the body and will be treated at length in Chapter 3.) The effect of hormones is selective; they act only on certain metabolic reactions in selected tissues. It appears that some hormones are enzyme inhibitors—they block certain metabolic reactions to allow competing metabolic reactions to proceed. Other hormones seem to act on the DNA or RNA molecules of cells to alter the way they govern cell function by these and other means; hormones control growth, general metabolic rate, sexual and pregnancy processes, and the metabolism of many chemicals vital to normal metabolism and behavior.

Genes, enzyme action, cell metabolism, and heredity

The nucleus of each cell in the human body contains 23 pairs of **chromosomes,** 46 in all. One of each pair of chromosomes is inherited from one parent, the other chromosome coming from the other parent. Each chromosome contains genes, complex chemicals that determine the organism's inherited characteristics. Genes also determine the particular specialization of each cell in the organism and the metabolic processes that go on within that cell. Each chromosome contains perhaps 3000 genes, and each gene is responsible for determining one or more of the characteristics of the cell. Genes are made up of a chemical called DNA (deoxyribonucleic acid), and the DNA molecule looks like a twisted ladder (Fig. 2-4), with pairs of amino acids forming the steps of the ladder. When a cell divides to reproduce itself, the chromosomes and genes also divide, leaving two spiral "half-ladders" for each gene. Each of the two new cells thus contain 46 "half-chromosomes" containing thousands of "half-DNA" molecules. Each half-ladder of DNA forms a pattern to assemble the other half from raw materials that are readily available in the new cell. Thereby each gene reproduces itself in cell division. The specialized characteristics of the new cells are the same as those of the old cell.

The specialized features of a cell depend on the type and quantity of the proteins that are the building blocks of that cell, proteins the cells itself manufactures. The

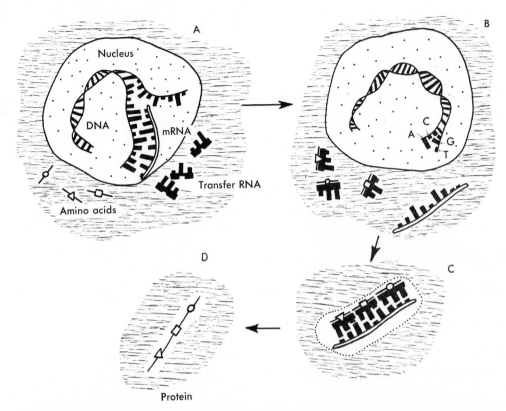

Fig. 2-4. Sequence of events in the manufacture of an enzyme by the cell. In **A** the DNA molecule "divides" to form a messenger RNA (mRNA) molecule on part of its structure. The sequence of amino acids on the DNA molecule *(A, C, G,* and *T* labelled in **B)** determine the shape of the RNA molecule that is assembled. In **B** the mRNA has left the cell nucleus. In **C** the mRNA is assembling transfer RNA in a cell inclusion, called a ribosome, by serving as a template for the amino acid sequence of the transfer RNA molecule. The transfer RNA, in turn, is assembling three amino acids (represented by the triangle, square, and circle) into a protein enzyme. In **D** the enzyme has left the ribosome to catalyze a chemical reaction in another part of the cell.

synthesis of cell proteins is controlled by the sequence of molecules in the DNA of its genes; some cells use one part of the DNA molecule to specialize as skin cells, others use another part to specialize as liver cells. The DNA molecule synthesizes a **messenger RNA** (mRNA) molecule on part of its structure (Fig. 2-4). The messenger RNA moves out of the nucleus of the cell to cell inclusions in the cytoplasm called **ribosomes**, which also contain RNA. Here the messenger RNA acts as a pattern for a third kind of RNA, called **transfer RNA.** An amino acid molecule is attached to each part of the transfer RNA that is assembled on the messenger RNA. The amino acids are thereby lined up in the proper sequence to form a specific protein. The protein thus produced is an enzyme that speeds specific chemical reactions. The reactions manufacture specialized parts of the cell, making it a skin cell or a liver cell as the case may be.

Cell mechanisms in heredity

A gene is the part of a DNA molecule that determines an inherited characteristic that can be identified, such as brown hair or blue eyes. Inheritance and cell specialization depend on the DNA of genes, but genes are packaged in chromosomes and chromosomes occur in pairs—only half of the chromosomes (23) are inherited from each parent; therefore only half of the genes and inherited characteristics come from each parent. The chromosomes come in pairs because the half received from one parent must concern the same structures as the half the other parent contributes. If the 46 chromosomes were composed of two random groups of 23 from each parent, some characteristics would be repeated and some would be missing.

Some of the cells of the body are specialized for reproduction; these cells contain the same chromosomes and genes as other cells of the body, but are isolated from them by being contained in the reproductive tissue of the male (**testes**) and female (**ovaries**). The reproductive cells of the male and female **gonads** (reproductive organs) multiply in the same fashion as other cells in the body as long as they are in an immature state, that is, each cell splits each of its 46 chromosomes and each of the DNA molecules they contain in forming two new cells by cellular mitosis, or **mitotic division** (Figs. 2-3 and 2-4). In the final division save one, called a *reduction division,* the chromosomes line up by pairs instead of splitting, and each cell receives only one of each pair of chromosomes, ending up with two cells of 23 chromosomes each instead of two cells of 46. Which one of each pair each new cell receives is apparently determined by chance. One of a single pair might wind up in either of the two new cells. In the male a final mitotic division produces four **sperm cells.** In the female one cell of the reduction division and one cell of the final meiotic division

are discarded so that only one **ovum** (egg cell) remains. In fertilization one of the sperm cells penetrates the ovum to contribute its 23 chromosomes to the 23 of the ovum so that a single cell of 46 chromosomes results. It is from this cell that the mature and complex multicellular organism develops by mitotic division; half of the chromosomes, and therefore half of the genes of each subsequent cell, originate with the female and half with the male.

The arithmetic of heredity. The single cell that is to form the complete individual begins with 23 pairs of chromosomes and therefore 23 pairs of gene assemblies, one member of each pair having been contributed by the mother and one by the father. Each chromosome pair contains many pairs of genes, each gene regulating the same inherited characteristics in the future offspring. To simplify, consider only one gene pair from a single pair of chromosomes that determine a given characteristics, such as eye color. Assume for the moment that the male contributed a gene for brown eyes (Br) and the female contributed a matching gene for blue eyes (bl). Further assume that the Br gene is **dominant** and the bl gene is **recessive**. This means that an individual having only Br in both members of a gene pair (BrBr) will have brown eyes, an individual with only bl genes (blbl) will be blue-eyed, and an individual with one of each gene (Brbl) will be brown-eyed since the brown-eyed (Br) gene is dominant over the recessive blue-eyed (bl) gene. However, the Brbl individual may contribute a bl gene to his offspring. This is true because, if he carries Brbl in his genes, the reduction division will mean that half the sperm cells will carry Br and half will carry bl. Since it is a matter of chance in the reduction division which sperm or ovum gets which of the gene-chromosome groups, the odds are 50-50 that a Brbl individual will contribute a Br gene and 50-50 that he will contribute a bl gene to his offspring. To illustrate further consequences let us consider two generations:

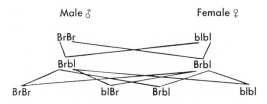

Male ♂   Female ♀

BrBr   blbl

Brbl   Brbl

BrBr   blBr   Brbl   blbl

Mating a BrBr with a blbl can only result in Brbl individuals, brown-eyed but **carriers** of the recessive gene for blue eyes. If two carriers are mated, there are four possible crosses, BrBr, blBr, Brbl, blbl. One in four (on the average) will be brown-eyed and carry only that gene, one in four will be blue-eyed and carry only that gene, and two will be brown-eyed (Br) but carriers of the recessive gene (bl) for blue eyes.

The genes of the inherited DNA molecules determine the physical characteristics by the way they control the manufacture of enzymes in the cell. Enzymes that control hair and eye color are examples. In the inheritance of human characteristics some genes act as simple dominants and recessives, such as brown eye color over blue, curly hair over straight, dark hair over light. Some abnormalities may be inherited as dominants, such as short digits or hereditary cataracts, and others as recessives, such as albinism or epilepsy. In the human, however, **gene linkage, sex linkage,** and **crossovers**, complicate the picture.

Gene linkage

When the chromosomes divide by pairs, each chromosome constitutes a "package" of gene-determined characteristics. If the individual inherits chromosome A instead of B, he will receive each of the thousands of DNA genes in A. The gene for dark hair will be found in the same chromosome as the gene for brown eyes so that both characteristics will usually be inherited or else neither.

Crossovers

When the chromosomes line up into pairs during reduction division, they sometimes

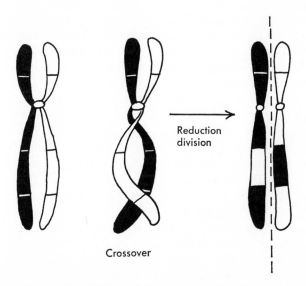

Reduction division

Crossover

Fig. 2-5. Diagram of reduction division of chromosomes showing crossover. As a result of crossover, the sperm or egg cell receives neither all the white chromosome nor all the black chromosome in the reduction division, but takes genes (DNA molecules) from each.

get twisted (Fig. 2-5). When the division of genes and chromosomes occurs, it cuts across chromosome lines, and the individual may inherit some genes from chromosome A and some from B. As a result the gene for dark hair may wind up in the same chromosome as the gene for blue eyes instead of the one for brown eyes.

Sex-linked characteristics

The sex of offspring is also determined by gene pairs, with the masculine (Y) gene being dominant over the feminine gene (X). The female carries XX and the male XY. Therefore, in reduction division the female contributes only X genes, while the male contributes either an X or Y since he carries one of each:

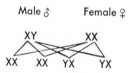

Male ♂   Female ♀

XY   XX

XX   XX   YX   YX

Half the offspring will be males and half females, on the average. However, other gene pairs are carried in the X chromosome and the Y chromosome besides those determining sex. These genes are called sex-linked characteristics because they are found in the same chromosomes as the genes for sex. Moreover, the Y chromosome is smaller than the X chromosome and therefore does not contain as many DNA genes. There are, therefore, characteristics carried by only the larger X chromosome that are not carried by the smaller matching Y chromosome. Hemophilia is one of these characteristics; when the metabolism of blood is controlled by the recessive gene h, an enzyme necessary for blood clotting is missing. The dominant gene H permits normal clotting. A female never displays hemophilia since her chromosome-gene linkage is either $X_H X_h$ or $X_H X_H$, but the $X_H X_h$ female will contribute the X_h chromosome to half her offspring. The $X_h Y$ males will be hemophilic because the male has

no H genes in his small Y chromosome to offset the recessive h gene, while the $X_H Y$ males will be normal. Therefore, half of the *male* offspring ($X_h Y$) of a hemophilic carrier female ($X_H X_h$) will be hemophilic and half will be normal ($X_H Y$). There is at least one famous example of this mechanism; Queen Victoria was a carrier of hemophilia and her carrier daughters introduced the gene into the Russian and Spanish royal families, although her son, King Edward VII, was an $X_H Y$ male who did not inherit the gene for the disease to pass on to the English royal family.

CONTROL OF METABOLISM BY THE CIRCULATORY SYSTEM

Intermediary metabolism that supplies the cells with food and oxygen and removes carbon dioxide and waste material is completely dependent on the **circulatory system** as a transporting medium. The human body is 96% fluid and the circulatory system is responsible for maintaining the chemical and physical consistancy of that fluid. The fluid content of the body may be subdivided into the following: (1) the **intracellular fluid**, which is the fluid medium of the cytoplasm inside cells, a medium necessary to the chemical reactions of cell metabolism; (2) the **extracellular fluid** outside of and surrounding the cells, which serves as a "middleman" for the physical transport of food, oxygen, waste, and carbon dioxide between the cells and the circulatory system; and (3) the blood of the circulatory system, which transports oxygen and carbon dioxide between the lungs and the extracellular fluid, transports food from the digestive system to the extracellular fluid, and transports waste from that fluid to the kidneys.

Circulatory system

The circulatory system consists of (1) the heart, which maintains the flow of blood by its pumping action; (2) the **pulmonary circulation** system of blood vessels, which carry oxygen between the heart and the lungs; and (3) the **systemic circulation,** which carries blood from the heart to all the other tissues of the body and back again to the heart.

The pulmonary circulation is the means for loading the blood with oxygen for the tissues of the body and removing carbon dioxide from blood returned to the heart from the tissues. Inspired air contains 20% oxygen, and blood returned to the heart from the tissues is high in carbon dioxide. Blood circulated by the pulmonary circulation between heart and lungs thus loses carbon dioxide and acquires oxygen by simple diffusion of gases through the walls of the **capillaries** (thin-walled blood vessels) in the lungs, that is, oxygen goes into solution in the blood while carbon dioxide comes out of solution to be exhaled. Far more important, however, are chemical reactions that go on in the **red blood cells**. In the tissues they have reacted chemically to bind carbon dioxide. After transport to the lungs, the reverse chemical reaction occurs to release carbon dioxide and bind oxygen. Accompanying these reactions is a change in color so that blood returning from the tissues (venous blood) is not as bright red as blood going to the tissues (arterial blood).

The systemic circulation moves blood between the heart and the tissues. It includes (1) the **arteries,** which carry blood from the heart to the tissues; (2) the **capillaries** in the tissues, through whose thin walls the exchange between blood and extracellular fluid occurs; (3) the **veins,** which return blood from the tissues to the heart; and (4) the **lymph vessels,** which serve as an auxiliary return system. The rhythmic contractions of the heart pump blood out through the arteries, whose muscular walls may contract or relax in reaction to vary their size and therefore the pressure of the blood within them. The pressure and rate of flow of the blood gradually diminishes as the arteries branch and rebranch to finally form the thin-walled *capillaries* through whose walls the exchange between blood and extracellular fluid occurs. Blood entering the tissue capillaries is higher in oxygen and glucose and that leaving the tissues is high in carbon dioxide and waste. A free exchange (**diffusion**) of fluid and gases occurs between blood and extracellular fluid in the capillaries, whose thin walls retain only solid particles from the blood, such as the red cells. The red cells also react chemically to lose oxygen to the tissues and bind carbon dioxide from them. The system of diffusion is used to transport glucose from the digestive system to the blood and from the blood to the tissues as well as to carry waste (such as lactic acid) from the cells to the blood, and from the blood to the kidney for disposal.

Upon leaving the tissues the capillaries reform into larger veins that return the blood of the systemic circulation to the heart under low pressure. In addition, a further system of lymph vessels collect surplus extracellular fluid for return to veins near the heart. Circulation in the lymph vessels is maintained only by contraction of the muscles of the body in ordinary exercise. These contractions squeeze the thin walls of the lymph vessels passing through the muscles to move their fluid contents along.

HOMEOSTASIS AND THE INTERNAL ENVIRONMENT
Homeostasis

Because of the extreme specialization of the cells of the body, the ability to perform many functions that other (differently specialized) cells perform for them has been lost. Many conditions of the internal environment must be kept within narrow limits so that such specialized cells may survive. Changes in the external environment and even internal changes caused by metabolism are reacted to by the tissues, organs, and systems of the body to keep the internal environment within narrow limits of pressure, oxygen content, acid-base balance, blood-sugar level, chemical composition, and temperature. As explained before, these reactions are collectively referred to as **homeostasis**.

Blood pressure changes

Changes in blood pressure occur from changes in posture and exercise, as well as from other causes. They are kept within limits by pressure receptors in the aorta (a large blood vessel) and the carotid artery. Stimulation of these receptors by an increase in blood pressure sends impulses in nerves that act to slow down the heart by the way of centers in the brain. *Oxygen and carbon dioxide* content of the blood are controlled by the CO_2 level. High CO_2 speeds up the heart rate (by way of brain centers) to carry more CO_2 to the lungs for elimination. It also acts to speed up centers in the brain that control breathing. The *acidity of the blood* is also critical. Normally it is slightly alkaline. More CO_2 increases acidity, but the above mechanisms rid the blood of acidity. Acidity is an excess of H ions; alkalinity is too many OH ions. *Buffer* substances in the blood can bind either excess and deliver them to the kidneys for elimination. *Blood sugar level* is maintained between 60 and 130 mg/100 ml. of blood. Excess sugar is converted to glycogen by the liver, or it can be restored to the blood by the opposite process. The liver can also make glucose out of fat and protein. The hormone adrenaline from the adrenal glands stimulates glucose manufacture from glycogen, whereas insulin from the pancreas stimulates the reverse process. The endocrine glands, as well as the nervous system, organize the body's response to change. The *chemical composition* of the blood is also regulated by such mechanisms. For example, hormones of the pituitary gland regulate the potassium and calcium balance of the body fluids. The *body temperature* must be kept within narrow limits. Changes in blood temperature affect the hypothalamus (a part of the brain) so as to cause shivering (a reflex) if too cold, and sweating if too hot. *Regulatory behavior* is a part of the homeostatic process. Changes in blood sugar may cause an animal to seek or shun food. Changes in body temperature may result in movement to sun or shade or in nest-building. Behavior is usually *aroused* by internal changes called needs; such arousal is a **drive**. Some lower animals have inherited patterns of behavior, in response to arousal, called **instincts**. Man usually relies on learning to develop behavior that is appropriate to his needs and drives (**learned reactions**).

SUMMARY

All life, from single-celled organisms to man, shows the basic characteristics of irritability, conduction, contraction, secretion, elimination, growth, reproduction, and metabolism. All are necessary to behavior. Each of these characteristics depends on one or more specialized parts of each cell. In the course of evolution, complex, many-celled organisms have developed because they are better able to survive under the varied conditions of life. Different cells of these complex organisms have become specialized in one or more of the functions of life, depending on differently specialized cells to carry on other life functions for them. Groups of specialized cells, called tissues, are assembled into organs and systems as the many functions of the organism are integrated. Further integration is assured by the endocrine glands and nervous system.

Specialization means loss of versatility; therefore, the internal environment surrounding the cells must be held constant so that the cells can survive. The cells take food and oxygen from that environment and eliminate carbon dioxide and waste through the chemical reactions of cell metabolism. Since the cells are so specialized, other cells must provide the food and oxygen from the external environment and remove the carbon dioxide and waste in chemical reactions, called intermediary metabolism. All of these reactions either store energy (anabolism) or release energy (catabolism). The source of food for the cells is glucose and the source of energy is phosphate-bonded compounds built up by anabolism from breaking down glucose (catabolism). In intermediary metabolism, glucose is provided by carbohydrates, and the amino and fatty acids the cell uses in its structure are broken down from protein and fat. Minerals and vitamins are also necessary. The whole process can be measured in terms of the oxygen consumed and carbon dioxide given off by the body in oxidation.

Metabolism includes all the chemical reactions of life, which are controlled by enzymes that selectively control the speed of chemical reactions without being used up in those reactions. Enzymes form a "pattern" upon which molecules are assembled to break them down (catabolism) or build them up (anabolism). Some vitamins act as antienzymes and selectively prevent certain reactions.

Heredity is also determined by enzyme-manufacturing arrangements in the cell nucleus. Half the chromosomes in the nucleus of every cell are inherited from each parent. Each chromosome contains many DNA molecules that act as genes, or units of heredity. The sequence of four elements in the DNA molecule acts as a pattern to form messenger RNA molecules. Messenger RNA migrates out into the cell to assemble transfer RNA which, in turn, assembles cell proteins that are enzymes. The enzymes control the nature of the cell.

Dominant and recessive genes may be inherited, one from each parent. If two dominant or one dominant and one recessive are inherited, the offspring will show the dominant characteristic. If one dominant gene and one recessive gene or two recessives are present, the individual may pass the recessive characteristics on to its offspring. These relationships are modified by sex-linked characteristics and crossovers in the chromosomes.

The circulatory system is important to metabolism because it is the transportation system for interchanges between the internal and external environment. Many of the reactions of homeostasis that maintain the constancy of the internal environment are carried out by way of the circulatory system.

READINGS

Allfrey, V., and Mirsky, A.: How cells make molecules, Sci. Amer. **205**:74-82, Sept., 1961. (W. H. Freeman Co. Reprint No. 92.)

Asimov, I.: The genetic code, New York, 1962, Signet Science Library. (New American Library of World Literature, New York; also Clarkson N. Potter, Inc., N. Y.)

Asimov, I.: The human body, Boston, 1964, Houghton Miffin Co.

Brachet, J.: The living cell, Sci. Amer. **205**:50-61, Sept., 1961. (W. H. Freeman Co. Reprint No. 90.)

Carter, C. O.: Human heredity, Baltimore, 1962, Penguin Books, Inc.

Changuex, J. P.: The control of biochemical reactions, Sci. Amer. **212**:36-45, April, 1965. (W. H. Freeman Co. Reprint No. 1008.)

Comroe, J. H.: The lung, Sci. Amer. **214**:56-68, Feb. 1966, (W. H. Freeman Co. Reprint No. 1034.)

Crick, F. H. C.: The genetic code III, Sci. Amer. **215**:55-62, Oct. 1966, (W. H. Freeman Co. Reprint No. 1052.)

Fisschburg, M., and Blackler, A. W.: How cells specialize, Sci. Amer. **205**:124-140, Sept., 1961. (W. H. Freeman Co. Reprint No. 94.)

Hurwitz, J., and Furth, J. J.: Messenger RNA, Sci. Amer. **206**:41-49, Feb., 1962. (W. H. Freeman Co. Reprint No. 119.)

Mazia, D.: How cells divide, Sci. Amer. **205**:100-120, Sept., 1961. (W. H. Freeman Co. Reprint No. 93.)

McKusick, V. A.: The royal hemophilia, Sci. Amer. **213**:88-95, Aug., 1965.

Mittwoch, U.: Sex differences in cells, Sci. Amer. **209**:54-62, July, 1963. (W. H. Freeman Co. Reprint No. 161.)

Steen, E. B., and Montagu, A.: Anatomy and physiology, vols. 1 and 2, New York, 1959, Barnes & Nobles, Inc.

Part II

Integrating and response systems

Chapter 3

Endocrine glands

OVERVIEW

The cells and tissues of the body are diverse and specialized. A need for *integrating* their varied activities to maintain a *constant internal environment* has resulted. The body is integrated by (1) the organization of cells into tissues, organs, and systems, as explained in Chapter 2, (2) the integration of tissue, organ, and system activities by the nervous system, to be covered in Chapter 6, and (3) the integration of these activities by the endocrine glands, whose chemical secretions may have similar effects in widely separated locations in the body.

The specialized secretions of the endocrine glands, called hormones, are carried throughout the body by the bloodstream and have widespread effects. Some of these glands are under the control of the nervous system and are part of the organism's response to external and internal events; other glands react directly to conditions in the internal environment. The endocrine glands are important, directly or indirectly, to behavior.

The defining characteristics of the endocrine glands will be explained first. A few remarks on methods of investigation will follow to explain the functions of the glands and reveal the reasons for flaws in our knowledge. Then the chemical variety of the endocrine hormones can be briefly

noted. The various ways in which hormones can act on their "target" cells and tissues will be explained. After this introduction the endocrine glands will be discussed, one at a time. In each case their normal function will be explained first. The effects of undersecretion and of oversecretion of the gland can then be appreciated. These effects show the importance of the gland to individual differences in vigor, muscle and nerve excitability, emotional balance, metabolism, growth and sexual development, and other factors important to behavior. The endocrine glands discussed will include the thyroid, parathyroids, adrenals, pancreas, pituitary, gonads, pineal, and thymus.

CHARACTERISTICS OF THE ENDOCRINE GLANDS
Endocrine and exocrine glands

All glands are *organs,* made up of a variety of tissues that aid in *secretion* of substances needed by the body. All cells have secretory functions (Chapter 2), but glands contain cells that are specialized for secretion. Exocrine glands are duct glands, so called because they discharge their secretions into a duct or "pipeline" that carries the secretions to their destination. The destination may be a part of the digestive tract, as in the case of the salivary glands and glands of the intestines; it may be the surface of the body, as in the case of the sebaceous (oil-producing) and sweat glands of the skin. However, the exocrine glands are not treated in this chapter; the endocrine glands are. The endocrine glands, or ductless glands, have no "pipelines" for their secretions. Endocrine glands discharge their secretions directly into the blood vessels that pass through them. The endocrine gland secretions, called hormones, are carried throughout the body by the circulatory system. Depending on the nature of the hormone produced and the characteristics of the cells it encounters, an endocrine gland may affect the functioning of cells, organs, and tissues in widespread locations throughout the body. A gland is endocrine, then, if it produces a hormone that (1) is specific to that gland, (2) is distributed by the bloodstream throughout the body, and (3) has a specific influence on some other part of the body—**target tissue** or organ.

Hormone characteristics

Hormones include a variety of compounds (for example, steroids, polypeptides, and amino acids) that have specific effects on different kinds of specialized tissue. Some hormones affect most of the cells of the body, irrespective of their specialized structure and functioning. Other hormones affect only cells that are specialized in certain ways, for example, a hormone that affects the ability of kidney tubule cells to reabsorb water from the urine. In this instance the target tissue of the hormone is found only in a single organ, the kidney. However, a given endocrine gland may produce several different hormones if it has several different kinds of secreting cells or if its cells produce more than one kind of secretion. In this case the hormones would act on a variety of target tissues with different effects on each tissue. To fully understand the function of an endocrine gland, each of its hormones would have to be isolated and its effects tested.

The problem is further complicated by the fact that endocrine glands affect each other. Hormones from one endocrine gland may excite or inhibit the production of hormones by another endocrine gland, that is, *interactions* occur between endocrine glands. Finally, antihormones have been found that chemically inhibit the production of hormones by a given gland or else prevent the action of its hormone in the target tissue.

Methods of investigation

Since each endocrine gland may produce several hormones and some of these hormones may affect other endocrine glands, the study of endocrine function has been a baffling and complex task. Three methods have been used that represent steps in increasing knowledge of each gland: (1) removal of the gland from an animal and observing the effects of the lack of its hormone(s) on physiology and behavior; (2) injecting a normal animal with hormones from the gland to observe the effects of an oversupply of the hormones (these hormones are obtained by "grinding up" the gland from another animal to form an extract or injection, by chemical isolation of the various hormones from the gland, or by chemically synthesizing the hormone if its structure is understood); and (3) removal of the gland and "replacement therapy," that is, injecting gland extracts, isolated hormones, or synthesized ones.

The effects of the lack of only one of several hormones produced by the gland can be studied through replacement therapy. Using all the known hormones isolated from the gland, the investigator may assume that he has found them all if the animal's physiology and behavior remain normal without the gland and with replacement therapy. The errors in these methods are chiefly caused by interactions between glands. If one gland is removed and an animal develops a symptom—for example, low blood calcium and resulting irritability of the nervous system—the investigator may assume that the gland maintains the calcium level of the blood. However, the gland may produce a hormone that stimulates another gland to perform this function. Even when the hormone has been isolated or synthesized, the effect of the hormone on the other glands must be understood.

Mechanisms of hormone functions

Table 3-1 lists the major endocrine glands, their hormones, the chemical nature of these hormones, the target tissue of each, their major functions, and their mode of action. There is far more detail in the table than the student needs; a knowledge of the major effects of each hormone group is sufficient. However, the details given in the table illustrate some major conclusions about the nature of hormones and their action that are important. The fourteen endocrine glands listed produce at least twenty-seven different hormones, although all their effects are not fully understood. Nearly all the hormones produced have very complex molecular structures, particularly steroids or proteins and the polypeptides out of which proteins are made. The steroids are secreted by the adrenals and gonads, and the proteins and polypeptides by the pituitary, pancreas, thyroid, and parathyroids. New methods of separating complex proteins have made it possible to isolate many protein hormones in pure form in recent years. A survey of the variety of target tissue affected by the hormones listed will show that some hormones affect only a few structures, while others affect most of the cells of the body. Some hormones, chiefly those of the anterior pituitary, act by stimulating or suppressing the output of other endocrine glands.

The hormones listed have a variety of effects on a variety of target tissues. Some hormones are involved in organized responses to external stimuli, such as the reaction of the adrenal medulla in sympathetic stimulation (Chapter 6). Others are concerned with the consistency of the internal environment, such as the parathyroids and calcium level or the pancreas and blood sugar level. Some endocrine glands of this group are stimulated directly to produce a hormone that corrects a lack of balance in internal conditions whenever the imbalance occurs; for example, the pancreas produces more insulin when the blood sugar is too high and less insulin when the blood sugar is too low. (The effect of insulin is to help cells use up blood sugar.) As would be expected from the variety of hormone effects on so many kinds of target tissue, several modes of hormone action are found, some hormones acting in more than one of the following ways: (1) some hormones are *coenzymes* (Chapter 2) and therefore aid in activating chemical reactions in the cells of their target tissue, for example, the thyroxin of the thyroid gland; (2) some hormones modify the membranes of the cells they encounter, adhering to the membrane to make it more or less permeable to specific substances; for example, insulin from the pancreas, which enhances the permeability of cell membranes to blood sugar; (3) some hormones act directly on structures within the cell; for example, the effect of action of adrenal norepinephrine on the smooth muscle cells of the arteries; and (4) some hormones act on cells by regulating the genetic apparatus by which they repair and reproduce themselves, for example, the androgens and estrogens of the gonads. (For a review of the operation of the genetic apparatus see Chapter 2.)

In summarizing the mode of action of hormones the following conclusions can be made: (1) steroid hormones appear to act by gene activation, (2) other hormones such as thyroxin act directly by dissociating cell enzymes to change cell reactions, (3) still other hormones such as insulin and vasopressin act on the permeability or transport features of the cell membrane,

Table 3-1. Endocrine glands and their functions

Gland	*Hormone(s)*	*Chemical nature*	*Target tissue*
Thyroid	Thyroxin	Thyronine deriva-tive	Probably all tissue
	Thyrocalcitron	Polypeptide	All cells
Parathyroid	Parathormone Thyrocalcitron-releasing factor (TCRF)	Protein	Gastrointestinal tract, bone, kidney
Skin	Vitamin D		Gastrointestinal tract, kidney
Adrenal cortex	Cortisol Corticosterone Aldosterone	Steroids (enzyme)	Probably all cell membranes, liver, gonads
Adrenal medulla	Epinephrine Norepinephrine	Catechol Amines	Heart Arteries Liver Anterior pituitary
Pancreas			
Alpha cells	Glucagon	Polypeptides	Liver
Beta cells	Insulin		Almost all cells
Posterior pituitary (neurohypophysis)	Vasopressin	Polypeptides	Arteries Kidney
	Oxytoxin		Uterus Mammary glands
Anterior pituitary (adenohypophysis)	Somatotropic hormone (STH) Thyrotropic hormone (TH) Adrenal corticotropic hormone (ACTH)	Polypeptides	Bone Thyroid gland Adrenal cortex and fat tissues
	Follicle-stimulating hormone (FSH)	Protein	Gonads and other tissues
	Luteinizing hormone (LH) Lactogenic hormone (prolactin) or Luteotropic hormone		Gonads Gonads and mammary glands
Testes	Androgens Testosterone Andosterone	Steroids	All tissues
Ovaries	Estrogens Estradiol Esterone	Steroids	All tissues
	Progesterone	Steroid	Uterus
Placenta	Anterior pituitary–like hormones (APL) or chorionic hormones	Steroids	All tissues
Pineal	Melatonin	Indole	Gonads
Thymus	(Not an endocrine gland— see text)		

Major function(s)	*Mode of action*
Raises metabolic rate, increases protein synthesis, carbohydrate synthesis, and transport Lowers blood calcium	Promotes enzyme dissociation, stimulates RNA production by specific cells
Raises blood calcium level, lowers phosphate level	Stimulates calcium and decreases phosphate absorption from the gastrointestinal tract and new bone, decreases calcium excretion, increases phosphate secretion by kidney (by action of vitamin D)
Promotes retention of both calcium and phosphate	
Sodium retention, potassium loss, increased carbohydrate metabolism, and less glycogen produced in liver, electrolyte and estrogenic effects	Stimulates specific RNA production
Increases heart rate Vasoconstriction (both increase glycogen release)	
Release of ACTH	
Increase production glucose Promotes *glucose*, amino acid, cation, fatty acid *absorption* by cells, inhibits glucogenesis by liver	Affects glucose transport by cell membrane by attaching to membrane, changes protein synthesis by cells through RNA mechanisms
Raises blood pressure Stimulates water reabsorption Stimulates contractions Stimulates milk secretion	Attaches to cell membrane to increase permeability
Stimulates growth Stimulates thyroxin secretion Stimulates steroid secretion by adrenal cortex, breaks down fat tissues Development of ova or sperm cells Stimulates estrogen and androgen output	Enzyme activation Stimulates anabolism
Corpus luteum development and milk output	
Sexual arousal; primary and secondary sex characteristics	
Sexual arousal; primary and secondary sex characteristics	Stimulates RNA production by the cell
Prepares for embryo Maintains pregnancy	
GTH-like effects	
Suppresses hormone output by gonads	Light to eye stimulates SNS, whose neurohumors block enzyme for hormone production

(4) additional hormones such as ACTH activate enzymes in cells to promote specific reactions, and (5) some hormones such as thyroxin have both genetic and nongenetic effects.

MAJOR ENDOCRINE GLANDS

The locations of the major endocrine glands are shown in Fig. 3-1. Some glands occur in pairs (adrenals and gonads); others form a single structure (the pineal). Some glands are paired parts of a single structure (adrenal cortex and medulla and anterior and posterior pituitary), or form a cluster of cells (islet cells of the pancreas). Each gland will be referred to as a single unit, whether one, a pair, or more structures are involved.

Lists of the major endocrine glands vary according to who makes the list and for what purpose. Those glands whose function is either uncertain (intermediate pituitary), specific to digestion (stomach gastrin and small intestine secretin), or only suspected (kidneys and blood pressure, liver and anemia) have been omitted. This leaves the following (Table 3-1 and Fig. 3-1): (1) thyroid, (2) parathyroid, (3) adrenal cortex, (4) adrenal medulla, (5) pancreas (islet alpha and beta cells), (6) posterior pituitary, (7) anterior pituitary, (8) gonads (testes, ovaries, related placenta), (9) pineal, and (10) thymus. The adrenal cortex, thyroid, and gonads are controlled partly by the anterior pituitary. The adrenal medulla, pancreas, posterior pituitary, and pineal are under nervous as well as endocrine control, so that they react to external as well as internal events. In taking up the specific function of each gland, what is known of its normal role will be given first, followed by the effects of *hypo-*

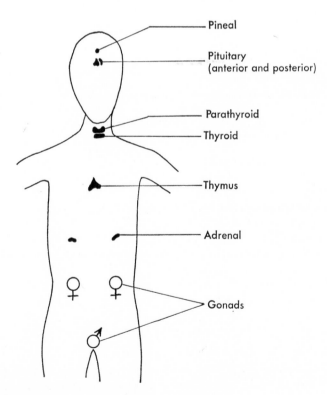

Fig. 3-1. Diagram of the location of major endocrine glands in the human body.

secretion (undersecretion) and *hypersecretion* (oversecretion) of its hormone in cases of glandular abnormality. In each case abnormal function helps in understanding the role of the gland in normal control of body function and therefore behavior.

Thyroid gland

The **thyroid gland** lies on either side of the trachea (windpipe) just below the larynx (voice box). It is a good place to begin study of the endocrine glands because its major hormone, **thyroxin,** is a relatively simple one. Thyroxin is manufactured in the gland by combining iodine and an amino acid (tyrosine). The hormone probably affects all the cells of the body as target tissue. Thyroxin raises the metabolic rate of all the cells of the body and therefore is necessary for a normal level of energy and activity. A minimum level of thyroxin in the blood and tissue fluid is necessary for a normal metabolic rate. Oversecretion of thyroxin raises the metabolic rate to abnormal levels. The functioning of the thyroid gland can therefore be tested by testing the metabolic rate. When the test is conducted under resting conditions, the results are called the basal metabolic rate, or BMR. As described in Chapter 2, the test measures the rate of oxygen consumption in the body caused by the metabolism of cells. (Since the hormone is made by combining amino acids and iodine, a more direct test of protein-bound iodine content of the blood may be made). Under normal conditions the thyroid gland may have much to do with the amount of energy and drive displayed by the individual and with how adequately he responds to stress situations that demand vigorous physical arousal.

Hypothyroidism. When the thyroid does not produce enough thyroxin to maintain a normal metabolic rate, **hypothyroidism** occurs. The effects of hypothyroidism depend on when the condition occurs, during growth or after maturity. The effects are usually more severe when they occur during childhood growth because metabolism must be higher to support growth and development than to support adult body functions; more thyroxin is therefore needed during childhood. If hypothyroidism develops at birth or during early childhood, it causes symptoms called **cretinism.** The cretin fails to develop normally either physically or mentally. He is dwarfed because of inadequate bone growth, although the connective tissue of the body is overdeveloped—puffy face, protruding tongue, and "potbelly." He is "feebleminded" because of inadequate development of the nervous system. Cretinism can be prevented with supplementary doses of thyroxin if the hypothyroid condition is discovered in time.

Adult hypothyroidism is called **myxedema.** The name comes from the collection of body fluid in connective tissue (edema) that gives the individual a puffy, bloated appearance. Myxedema, caused by an onset of thyroid deficiency in the adult, reduces the BMR by 35 to 40%. This results in sluggishness, chills from inability to maintain body temperature, and reduced muscle tone. Motivation, vigor, and alertness diminish, and the individual sleeps much of the time. The central nervous system may deteriorate until the individual becomes an imbecile. Supplementary thyroxin can effect complete recovery.

Hyperthyroidism. Overproduction of thyroxin by the thyroid, or **hyperthyroidism,** is less common than hypothyroidism. The BMR in this condition may be 50 to 75% above normal. As a result the individual is hyperactive and "nervous." He has a huge appetite but cannot gain weight because all that he eats is consumed in maintaining a high BMR. He sleeps little, is irritable, and is unable to concentrate. "Exophthalamus" (bulging eyes) is a prominent symptom. Hyperthyroidism can be cured by surgically removing part of the gland. It usually leaves no permanent impairment if treated successfully.

Goiter is an enlargement of the thyroid gland that is apparent as a swelling in the neck region. It may accompany hyperthyroidism for unknown reasons, or it may result from hypothyroidism when the cells of the thyroid multiply to increase their inadequate output of thyroxin. Simple goiter often resulted from a lack of iodine in the diet for the manufacture of thyroxin and occurred in areas of the world where there was no iodine in the soil of crops grown for food. Iodine is now added to most table salt (iodized salt) to prevent the condition.

Studies of abnormal thyroid conditions show, in exaggerated form, the probable importance of the thyroid to normal behavior. Individual differences in normal thyroid functioning may help account for individual differences in energy, motivation, attention, and general alertness. Some recent evidence showed that the thyroid may have a role in regulating blood calcium under stimulation of the parathyroid glands (Table 3-1).

Parathyroid gland

The parathyroid gland consists of four tiny organs, shaped like slightly flattened peas, embedded in, or attached to, the thyroid gland. The parathyroids produce **parathormone,** a hormone essential to controlling the calcium level and calcium to phosphate ratio in the blood and tissue fluid—factors required for normal nerve and muscle cell functioning and therefore normal behavior. The higher the blood calcium level, the less excitable the muscles and nervous system are; low blood calcium makes these tissues irritable and may cause convulsive seizures and muscle contractions. Parathormone acts to increase blood calcium levels and therefore to decrease nerve and muscle excitability. The parathyroid is stimulated to release the hor-

mone by low blood calcium and suppressed by high blood calcium, a simple feedback mechanism that keeps the calcium level within the narrow limits required for normal muscle and nerve excitability. Parathormone also lowers blood phosphate levels for a proper calcium-phosphate ratio. Some believe that low blood calcium stimulates the parathyroid to release a second hormone that causes the thyroid to secrete a calcium-lowering hormone (Table 3-1).

The parathyroids require **vitamin D** to adequately regulate calcium and phosphate levels. The vitamin prevents the loss of calcium in the feces and phosphate in the urine. Thus the vitamin and the hormone act together in maintaining calcium levels but in opposition on phosphates. Vitamin D can compensate for a lack of parathormone in maintaining blood calcium, but the hormone is not effective without the vitamin. (Lack of vitamin D causes rickets in children, a bone-wasting disease caused by a loss of the calcium and phosphates that make up bone.) Vitamin D can be considered a hormone because it is manufactured by an organ (the skin); when the skin is exposed to sunlight, the hormone is released into the bloodstream to have effects elsewhere in the body. Because man shields his skin from the sun with clothing, a substance made by the body (a hormone) has become an essential factor (a vitamin) in the diet.

Given an adequate supply of vitamin D for retention of calcium by the body, parathormone has two mechanisms for raising the blood calcium level. One is rapid and of limited extent; the other takes more time but can cause a greater change in calcium level. Parathormone acts rapidly to increase absorption of calcium from the intestine and to prevent its loss in the urine (kidney reabsorption). The hormone acts more slowly on bone to provide a "reserve supply" of calcium. (Bone is made of calcium and phosphate.) Parathormone breaks down bone into a form that can be taken up by the tissue fluids to supply more calcium and phosphate. At the same time it stimulates excretion of phosphate in the urine so that a proper calcium-phosphate ratio is maintained; the blood calcium rises and blood phosphate is reduced.

Hyposecretion of parathormone is rare in man (parathyroid tissue is sometimes removed in tumor operations) and is easily treated with parathormone or vitamin D. Complete removal of the parathyroids in animals has the expected effect. The nervous system and muscles become hyperexcitable because of lowered blood calcium. (Calcium is not absorbed from intestine or bone and is excreted in the urine.) Muscle twitches (**clonus,** Chapter 5) result, giving way to muscle spasms (**tetany**) and convulsive seizures similar to epilepsy.

Hypersecretion of parathormone is equally rare in man, usually being associated with tumors that enlarge the parathyroid glands. As would be expected, an increased parathormone level in man or experimental animals raises the calcium level and lowers the phosphate level of the blood. The calcium level may rise so high that the kidney cannot reabsorb it all, and excess calcium may be found in the urine. Calcium and phosphates are drawn from the bones, deforming them. Muscle tone is reduced, the central nervous system (CNS) is less excitable, and the individual becomes dull and sluggish. Removal of part of the gland restores normality.

It should be noted that low blood calcium with the same symptoms as hyposecretion of parathormone can result from a diet low in calcium or vitamin D, even when parathormone secretion is normal. This often happens during pregnancy and lactation (nursing) when extra demands are put on the calcium levels of the body.

Under normal conditions individual differences in parathormone and vitamin D levels in the blood could mean differences between individuals in nervous system functioning. This could affect all levels of behavior from alertness and coordination to intelligence.

Adrenal cortex

The adrenal glands are named for their location atop the kidneys (renal = kidney), but they are not directly related to the kidneys. Further, the adrenals consist of two parts that bear little relation to each other. The core, or **adrenal medulla,** of each gland is derived from neural tissue and is innervated by the autonomic nervous system (Chapter 5). The covering, or **cortex,** of the gland is derived from the same type of tissue as the gonads and bears a functional relationship to them. The most important hormones produced by the **adrenal cortex** are steroids. These hormones are therefore called **corticoids.** They regulate the sodium and potassium balance of the body, govern carbohydrate metabolism, and seem to have something to do with sexual functioning. Corticoids also promote sodium retention and potassium loss via the kidney. An excess of sodium outside the cells and an excess of potassium inside the cells, where it is not available for excretion, is the basis of the excitability of the nervous system, the resting potential and the nerve impulse (Chapter 4). Thus corticoids maintain the excitability of cells.

Corticoids also stimulate the storage of blood sugar in the liver as glycogen and increase carbohydrate metabolism to raise the basal metabolic rate. The corticoids seem to mimic the gonads in supporting vigor and secondary sex characteristics, and the adrenal cortex produces a male sex hormone (an **androgen**). The production of corticoids by the adrenal cortex is under the control of a stimulating hormone of the anterior pituitary gland (adrenocorticotropic hormone, or ACTH, Table 3-1).

Hyposecretion of adrenal corticoids (Addison's disease) results in too much elimination of sodium (Na) and too much retention of potassium (K) by the kidneys. Since the excitability mechanism for all cells depends on an excess of Na outside the cell membrane and an excess of K inside (Chapter 4), the excitability of nerves and muscles is reduced. In maintaining a constant *concentration* of NaCl (salt) solution during loss of Na, body fluids are also lost. Changes in carbohydrate metabolism involve less storage of reserve blood sugar as glycogen in the liver and muscles for use when needed by the body. Carbohydrate utilization is also reduced, lowering the BMR. Lack of vigor, muscle weakness, lower body temperature, and weight loss result. Unless supplementary salt (NaCl) is available in quantities, an animal dies soon after removal of the gland. Death follows later in any case unless replacement therapy is given.

Hypersecretion of corticoids is rare in man. The sexual effects of the hormone are the most observable features of hypersecretion since sexual precocity in children and masculinity in women (for example, circus bearded ladies) result. (Stimulating the adrenal cortex with pituitary ACTH has been used as a cure for rheumatism, with some unfortunate side effects!)

Normal functioning of the adrenal cortex is required for normal nerve and muscle excitability. The corticoids interact with the adrenal medulla and pituitary in determining resistance to environmental stress. Individual stress tolerance, sexual vigor, and nervous system efficiency are affected by the functioning of the gland.

Adrenal medulla

The "core" of the adrenal glands is closely related to the autonomic (visceral) nervous system (ANS) and is derived from the same kind of tissue (Chapter 6). The gland secretes **norepinephrine and epinephrine,** (also called **noradrenaline** and **adrenaline**) when stimulated by sympathetic nerves of the ANS, a feature of arousal of the body in response to stress. Norepineph-

rine resembles the transmitter substance of sympathetic nerve endings and reinforces their effects on the viscera. This includes raising the blood pressure by constricting the arteries (vasoconstriction). Epinephrine is derived from norepinephrine and has similar effects except for raising the blood pressure by accelerating the heart rate rather than by vasoconstriction. There is evidence that epinephrine predominates in states of fear and norepinephrine in states of rage (Chapter 16). This could account for the "pounding heart" when frightened and a "pale" appearance from vasoconstriction near the skin when angry.

Stress and alarm reactions involve both the adrenal cortex and adrenal medulla (Fig. 3-2). Under the influence of sympathetic stimulation, epinephrine is released with the effects noted above. Epinephrine also stimulates the anterior pituitary gland to secrete ACTH, which, in turn, stimulates the release of corticoids from the adrenal cortex to improve tissue excitability and increase the BMR.

Hypersecretion of the adrenal medulla is not a known gland abnormality. It is a feature of stressful conditions along with sympathetic arousal and the effects on the adrenal cortex previously noted.

Hyposecretion can be imitated by removing the gland in animals without removing the adrenal cortex. The animal remains normal except for inability to tolerate environmental stress. Mobilization to maintain body temperature in cold environment, vigor, and response to arousing stimuli are reduced.

It has been shown that prolonged stress causes adrenal enlargement that probably involves both the cortex and medulla since both are involved in response to stress. The result would be an increased capacity to mobilize the resources of the body to meet future stressful conditions and enhance chances for survival in animal or man living under primitive conditions.

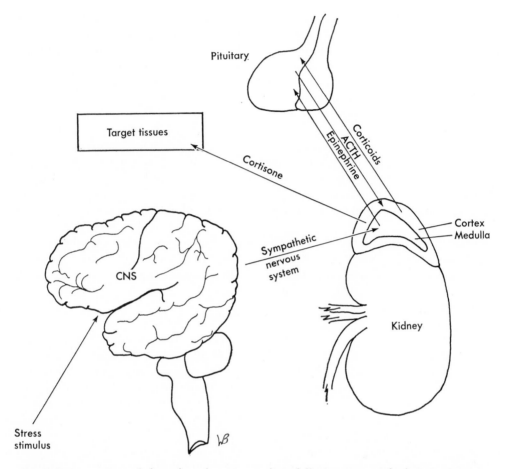

Fig. 3-2. Interaction of the adrenal cortex and medulla in stress and alarm reactions. Perception of a stress stimulus results in sympathetic nervous system response, including increased epinephrine reaction by the adrenal medulla. Epinephrine stimulates ACTH output by the anterior pituitary gland. ACTH stimulates the adrenal cortex to increase corticoid output. Corticoids improve nerve tissue excitability and raise the metabolic rate, both adaptive reactions to stress.

Pancreas

The **pancreas** is an organ that lies in a curve of the gut between the stomach and the small intestine and has both exocrine and endocrine functions. It is a digestive gland that discharges into the small intestine, a function that is of little interest to the present topic. Embedded into the pancreas (in the islets of Langerhans) are two kinds of endocrine cells, the **alpha** and **beta cells**. The alpha cells seem relatively unim-

portant in the body's economy. They comprise only about 25% of the total endocrine cells and produce a hormone (**glucagon**) that opposes the action of the beta cells by stimulating the liver to produce blood sugar. Glucagon is released for a brief period by the alpha cells in response to low blood sugar.

The *beta cells* produce **insulin,** a hormone that inhibits the liver in either making or releasing blood sugar and further lowers blood sugar by increasing its use by the muscles and other nonnervous tissue of the body. Insulin appears to make these cells more permeable to blood sugar and is essential for blood sugar utilization. The beta cells release insulin in response to a high level of sugar in the blood; their secretion is inhibited when the blood sugar drops as a result of liver storage and muscle utilization. The gland and the effect of its secretion form a self-regulating feedback loop. Insulin is also released when the gland is stimulated by the vagus nerves (Chapter 6).

Hyposecretion of insulin by the beta cells of the pancreas may cause a common disorder in man called **diabetes mellitus,** although recent evidence indicates that a pituitary hormone may also cause this disorder, as will be explained later. Without sufficient insulin, blood sugar is neither used by the muscles and other tissues nor stored as glycogen by the liver. This causes an increase in the amount of glucose (blood sugar) in the blood, and some of the oversupply is secreted in the urine. (Sugar in the urine is a test for diabetes.) In their attempt to rid the blood of excess sugar, the kidneys excrete more water than usual, and the individual becomes dehydrated. Poisonous waste products accumulate in the blood because the tissues cannot completely metabolize fats and proteins in place of the carbohydrate glucose (Chapter 2). A **diabetic coma** and death may ensue. Insulin replacement therapy can prevent these symptoms since the hormone has been isolated and synthesized. The insulin injections must be balanced against the amount and type of food intake to assure normal blood sugar levels.

Hypersecretion of insulin is rare in man and is cured by removal of islet tissue. An oversupply of insulin, or an overdose of insulin in a diabetic, results in **hypoglycemia** (low blood sugar level) since all the stored blood sugar is utilized. **Insulin shock** convulsions result and cause death unless glucose is quickly administered. Induced insulin hypoglycemia and insulin shock have been used in the treatment of mental patients (Chapter 18).

It is doubtful if individual differences in insulin secretion that are within the normal range are important to behavior. Insulin is not required by the cells of the nervous system for their utilization of blood sugar, and insulin does not pass the blood-brain barrier (Chapter 6). The nervous system is, however, very dependent on a constant supply of blood sugar at a concentration in the body fluid that lies within the normal range. Insulin coma and insulin shock result from extremes of blood sugar concentration that affect the brain.

Posterior pituitary

The pituitary gland, or **hypophysis,** hangs from the base of the brain; it is connected to the hypothalamus by a narrow "stalk." The posterior part of the pituitary gland is called the **neurohypophysis** because it receives nerve fibers from the hypothalamus and seems to be under nervous control. Two hormones have been isolated from posterior pituitary extracts: **vasopressin** and **oxytocin.** These two hormones have the following four overlapping effects: (1) they constrict blood vessels in the smaller arteries, which raises the blood pressure (a *pressor* effect); (2) they stimulate contraction of other smooth muscles besides those in the walls of arteries, particularly the uterus; (3) they stimulate milk production by the mammary glands; and (4) they stimulate the kidney to reabsorb water from the urine (an **antidiuretic** effect). Vasopressin is more effective in causing the pressor and antidiuretic effects, whereas oxytoxin has more to do with contractions of the uterus and with milk production. Oxytoxin is believed to play a role in the strong uterine contractions of labor in childbirth and in subsequent readiness to nurse the young. A combination of oxytoxin and vasopressin is therefore used to aid childbirth. The pressor role of these hormones in nomal body functioning is little understood, but removal of the gland or injection of its hormone affects blood pressure.

The *antidiuretic* role of the **posterior pituitary** is important in controlling the water balance of the body. Dehydration (lack of water) in nerve cells in the hypothalamus results in stimulation of the posterior pituitary via nerves reaching it from the hypothalamus. The posterior pituitary secretes its hormones. The hormones, in turn, stimulate the kidney to reabsorb up to a third of the water it uses to pass wastes. Hydration (the presence of water) in hypothalamic cells results. This stops the stimulation of the posterior pituitary in another interesting feedback loop. The mechanism is an important part of the thirst drive, which will be discussed in Chapter 15.

Hyposecretion of the posterior pituitary leads to **diabetes insipidus,** with the excretion of large amounts of water, together with a strong thirst and a large water intake to maintain the water balance of the body and prevent death by dehydration. The condition can be cured by posterior pituitary extract. Posterior pituitary hypersecretion is not a known disorder.

The neurohypophysis is important, then, to the psychological areas of maternal behavior and the thirst drive. In addition, the nerve fibers reaching the pituitary are believed to secret transmitter substances (**neurohumors**) into blood vessels reaching the anterior pituitary in a **portal system** of the circulation. (A portal system carries substances in the bloodstream from one specific point to another; the substances do not reach the rest of the circulation.) The transmitter substances can excite or inhibit the secretions of the anterior pituitary. Thus the hypothalamus, which is an important center for governing motivated behavior, controls some of the secretions of

both the posterior and anterior pituitary glands.

Anterior pituitary

The *anterior pituitary* gland, or **adenohypophysis**, has been called the "master gland" since it regulates the output of three "target" endocrine glands with five "tropic" hormones. It controls, at least to some extent, the adrenal cortex, the thyroid, and three activities of the gonads (germ tissue growth and the production of sex and pregnancy hormones). It produces an additional hormone with widespread effects on the growth of the body. There may also be influences from the pituitary on carbohydrate metabolism and the pancreas, but these are not well enough established for discussion here. Parts of the body affected by both anterior and posterior pituitary glands are sketched in Fig. 3-3.

The **somatotropic hormone (STH)** does not affect other glands. It acts directly to stimulate normal growth over the entire body in the developing organism. Growth naturally occurs by cell multiplication in all tissues, but it is most noticeable in the long bones of the body, particularly in the bones of the limbs. Growth in man seems normally to occur over two periods, the first from birth to puberty (the beginnings of adolescence) at a diminishing rate and the second a marked growth spurt during adolescence, the period from puberty to maturity, which is accompanied by sexual development. The timing and extent of growth is governed by STH, whereas the sexual changes are regulated by other hormones of the anterior pituitary gland.

Hyposecretion of STH inhibits growth and results in a **pituitary dwarf** or midget. The pituitary dwarf is usually of normal intelligence and normal body proportions and should not be confused with the inherited gland abnormalities that result in the achondroplastic dwarf with a normal head and body but underdeveloped limbs. The pituitary dwarf may or may not show

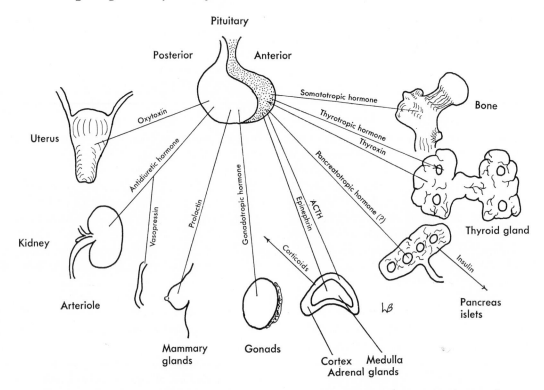

Fig. 3-3. Hormones and target tissue of anterior and posterior pituitary glands. For details, see text.

retarded sexual development. He may be only 3 or 4 feet tall at maturity. Hormone therapy will prevent this condition if begun early enough.

Hypersecretion of STH varies in its effect on the body, depending on whether it began before or after maturity. Hypersecretion during otherwise normal growth results in a **pituitary giant** of normal body proportions who may be 8 or 9 feet tall. There are no known effects on the nervous system, and the pituitary giant is usually of normal intelligence. If hypersecretion of STH begins after maturity, that is, after normal growth ends, a condition called **acromegaly** results. The cartilage at the ends of the long bones of the limbs and jaw, where growth is most noticeable, hardens into bone; normal growth in a proportionate "lengthwise" fashion is no longer possible. The bones become misshapen and

thickened, especially those of the limbs, nose, and jaw. Fibrous tissue of the face and tongue is enlarged, and the abdomen protrudes. The individual has a coarse and apelike appearance.

Recent evidence suggests that hypersecretion of STH may cause diabetes mellitus in some individuals whose pancreas secretes a normal amount of insulin. In these individuals STH stimulates the formation of blood glucose and interferes with its use by the cells of the body. There appears to be no cure for pituitary hypersecretion because the gland is inaccessible to surgery.

The **thyrotropic hormone (TTH)** output of the anterior pituitary gland is controlled by the level of thyroxin in the blood. TTH stimulates iodine uptake and thyroxin synthesis by the thyroid gland. In an interesting feedback mechanism the increased level of blood thyroxin inhibits output of TTH by the pituitary. The blood sugar is therefore maintained at a level consistent with the needs of the body during rest or exercise.

The **adrenocorticotropic hormone (ACTH)** stimulates and regulates the output of hormones by the adrenal cortex. As previously described, ACTH output is increased by epinephrine from the adrenal medulla under stress stimulation. Other stimuli to ACTH output are uncertain, but the hypothalamus and portal system from the posterior pituitary are probably involved. ACTH stimulates the adrenal cortex to increase corticoid output. As previously explained, the corticoids govern the sodium and potassium balance of the body for nervous system excitability, regulate carbohydrate metabolism, and support sexual vigor and the development of secondary sex characteristics.

Three **gonadotropic hormones (GTH)** are produced by the anterior pituitary gland. Their effects on the hormone output of the gonads will be mentioned here and more thoroughly explained in the section on the gonads.

1. **Follicle-stimulating hormone (FSH)** stimulates the development of sperm cells in the testicles of the male and the development of ova, or egg cells, in the ovaries of the female. In the female FSH also brings the follicle containing the ovum to maturity.

2. **Luteinizing hormone (LH)** stimulates the output of sex hormones by the gonads, estrogens from the corpus luteum of the female ovaries and androgens from the interstitial tissue of the testes of the male. LH also causes the mature follicle of the ovary to rupture and release the ovum and then changes the follicle into the corpus luteum.

3. **Lactogenic hormone (prolactin)** brings the corpus luteum to maturity in the female and stimulates its output of progesterone. It also has a direct role in stimulating the development and milk production of the female mammary glands. Its role in the male is not clear.

The anterior pituitary gland controls the output of several other endocrine glands and is closely related to the hypothalamus that governs "drives" (hunger, thirst, and so on) by way of the posterior pituitary and the portal system of blood vessels. For these two reasons the anterior pituitary is probably the most important of the endocrine glands to behavior. By its dominance of the adrenal cortex and feedback relationship to the adrenal medulla, it has much to do with the individual's vigor and ability to withstand stress. Its control of corticoids further governs the excitability of the nervous system that integrates behavior. Its interaction with the thyroid determines the individual's metabolic level and therefore his responsiveness to the world about him. Normal or abnormal sexual development with its consequences for personality depend on how the anterior pituitary governs the activity of the gonads. Physical stature depends on the growth hormone of the pituitary, and abnormalities of size have a profound influence on personality. All in all, the anterior pituitary has a pivotal role in behavior.

Gonads

The reproductive organs of the male and the female have dual roles. One function involves maturation of the reproductive organs and development of the secondary sexual characteristics (distribution of body fat, development of pubic, armpit, and chest hair, deepening of the voice, etc.). The other function involves growth and development of the **germ tissue** or **germ cells** (sperm or ova) in both sexes and an orderly sequence of reproductive events in the female.

Male reproductive system. The male reproductive system is based on paired testes contained in a sac, or **scrotum.** Their location outside the body cavity lowers their temperature to a point that permits the growth of sperm cells in the **seminiferous tubules.** The tubular tissue of the testes gives rise to the **seminal duct,** which ascends into the abdomen to unit with the duct from the other testicle and is joined here by the *prostate gland.* Gland secretions and sperm form **semen,** which is collected in the **seminal vesicle.** During copulation (sexual intercourse) the vesicles and outgoing **urethra** of the **penis** contract to ejaculate the semen that contains the sperm cells.

The male reproductive hormones are androgens, secreted by the **interstitial tissue** that surrounds the seminiferous tubules of the testes. The secretion of androgens by this tissue is stimulated by FSH from the anterior pituitary. Androgens are derived from progesterone, which is an important female sex hormone; they are also secreted in some degree by the ovaries, adrenal cortex, and female placenta.

Removal of the gonads is called castration. Lack of androgen caused by castration before puberty results in loss of vigor and failure to develop secondary sexual characteristics (that is, a eunuch). Early injections of the hormones in a castrate reverses these effects. After maturity, castration often abolishes sexual behavior in animals, but merely reduces its frequency in men. (It's all in your head!) The same is true of lack of androgen production in old age.

Female reproductive system. The female reproductive system includes paired ovaries in the abdomen that contain immature **follicles,** each of which has an ovum, or egg cell. The open ends of the **fallopian tubes** (oviducts) lie near the ovaries; when **ovulation** produces a mature ovum, the fallopian tubes carry it to the **uterus.** If the ovum is fertilized by a sperm cell, it develops into an **embryo** in the wall of the uterus. At birth, the **fetus** (developed embryo) is discharged via the **cervix** and **vagina.**

The female reproductive cycle is illustrated in Fig. 3-4. The cycle averages twenty-eight days and begins at the end of menstruation with increased output of FSH by the anterior pituitary gland. The hormone causes increased growth of a follicle in the ovary. The growing follicle secretes **estrogens** that promote the growth of vascular and connective tissue in the wall of the uterus, preparing it to receive the ovum. Estrogens also stimulate LH secretion by the anterior pituitary gland.

The dual influence of pituitary LH and FSH stimulates the follicle to reach the surface of the ovary and release the ovum (ovulation) about the fourteenth day. The ovum is carried by the fallopian tubes of the uterus and buries itself in the wall of the uterus at about the seventeenth day. This interval (fourteenth to seventeenth day) is the period of greatest fertility.

Meanwhile, pituitary LH and prolactin stimulate the follicle to become an enlarged **corpus luteum** and to secrete **progesterone.** Progesterone stops the output of FSH by the pituitary to prevent further follicles from maturing and producing eggs—the status quo is maintained. LH and prolactin also stimulate the continued output of estrogen by the corpus luteum. Estrogen acts to continue development of the wall of the uterus. Prolactin also prepares the mammary glands for milk production.

If pregnancy occurs, a **placenta** develops in the wall of the uterus to support and nourish the embryo. The placenta secretes both progesterone and **chorionic hormone.** These hormones replace progesterone from the corpus luteum in inhibiting FSH production and maintaining the status quo for pregnancy.

Under the influence of progesterone and/or chorionic hormones, ovulation and further fertilizations cannot occur. The birth control pills now in wide use imitate progesterone and are taken to prevent ovulation. If pregnancy does not occur, the corpus luteum degenerates and estrogen and progesterone production are reduced.

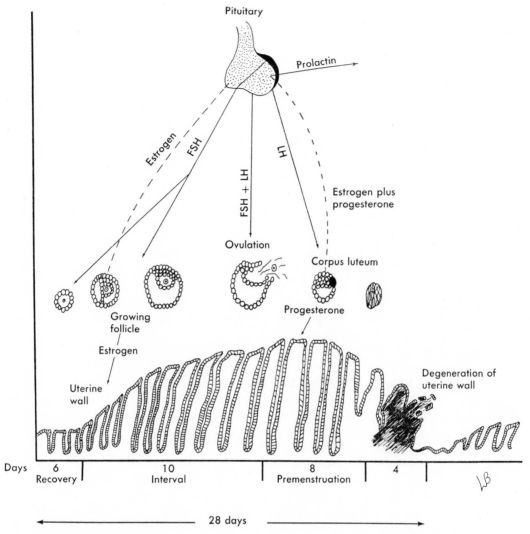

Fig. 3-4. Female reproductive cycle. For details of the sequence of events diagrammed here, see text.

The uterine wall sheds, causing bleeding (menstruation) from the vascular structures built up there.

Pineal gland

The **pineal gland** is a small pea-shaped structure that is found on top of the posterior part of the third ventricle (Chapter 6). In cold-blooded animals such as the frog it is a primitive visual receptor, a "third eye." Its hormone, **melatonin**, prob-

ably acts to bleach the skin pigment cells from which the hormone takes its name. The function of the pineal gland has changed drastically in mammals through evolution, and its role in human physiology and behavior was a mystery until recently. Now it is known to govern the activity of the reproductive system in response to the light changes that accompany the light-dark cycle of each day or the changes in daylight with the seasons. The pineal gland no longer contains visual receptors in man, but it is stimulated by excitation that originates in the eye. The excitation reaches the gland by way of the sympathetic nervous system. Of the glands studied, the pineal gland is the fifth to respond to nerve stimulation (neurosecretory). The other four were the adrenal medulla, the pancreas, the posterior pituitary, and the anterior pituitary response to secretions from the nerve cells of the posterior pituitary and hypothalamus.

The melatonin released by the pineal gland suppresses or inhibits the activity of the gonads and sexual behavior. Since light suppresses the pineal gland secretion, gonadal activity is released by light. This means that sexual activity is increased by light and reduced by dark in the daily light-dark cycle. The increased sunlight of longer days during the spring triggers annual growth of the gonads and sex activity in some species of animals.

The way in which light controls gonadal activity through its effect on the pineal gland is involved. Light stimulates the retina of the eye. Excitation reaches the pineal gland by way of sympathetic nervous system fibers (from the superior cervical ganglion). These fibers release noradrenaline. Noradrenaline blocks the activity of an enzyme that is needed by the gland to make its hormone, melatonin. Melatonin production is reduced. Since melatonin normally inhibits the gonads, the gonads are released from inhibition. They secrete more sex hormones, the **estrus cycle** in the female is accelerated, germ cell production in both sexes increases, and sexual behavior is stimulated. The enzyme blocked by the sympathetic nervous system has a long and complex name (hydroxyindole-O-methyl transferase) that no one need learn since it is usually known by its initials, **HIOMT.** HIOMT activity is governed directly by the light-dark cycle. The pineal gland makes melatonin out of serotonin and serotonin supply depends on brain reactions to the

light-dark cycle. Two control mechanisms are therefore possible.

Pineal gland malfunction is rare in man. It is usually caused by tumors of the gland or of adjacent tissue. If the tumor is in the gland itself, the cells multiply and secrete more melatonin; thus, *hypersecretion* in children results in delayed sexual development. If the tumor is in the surrounding tissue, it interferes with the function of the gland. *Hyposecretion* of melatonin results, causing precocious puberty in children. Little is known of abnormalities of the gland in adults.

The importance of pineal function to behavior is obvious. It is an important factor governing the onset of puberty in man and may explain why sexual maturation occurs earlier in tropical regions where there is more sunlight. It regulates the sexual behavior of some animals according to the daily light-dark cycle. It may regulate the timing of the estrus (menstrual) cycle in man as well as in animals. Finally, it governs the seasonal cycle of sexual behavior found in some animals.

Thymus gland

The **thymus gland** develops as a large "gland" of two roughly equal lobes that lie between the breastbone (sternum) and the heart. In young calves it forms a food delicacy known as sweetbread. The size of the thymus increases in step with general growth in the human until the child is 8 to 10 years old. It slowly atrophies thereafter and is not functional in the adult.

The thymus is not actually an endocrine gland since it does not appear to produce hormones. It is included here only because it is listed with the endocrine glands in older references. Recently the thymus gland has been found to be the primary source of **lymphocytes**—white blood cells that combat disease bacteria and viruses and react to the presence of foreign proteins (infections). The lymphocytes are released into the bloodstream by the thymus and stored by the lymph glands and spleen. Production of lymphocytes by the thymus is at its peak in the last few days before birth and the first few days after birth.

Lymphocytes appear to have two functions: (1) they produce "antibodies" that neutralize disease bacteria and viruses and (2) they "recognize" and react against foreign proteins, for example, tissue transplanted from another animal or a splinter under the skin. The thymus is believed to manufacture the original lymphocytes, expose them to the body's own proteins and destroy those that react, and then release the rest to the spleen and lymph glands for storage and future multiplication when needed. Autoimmune diseases, in which the body reacts against its own proteins as in leukemia and myasthenia gravis, may be caused by failure in the sorting mechanism of the thymus.

The thymus is probably of little importance to behavior except that its functioning contributes to the ability of the individual to withstand stress, particularly the stress of disease or injury.

SUMMARY

The endocrine glands are organs specialized to secrete hormones directly into the bloodstream. Hormones have a specific effect on specialized target tissue wherever they encounter it. The effect depends on both the specialized nature of the target tissue and the nature of the hormone. Their effects have been investigated by gland removal, by injections of natural or synthesized hormones, and by a combination of these two methods. They affect their target tissues in a variety of ways, including enzyme activation or dissociation, altering cell membrane permeability, affecting other structures in the cell, changing the genetic apparatus in the cell nucleus, or a combination of these effects.

Some endocrine glands are stimulated by the presence of hormones from other endocrine glands or other changes in the internal environment of the body. Other endocrine glands are under nervous as well as chemical control. The output of thyroxin from the thyroid gland is stimulated by TTH from the anterior pituitary; TTH output, in turn, is regulated by blood thyroxin level. Thyroxin stimulates metabolism in all the cells of the body. Hypothyroidism in childhood results in cretinism, a failure to develop either physically or mentally. In the adult it causes myxedema, with subnormal vigor and alertness. Hyperthyroidism causes a high BMR, hyperactivity, nervousness, and weight loss.

The parathyroid glands produce parathormone in response to a low level of blood calcium. Parathormone, in cooperation with vitamin D, raises the blood calcium level and reduces the phosphate level to lower nerve cell excitability. This is done by increasing calcium intake, reducing its loss, and taking reserve supplies from the bone. Hyposecretion of parathormone or lack of vitamin D causes hyperexcitability, muscle clonus, tetany, and convulsions. Hypersecretion causes sluggishness, apathy, and wasting of the bones (rickets).

The adrenal cortex secretes corticoids that regulate the sodium and potassium levels of the body, govern carbohydrate metabolism, and mimic the sex hormones. Hyposecretion of corticoids (Addison's disease) depresses the excitability of the nervous system and muscles, which is based on the sodium and potassium balance. Body fluids are lost with sodium excretion, and less blood sugar is stored. Lack of vigor, muscle weakness, low body temperature, and weight loss result. Hypersecretion causes sexual precocity in children and masculinity in women.

The adrenal medulla is stimulated by the sympathetic nervous system (SNS) to secrete norepinephrine and epinephrine (noradrenaline and adrenaline). Norepinephine mimics SNS effects on target tissue and raises the blood pressure by vasoconstriction. Epinephrine raises blood pressure by increased heart rate and also stimulates ACTH release by the anterior pituitary. ACTH stimulates corticoid output by the adrenal cortex, which increases the BMR and improves tissue excitability. Both the adrenal cortex and medulla increase their secretions in response to stress.

The pancreas reacts to nerve excitation and to the level of blood sugar. Its major hormone is insulin, produced by the beta cells. Insulin inhibits the liver in making or releasing blood sugar and causes increased use of blood sugar by the muscles and other tissue. Hyposecretion of insulin causes diabetes mellitus, with an oversupply of blood glucose (hyperglycemia) secreted in the urine and an accumulation of wastes from fat and protein metabolism, and leads to a diabetic coma. Hypersecretion of insulin causes hypoglycemia and insulin shock convulsions.

The posterior pituitary gland, or neurohypophysis, is under nervous control by the hypothalamus. Its hormones, vasopressin and oxytoxin, raise the blood pressure by arterial constriction (pressor effect), cause contractions in the uterus, stimulate milk production by the mammary glands, and have an antidiuretic effect on the kidney. The main effect of hyposecretion is diabetes insipidus, with excretion of much urine. Hypersecretion is unknown. Posterior pituitary secretions are important to the thirst drive and to maternal behavior. In addition, the nerve fibers reaching the posterior pituitary from the hypothalamus secrete neurohumors, which reach the anterior pituitary via a portal system of blood vessels, influence its activity, and bring it under the influence of the hypothalamus, an important center for drives.

The anterior pituitary gland, or adenohypophysis, controls the activity of the thyroid gland, adrenal cortex, and gonads, in addition to secreting a somatotropic hormone (STH) that stimulates body growth. Hyposecretion of STH in childhood results in a pituitary dwarf. Hypersecretion in childhood results in a pituitary giant, whereas adult hypersecretion causes acromegaly with thickened bones and coarse features. The thyrotropic hormone (TTH) output of the pituitary gland is controlled by the level of blood thyroxin and controls, in turn, the output of the thyroid gland. The adrenocorticotropic hormone (ACTH) of the pituitary controls the adrenal output of the cortical steroids.

The gonadotropic hormones stimulate the gonads to produce hormones and regulate sexual cycles in the female and sexual drive in the male. The follicle-stimulating hormone stimulates the development of ova by the female follicles and sperm by the male testes. Luteinizing hormone (LH) stimulates sex hormone output by both sexes and ovulation in the female. Lactogenic hormone (prolactin) aids in turning the follicles into the corpus luteum and stimulates its output of progesterone. It also stimulates female milk production. The gonads are thus under the control of the adenohypophysis. In both sexes the gonads have the two functions of producing germ tissue and sex hormones. The male testes produce androgens and sperm cells. Lack of female estrogens or male androgens in childhood results in failure to mature sexually and failure to develop a sex drive. After castration in adult animals the sex drive often fails, but is little affected in adult humans. In the female pituitary FSH initiates the estrus cycle by stimulating the follicles of the ovaries to produce an ovum, which is carried to the uterus by the fallopian tubes. The follicles secrete estrogens that stimulate growth of the placenta in the uterus and excite the pituitary to secrete LH. FSH and LH cause ovulation. Pituitary LH and prolactin change the follicle into the corpus luteum, which secretes progesterone. Progesterone stops FSH production and prevents further ovulation. LH and prolactin keep up estrogen secretion of the corpus luteum, and prolactin prepares the mammary glands for milk production. The placenta secretes chorionic hormone and progesterone to maintain the status quo if pregnancy occurs. Otherwise, the uterine wall is stripped away in menstruation.

The pineal gland produces a hormone called melatonin. SNS stimulation in response to light inhibits melatonin production by blocking its enzyme, HIOMT. Melatonin inhibits gonadal activity in the absence of light. The pineal gland helps regulate day and night cycles of sexual activity in man and other animals and regulates seasonal sexual activity in some animals.

The thymus gland is of little importance to behavior. It is not an endocrine gland since it produces white blood cells (lymphocytes) instead of hormones. Lymphocytes are produced at birth and until 8 to 10 years of age; after this the gland atrophies. Lymphatocytes reacts against bacteria and viruses as well as foreign proteins in the body and thereby combat infection.

READINGS

Asimov, I.: The human brain, Boston, 1964, Houghton Miffin Co.

Burnet, M.: The thymus gland, Sci. Amer. **207**:50-57, Nov., 1962.

Csapo, A.: Progesterone, Sci. Amer. **198**:40-46, April, 1958. (W. H. Freeman Co. Reprint No. 138.)

Davidson, E. H.: Hormones and genes, Sci. Amer. **212**:36-45, June, 1965. (W. H. Freeman Co. Reprint No. 1013.)

Levey, R. W.: The thymus hormone, Sci. Amer. July, 1964. (W. H. Freeman Co. Reprint No. 188.)

Levine, S.: Sex differences in the brain, Sci. Amer. **214**:84-90, April, 1966. (W. H. Freeman Co. Reprint No. 498.)

Li, C. H.: The ACTH molecule, Sci. Amer. **209**: 46-53, July, 1963. (W. H. Freeman Co. Reprint No. 160.)

Rasmussen, H.: The parathyroid hormone, Sci. Amer. **204**:56-63, April, 1961. (W. H. Freeman Co. Reprint No. 86.)

Whalen, R. E., editor: Hormones and behavior, Princeton, N. J., 1967, D. Van Nostrand Co., Inc.

Wurtman, R. J., and Axelrod, J.: The pineal gland, Sci. Amer. **213**:50-60, July, 1965. (W. H. Freeman Co. Reprint No. 1015.)

Chapter 4

Nerve physiology

OVERVIEW

Chapter 2 explained how life is *organized* from a chemical level up to the level of tissues, organs, and systems. Chapter 3 was devoted to the system of endocrine glands whose function is integration of the other tissues and systems of the body. This chapter will be devoted to a kind of *tissue* that is also specialized for organizing the reactions of the body—nerve tissue. Nerve tissue is specialized for conduction. Nerve tissue makes up the nervous system, which integrates the varied functions of man's specialized cells by conducting excitation from one part of the body to another. In this fashion activity in one part of the body affects activity in another part of the body so that internal consistency, or homeostasis, can be maintained.

Before the nervous system is studied as a whole (Chapter 6), the structure and functioning of its cells should be understood. The cell unit of structure and function in the nervous system is the neuron, or nerve cell. Neuron function depends on certain features of neuron structure, which will be presented first. A general idea of the methods the anatomist uses will help in the presentation. Then ways of measuring the electrical and chemical events that signal conduction in neurons can be explained so that the signs of neuron functioning will be meaningful. Electrical and chemical

characteristics of neuron function will be outlined. Finally, the way in which neurons pass on excitation from one cell to another at synapses concludes the chapter. Excitation and inhibition at synapses, or points of functional contact between cells, determine what part of the body receives a "message" from another part of the body via the nervous system.

THE NEURON: ANATOMY

A simplified sketch of a "typical" **neuron** is presented in Fig. 4-1. Nerve cells in man are too small to be seen except under a microscope (see below) and vary widely in their characteristics, but all nerve cells feature the parts labeled in Fig. 4-1 with the exception of the neurolemma and myelin sheath. **Synapses** between two neurons are shown so that the role of certain parts of the cell may be appreciated. The nerve cell shown is a long slender one, obviously designed to carry excitation from one part of the body to another. In life the neuron receives excitation at synapses from the **terminal arborization** of another neuron. At this point the terminal arborization contacts the **dendrites** and **cell body** of the neuron, each contact being a synapse. The transferred excitation is focused by the **axon hillock** on the **axon** and carried down the axon to its terminal arborization at the next set of synapses. Excitation continues to be

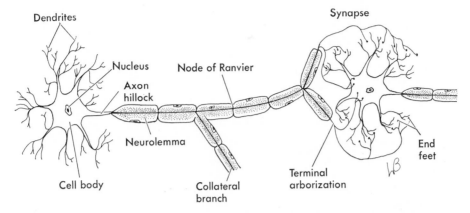

Fig. 4-1. Semidiagrammatic view of a "typical" neuron, showing its major parts and synapses with a second neuron. The role of each part of the neuron is described in the text.

passed from cell to cell in this manner. The axon of a neuron may or may not have a **myelin sheath,** a fatty covering interrupted at the **nodes of Ranvier.** Since the conduction process is an electrical event, excitation was once thought to jump from one node of Ranvier to another (saltatory conduction), but recent evidence indicates this is not the case. In any event nerve cells with myelin sheaths conduct faster than nerve cells that have no myelin sheath. The **neurolemma** is a covering for the neuron, made up of a separate cell (the Schwann cell) that is thought to secrete the fatty myelin sheath. Its main function seems to be protective, holding together the long thin axon.

The **nerves** of the body are bundles of axons connecting the brain and spinal cord to the sense organs and muscles. The nerves make up the **peripheral nervous system.** Their axons each have a neurolemma but may or may not have a myelin sheath, although most of them do. The axons that lie altogether inside the brain and spinal cord are in the **central nervous system** and have no neurolemma; they may or may not have a myelin sheath. Their myelin sheaths are thought to be secreted by glial cells, another kind of supporting cell. In any case

bundles of individually conducting fibers that are held together by connective tissue constitute the nerves of the peripheral nervous system. Bundles of individually conducting axons running from one part of the brain and spinal cord to another inside the central nervous system are called **tracts.**

Types of neurons

As mentioned previously, individual nerve cells vary widely in appearance. It is useful, however, to classify them into anatomical categories that have functional significance (Fig. 4-2). Although there are many varieties of neurons, the classification shown types them according to the number of processes that extend directly from the cell body. The **bipolar** (two-process) **neuron,** which has a single axon and a single dendrite, is thought to be the primitive or early form of all nerve cells. In man such cells can be seen in the retina of the eye, where their functional characteristics are important (Chapter 12).

Most of the nerves conducting excitation from the sense organs of the skin to the brain and spinal cord—sensory nerves—are made up of **unipolar neurons.** A single process connects both axon and dendrite to the cell body, and the dendrite takes on all the

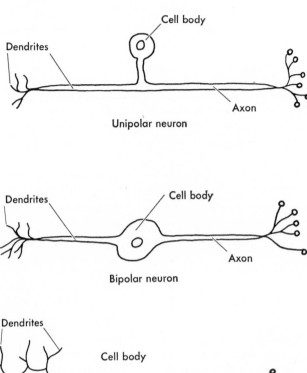

Fig. 4-2. Types of neurons classified according to the number of processes attached directly to the cell body. A unipolar neuron has one, a bipolar neuron has two (one axon and one dendrite), and a multipolar neuron has several (one axon and several dendrites).

characteristics of an axon, including, in many cases, a myelin sheath. A review of the "typical" neuron (Fig. 4-1) will show that conduction proceeds in the direction from dendrites to cell body to axon. The unipolar neuron connects the dendrite to the axon. Since the cell body lies near the brain and spinal cord, the dendrite must be long to reach the skin surface and must conduct rapidly like an axon.

A **multipolar** (many-process) **neuron,** on the other hand, has several short dendrites and a single axon, and therefore many pro-

cesses are connected to the cell body. Multipolar neurons are the most common, being found throughout the central nervous system. Their axons also make up the tracts of the brain and the **motor nerves** that extend from the central nervous system to the muscles to excite muscular contraction. Multipolar neurons are classified as **Golgi type I** and **Golgi type II** according to the length and branching of their axons. If they are to carry excitation for some distance, as do tracts and motor nerves, they are Golgi type I neurons, with long axons having few branches. If their axons are short and branch repeatedly, they are Golgi type II neurons, whose function is to spread excitation to nearby neurons.

Anatomical methods for studying neurons

To appreciate what nerve cells look like and what mistakes the anatomist can make in studying their connections with one another, at least a simplified form of the methods used by the anatomist should be understood. It is difficult to study neurons because of their small size and still more difficult to trace their many connections with one another at synapses. To overcome these difficulties, the anatomist uses several different procedures: light microscope observations, degeneration methods, and electron microscope observations.

Light microscope observations. The largest neurons vary from 50 millimicrons ($m\mu$) (thousandths of a millionth of a meter) thick at the cell body to 20 $m\mu$ (about one thousandth of an inch) thick at the axon. Cells of this size can be seen only through a **microscope.** The tissue must be sliced thin enough so that light will pass through it (about 40μ) and placed on a glass slide for observation under the microscope. Before a section of brain or spinal cord can be sliced this thin, it must be hardened with formaldehyde (formalin). When the animal is sacrificed, a tube from a formalin bottle is inserted into the heart, which pumps the solution throughout the circulatory system, replacing the blood. The nervous tissue is thus hardened from the inside out. The tissue is then removed from the animal and further hardened by freezing or embedding in paraffin, and thin cross sections are sliced from the desired portion with a **microtome,** a precision slicing instrument. The thin sections are placed in alcohol to remove water and then stained, or dyed with solutions that react chemically with one part or another of the nerve cells to color them for clear observation under the microscope. For exam-

ple, some stains react with the myelin sheath of axons to enable the anatomist to trace the axons from section to section in the tracts of the brain and spinal cord. Other stains color only cells without a myelin sheath or the cell bodies and terminal arborizations of neurons for studying synapses. Many different specialized types of stains can be used. Stained sections are placed on glass slides and covered for protection. They are then ready for observation.

Degeneration methods. Even after proper staining the anatomist cannot distinguish one tract from another under the microscope because the stained axons or myelin sheaths carry no "labels" and the axons of adjoining tracts become intermingled or overlap. To overcome this difficulty, the anatomist damages a tract in the living animal at a point where its location is known. After waiting for the effects of the damage to reach other levels of the brain and spinal cord, he sacrifices the animal, makes slides, and identifies the tract at other levels by observing the effects of the original damage at these levels. For example, cutting a tract in the central nervous system will cause the axons to degenerate between the cut and their terminal arborization (wallerian degeneration). Slides of sections taken at other levels will reveal the location of the tract by the absence of its axons. The same cut will cause changes in the cell bodies of the damaged neurons (secondary, or retrograde, degeneration). When the anatomist finds a group of cell bodies (a **center,** or **nucleus**) showing the changes indicated, he knows that the axons of the tract he cut originated in that group of cell bodies. Finally, when a tract degenerates, the cell bodies of neurons on which the tract ended are deprived of synaptic connections (innervation) from the cut neurons. This sometimes causes these cells to degenerate in turn. Their axons can then be traced by their absence to the next synapses in the chain of cell connections.

Electron microscope observations. The **electron microscope** allows a magnification of ten to a hundred times that of the light microscope. Through its use in anatomy, physiology, and physiological psychology, much has been learned regarding the physical and chemical characteristics of synapses. Synapse function must be understood if knowledge of how changes in nerve cell excitability at synapses can occur in sensitization, adaptation, and learning is to be gained. Synaptic change lies at the heart of these problems.

To oversimplify, the tissue is bombarded with a stream of electrons, or negative particles, in a vacuum. The stream of **electrons** can be focused by magnetic means, just as light can be focused by a lens. The resulting magnification reveals the smallest structures at the synapses and can show the structure of viruses, crystals, and even large organic molecules (Chapter 10). The magnified image is projected on a fluorescent screen at the end of the evacuated tube.

THE NEURON: FUNCTION
Instrumentation

The functioning of neurons in carrying nerve impulses along the length of the axon and in exciting other neurons at synapses is usually studied through the electrical activity that constitutes the nerve impulse. In the past the major obstacles to studying the electrical activity of neurons were (1) the small size of the neuron, (2) the minuteness of the electrical change (10 to 70 thousandths of a **volt**), and (3) the lag in recording instruments that could not follow electrical events that last only a thousandth of a second. The first problem has been solved by the development of the **microelectrode,** which is small enough to penetrate a single nerve cell so that the difference in electrical potential between the inside and outside of the single cell can be measured. The second problem has yielded to the **vacuum-tube amplifier,** which can magnify voltage

differences by as much as a million times. The third problem has been overcome by the **cathode-ray oscilloscope,** which measures voltage change as the movement of a stream of electrons, an event that has almost no inertia or lag.

In practice, the microelectrode is made by stretching a heated glass tube out until it breaks with a hollow end as tiny as 0.5μ thick. The tube is filled with an electrically conducting salt solution (KCl) and inserted into the tissue. When the microelectrode enters a single axon, such as a giant squid axon, a potential difference with respect to another electrode located outside the axon at an indifferent point is registered. The difference in potential is usually about 70 millivolts (mv.) (70/1,000 volt) and represents the **resting potential** of the nerve cell. The outside of the nerve cell is positively charged with respect to the inside. This **polarized condition** reverses during passage of the nerve impulse down the axon (Fig. 4-3).

Recording the nerve impulse (Fig. 4-3)

The microelectrode inside the axon is negative with respect to an electrode outside the axon. This difference in charge is magnified by the vacuum-tube amplifier and applied to the cathode-ray oscilloscope. Now the cathode-ray oscilloscope amounts to a simplified version of a television set. The cathode tube itself is an elongated vacuum tube with an electron source at one end. The electron source, or cathode, discharges negative charges or electrons at high speed to strike the face of the tube at the other end. The tube face is coated inside with a fluorescent paint so that the electrons make a bright spot on the face of the tube when they strike it. The spot can be made to move across the face of the tube at a known rate by charging plates to either side of the stream of electrons to deflect them back and forth (the X plates). When the amplified charge between the inside and outside of the axon is applied to

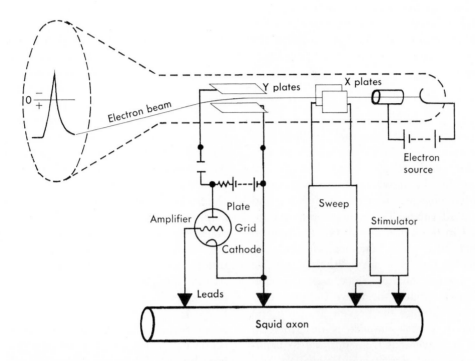

Fig. 4-3. Diagram of the arrangements for recording the nerve impulse. The micro-electrode and the operation of the cathode-ray oscilloscope are described in the text. The vacuum tube controls the flow of electrons (negative charges) from a negatively charged *cathode* to a positively charged *plate* in a vacuum. Negative charges reduce the positive charge of the plate. These charges must pass through apertures in a screen *grid* to reach the plate from the cathode. The grid is connected to the microelectrode, which has a negative charge from the inside of the nerve cell. The plate is indirectly connected to the outside of the cell. The negative electrons on the grid turn back many times their number in electrons that would normally flow from cathode to plate (like charges repel each other). Thus a small charge at the grid makes a large difference in the number of electrons reaching the plate and therefore a large difference in the voltage of the plate. The voltage difference between the inside and outside of the nerve cell is therefore *amplified* many times.

plates above and below the electron stream (the Y plates), the moving spot on the face of the tube is deflected downward. If the nerve cell is stimulated, a reversal of its normal polarized condition results, and the outside of the nerve cell becomes negative with respect to the inside at that point. This change will then sweep down the length of the axon. If the axon is stimulated at the same time that the sweep of the electron beam is started across the face of the tube, a picture of the reversal of the polarized condition of the axon as the nerve impulse passes the microelectrode will be obtained. The reversal of polarization in the axon as the electron beam passes across the face of the tube will, so to speak, "draw its own picture," with time as the horizontal axis of the graph and voltage change as the vertical axes (Figs. 4-3 and 4-5). Placing the microelectrode *near* the cell is enough to record nerve impulses in many experiments since the fluid surrounding the cells is a good conductor of electrical changes.

Electrical characteristics of the nerve impulse

The changes in potential (voltage) or **currents** involved in the stimulator, sweep, amplifier, and cathode-ray oscilloscope are caused by the movement of electrons or negative charges through **conductors** and evacuated tubes. The voltage changes involved in the nerve impulse of the neuron are caused by **ions,** chemical elements, or molecules that can carry either a positive or a negative charge. Since a positive ion (sodium) initiates the nerve impulse, current flow through the nerve cell membrane during the nerve impulse is described in terms of movement from *positive* to *negative*. Actually, positive and negative ions move in both directions as will be described later.

Electrotonus

The outside of a "resting" nerve cell is positively charged with respect to the inside of the nerve cell. This polarized condition is caused by the physical and chemical characteristics of the **nerve membrane. Electrotonus** is the result of adding to, or subtracting from, the polarized condition of the nerve membrane without exciting the fiber (that is, axon) enough to reverse its potential, and thus set off a nerve impulse (Fig. 4-4). If the axon has a negative electrode or **cathode** applied to one point along its length and an **anode** or positive electrode applied to another point along its length, the polarized condition of the membrane will be altered at these two points. At the cathode the polarized condition will be reduced (**catelectrotonus**). The membrane is *more excitable* at the cathode because further reducing the polarized condition of the axon would set off the nerve impulse. At the anode the polarized condition of the membrane will be increased (**anelectrotonus**). This change is oppo-

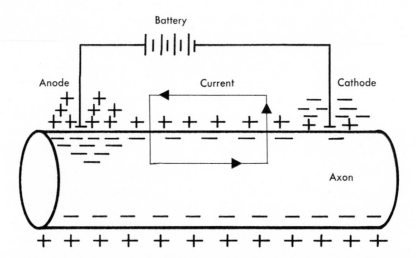

Fig. 4-4. Electrotonus, or changing the polarized condition of the neuron by less than the amount required to excite it. Polarization is increased at the anode (anelectrotonus), where the axon is less excitable than normal. Polarization is decreased at the cathode (catelectrotonus), where the axon is more excitable than normal.

site to the change that causes a nerve impulse so that the axon is less excitable at the anode than normal. There is a flow of current along and through the membrane between the anode and cathode.

Although the flow consists of the movement of both positive and negative ions, it is depicted as being a flow from positive to negative, as described previously. In these terms, currents that flow inward through the membrane (anodal currents) are inhibiting, whereas currents that flow outward through the membrane are exciting (cathodal currents). Such conventions of current flow are clumsy but still widely used; there-fore, they should be understood. For other purposes it is well to keep in mind that positive and negative ions are actually moving in both directions.

All-or-none law

The nerve impulse consists of a rapid exchange of positive and negative ions across the nerve cell membrane when the degree of electrotonus reaches a critical value at the cathode. That is, when the polarized condition of the nerve membrane is reduced by a certain amount, the membrane "takes over" and continues the depolarization past the neutral point so that

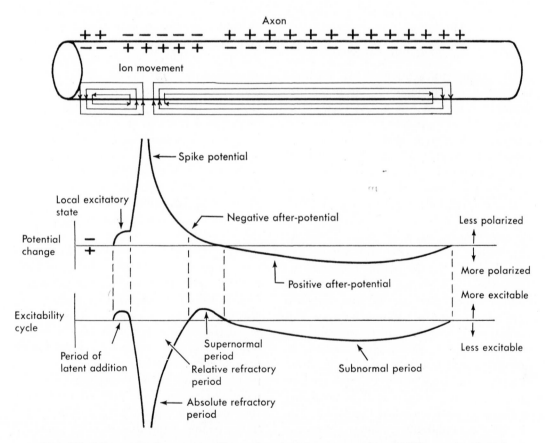

Fig. 4-5. Nerve impulse: current flow, potential changes, and excitability cycle plotted on a common time axis. For details, see text. (From Morgan, C. T.: Physiological psychology, ed. 3, New York, 1965, McGraw-Hill Book Co.)

the outside of the nerve cell membrane becomes negative with respect to the inside. The impulse is self-propagating; that is, the energy for the polarization reversal is supplied by the nerve cell itself, and not by the stimulus that triggers it. Once initiated, the impulse spreads along the axon by ion shifts through the membrane down the whole length of the axon; the energy for the spread comes from the nerve cell membrane. The **all-or-none law** states that a nerve cell responds with the total voltage change that its polarized condition permits if, and only if, the stimulus intensity reaches a critical threshold value. Stronger stimuli will not result in a larger or faster nerve impulse since the nerve cell itself, and not the stimulus, provides the energy for the nerve impulse.

Electrical and excitability events

The complete sequence of electrical changes that accompanies the nerve impulse are shown in Fig. 4-5. A diagram of the changes in excitability of the axon occurring at the same time is also shown. Finally, the current flow accompanying the various phases of the **action potential** is given in a conventional term of positive to negative current flow. As the current flow that causes the nerve impulse approaches the point on the axon being measured, an electrotonic change (catelectrotonus, discussed above) in the action potential occurs; this change is called a **local excitatory state.** Because of the outward (positive to negative) flow of current, this portion of the membrane is partially depolarized, that is, less positive outside to negative inside than normal. The local excitatory state lasts about 0.5 milliseconds (msec.). At the same time the excitability of the axon is increased at that point. The change in excitability accompanying the local excitatory state is graphed as the **period of latent addition** on the excitability cycle. When the electrotonic change reaches the threshold of the nerve membrane, the membrane "takes over" and continues the electrical change, as indicated in the all-or-none law. The membrane reverses potential, becoming negative on the outside and positive on the inside, an event of the action potential called the **spike potential.** The spike potential lasts about 1 msec. During this time the axon cannot be deporalized since it has already reversed polarization. The axon is completely unexcitable, an event of the excitability cycle called the **absolute refractory period.** The axon then begins recovering its polarized condition as indicated in the current flow diagram. This event occurs rapidly at first, and then more slowly, as shown by the action potential. The period during which the axon is recovering its normal polarized condition is the **negative after-potential** and lasts about 20 msec. in a "typical" neuron. During the early part of the negative after-potential, the axon has recovered enough polarization to be excitable again. However, the current flow of recovery must be reversed to excite it, so that a stronger-than-normal stimulus is required; the threshold of the axon is raised during the early part of the negative after-potential. This part of the excitability cycle is called the **relative refractory period.** During the later part of the negative after-potential, the current flow causing recovery slows down and is therefore easier to reverse by a new stimulus. In addition, the axon is still partially depolarized—it has not yet recovered its fully polarized state. For these two reasons the axon is easier to stimulate (or depolarize again) than normal. The excitability cycle is therefore in a **supernormal period,** and a weaker stimulus will excite it in comparison with its resting state. Finally, the current flow involved in recovery "overshoots" the polarized condition found in the resting axon; that is, for a period of about 80 msec. the axon becomes more polarized than normal, the **positive after-potential.** During the overpolarized condition of the positive after-potential, a stronger-than-normal stimulus is required to reduce the polarized condition of the axon enough to fire it—its threshold is increased. Therefore, the **subnormal period** of the excitability cycle accompanies the positive after-potential, and the nerve cell is harder to stimulate than usual during this period.

The sequence and timing of the electrical and excitatory events varies widely from one nerve cell to another. Some types of nerve cells show no positive after-potential or subnormal period. The duration of the phases of the action potential and excitability cycle, as well as conduction velocity, differs according to cell size and type (Table 4-1). Finally, cells in the living brain probably fire at slower rates than the excitability cycle given here would allow (the information presented has been taken from peripheral nerves). However, the principles outlined are valid and have important consequences for physiological psychology.

It is important to realize that the only information the brain receives from the outside world is coded in terms of nerve impulses. Events in the physical world stimulate the *receptors,* which, in turn, stimulate nerve cells whose impulses reach the brain, either directly or indirectly. Now, if the *stimulus* to the receptor is *just* strong enough to fire the sensory nerve cells—a threshold stimulus—the nerve cell will fire, and fire again only after the first part of the negative after-potential is over and the supernormal period begins. That is, the nerve cell will have to recover full sensitivity before it can fire a second time in response to a barely sufficient, or threshold, stimulus. This means that the *frequency* of impulses will be at a *minimum.* However, the *spike size* (amount of polarization change in the nerve impulse) will be at a *maximum.* The spike will be large because the sensory nerve cell membrane will be fully repolarized or recovered each time it fires. Now, if the stimulus to the receptor is increased in *intensity,* how can this change be communicated to the brain? With a stimulus well above threshold, the nerve cell need not recover fully before it can be fired

Table 4-1. Properties of nerve fibers*

	A	Alpha	Beta	Gamma	Delta	B	s.C†	d.r.C‡
Fiber diameter (μ)	1–22	6– 19	12–8	8–2	1–6	≤ 3	0.3–1.3	0.4–1.2
Conduction speed (m./sec.)	5–120	5–120				3–15	0.7–2.3	0.6–2.0
Spike duration (msec.)	0.4–0.5					1.2	2.0	2.0
Absolutely refractory period (msec.)	0.4–1.0					1.2	2.0	2.0
Negative after-potential amplitude, per cent of spike	3–5					None	3–5	None
Duration (msec.)	12–20						50–80	
Positive after-potential amplitude, per cent of spike	0.2					1.5–4.0	1.5	
Duration (msec.)	40–60					100–300	300–1000	
Order of susceptibility to asphyxia	2					1	3	3
Velocity/diameter ratio	6					?	?	1.73 average

*Modified from Patton, H. D.: Special properties of nerve trunks and tracts. In Ruch, T. C., Patton, H. D., Woodbury, J. W., and Towe, A. L.: Neurophysiology, ed. 2, Philadelphia, 1965, W. B. Saunders Co.
†Unmyelinated C fibers of the sympathetic nervous system.
‡Unmyelinated sensory nerve fibers for pain.

again—it will fire during the relative refractory period that occurs during the early part of the negative after-potential. An increase in stimulus intensity will result in more frequent nerve impulses to the brain. Further, each spike potential after the first will be smaller—represent a lesser potential change—because the nerve cell will not be fully repolarized or recovered before it is fired each time. The cell will be fired during the negative after-potential. Increases in intensity of stimulus can therefore be signaled to the brain by increases in the frequency of nerve impulses and decreases in their spike size. Finally, it should be noted that receptors and sensory neurons differ in threshold. A weak stimulus may fire only the most sensitive ones. As stimulus strength increases, then, more receptors and therefore more sensory neurons will be firing. Such changes must relay information to the brain as changes in the brightness of lights, loudness of sounds, intensity of pressure on the skin, etc.

Generator potentials

Axons, apparently, are the only receptor or nervous structures that show spike potentials. Receptors stimulate nerve cells, and nerve cells stimulate each other at synapses by means of graded, or generator, potentials. These potentials resemble the electrotonic changes and the local excitatory state previously described. That is, they represent *partial* depolarization at the receptor or at synapses—depolarization that does not become complete, or at least does not reverse, the polarized condition at that point. As such, graded potentials do not follow the all-or-none law. The signal increases in intensity of a stimulus at a receptor or increases in the number of active synapses on the cell body and dendrites by an increase in the *extent* and *degree* of depolarization. The ion shifts that result depolarize the axon to result in nerve impulses. Graded potentials can *summate,* one partial depolarization adding to the effect of the previous one, if they occur close enough together. In receptors, **generator potentials** usually arise only in response to the type of stimulus for which the receptor is specialized, for example, pressure in the pacinian corpuscle or light in the rods and cones of the eye. At synapses, as will be seen later, chemical events seem to cause **graded potentials** on the dendrites and cell bodies they contact, structures that do not normally respond to electrical changes. The sequence of events at the synapses would be as follows: axon spike, chemical event, graded potential, and axon spike.

Chemical characteristics of resting potential and nerve impulse

Recent research has made clear what shifts in ions or charged chemical particles are responsible for the resting potential and for the nerve impulse. The ionic basis of the resting potential and the ion shifts responsible for the nerve impulse have been largely worked out over the past few years by an ingenious set of experiments carried out on giant squid axons. These axons are unmyelinated and as large as a millimeter in diameter. As a result of their size, investigators have been able to sample and to alter the chemical and electrical characteristics of squid axons while firing them at the same time. The resulting information shows the dependence of the nervous system on the ions in its fluid environment; that is, the functioning of nerve cells and therefore sensation, imagination, thinking, and behavior, all depend on that environment.

Resting potential. The polarized condition of the nerve cell axon is caused by certain properties of the nerve cell membrane with respect to ions, or charged chemical elements and molecules. As a result of the characteristics of the nerve cell membrane, there are more positive than negative ions outside the membrane and more negative than positive ions inside the membrane. The imbalance in ions results in a positive charge outside the membrane and a negative charge inside the membrane. The ion imbalance and the consequent resting potential between the inside and outside of the cell membrane is the result of four factors (Fig. 4-6):

1. *Sodium pump.* For reasons that are still not understood the nerve cell membrane actively excludes **sodium** ions (Na+) from the cell. Sodium ions carry a positive charge so that there are more positively charged sodium ions outside the membrane than inside the membrane.

2. *Potassium pump.* Theorists believe that the membrane actively *includes* **potassium (K+)**; that is, it takes any potassium ions encountered in the fluid environment and actively transports them inside the cell. Potassium ions are positively charged, but there are not enough of them inside the cell to offset the positively charged sodium ions outside the cell. The cell remains, on balance, more positively charged outside than inside.

3. *Ion size.* The cell contains many nega-tively charged acid molecules (acid anions) that are too large to pass through the pores of the cell membrane. Because of their size, they cannot pass through the membrane pores any more than buckshot will pass through a sieve. This further makes the inside of the cell negative with respect to the outside.

4. *Principle of diffusion.* **Chlorine (Cl−)** ions carry a negative charge and are free to move back and forth through the membrane. Now substances tend to move from a region of high concentration to a region of low concentration, according to the principle of diffusion. To demonstrate this one need only place a drop of ink into a glass of water and in minutes the ink particles will diffuse throughout the water. According to the principle of diffusion one would expect to find an equal number of chlorine ions inside and outside the nerve cell membrane. But chlorine ions carry a negative charge and therefore are attracted by positively charged ions and repelled by negatively charged ions. As shown earlier, there

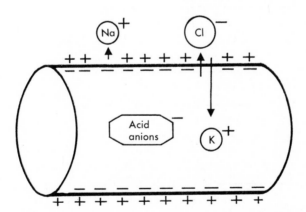

Fig. 4-6. Chemical basis of the resting potential. Negatively charged acid anions are trapped inside the cell membrane because of their size, and positive sodium cations (Na+) are actively excluded by the membrane ("sodium pump"). A concentration gradient of potassium (K+) and chlorine (Cl−) ions result, the Cl− ions attracted by the Na+ and the K+ by the negative acid anions. Cl− ions tend to diffuse back inside the membrane, and K+ ions back outside to some extent. As a net result, the membrane is polarized, being positive on the outside with respect to the inside of the cell.

are more negative acid anions inside the membrane than outside, and more positive sodium ions outside the membrane than positive potassium ions inside the membrane. Therefore, there is an imbalance in favor of positive ions outside the membrane and negative ions inside the membrane. Negative chlorine ions are repelled by the negative ions inside the membrane and attracted by the positive ions outside the membrane; a **concentration gradient** of chlorine ions is built up, with more chlorine ions outside than inside the membrane. For reasons explained above, there is a similar concentration gradient of sodium (more outside) and opposite concentration gradi-

ents of potassium and acid anions (more inside). The measured size of these gradients of charged particles is enough to account for the size of the resting potential, 40 mv. or more. The resting potential is accounted for by the imbalance of known positive ions outside the nerve cell membrane and known negative ions inside the nerve cell membrane. These principles are not confined to nerve cells—all living cells seem to be polarized and for the same reasons. However, the specialized feature of nerve cells is shown in their greater ability to alter their polarized condition to produce the nerve impulse.

Nerve impulse. Actually since a single

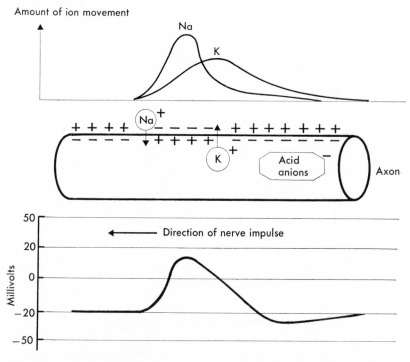

Fig. 4-7. Chemical basis of the nerve impulse. Polarization reversal is caused by an influx of sodium (Na+) ions when the membrane ceases to exclude them. Recovery of polarization occurs when potassium ions (K+) move outside the membrane to replace sodium ions. Ion movements are shown in the top graph, events in the axon are sketched in the middle, and electrical changes (millivolts of polarization) are at the bottom, with a common time axis for the three sets of events reading from left to right.

axon rather than a bundle of axons in a nerve is being discussed, the term should be neuron impulse. The term nerve impulse comes from earlier experiments in which the electrical activity of nerve trunks rather than a single axon was all the experimenters could measure. To simplify, the nerve impulse in an axon occurs when its polarized condition is reduced enough to "turn off" the sodium and potassium "pumps" (Fig. 4-7). The initial result is a rapid movement of positive sodium ions (Na^+) into the negatively charged interior of the axon. This event reverses the polarized condition of the membrane so that it becomes positive inside and negative outside—the spike potential. Recovery is initiated by the movement of positive potassium (K^+) ions out of the axon to replace the sodium ions. Potassium ion movement causes the recovery of the normal polarized condition of the axon, that is, the downward limb of the spike potential and parts of the negative and positive after-potentials. The cell is depolarized by sodium ion movement and repolarized by potassium ion movement through its membrane. Negative chlorine ions move first inside and then back outside the membrane in response to changes in its polarized condition. After the action potential is over, the sodium and potassium "pumps" become active again—the sodium is transferred back out of the cell and the potassium back inside the cell while the resting potential is maintained.

THE SYNAPSE

Refer again to Fig. 4-1. It can be seen that nerve cells contact one another when the terminal arborization of one cell "contacts" the cell body and dendrites of a second cell. Every such contact is a **synapse.** Although there are several kinds of synapses, the variety sketched here is most typical. Each branch of the terminal arborization of the first cell ends in a knob-like structure called an axon terminal, or **synaptic knob.** The synaptic knobs do not touch the surface of the dendrites or cell bodies, but come very close to them, leaving a uniform gap or about 100 angstrom units (Å) (1/1000 of a millimeter). In Fig. 4-8 three types of junctions between synaptic knobs and dendrites or cell bodies are shown as they can be seen under the electron microscope. Notice the small globules that concentrate inside the synaptic knobs near the synaptic cleft, or gap between knob and cell body or dendrites. These are the **synaptic vesicles** that are believed to contain the specific chemical substances by which one nerve cell excites another at synapses. Two of these *chemical transmitters* are known to be **norepinephrine** and **acetylcholine (ACh),** but there may be others. There are also neurons whose end-feet probably release inhibitory chemical transmitters such as gamma-aminobutyric acid (GABA) that increase the polarization of dendrites and cell bodies at synapses. This can prevent excitation at nearby synapses from excitatory neurons that end on the same cell.

Postsynaptic potentials

When an excitatory neuron releases ACh onto another neuron at its synapses, the chemical transmitter acts to partly depolarize the second cell. The resulting depolarization is called an **excitatory postsynaptic potential,** or **EPSP.** The vesicles in the synaptic knob probably release ACh molecules through the membrane of the synaptic knobs. The ACh molecules drift rapidly across the synaptic cleft to act on the cell body and dendrites of the second cell. They appear to make the cell body and dendrites of the second cell more permeable to positively charged sodium and potassium ions. The result is an electrotonic potential described as initiating the nerve impulse in a previous section. The cell body and dendrites do not reverse polarization immediately as an axon does. Ions shift from the area of the axon hillock (Fig. 4-1) to replace those that move across the mem-

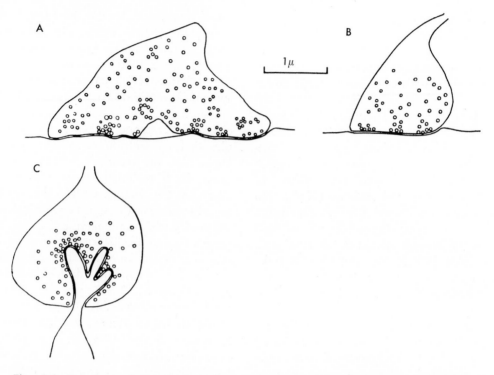

Fig. 4-8. Drawings of three types of synapses seen under the electron microscope. Presynaptic endings (synaptic knobs) are on top in each illustration, the postsynaptic endings below. **A,** Synapse on a large motoneuron cell body. **B,** A smaller interneuron synapse of the same variety. **C,** A synapse between a visual receptor cell in the retina and a nerve cell. Note synaptic vesicles of transmitter substance in each presynaptic ending. (**A** from Paley, S. L.: J. Biophys. Biochem. Cytol. (supp.) **2:**193-202, 1956; **B** from DeRobertis, E. D. P.: J. Biophys. Biochem. Cytol. **2:**503-512, 1956; **C** from DeRobertis, E. D. P., and Franchi, C. M.: J. Biophys. Biochem. Cytol. **2:**307-317, 1956.)

brane of the cell body. Depolarization of the axon hillock results in a nerve impulse, initiated in the axon. The nerve impulse then sweeps down the axon to the next set of synapses, as previously described. As long as a negative EPSP is maintained by synapses on the dendrites and cell body, the axon will continue to fire. When fresh ACh is no longer being released at the synapses, the neuron does not continue to fire because the remaining ACh is rapidly broken down by an enzyme, **acetylcholinesterase** (AChE).

Other types of neurons that are excited in the normal way act to prevent the depolari-

zation of neurons upon which they have synapses. One type of inhibitory cell known to be important in reflexes is a Golgi type II neuron called a Renshaw cell. Its synaptic knobs have vesicles that probably contain gamma-aminobutyric acid (GABA). Such transmitters *hyperpolarize*, or increase, the polarized condition of the cell body and dendrites upon which they are released. The change in potential is called an **inhibitory postsynaptic potential (IPSP).** A hyperpolarized cell is harder to excite with the EPSP produced at excitatory synapses. The cell body and dendrites of a cell may have both excitatory and inhibitory

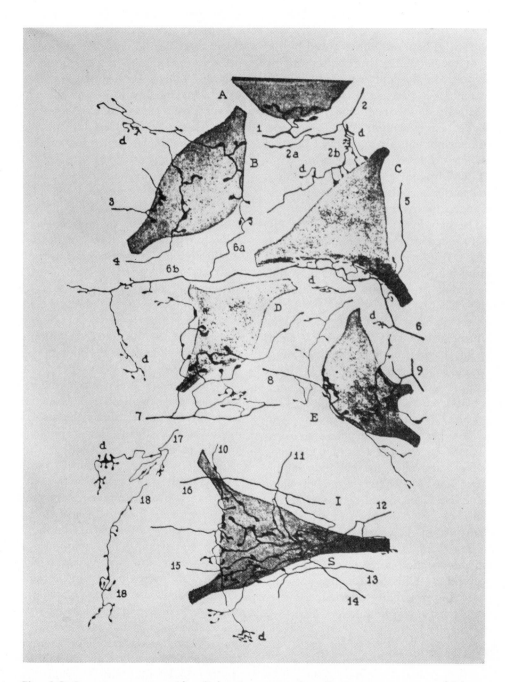

Fig. 4-9. Synapses as seen with a light microscope. **A** to **E** are motoneurons and **I** is an interneuron. Numbered fibers are presynaptic axon terminals ending in synaptic knobs on dendrites and cell bodies of **A** to **E** and **I**. (From Lorenti de No, R.: J. Neurophysiol. **1**:195-206, 1938.)

synapses on it; whether or not it fires depends on the algebraic sum of the EPSP and IPSP influences, which are called **facilitation** and **inhibition,** respectively.

The IPSP is believed to be caused by the effect of the inhibitory transmitter on the membrane. The transmitter probably makes the membrane permeable to potassium ($K+$) ions inside the membrane, but not to the slightly larger sodium ($Na+$) ions outside the membrane. The outflow of positive potassium ions through the membrane without a corresponding inflow of positive sodium ions makes the cell body and dendrites more positive outside to negative inside. The hyperpolarized cell is more difficult to depolarize or excite. Potassium salts have been used to hyperpolarize and therefore inhibit parts of the brain in animal learning experiments (spreading depression, Chapter 17).

The diagrams and figures used to illustrate principles of synaptic function up to this point have been oversimplified. Fig. 4-9, taken from a microscope slide, gives some appreciation of the number and complexity of synapses on each single cell. It should also be noted that axo-axonic synapses have been observed where the synaptic knobs end on the terminal filaments of another fiber. These are probably inhibitory, but until researchers agree on their mode of action this is not certain. The importance of synaptic mechanisms to the psychologist is, however, no longer in doubt. For example, it has been shown that blocking destruction of the transmitter ACh by preventing AChE from acting not only increases the excitability of synapses, but, in animals, improves the rate at which they learn (Chapter 17).

SUMMARY

As a background to understanding how the nervous system maintains homeostasis and regulates behavior, this chapter has been devoted to study of the unit of nervous system structure and function—the neuron or nerve cell. Although neurons vary widely in appearance, they all feature a cell body, one or more dendrites, an axon, and a terminal arborization. Bundles of neuron fibers make up the nerves of the peripheral nervous system and tracts of the central nervous system. Axons may or may not have a myelin sheath, but all the axons of nerves have a neurolemma. Varied as they are, neurons can be classed as unipolar, bipolar, or multipolar, depending on the number of processes attached to the cell body.

Neurons are too small to be observed except under a microscope. Even then, special hardening, staining, and slicing techniques must be used to prepare the tissue. Anatomists trace the tracts of the nervous system by the effect of damaging the axons of tracts at levels where their location is known—the tracts can be traced at other levels by changes in the affected cells. Extremely small parts of the neuron can be observed with the electron microscope, which is much more powerful than the light microscope.

The function of neurons is studied by observation of their electrical characteristics. Such observations require the use of the microelectrode, the vacuum-tube amplifier, and the cathode-ray oscilloscope. The neuron exhibits a resting potential, with the outside of the cell positive with respect to the inside. When stimulated, this state of affairs is reversed, and the change sweeps down the axon as the nerve impulse or action potential. The nerve impulse obeys the all-or-none law, the energy being supplied by the nerve membrane. The action potential shows a sequence of polarization changes, including the local excitatory state, spike potential, negative after-potential, and positive after-potential. The axon shows corresponding changes in excitability, including the latent addition period, absolute refractory period, relative refractory period, supernormal period, and subnormal period. These facts have important consequences for the way the brain detects intensity change in receptors as a function of changes in the frequency and spike size of nerve impulses. Nerve impulses are apparently confined to axons, receptors and neuron cell bodies showing a partial depolarization called a generator potential or a graded potential, respectively.

Both the resting potential and the action potential are caused by the behavior of the nerve membrane with respect to positively and negatively charged ions, particularly the exclusion of sodium and the inclusion of potassium. The resulting differences in concentration (concentration gradient) of charged ions causes the resting potential. The action potential and nerve impulse result when the nerve membrane momentarily quits excluding sodium and including potassium—ion shifts power the nerve impulse.

Nerve cells excite one another at synapses. The terminal arborization of the axon ends in synaptic knobs that contact the cell body and dendrites of a second cell. These knobs contain synaptic vesicles that release either an excitatory or inhibitory transmitter when the nerve impulse reaches them. Excitatory transmitters such as ACh depolarize the cell body and dendrites of the second cell, causing an EPSP. The EPSP depolarizes the axon to cause a nerve impulse. Inhibitory transmitters hyperpolarize the second cell to result in an IPSP. The effect of excitatory and inhibitory synapses on the same cell is one of algebraic summation. The EPSP is caused by an increase in membrane permeability to sodium and potassium while the IPSP results from an increase in permeability to potassium alone. The understanding of synaptic phenomena is important to the physiological psychology of sensation, perception, and learning.

READINGS

Baker, P. F.: The nerve axon, Sci. Amer. 214:74-82, March, 1966. (W. H. Freeman Co. Reprint No. 1038.)

Eccles, J.: The synapse, Sci. Amer. 212:56-66, Jan., 1965. (W. H. Freeman Co. Reprint No. 1001.)

Freeman, I. M.: Physics made simple, Garden City, N. Y., 1954, Doubleday & Co. Inc.

Galambos, R.: Nerves and muscles, Garden City, N. Y., 1962, Doubleday & Co. Inc.

Katz, B.: The nerve impulse, Sci. Amer. 187:55-64, Nov., 1952, (W. H. Freeman Co. Reprint No. 20.)

Keynes, R.: The nerve impulse and the squid, Sci. Amer. 199:88-90, Dec., 1958. (W. H. Freeman Co. Reprint No. 58.)

Chapter 5

Muscle physiology

OVERVIEW

Preceding chapters have sketched the manner in which many-celled organisms are composed of different types of specialized tissue and how nerve cells function in co-ordinating the varied activities of the body. Among these activities are the responses of glands and muscles, both excited by nerve cells. The responses of the ductless, or endocrine, glands were studied in Chapter 3; most of the duct, or exocrine, glands are digestive in function and add little to understanding other kinds of behavior. The reactions of muscles will be discussed in the present chapter since understanding their structure and function helps in seeing how the nervous system is organized to control muscle responses and therefore behavior. The organization of the nervous system will be explained in Chapter 6.

This chapter will begin by classifying muscle tissue according to its structure and function, followed by a discussion of how each of the three kinds of muscle tissue—smooth, cardiac, and striate—is organized into muscles. Most observable behavior is caused by striate, or skeletal, muscle, which controls the movements of the body in a coordinated fashion. Discussion of how nerve cells excite striate muscle response will conclude the chapter.

CLASSIFICATION OF MUSCLE TISSUE

Muscle tissue is made up of cells that are specialized for changing shape by shortening their elongated form. When muscle cells are attached to one another and to other tissues of the body, they are organized into muscles. Muscles are made up of muscle cells (for contraction), connective tissue (to hold the cells together), vascular, or blood vessel, tissue (to nourish the other cells), etc. Muscles are therefore *organs* made up of several kinds of specialized tissue.

The way in which muscle cells and other muscle tissue have specialized hinges largely on the rate of contraction required of a given type of muscle and how dependent it is on stimulation from the nervous system. *Contraction rate* and *automaticity* (independence of stimulation by the nervous system) determine the structure and function of muscle cells as organized into muscles. Three types of muscle tissue have resulted: **smooth, striate,** and **cardiac.** Smooth and cardiac (heart) muscles contract slowly and are relatively automatic, contracting without nervous stimulation. Smooth and cardiac muscle tissue are found in the *viscera*, or internal organs, and therefore form **visceral muscles.** Striate muscles react rapidly and depend on the nervous system for excitation. Striate muscles move the body (Gr., *soma*) about by pulling on the bony "levers" of the skeleton and are therefore called **somatic muscles.** Visceral muscle has often been called involuntary since its contractions are largely automatic and one is not aware of them; the contractions involved in the beating of the heart and the digestion of food are examples. Somatic muscle has been called voluntary since one is often aware of the muscle contractions that control movements, and body movements are said to be under the control of the "will." The distinction fails in several ways. Humans and animals learn voluntary control of certain visceral smooth muscles, for example, those involved in the control of the bowel and bladder in becoming housebroken or toilet trained. Somatic, striate, or skeletal muscles, on the other hand, often react without awareness in reflexes such as those of breathing or in more complex automatic movements such as walking.

STRUCTURE OF MUSCLE TISSUE
Smooth muscles

Smooth muscles form the walls of the hollow tubular structures of the viscera such as the arteries or the stomach and intestines. Smooth muscles also form the **sphincters** that can close off the visceral "tubes" at selected points, such as those at the end of the stomach, the rectum, or the bladder. They sometimes take a nontubular form as in the **piloerector muscles** that erect the hairs on the head and body. The muscle cells of smooth muscle are the simplest of all muscle cells (Fig. 5-1). The individual muscle cells *(muscle fibers)* are small (0.03 to 0.1 mm. long and 0.006 to 0.012 mm. thick) and can be seen only under a microscope. They are spindle-shaped, with a single nucleus centrally placed. The muscle cell cytoplasm is called **sarcoplasm,** and it contains threadlike **myofibrils** that run the length of the cell. The myofibrils are often called simply **fibrils.** They are made of a chemical called **actomysin** and are the contracting mechanism of the cell. The myo-

fibrils shorten as their molecules slide past one another—this pulls on the ends of the cell to shorten the whole cell.

The excitation mechanism that activates the myofibrils is found in the cell membrane (**sarcolemma**). The muscle cell membrane conducts excitation over the length of the cell in the same way that the nerve cell membrane conducts excitation down the length of its axon (Chapter 4). The membrane of the resting muscle cell is therefore *polarized* and reverses polarization when excited. Smooth muscle cells form muscles that show slow (5 to 15 seconds), sustained contractions.

Striate muscles

The skeletal muscles of the limbs and body trunk allow one to move about in space by pulling on the bony levers of the body. Their contractions are readily observable in watching a weight lifter, for example. Skeletal muscles are made up of striate muscle tissue, so called because of the striped appearance of its cells under the microscope (Fig. 5-1). The individual cells or fibers are larger than those of smooth muscle, being from 1 to 50 mm. long and 0.01 to 0.1 mm. in diameter. Striate muscle fibers are circular or prism-shaped in cross section and have rounded, thinned-out ends. Each cell has several nuclei (a **multinuclear cell**) located just beneath the membrane of the cell. Connective tissue divides the cell into segments (sarcomers) at Krause's lines, or the **Z lines.** The striate appearance is caused by the alternately light- and dark-banded portions of the myofibrils that run the length of the cell. The Z line connective tissue that divides the cell into segments runs across the middle of the light area (I band, or isotropic band), keeping all the light bands of each myofibril lined up with the other myofibrils. The dark bands (A bands, or anisotropic bands) are therefore parallel with one another as well. The A and I bands are named for their transparency to light—the

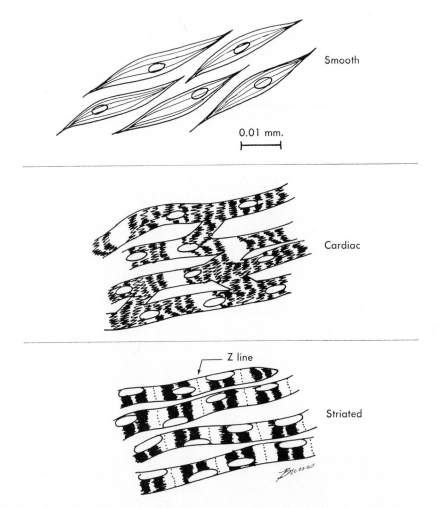

Smooth

0.01 mm.

Cardiac

Z line

Striated

Fig. 5-1. Smooth, cardiac, and striated muscle cells, sketched as they appear under the microscope. For an explanation of the differences in their appearance, see text.

I bands are more transparent than the A bands.

These anatomical features have functional significance in making the striate muscle cells contract more rapidly than smooth muscle cells, yet leaving them more dependent on excitation by nerve cells. Just as in smooth muscle, striate muscle cells shorten when the threadlike myofibrils shorten. But in striate muscle cells only the light-banded parts of each myofibril shorten during contraction—the dark bands do not shorten. It can be shown that the banded

appearance of the myofibrils is the result of a more efficient arrangement of their molecules for contraction, but this need not concern us here. What does concern us is how the myofibrils react so rapidly to stimulation of the muscle cell membrane. It has been shown that the Z lines connect all the light bands and that only the light bands shorten during contraction. Under the electron microscope the membrane is seen to be ringed with "pores" at the Z line, which lead to tubes traveling along the Z-line membrane directly to the active light bands of the myofibrils. When the membrane changes polarization to excite the cell, the electrical changes are carried directly to the myofibrils down these tubes (the sarcoplasmic reticulum). The myofibrils are thus excited more directly in striate muscles than in smooth muscles and can react more quickly. Such "plumbing" in striate muscles also serves for rapid exchange of energy-giving compounds and waste with the circulation.

Red and white striate muscles. Striate muscles are made up of muscle cells that differ in the degree of specialized structure and function outlined above. The muscles that are most specialized for rapid contraction are called **white muscles.** They have a large proportion of muscle cells showing complete and regular striations in their myofibrils and well-developed sarcoplasmic reticulum "plumbing." White muscles contract more rapidly than do red muscles, but cannot maintain contraction for as long because they depend on a constant supply of oxygen and blood sugar from the circulatory system. White muscles are usually **flexor muscles** that bend the limbs, digits (fingers), and body. For example, the white meat of the chicken breast is made up of flexor muscles that cause the rapid beat of the wings of a fowl in flight.

Red muscles, on the other hand, show less well-developed striations in the myofibrils of many of their cells and less extensive reticular plumbing in these cells. They do not contract as rapidly as do white muscles because the myofibrils are neither as efficiently arranged nor as directly stimulated by the membrane. Red fibers take their name from the presence of red-colored particles (myoglobin) in their cytoplasm that store oxygen. These fibers carry, therefore, a larger reserve oxygen supply and can maintain contraction for a longer period of time without a constant supply of oxygen by the circulatory system. **Extensor muscles,** which hold the body erect by extend-ing the body trunk and limbs, are usually red muscles, for example, the extensor muscles in the thighs of chicken, the so-called dark meat. In man extensor muscles include the large muscles of the thighs and back.

The anatomical distinction and color difference between red and white muscle is obvious in certain birds and in rodents, is less so in dogs and cats, and is nearly absent in monkey and man. The functional differences between flexor and extensor muscles remain in man, however, and are important to the coordination involved in behavior.

Cardiac muscle

Cardiac muscle is found only in the heart and is intermediate in structure and function between striate and smooth muscle tissue. This muscle resembles both smooth and striate muscle in certain features because of the conflicting demands made on the heart. Cardiac muscle must show a high degree of automaticity, or independence of nervous stimulation, like smooth muscle, to maintain life—beating regularly, regardless of what is going on in the nervous system. On the other hand, the heart must contract fairly *rapidly,* like striate muscle, to provide for rapid circulation of the blood. The cells of heart muscle tissue are multinuclear and striated, but the striations of the myofibrils are not so regular or clear as those of striate muscle tissue (Fig. 5-1). Cardiac muscle does not contract so rapidly as striate muscle, but can contract rapidly enough to beat more than a hundred times a minute. It contracts automatically and regularly. The individual cell membranes are so close together that excitation spreads rapidly from cell to cell; if one cell is excited, all the others soon react. Functionally, the heart contracts like one huge cell, with excitation and contraction spreading to all its parts (a functional syncytium). Regularity of contraction is assured because the heart has built-in nerve tissue (the nodes) that automatically time the contractions by stimulating the heart muscle at regular intervals. The functional syncytium and built-in (intrinsic) nerve tissue are features also seen in the smooth muscle of the intestine, whose regular contractions (**peristalsis**) aid in the digestion of food.

STRUCTURE AND FUNCTION OF MUSCLES AS ORGANS
Smooth muscle

As previously explained, smooth muscle is specialized for slow, sustained, and often automatic contraction and relaxation and is the type of muscle that forms much of the viscera, or internal organs. When smooth muscle takes a tubular form, as in the arteries and intestines, the tubular structure is often made up of opposed groups of muscle fibers (Fig. 5-2). One set of fibers may be oriented in a circular fashion around the tube. Contraction of these fibers *constricts* the "bore" of the tube to reduce the flow of blood through an artery, to reduce the flow of air through the

trachea, or windpipe, or to move food along in the intestine. The opposed set of fibers is oriented in a longitudinal direction. Contraction of these fibers tend to shorten the tube and, more importantly, to *increase* its bore. Despite their automatic contractions, smooth muscles of the arteries, intestines, etc. are supplied with nerve fibers (axons) from the brain and spinal cord via the nerves of the peripheral nervous system. These motor nerves form a special subdivision of the peripheral nervous system called the **autonomic nervous system (ANS)** (Chapter 6), which has two divisions, the **parasympathetic division** and the **sympathetic division.** Both divisions supply the tubular type of muscle described here, but in many cases the sympathetic division supplies one set of fibers (for example, the circular fibers), whereas the parasympathetic division supplies the other set of fibers (for example, the longitudinal fibers). In the arteries excitation by one division of the ANS can restrict the flow of blood to an organ by constricting the artery while exci-

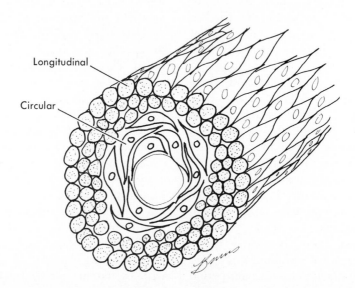

Longitudinal

Circular

Fig. 5-2. Diagram of how muscle cells are organized in tubular smooth muscle tissue, as in arteries or intestine. Contraction of circular fibers constricts the "bore" of the tube, whereas contraction of longitudinal fibers has the opposite effect.

tation by the other division dilates the artery to increase the flow of blood to the organ. The iris, or colored portion of the eye that surrounds the pupil, is made up of circular and radial fibers that are opposed, and the opposed fibers are supplied by the opposed divisions of the ANS. Sympathetic stimulation contracts the radial fibers to enlarge the pupil and admit more light to the eye, whereas parasympathetic stimulation contracts the circular fibers to constrict the pupil and admit less light to the eye.

In the case of the intestine, as previously noted, the contractions of the circular and longitudinal fibers are largely automatic, like those of the heart, although stimulated by local factors such as the presence of wastes. In this case stimulation by the parasympathetic division increases the rate of regular contractions, whereas sympathetic stimulation inhibits regular contractions.

Smooth muscles sometimes take a form such as that of striate muscles in gross appearance, with all the fibers oriented in the same direction. This is true of the piloerector muscles that erect the body hair and of the sphincters (all circular fibers), whose contraction closes the bowel and bladder openings. In these two cases, sympathetic stimulation contracts the muscle to raise the body hair or close the sphincter opening, while parasympathetic stimulation inhibits contraction by these muscles. The reasons for these effects will be studied later (Chapter 6).

Cardiac muscle

As previously described, the cells of cardiac muscle are intermediate in structure between those of smooth muscle and those of striate muscle. As a result cardiac muscle is intermediate in functional characteristics between smooth and striate muscle—the heart contracts rapidly like striate muscle, but automatically like many smooth muscles. The membrances of the muscle cells are so closely interwoven that excita-

tion spreads from cell to cell so that the whole heart muscle contracts almost as a unit, although some parts contract before others. The heart is regularly excited by intrinsic nerve tissue (the nodes) and will continue to beat if its nerve supply from the central nervous system fails. This has obvious survival value for the organism. In addition, the nodes and their nerve fibers act to time the wave of contraction over the four chambers of the heart so that the heart may act as an efficient pump, with its chambers contracting and its valves opening and closing in proper sequence. Like smooth muscle, the heart is supplied by the ANS, sympathetic stimulation serving to increase its rate of automatic beating (pumping), while the parasympathetic stimulation slows the heart beat, all in response to the circulatory needs of the body.

Striate muscle

Striate, or somatic, muscle is the most rapid in contraction of the three types of muscle. However, it cannot maintain a strong contraction or series of contractions for as long as smooth or cardiac muscle. Neither is it automatic in action such as most visceral muscle; somatic muscle must receive excitation from the central nervous system, via the motor nerves of the peripheral nervous system, to contract under normal circumstances.

The way in which the cells or fibers are organized in striate muscle becomes important in understanding its function (Fig. 5-3). All muscle cells are oriented in the long axis of nearly all striate muscles. Connective tissue plays a major role in the structural organization of the muscle. All the cells are linked together by connective tissue, which ultimately connects to tendons on either end of the muscle; thus, shortening of the individual cells ultimately exerts a pull on the tendons at either end and acts so as to shorten the muscle. The tendons are attached to bone at either end to flex or extend the arms, legs, etc. In cross section

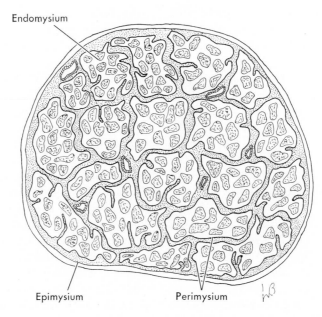

Fig. 5-3. Diagram of a cross section of a striate muscle, showing how cells are organized by connective tissue. Endomysium surrounds each cell, perimysium divides the muscle into segments, and epimysium surrounds the whole muscle.

it can be seen that there is a layer of connective tissue around each individual cell; other sheets of connective tissue divide the muscle into segments, and still more connective tissue surround the whole muscle. The connective tissue acts to bind the cells together and strengthen their attachments.

Flexors and extensors. Somatic muscles occur in opposed pairs, called flexors and extensors. Flexors act to bend the digits, limbs, and body; they react more rapidly than extensors and contain more white muscle fibers, as previously noted. Extensors act to extend the digits, limbs, and body; they react more slowly than flexors (but can maintain contraction for longer) and contain more red muscle fibers. Extensors are also called antigravity muscles since their action in extending the limbs and body opposes the pull of gravity and maintains the upright position. An exception in man is the muscles of the arms, in which flexing the arm and fingers opposes the pull of gravity.

Reciprocal innervation. The muscles involved in any given body movement, whether flexors or extensors, are called the **agonist muscles** for that moment. If a flexor is the agonist muscle for a given movement (for example, bending the leg), the extensor muscle that would perform the opposite movement (straightening the leg) is the **antagonist muscle** for that movement. Since they occur in opposed pairs, an antagonist muscle must relax for an antagonist muscle to perform a movement—the triceps muscle of the arm must relax for the biceps muscle to bend the elbow. Both agonist and antagonist muscles are **innervated** (receive nerve fibers) from the central nervous system (CNS) via the motor nerves of the peripheral nervous system. The CNS is so arranged that, when an agonist muscle is excited, its antagonist is inhibited. This is called **reciprocal innervation.**

Isotonic and isometric contraction. If a muscle shortens in flexing a limb, the contraction of that muscle is called an **isotonic**

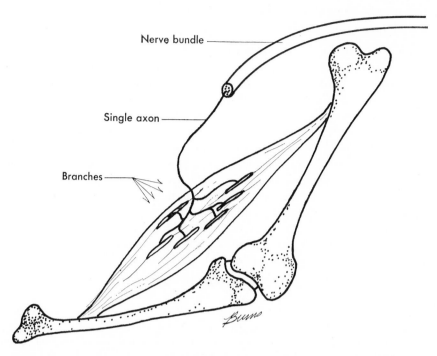

Nerve bundle

Single axon

Branches

Fig. 5-4. Sketch of the motor unit, consisting of a single motoneuron (whose axon is shown) and individual muscle cells innervated by branches of that motoneuron.

contraction (*iso,* the same; *tonus,* tension). The contraction is termed isotonic because the amount of tension exerted by the muscle during the movement remains relatively constant while the length of the muscle changes. Under these circumstances the muscle is performing "work" as a physicist defines it, that is, it is exerting a force upon a mass over a distance (work = force × distance). Lifting weights would be an example of the isotonic contraction of muscles. If a muscle does not shorten, but merely maintains tension, the contraction is called **isometric** because the length of the muscle remains the same (*iso,* the same; *metric,* length). In standing, the extensors of the legs would be contracting isometrically since they are merely maintaining tension in opposition to the pull of gravity that tends to bend the legs, and their length would remain constant. In the physicist's terms no useful work is done since the force

involved does not act to displace mass over a perceptible distance.

Actually, contraction always implies shortening of the individual cells of the muscle. Muscle cells actually shorten in isometric contraction, but at the expense of the elastic connective tissue that attaches them to the tendons at either end of the muscle so that the length of the whole muscle remains the same. Muscle cells may contract while the muscle is shortening (isotonic contraction), tensing (isometric contraction), or even lengthening. Muscle cells may contract in resisting the force of gravity while the muscle lengthens in walking, or they may contract while the muscle lengthens in checking the motion of a limb that was initiated by an antagonist muscle. In swinging the arms while walking, muscles contract to stop the swing even as they are being stretched by momentum. In such cases "negative work" would be done.

INNERVATION OF STRIATE MUSCLE
Motor unit and innervation ratio

Striate muscle contraction is organized by the way it is innervated (receives nerve fibers for excitation). Each axon of the motor nerve supplying a muscle breaks up into a number of branches (Fig. 5-4). Each branch makes contact with a single muscle cell. If the axon of a neuron has 50 branches, that neuron contacts and excites 50 muscle cells at once, whenever it fires. The single nerve cell and all the muscle cells it contacts is a **motor unit,** and this is the unit of contraction for the muscle. If, on the average, each axon in the motor nerve to a muscle contacts 50 muscle cells to excite them, 50 is the size of the motor unit. The minimum contraction the muscle can make would involve firing one motoneuron, which would excite 50 cells. Exciting a second neuron to increase the response would involve adding another "set" of 50 muscle cells to the muscle contraction, for a total of 100. Further increases in contraction would involve stepwise increments in motor unit involvement, 50 muscle cells at a time. This does not imply that all active motor units fire simultaneously. (See the discussion on muscle twitch, clonus, and tetanus.)

The size of the motor unit in a muscle may be arrived at by the **innervation ratio,** which is a ratio between the number of nerve cell axons in a motor nerve and the number of muscle cells in the muscle it supplies. If the motor nerve to a muscle has 100 fibers (axons) and the muscle has 5000 muscle cells, the innervation ration is 100:5000, which is expressed as 1:50. The motor unit contains 50 muscle cells supplied by each nerve cell, on the average.

The size of the innervation ratio and therefore the size of the motor unit for a given muscle depends on the kind of response that muscle will be called on to perform. Muscles involved in gross movements that require only a few gradations of contraction have large innervation ratios and large motor units. Extensors such as those of the thighs and back are examples in which innervation ratios may run as high as 1:150. When only a few different strengths of contraction are needed for gross movements controlled by the muscle, the motor unit can be large. On the other hand, flexor muscles that control precise movements are called on to contract in many small gradations. The innervation ratio and motor unit must therefore be small, permitting the muscle to increase its contraction a few cells at a time. The flexors controlling the fingers may have ratios of 1:10, and the muscles controlling eye movements may have ratios running down to 1:3. Mathematically, a ratio of 1:10 is smaller than one of 1:3, but size, large or small, of the innervation ratio is judged by the physiologist in terms of the size of the motor unit, the denominator of the innervation ratio.

Muscle twitch, clonus, and tetanus

If contraction in a muscle increases several muscle cells at a time, why is the contraction smooth and not "jerky"? For that matter, why is a sustained contraction a smooth pull and not a series of "twitch-like" contractions of all motor units at once? The answers to these questions and others are best understood after a look at some methods used by the muscle physiologist and the results he obtains using these methods.

Fig. 5-5 shows a nerve-muscle preparation setup for recording muscle responses and the records obtained with the preparation. A muscle and a segment of its motor nerve are removed intact from an animal and mounted so that when the muscle contracts, it moves a lever that records the contraction on a revolving drum (a kymograph). The nerve is placed on electrodes so that its axons may be stimulated electrically. The resulting nerve impulses cause the muscle to contract.

If the experimenter uses a strong enough

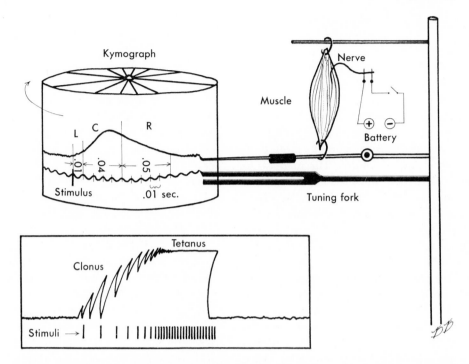

Fig. 5-5. Sketch of a nerve-muscle preparation setup for recording, and types of records obtained. Stimulation of the nerve causes muscle contraction, which is recorded on the rotating kymograph as a moving line. A time record is made by the constant rate of vibration of a tuning fork. A muscle twitch from a single nerve stimulus is being recorded on the kymograph. Below this is the record obtained by repetitive stimulation at an increasing rate, showing clonus and tetanus responses.

stimulus to fire all the axons in the nerve, the resulting impulses would reach all the motor units of the muscle at the same time and a single large contraction would result. A single response of this kind is called a **muscle twitch,** and such a record is shown in Fig. 5-5. The time elapsed between the stimulus, shown on the drum by a signal marker, and the onset of the muscle contraction is called the **latent period** of the muscle twitch (here, 0.01 second). A small portion of this period is due to conduction time in the axons and the time required for the axon to excite the muscle cell membrane. Most of the period, however, results from the time required by the myofibrils to begin contracting after they are excited by the muscle cell membrane.

The time required for the muscle to reach *full* contraction after it begins to react (0.04 second in this instance) is called the **contraction time** and represents the time required by the slowest muscle cells to reach full contraction. The time taken by the muscle to reach its resting length after a contraction is called the **relaxation time** (0.05 second for this muscle).

Muscles with various functions differ in the above characteristics. Slow extensor muscles of the red variety, with large innervation ratios and motor units, have long latent periods, contraction times, and relaxation times. Fast flexor muscles of the white variety, with small innervation ratios and motor units, show short latent periods, contraction times, and relaxation times.

Regardless of the kind of muscle being stimulated, what happens if the nerve is stimulated a second time before relaxation is complete from the first response? The nerve cells recover and can be fired again long before the muscle even begins contracting. Such a record is shown in Fig. 5-5. The second response begins "on top of" the first and the muscle contracts more than it does to a single stimulus. The increase in response is called **summation.** Summation is as true for the individual muscle cell as it is for the whole muscle; the mechanical shortening of the myofibrils far outlasts the electrical response of the axon and muscle cell membrane that excites them, and the myofibrils can be excited to contract again before they relax completely. A series of stimuli delivered during the relaxation periods of each response may give a series of summated responses (the staircase phenomenon), leading to a pull about twice as great as a single twitch. If the muscle has time to partially relax after each response before contracting again, a jerky series of summated contractions, called **clonus,** occurs. Clonus can be observed in fatigued muscles or in certain abnormal reflexes.

What happens if the experimenter increases his rate of successive stimulations so that the muscle cells are stimulated each time before they have begun to relax? As seen in Fig. 5-5, a smooth maintained contraction of as much as four times the strength of a single twitch results. Such a response is called **tetanus** and occurs during normal, strong muscle contractions such as those involved in lifting heavy weights. In normal movement the rate of nerve firing required to maintain tetanus in a muscle will depend on the contraction time for that muscle and will be higher for flexors than for extensors because of their shorter contraction and relaxation times (up to 50 per second in the fastest muscles).

How can a muscle contract with less than the pull of tetanus and yet not show a jerky clonus? If each motor unit relaxes before contracting again, each motor unit would show clonus. In the normal muscle contractions of life, all the motor axons are not firing at the same rate or at the same time like they are in a nerve-muscle preparation. Those motor axons that are stimulating motor units are firing *asynchronously.* Different motoneurons are firing at different times so that some motor units begin to relax as others contract to take their place. The result is a smooth maintained average pull. The rate of firing (as low as 5 per second in individual neurons), is subtetanic, or clonic, for each motor unit, but the asynchronous firing of the units makes the average contraction smooth.

Finally, it is interesting to observe that the amount of pull exerted by a muscle depends on the length to which it is stretched prior to contraction—the length-tension relationship. Up to a point, the more the muscle is stretched prior to contraction, the more tension it will develop. The length to which striate muscles are stretched between their bony attachments in life is near the optimum. The length-tension relationship holds for cardiac muscle as well; the more the heart is filled—stretched—by increased circulation during exercise, the greater the strength of its pumping contraction in each heartbeat.

Muscle tone and the stretch reflex

A few of the motor units of any healthy muscle are always contracting, especially in extensor muscles. This resting contraction is called **muscle tone** and gives healthy muscles their rubbery hard feel to the touch. Muscle tone is increased when the muscle is stretched by body position. As an example, lay your arm on the table, relax it with the elbow bent, and feel the biceps with the other hand. Now straighten your arm out on the table, relax it again, and again feel the biceps. The stretched, or lengthened, muscle will feel firmer to the touch—its tone has increased.

Muscle tone is partial resting contraction of a muscle in response to a reflex called the **stretch reflex.** Receptors in the muscle respond to stretch of the muscle; sensory neurons are excited, which, in turn, fire some of the motoneurons going to motor units in the same muscle (Chapter 9). The more the muscle is stretched, the more stretch receptors will be stimulated and more motor units will be excited. On the other hand, if the tendon attaching a muscle is cut, it will shorten by one fourth to one third of its length because of its own elasticity and become completely "limp"— none of the stretch receptors will be firing and therefore none of the motor units of the muscle is active.

Structure and function of the myoneural junction

The **myoneural junction** is the region of contact between branches of the motor nerve cell and each muscle cell in striate muscles. It will be recalled that the axon breaks up into branches, whose number depends on the average size of the motor unit. Each branch reaches a muscle cell to establish a myoneural junction. Myoneural junctions are diagrammed in Fig. 5-6 as they are seen under the high magnification of the electron microscope. It can be seen that the nerve branch forming the myoneural junction loses its myelin sheath covering before spreading out into a nerve ending that appears buried in a thickened indentation of the sarcolemma of the muscle, the **end-plate,** or subsynaptic region. A 100 Å gap is evident between the nerve ending and the muscle end-plate, and the end-plate is extensively folded to increase the area exposed to the fluid of the gap. When the nerve impulse arrives down the axon branch, it is unable to provide enough current to depolarize the muscle cell membrane because the membrane of the muscle cell has an area at least one thousand times as large as the nerve cell ending; therefore, a chemical event must intervene. The nerve ending contains many **vesicles** as seen under the electron micro-

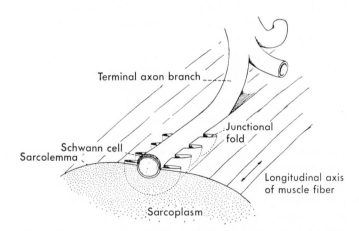

Fig. 5-6. Myoneural junction, drawn as it is seen under the electron microscope. The axon branch loses its myelin sheath and runs in the longitudinal axis of the muscle fiber. The neurolemma (Schwann cell) forms a folded structure near the thickened part of the sarcolemma that forms the end-plate (see text). (After Birks, R., Huxley, H. E., and Katz, B.: J. Physiol. [London] **150**:134-144, 1960.)

scope. Chemical studies show that the vesicles probably contain acetylcholine (ACh), which acts as a chemical transmitter over the gap between nerve ending and muscle end-plate. As explained in Chapter 4 for synapses between nerve cells, arrival of the nerve impulse at the nerve ending is believed to release ACh from the vesicles into the gap between nerve ending and muscle cell end-plate. Like nerve cells, the muscle cell has a polarized membrane—positive outside and negative inside—with a concentration of sodium (Na) outside the cell and postassium (K) inside the cell. The ACh *depolarizes* the end-plate by making it permeable to both of these ions in the same fashion as its action at nerve cell synapses ("short-circuit" theory). This depolarization results in a change in potential across the end-plate region of the muscle cell membrane, called the **end-plate potential** (epp). The epp does not completely depolarize the membrane at the end-plate because of the influx of ions from other regions of the membrane. Other regions, however, are depolarized enough by ion movement to initiate a **muscle action potential**—a polarization reversal that sweeps over the entire muscle cell and has the same electrical and chemical basis in excitation and recovery as described for the nerve cell in the previous chapter. The muscle action potential activates the myofibril contraction mechanism of the cell that has already been described. The sequence of events at the myoneural junction is as follows: nerve impulse → ACh transmitter release → end-plate potential → muscle action potential → muscle cell contraction. After it has acted to stimulate the end-plate, ACh is destroyed by hydrolysis. The reaction is speeded by the enzyme acetylcholinesterase (AChE) that is present in the tissue fluids, as described in Chapter 4.

As used in several experiments on the role of muscle action in learning (Chapter 17), drugs such as curare compete with ACh for receptor sites on the membrane and reduce the epp below the point where it will stimulate the muscle cell membrane, preventing muscle action. Drugs called anticholinesterases (erserine, physostigmine) compete with ACh for AChE, leaving more ACh free to stimulate the epp and increase the size of the epp. Anticholinesterases are useful in studying the role of ACh at nerve and muscle synapses.

SUMMARY

Muscle cells are specialized for contraction. Muscle tissue and other types of tissue make up muscles, where structure depends on the function they perform, primarily the *contraction rate* and the *automaticity* required for their function in the body. Visceral muscle includes smooth and cardiac muscle, which are slower in contraction and less dependent on excitation from the CNS than the somatic or striate muscle responsible for overt behavior. Smooth muscle cells show the simplest structure with a sarcolemma membrane as an excitation mechanism and myofibrils (in the sarcoplasm of the cell) of actomysin as a contraction mechanism. Smooth muscles often form tubes such as arteries with circular fibers innervated by one division of the autonomic nervous system (ANS) and with opposing longitudinal fibers innervated by the other division of the ANS. More automatic tubular muscles such as the intestines and other visceral muscles such as the sphincters or piloerector fibers are excited by the sympathetic division of the ANS and inhibited by the parasympathetic division.

Striate muscle cells are larger than smooth muscle cells and are multinuclear, with banded light and dark myofibrils that are lined up by a membrane, the Z line, which runs across the cell at the middle of each light band and divides the cell in segments. The Z lines carry tubes into the cell from pores in the membrane to increase the rate of excitation of the myofibrils and to improve their energy exchange with the cell environment. Only the light bands of the myofibrils narrow in contraction.

Striate muscles can also be classified as red or white, according to the regularity of the myofibrils in their cells and the proportion of cells with red-colored oxygen-carrying myoglobin in their sarcoplasm. White muscles are usually flexors and contract faster, but they cannot maintain contraction as long as red muscles can. Red muscles are usually extensors.

Cardiac muscle forms the blood-pumping chambers of the heart. It is intermediate in structure and function between smooth and striate muscle. It has semistriated myofibrils and reacts fairly rapidly like striate muscle, but it is automatic in contraction and has intrinsic nerve tissue for timing its contractions like some visceral muscle. Cardiac muscle forms a functional syncytium, with excitation spreading from cell to cell. Its automatic contractions are speeded by sympathetic excitation and slowed by parasympathetic inhibition.

Much of the way striate muscle functions depends on how it is innervated. Flexors and extensors perform opposite body movements and are therefore reciprocally innervated; when the agonist muscle for a movement is excited, its antagonist is inhibited. When a muscle shortens during contraction, the contraction is called isotonic; if the muscle does not shorten, isometric contraction has occurred. Striate muscle cells are innervated by groups, a motor nerve cell and the muscle cells innervated by its branches constituting the unit of contraction, the motor unit. The average number of muscle cells in the motor units of a muscle can be computed by a ratio between the number of nerve cells going to a muscle and the number of muscle cells in the muscle; reduced to a numerator of one, this is the innervation ratio. Flexor muscles have smaller motor units and innervation ratios than extensors because of the more precisely graded contractions they must perform.

If all the motor axons to a muscle are artificially stimulated at once, a muscle twitch results, with a defined latent period, contraction time, and relaxation time. If the stimulus is repeated during each relaxation period, a series of contractions called clonus occurs, with each contraction larger than the twitch because of the summation resulting from successive stimulation. If the stimuli follow one another before relaxation begins, maintained smooth tetanus of still greater summation occurs. In life, clonus rarely happens because the motor units fire asynchronously. The rate of stimulation required for tetanus is higher for white flexor muscles than for red extensor muscles because of their faster contraction and relaxation time.

The tone, or partial contraction of resting muscles, depends on how much they are stretched, and is caused by the stretch reflex. Moreover, the more a muscle is stretched, the greater its contraction in response to a stimulus, up to an optimum point. Muscles in the body are anatomically stretched to about that optimum degree.

Each striate muscle cell is stimulated by a branch of a motor axon at the myoneural junction. A chemical event intervenes between the nerve impulse and excitation of the muscle cell membrane. The nerve ending releases acetylcholine (ACh), a transmitter that "shorts out" the end-plate under the nerve ending, making it permeable to sodium and potassium and causing the end-plate potential (epp). The resulting ion shifts from all over the muscle cell membrane cause it to reverse polarization in a fashion identical to the nerve impulse. This activates the contraction mechanism of the myofibrils. The sequence of events is nerve impulse → transmitter → epp → muscle action potential → contraction.

READINGS

Hayashi, T.: How cells move, Sci. Amer. **205**:184-204, Sept., 1961. (W. H. Freeman Co. Reprint No. 97.)

Huxley, H. E.: The contraction of muscle, Sci. Amer. **199**:67-82, Nov., 1958. (W. H. Freeman Co. Reprint No. 19.)

Huxley, H. E.: The mechanism of muscle contraction, Sci. Amer. **213**:18-27, Dec., 1965. (W. H. Freeman Co. Reprint No. 1026.)

Porter, R. E., and Franzini—Armstrong, C.: The sarcoplasmic reticulum, Sci. Amer. **212**:72-80, March, 1965. (W. H. Freeman Co. Reprint No. 1007.)

Steen, E. B., and Montagu, A.: Anatomy and physiology, vol. 1, New York, 1959, Barnes & Noble, Inc.

Chapter 6

Nervous system

OVERVIEW

In Chapter 4 the structure and function of the nerve cell, or neuron, was explained. Neurons, in turn, are cell units of the tissue that makes up the nervous system. The nervous system is specialized for conducting excitation from one part of the body to another so that the organism can make responses to stimuli. Such stimuli, inside or outside the body, excite receptors or sense organs, which will be studied in Part III (Chapters 7 to 12). The organism responds by muscle contraction or gland secretion— even humans are able to only "twitch" or "squirt"—no matter how complex the response. Muscle cells and muscle contraction were surveyed in Chapter 5. The responses of gland cells and glandular systems were explained in Chapter 3. The present chapter concentrates on the nervous system, whose structure and function explain how the organism can make complex and patterned responses to a wide variety of stimuli.

The chapter begins with a simple classification of the major divisions of the nervous system, the central nervous system and the peripheral nervous system. Then the structure and function of the peripheral nervous system will be explained. Particular attention will be given to the autonomic nervous system, which controls the smooth muscles and glands, because of certain complexities of its structure and function.

The balance of the chapter will be devoted to the structure and function of the central nervous system. As a beginning model the anatomy and physiology of reflexes in the spinal cord will be outlined in simplified form. This reflex plan can be applied to the *function* of higher centers in the brain. Understanding the *structure* of the brain, however, requires a more extensive background because of its extreme complexity. To help visualize the brain in simplified form, the next section traces its embryological development, beginning with the single fertilized egg cell that develops into all the systems of the body. The developmental story will be interrupted at a point where the relationship of all the major parts of the nervous system to one another is still uncomplicated. Illustration of these parts in the generalized brain of a lower animal will help fix their relative locations in mind. The function of each of the major brain centers in behavior can then be explained. Finally, the changes that occur in further development in man's brain will be shown. The cranial nerves will be mentioned, and the anatomy and function of the "highest" part of the brain, the cerebral cortex, will be outlined. Some notes on the connective and circulatory tissue of the brain will conclude the chapter.

CLASSIFICATION OF THE NERVOUS SYSTEM

The **nervous system** consists of the **brain, spinal cord,** and the **nerves** that connect with the brain and spinal cord and run to and from the **effectors** (muscles and glands) and **receptors** (sense organs). The brain and spinal cord constitute the **central nervous system** and will be studied in detail in a later section. The nerves, made up of bundles of individually conducting nerve cells or fibers, make up the **peripheral nervous system.** The **sensory nerves** carry excitation from receptors to the central nervous system. The **motor nerves** carry excitation from the central nervous system to the glands and muscles. Sensory and motor nerves branch repeatedly as they reach receptors and effectors over the entire body, and their final branches may contain only sensory or only motor fibers and can be called sensory nerves or motor nerves, respectively. Near their origin in the brain or spinal cord, however, most nerves are *mixed* and contain both sensory and motor fibers.

PSNS and ANS

A further distinction can be made among the independently conducting fibers of the peripheral nervous system. Those sensory fibers coming from the receptors and those motor fibers that reach the somatic or striate muscles and move the body about form the **peripheral somatic nervous system (PSNS).** The PSNS is the part of the peripheral nervous system that is concerned with overt reactions to both internal and external stimuli. As treated here, the motor fibers to the smooth muscles and glands form the **autonomic nervous system (ANS),** a different part of the peripheral nervous system. As classified, the ANS is a *motor system only* and will be treated separately because of certain unique features of structure and function. The fibers of the PSNS and ANS may be mixed in nerve trunks near their origin from the brain and spinal cord. Certain features of the origin of the ANS are unique, however, as will be explained later.

Peripheral somatic nervous system. The motor nerves going to the striate muscles and the sensory nerves coming from the receptors form the PSNS. The PSNS originates in the **spinal nerves** that leave the spinal cord and the **cranial nerves** that leave the brain. Branches of the spinal and cranial nerves spread over the entire body to reach the receptors and somatic muscles. There are twelve pairs of cranial nerves whose functions will be discussed later. Both cranial and spinal nerves occur in pairs because the nervous system is **bilaterally symmetrical.** Just as there are pairs of identical arms, legs, ribs, eyes, ears, etc., the brain and spinal cord are made up of identical halves joined at the "center." The spinal cord lies within the **vertebral column,** or backbone, of jointed **vertebrae** (Fig. 6-1). There are thirty-one pairs of spinal nerves connecting the spinal cord with receptors and effectors. The eight pairs of nerves that emerge from within the vertebral column between the neck (cervical) vertebrae are called the **cervical** nerves (Fig. 6-1). The twelve pairs that emerge between vertebrae to which ribs are attached are called **thoracic** nerves. The five **lumbar** nerves lie between vertebrae of the lower back, the five **sacral** nerves lie between vertebrae of the hip cage, or pelvis, and a **coccygeal** pair emerges from the rudiment of a tail. The **segments** of the spinal cord to which these nerves are attached are named accordingly. The thoracic and lumbar segments of the cord contribute fibers to the sympathetic chain ganglia of the autonomic nervous system (ANS), as will be explained below. The sacral segment and some of the cranial nerves also contain fibers of the ANS.

Autonomic nervous system. The ANS has

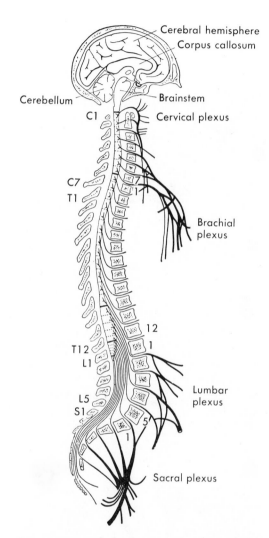

Cerebral hemisphere
Corpus callosum
Cerebellum
Brainstem
C1
Cervical plexus
C7
T1
Brachial plexus
12
T12
1
L1
Lumbar plexus
L5
S1
5
1
Sacral plexus

Fig. 6-1. Drawing of the brain and spinal cord in situ. The brain is shown in the median plane (a midline section), the spinal cord in external view, and the vertebrae cut away to show the enclosed cord. Note that the cord is shorter than the vertebral column; the spinal nerves must descend some distance before emerging between the vertebrae for which they are named (see text), especially those from the lower cord. (From Gardner, E. O.: Fundamentals of neurology, ed. 4, Philadelphia, 1963, W. B. Saunders Co.)

been defined as a *visceral motor system,* consisting of those motor nerve fibers of the peripheral nervous system that supply the smooth muscles and glands of the viscera (Chapter 5). The ANS differs from the motor fibers to the striate muscles in both structural and functional respects:

1. *Dual innervation.* There is only one system of motor fibers to the striate muscles, but each smooth muscle or gland receives two sets of fibers from the ANS (there are exceptions). One set of fibers is from the **sympathetic division** of the ANS, also called the **sympathetic nervous system (SNS).** The SNS originates in fibers leaving the spinal cord in the thoracic and lumbar regions. The other division of the ANS is the **parasympathetic division,** also called the **parasympathetic nervous system (PNS).** The PNS originates in fibers from the cranial nerves and from the sacral segment of the spinal cord. As can be seen in Fig. 6-2, each smooth muscle or gland receives both SNS and PNS fibers, a system of dual innervation.

2. *Peripheral ANS inhibition.* As explained in Chapter 5, the PNS and SNS have opposite effects on the smooth muscles and glands they innervate. If the SNS excites the visceral effector or speeds up its functioning, the PNS inhibits it or slows it down, and vice versa. For example, the SNS increases the heart rate and inhibits the digestive glands, whereas the PNS slows the heart rate and excites the digestive glands. These opposed influences act peripherally, that is, at the effector. By contrast, motor fibers to the striate muscles are excited or inhibited centrally, that is, inside the brain and spinal cord. Thus excitation of a somatic nerve cannot inhibit an effector.

3. *Two fibers in the ANS motor pathway* (Fig. 6-2). Somatic motor axons have their cell bodies in the brain or spinal cord, and their fibers take an uninterrupted course via cranial and spinal nerves to the somatic muscles. In both divisions of the

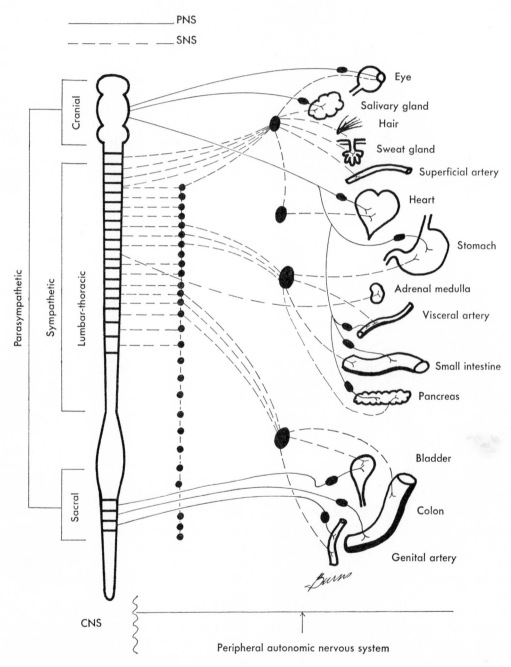

Fig. 6-2. Diagram of the autonomic nervous system, showing parasympathetic (PNS) and sympathetic (SNS) divisions. For further explanation, see text.

ANS there are two cells in the motor pathway. The **preganglionic** cells have their cell bodies in the spinal cord and brain, but their fibers terminate in **ganglia** (plural of ganglion) that lie outside of the CNS (Fig. 6-2). Here they synapse with **postganglionic** fibers that innervate the smooth muscles and glands. A **ganglion** is a collection of cell bodies that lies outside the CNS. The ganglia of the sympathetic division lie along the vertebrae in an interconnected chain (**sympathetic chain ganglia**) or in among the viscera (**collateral ganglia**) in the nerve network called a **plexus.** The **parasympathetic ganglia** are found near the organs that parasympathetic fibers innervate.

4. *Automaticity of effectors.* As noted in Chapter 5, the heart and some of the smooth muscles show automatic contractions, with their *rate* controlled by the ANS. Striate muscles do not normally contract unless excited by their motor nerves.

ANATOMY AND PHYSIOLOGY OF THE ANS

Details of the origin of the SNS and PNS within the brain and spinal cord will be treated in a later discussion of the reflex model of nervous system function. This section concerns the anatomy and physiology of those parts of the ANS that lie outside the brain and spinal cord.

Anatomy of the sympathetic division

The cell bodies of the preganglionic fibers of the SNS lie inside the spinal cord. Their axons are myelinated and leave the spinal cord via the spinal nerves, which will be described later. The preganglionic axons synapse with unmyelinated postganglionic cells in the sympathetic ganglia. Some of these ganglia lie in an interconnected chain that lies along the length of the vertebral column and extends up into the neck and head (sympathetic chain ganglia, Fig. 6-2). Other ganglia (collateral ganglia) are found in the body cavity, as

previously described. The preganglionic fibers are relatively short, reaching from the cord to nearby ganglia; the postganglionic fibers are long, reaching from ganglia to effectors. The preganglionic fibers are diffusely interconnected with many postganglionic cells, and there are more postganglionic than preganglionic fibers. This arrangement means that the SNS is anatomically connected to respond in a widespread or diffuse fashion—if a few of the preganglionic fibers are excited, many postganglionic fibers and effectors will respond.

Anatomy of the parasympathetic division

The PNS contains myelinated preganglionic fibers, unmyelinated postganglionic fibers, and ganglia where they synapse, but here the resemblance to the SNS ceases. The PNS preganglionic fibers emerge from the brain in the cranial nerves and from the sacral cord in the spinal nerves. The PNS ganglia lie on or near the organs innervated by the PNS so that the preganglionic fibers must be long, reaching from brain or cord to near the organ innervated. The postganglionic fibers are short, reaching from ganglia to nearby smooth muscles or glands. There is nearly a one-to-one relation between preganglionic and postganglionic neurons, with no interconnection between ganglia. This means that the PNS is organized to react in a discrete fashion, and one effector can be stimulated by PNS without other effectors being stimulated.

Physiology of the ANS

The SNS and PNS differ in function by having opposed effects on the visceral organs, as previously explained (Chapter 5)—speeding or slowing the heart or digestion, causing opposed contractions in the visceral smooth muscles, and inhibiting or exciting glands. The SNS and PNS also *interact* in complex responses involved in digestion, respiration, and other internal functions. As previously explained, the SNS is organized in a diffuse manner and tends to be aroused as a whole system. The SNS thereby sets off the widespread visceral responses characteristic of arousal and emotion—increased heart rate and rate of breathing and widespread changes in the blood vessels to prepare for exertion. The PNS is discretely organized to influence only a few visceral structures at a time. The PNS provides for the sequence of visceral reactions involved in digestion, food metabolism, and other metabolic responses. Widespread SNS excitation does, however, stimulate a more widespread PNS reaction so that there is a continual changing balance in the influence of the two systems on the viscera.

Secretions of the ANS (Fig. 6-3)

In both the SNS and PNS there are synapses between preganglionic neurons and postganglionic neurons in peripheral ganglia. These are the only synapses between neurons that lie outside the brain and spinal cord in the peripheral nervous system. Like many synapses in the central nervous system, the preganglionic neurons stimulate the postganglionic neurons by the release of **acetylcholine (ACh)** from synaptic vesicles (Chapter 4). After exciting the postganglionic neurons, ACh is rapidly broken down under the influence of the enzyme **acetylcholinesterase (AChE)** that is always present in the tissue fluid surrounding the cells. However, at the junction between the postganglionic neurons and their effectors the transmitter secretions of the SNS and PNS differ since they have opposite effects on the viscera. The PNS releases ACh to stimulate the effector. In the case of the heart the influence is inhibitory, but ACh selectively stimulates certain other smooth muscles such as those that constrict arteries going to somatic muscle and dilates arteries going to the digestive system. ACh also stimulates the digestive glands. Since the postganglionic fibers of the PNS excite visceral effectors as somatic motoneurons ex-

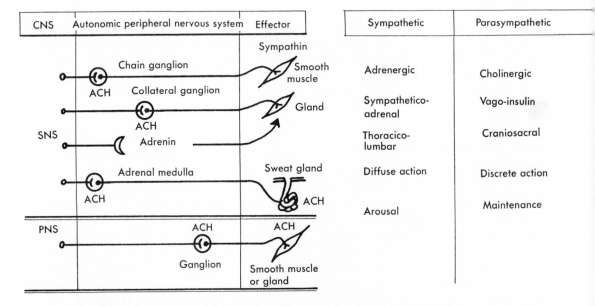

Fig. 6-3. Contrasts between the sympathetic nervous system (SNS) and the parasympathetic nervous system (PNS). Anatomical differences are diagrammed on the left, and the terminology applied to each system is shown on the right. For further details, see text.

cite striate muscles at the myoneural junction—by the release of acetylcholine—postganglionic PNS fibers are called **cholinergic** fibers.

By contrast, the SNS acts on the effector by the release of epinephrine or **norepinephrine,** depending on the postganglionic neurons and the organs they innervate. **Epinephrine** excites the heart to increase the heart rate, excites constricting fibers in the arteries to the digestive system, and excites dilating fibers in the arteries to the muscles to prepare the body for excretion. Norepinephrine, at other endings, inhibits the digestive glands. Since no substance like AChE is present in the blood to speed the removal of either, *diffuse* reactions result from the spread of these transmitters to nearby effectors. Epinephrine is chemically the same as adrenaline (see below), and thus the postganglionic fibers of the SNS are often called **adrenergic** (Fig. 6-3). The only exceptions are the smooth muscles that raise the body hairs—piloerector fibers and the sweat glands. These structures are innervated *only* by the SNS—there is no PNS innervation. The postganglionic SNS fibers release ACh to excite the piloerector fibers and sweat glands.

Glands innervated by the ANS

In addition to the digestive glands, the PNS sends fibers to the islets of Langerhans (beta cells) of the **pancreas** (Figs. 6-2 and 6-3) by way of the **vagus nerve** (Chapter 3). The PNS stimulates the pancreas to release **insulin** into the bloodstream. Insulin is necessary for blood sugar utilization by all the cells of the body with the exception of nerve tissue. Insulin appears to aid PNS reactions in a poorly understood fashion. Hence the PNS is sometimes called a **vago-insulin** system. The SNS, on the other hand, stimulates another gland, the **adrenal medulla,** which secretes the substances norepinephrine and epinephrine. The SNS is often called, therefore, a **sympatheticoadrenal** system. (It is interesting to note that no

postganglionic fibers are involved. Since the adrenal medulla secretes a substance that is like the postganglionic neuron secretions of epinephrine and norepinephrine, it is believed by many to have developed from a postganglionic neuron.) The hormones secreted by the adrenal medulla circulate in the bloodstream and have widespread effects on many visceral effectors. This, along with its diffuse anatomical arrangement and lack of an enzyme to destroy the hormones, increases the diffuse and widespread nature of SNS effects on the viscera.

The hypothalamus

The **hypothalamus** is a part of the brain that will be discussed in more detail later. However, it is meaningful to note that the hypothalamus controls the reactions of the ANS. Most of the nerve cells involved in control of the PNS lie in the anterior and medial (central) hypothalamus; those governing the SNS are found in the posterior and lateral (to the side) hypothalamus. Both sets of centers are sensitive to the internal conditions of the brain's tissue fluid—the internal environment—and respond, for instance, to changes in blood sugar level and salinity or fluid level. The ANS is involved in maintaining homeostasis, or constant internal conditions, in the body. Changes in internal conditions set off compensating SNS or PNS reactions to restore stability, reactions governed by the hypothalamus.

FUNCTIONS OF THE ANS

To the extent that the SNS and PNS could be said to have a purpose, the function of the SNS would be to organize widespread mobilization of the resources of an animal for vigorous physical activity in an "emergency," whereas the PNS functions to conserve the resources of the animal by a series of discrete reflex reactions involved in digestion, food storage, and other metabolic reactions. The interactions of the SNS and PNS are involved in complex responses of motivation and emotion.

Emergency theory

The emergency theory of Cannon was proposed as an explanation for the reactions of the SNS. He stated that the SNS mobilized the resources of the animal for "fight or flight" in an emergency. While somewhat different SNS patterns are found in rage than in fear (Chapter 16), the theory predicts most SNS effects on visceral structures. The Cannon theory is, therefore, a useful mnemonic device for the student. Arteries contract and relax in different locations to divert blood from the digestive system to the somatic muscles to "fuel" their exertions. Heart rate and blood pressure rise for the same reason. Respiration rate increases to provide more oxygen and the bronchial tubes to the lungs dilate. Sweating increases to cool the body, sphincters contract to "shut off" digestion, digestive contractions of stomach and intestine cease, and noradrenaline is released into the bloodstream to make these and other SNS reactions more widespread. To predict the SNS effect on a visceral structure, merely ask what that effect "should" be to prepare the body for exertion.

PNS effects

PNS effects can be predicted from the emergency theory as being the opposite of the emergency SNS effects. Thus the PNS should slow the heart rate and respiration, divert blood from the somatic muscles to the digestive system, and increase digestive functions. PNS effects can also be predicted from the reactions of the body during sleep, when automatic restorative functions such as digestion go on at an increased rate. The heart rate is slow, breathing is deep and regular, and sweating is inhibited.

The polygraph

ANS functioning in the intact human is most frequently measured with the **polygraph,** a group of measures of bodily reactions that graph PNS and SNS reactions on moving paper tape (*poly,* many; *graph,*

charts). Three measures are most frequently used: (1) depth and rate of breathing (**pneumograph**), (2) heart rate and blood pressure (**sphygmomanometer**), and (3) palmar sweating (**galvanic skin response, or GSR**). Heart rate, blood pressure, and rate of breathing are all increased by SNS activity and decreased by PNS activity. The sweat glands are innervated only by the SNS; thus palmar sweating provides a good measure of SNS activity apart from PNS reactions. Actually, SNS reactions and PNS counterreactions and responses are going on all the time. However, a sudden increase in the SNS activity, as indicated by the polygraph, suggests arousal, mobilization of the body's resources, and perhaps an "emotional state." The indicators would be a sudden increase in the rate of breathing or else catching the breath, an increase in heart rate and blood pressure, and the onset of palmar sweating as seen in the GSR. For this reason the polygraph is often used as a misnamed "lie detector," an emotional response to a question suggesting that the individual is lying. Needless to say the inference is often questionable because of individual differences in SNS reactions, the conditions under which the questioning is done, and other factors. The use of the polygraph as a lie detector is therefore best left in the hands of experts and even the data they gather should be interpreted cautiously.

Autonomic balance

PNS functioning, typically, is a series of discrete and timed responses regulating digestion or other visceral processes that occur as a sequence of reactions. More widespread PNS reactions do occur, however, in response to diffuse SNS arousal. Diffuse SNS reactions occur in some degree to almost every stimulus. A balance between SNS and PNS arousal is therefore always present, a balance that depends on individual differences in ANS sensitivity and on the current stimulus situation. Typical predominance of one system over the other —PNS or SNS dominance—in **autonomic balance ($\bar{A}$), SNS reactivity,** and **PNS compensation** are involved. There are individuals who show PNS dominance most of the time—they have excessive salivation, dry palms, a slow heart rate, and high intestinal motility (their stomach "growls"). Other individuals show SNS dominance most of the time—they have dry mouths, moist palms, and a fast resting heart rate. Most persons show slight dominance one way or the other and vary from day to day. Apart from autonomic balance, individuals differ in SNS reactivity—the extent to which mobilizing SNS reactions occur in response to a stimulus of a given magnitude or unexpectedness. Finally, stressful stimuli that produce extensive SNS arousal produce later PNS compensation—a reaction of the PNS. If individual PNS reactions achieve brief or lasting dominance over SNS influences, **parasympathetic overcompensation** has occurred. The PNS overcompensation may be momentary, as when a soldier relaxes his sphincters in combat and soils his trousers. It may be more lasting, as when oversecretion of digestive hydrochloric acid in the stomach produces stomach ulcers.

REFLEX PLAN OF THE CENTRAL NERVOUS SYSTEM

Despite the complexity of the responses mediated by the ANS and by the peripheral somatic nervous system, the organization of behavior must be sought in the central nervous system (CNS). The way in which neurons interconnect at synapses in the brain and spinal cord determines organized motor output in response to sensory input. Stimuli in the environment activate receptors, which leads to sensory nerve excitation and eventual motor nerve and muscle or gland response. Which stimulus leads to what response is governed by the "connections" between sensory and motor neurons that are made in the CNS.

Reflex model

One of the simplest stimulus-response, or S-R, relationships that can be observed in behavior is the reflex. Even the most oversimplified diagram of reflex anatomy involves parts of both the CNS and the peripheral nervous system. Five sets of component parts are involved (Fig. 6-4): (1) **receptors,** (2) **sensory neurons,** (3) **association neurons,** (4) **motor neurons,** and (5) **effectors.** Stimulation of receptors leads to sensory, or **afferent,** neuron impulses, which excite **association neurons** in the CNS. Association neurons, in turn, fire motor, or **efferent,** neurons which excite **effectors** that are muscles or glands. The synaptic connections between neurons are relatively fixed and invariable so that the response to the stimulus is always the same. Examples of reflexes include jerking the hand off a painfully hot surface, blinking the eyes in response to a puff of air in the face, or sneezing when the nasal passages are irritated. Once a given set of receptors is stimulated, the response is determined by the "fixed" synaptic connections in the pathway between stimulus and response. The reflex is then "stimulus-bound" or determined by the receptors stimulated. For example, stimulating pain receptors in the foot will cause an animal to reflexly withdraw his leg. Stimulating pressure receptors in the same foot will cause the animal to extend the same leg to support his weight. The pressure and pain receptors lead to different reflex pathways.

Anatomy of the reflex

Reflexes may include pathways in the cranial nerves and synapses in the brain, or they may involve the spinal nerves and the spinal cord. **Spinal reflex** anatomy will be used as an example here because of its relative simplicity. Refer again to Fig. 6-1. Note that the spinal nerves are attached to the spinal cord by two roots on either side. These are the **dorsal** (toward the back) **roots** and **ventral** (toward

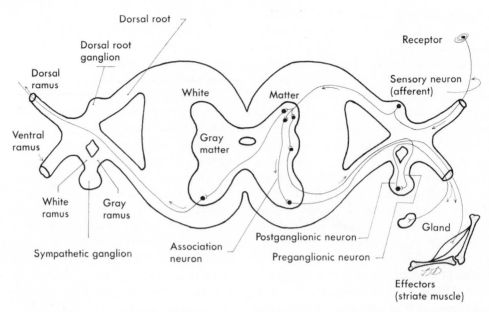

Fig. 6-4. Diagram of a cross section of the spinal cord, showing the parts of the nervous system involved in a spinal reflex. Major parts of the spinal cord and spinal nerves are labelled on the left-hand side of the figure. Elements involved in reflexes are labelled on right-hand side. For further explanation, see text.

the front) **roots.** Now refer to Fig. 6-4, a diagram of a cross section of the spinal cord at a level that shows these features. Also shown are the **dorsal** and **ventral rami** into which the spinal nerves divide on emerging from between the vertebrae. The cord itself is divided into the butterfly or H-shaped central **gray matter** and surrounding **white matter.** The white matter takes its color name from the whitish appearance of the myelin sheath coverings of its neurons. The neurons of the white matter form the **tracts** of the spinal cord, running up and down the cord to carry excitation from one level to another. The gray matter takes its color name from the unmyelinated neurons and many synapses found in this part of the cord. Neurons that lack myelin sheaths and unmyelinated nerve endings at synapses have a gray appearance. Tracts from the white matter and sensory and motor

neurons from the spinal nerves make their synaptic connections in the gray matter.

The spinal cord is connected to the receptors and effectors by way of the dorsal and ventral spinal roots and the dorsal and ventral spinal rami. The rami contain both sensory and motor neurons and are merely the first of many branches of the spinal nerves that eventually reach the receptors and effectors. The dorsal roots, however, contain only incoming sensory neurons and the ventral roots contain only outgoing motor neurons. The sensory neurons are unipolar, one process connecting the cell body with axon and dendrite (Chapter 4). The cell bodies of the sensory neurons are found in a ganglion (a collection of cell bodies outside the CNS) on each dorsal root, the **dorsal root ganglion.** There are thirty-one pairs of dorsal roots, ventral roots, and dorsal and ventral rami (eight cervical, twelve thoracic, five lumbar, five sacral, and one coccygeal, as previously classified).

The motor neurons to the smooth muscles and glands are also involved in reflexes. As previously explained, the motor pathway to smooth muscles and glands from the spinal cord forms the sympathetic division of the autonomic nervous system (the SNS). The SNS sends neurons to the sympathetic ganglia that are called preganglionic neurons. The preganglionic neurons have myelin sheaths and enter the sympathetic ganglia via the **white ramus** (Fig. 6-4), their myelin sheaths giving the ramus its white appearance. As previously explained, the preganglionic neurons may synapse with postganglionic neurons in the sympathetic ganglia, or they may continue through the sympathetic ganglia to reach collateral ganglia in the body cavity. In either case the preganglionic neurons synapse with postganglionic neurons that have no myelin sheaths. If the synapses occur in the chain ganglia, the postganglionic neurons may rejoin the spinal nerves by way of the **gray ramus,** so-called because of the color lent to the ramus by the unmyelinated fibers. After rejoining the spinal nerves, these postganglionic fibers are distributed to smooth muscles and glands by way of the dorsal and ventral rami of the spinal nerves. If the postganglionic neurons originate in the collateral ganglia, each will reach smooth muscles and glands by way of a nerve plexus, as previously described.

Finally, the major anatomical subdivisions within the spinal cord should be described. The H-shaped gray matter includes **dorsal** and **ventral horns** or **dorsal** and **ventral columns,** the extensions of the gray matter on each side of the midline that reach toward the dorsal and ventral portions of the cord. The white matter is divided into three areas on either side of the cord, called funiculi (sing., funiculus). On either side of the cord the area between the midline and the dorsal roots is called the **dorsal funiculus,** the area between the midline and the ventral roots is called the **ventral funiculus,** and the area between the dorsal and ventral roots is called the **lateral** (to the side) **funiculus.**

Physiology of the reflex

Refer to the right-hand side of Fig. 6-4. A **receptor** may be a separate cell or it may be a specialized ending on a nerve cell. In either case stimulation of the receptor will give rise to a **generator potential** (Chapter 4), an electrotonic potential that will initiate a spike potential in the sensory or afferent nerve fiber. The sensory neuron may reach the spinal nerves by way of either the dorsal or the ventral ramus. In either case it will enter the cord by way of the dorsal root and synapse with association neurons in the dorsal column of the gray matter. The association neurons carry the excitation to motor neurons, whose cell bodies are in the ventral horns of the gray matter. The motor neurons carry the excitation to striate muscle effectors via the ventral root and either the dorsal or the ventral rami. If a smooth muscle or gland is involved in the response, two motor neurons will carry the excitation. The preganglionic neurons will receive excitation from association neurons and transfer that excitation to postganglionic neurons via synapses located in either the sympathetic chain ganglia or collateral ganglia. The preganglionic neurons, in either case, pass out the ventral root and white ramus. Postganglionic neurons originating in the chain ganglia may rejoin the spinal nerves via the gray rami to reach effectors (smooth muscles or glands) by way of either the dorsal or ventral rami. Postganglionic neurons originating in collateral ganglia reach visceral effectors by rejoining other nerve branches in a plexus in the body cavity.

Reflex complexity

In a withdrawal reflex to pain, or a flexion reflex, for example, many receptors, sensory neurons, association neurons, motor neurons, and effectors are involved. Connections to the association neurons of the reflex from higher centers in the brain modify the response to conform to body position. Excitation from the sensory input to the reflex reaches higher centers to initiate further behavior. A pain or flexion reflex of one limb results in a **crossed-extension reflex** of the opposite limb to support the animal's weight. Association neurons reach the opposite ventral horn by way of the **gray commissure** (Fig. 6-4) to stimulate the motor neurons for extensor muscles of the opposite limb. Many other reflexes are associated with the pain reflex. Some involve the ANS since there are changes of breathing and circulation in response to pain.

Reflex plan of higher centers

Sensory input from the receptors involved in reflexes, and from many other receptors as well, reaches higher centers in the brain by way of ascending tracts in the white matter of the spinal cord. Depending on the complexity of the brain centers involved, many thousands of association neurons may be excited. Finally, excitation will return to the spinal cord via descending tracts in the white matter. The fibers of the descending spinal cord tracts will reach the motor neurons to excite response. Considered from this oversimplified point of view, the most complex stimulus-response relations are modeled after the reflex with three major differences: (1) many more association neurons are involved at all levels of the brain and spinal cord; (2) the response is not fixed, but varies according to which association neurons intervene between stimulus and response on a given occasion, that is, the S-R pathways vary and are not fixed as in the case of a reflex; and (3) **correlation** of input and **coordination** of output are greater than in the reflex. Excitation must be focused (correlation) from many widespread receptors and tracts on a single brain **center** (collection of synapses) vital to the response. In addition,

from such a single brain center, tracts lead to many motor neurons at all levels of the brain and cord. The widespread pattern of motor neuron excitation is such that many muscles are excited in a smooth reaction. This is coordination of output on the motor side. The reflex model of complex S-R relationships is not adequate to describe all behavior, but it is a useful beginning and adequate for the chapters on sensation. A more complete explanation will be deferred until Chapter 14, when it is required to understand the last section of the text.

EMBRYOLOGY OF THE NERVOUS SYSTEM

Further understanding of the functions of the nervous system in controlling behavior will depend on a greater knowledge of its structure. The adult human nervous system is a tremendously complex structure that is not yet fully understood. Much of what is known about the nervous system comes from studying its development from a single fertilized egg to a complex system in a mature animal. This **embryological** approach helps in understanding the nervous system because the relationship between its parts can be seen more clearly when the parts are at a primitive and simple stage of development.

Development of the germinal layers (Fig. 6-5)

All living animals, including man, begin as a single fertilized cell. This single cell develops into a multicellular or many-celled organism by a process of mitosis, or cell division (Chapter 2). The single cell divides to form two cells, the two cells to form four, the four cells to form eight, and so on. Geometrically, more than four cells in a "clump" cannot have an equal access to the fluid environment for nourishment and waste elimination. Some cells would be inside the cell colony and others on the outside surface. As a result, the cell colony

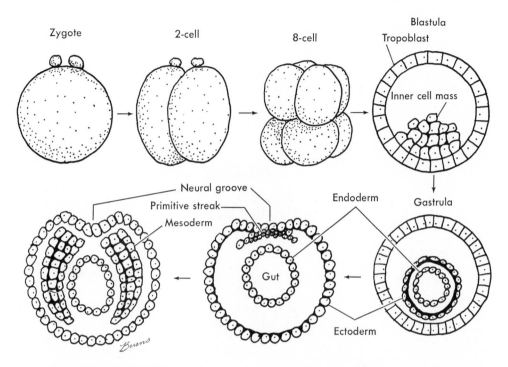

Fig. 6-5. Development of germinal layers. Simplified sketch shows some of the stages in the development of the embryo. For further explanation, see text.

forms a hollow "ball" of cells, called a **blastula** (Fig. 6-5).

Blastula. Cell specialization begins with the blastula. The "head" end of the blastula begins to grow at a faster rate than other parts. An inner cell mass forms in the hollow interior of the ball of cells. The cell colony now has an inside layer of cells, the primitive forerunner of the **gut,** or gastrointestinal tract, and of the muscles. At this stage the embryo is called the **blastula.**

Germinal layers. The inner cell mass forms both the **ectoderm** and the **endoderm,** the outermost and innermost layers of the embryo (Fig. 6-5). At this stage the embryo is called a **gastrula.** The gastrula develops a dorsal and a ventral side as the **neural groove** and primitive streak form along its middorsal line. The middle layer, or **mesoderm,** develops as an outgrowth of the primitive streak. The striate muscles develop from the mesoderm. The inner layer, or endoderm (*endo,* within), develops into the smooth muscle of the viscera. The outer layer, or ectoderm (*ecto,* outside), forms the skin, teeth, hair, and nervous system.

Formation and development of the neural tube (Fig. 6-6)

Along the middorsal line (midline of the back) of the embryo, the ectoderm develops a groove, the **neural groove,** which deepens and then "pinches off" from the surface to form a "tube" beneath the surface layer of cells, called the **neural tube.** The cells that originally connected the neural tube to the ectoderm migrate to either side of the tube to form the dorsal root ganglia. They send processes, or fibers, into the neural tube to form the dorsal roots of the spinal cord and other fibers out to the receptors to form the sensory nerves. As the neural tube develops into the spinal cord, cells in its ventral part

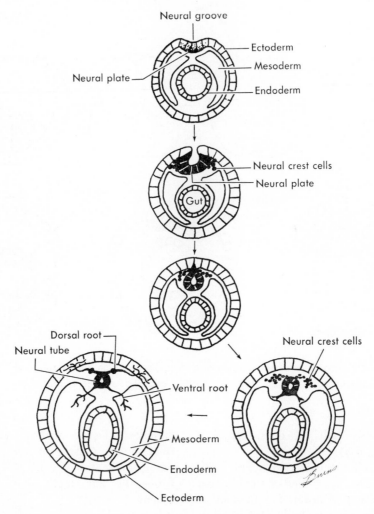

Neural groove

Ectoderm

Mesoderm

Neural plate

Endoderm

Neural crest cells

Neural plate

Gut

Dorsal root

Neural tube

Neural crest cells

Ventral root

Mesoderm

Endoderm

Ectoderm

Fig. 6-6. Development of the neural tube, forerunner of the spinal cord. Note the dorsal roots of the spinal cord are formed from the crest cells, and the ventral roots grow out of the neural tube to the muscles (mesoderm). For further explanation, see text.

send out fibers to form the ventral roots of the cord and the motor nerves.

Formation and development of the brain (Fig. 6-7)

Cells at the **anterior** (head) end of the neural tube begin to develop and multiply faster than cells in the **posterior** (tail) region. This rapid growth begins formation of the brain while the remainder of the neural tube forms the spinal cord. The hollow

developing brain soon shows three enlargements, the **forebrain,** the **midbrain,** and the **hindbrain.** The forebrain then divides into the **endbrain,** which includes the **cerebral hemispheres,** and the **diencephalon** (*di,* second; *encephalon,* brain). The diencephalon forms the egg-shaped **thalamus** in each of its walls and the **hypothalamus** in its "floor." The midbrain remains relatively simple, but it does develop four pea-shaped enlargements on its dorsal side, the **colliculi.**

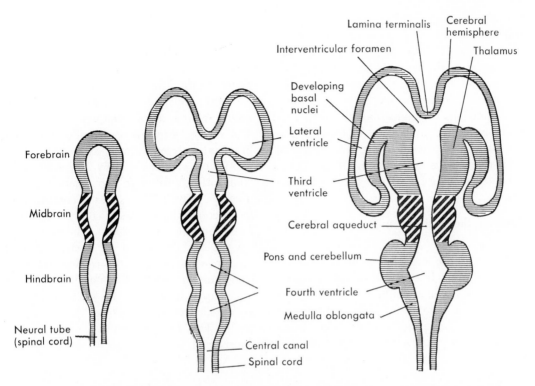

Lamina terminalis
Cerebral hemisphere
Interventricular foramen
Thalamus
Developing basal nuclei
Lateral ventricle
Third ventricle
Cerebral aqueduct
Pons and cerebellum
Fourth ventricle
Medulla oblongata

Forebrain
Midbrain
Hindbrain
Neural tube (spinal cord)
Central canal
Spinal cord

Fig. 6-7. Development of the brain. A dorsal (from above) view of the head end of the neural tube, cut away in this diagram to show its hollow interior. Three stages are shown in the development of the brain from three primary enlargements to five. (From Gardner, E. O.: Fundamentals of neurology, ed. 4, Philadelphia, 1963, W. B. Saunders Co.)

The ventral part of the midbrain is made up of tracts, including the **cerebral peduncles,** fibers going from the cerebral hemispheres to lower centers. The anterior half of the hindbrain develops a surface enlargement, the **pons,** on its ventral side. The pons is made up of fibers crossing to enter the **cerebellum.** The cerebellum develops as two large hemispheres (**cerebellar hemispheres**), outgrowths from the "walls" and "roof" of the anterior hindbrain. The posterior portion of the hindbrain forms the **medulla** with the development of its walls and floor.

Brainstem

The brainstem consists of those parts of the brain that retain, in a modified fashion, the tubular form of the neural tube and spinal cord (Fig. 6-7). The brainstem includes all the parts of the brain mentioned so far except the cerebral hemispheres and cerebellar hemispheres, which are outgrowths from the brainstem. Although there are many **centers** and **nuclei** (concentrations of synapses) to form gray matter in the brainstem, the white matter of tracts still surrounds the gray matter as in the spinal cord. In the cerebral and cerebellar hemispheres, the gray matter is on the surface and the white matter of tracts leading to the brainstem is on the inside.

Ventricles

The **ventricles** (Fig. 6-7) of the brain are found where the hollow center of the neural tube is widened or enlarged in forming the specialized parts of the brain described above. Two **lateral ventricles** are formed inside the cerebral hemispheres during development. The **third ventricle** is the tall narrow hollow space inside the diencephalon. The diamond-shaped **fourth ventricle** is formed inside the hindbrain. The tubular passage connecting the third and fourth ventricles inside the midbrain is not a ventricle; it is called the **cerebral aqueduct.**

Parts of the brain (compare Figs. 6-7 and 6-8)

The endbrain is the most anterior part of the forebrain. It consists of the cerebral hemispheres, which contain two major sets of centers, the interior **basal ganglia** and the surface **cerebral cortex.** The basal ganglia, or **corpus striatum** (striped bodies),

are centers that develop in the inner walls of the cerebral hemispheres. They have a striped appearance because the white matter of the tracts alternates with the gray matter of the centers. The remainder of the cerebral hemispheres develops surface gray matter where many synapses are formed. The surface gray matter is called the **cerebral cortex** (*cortex,* bark, as the bark on a tree) and is often simply referred to as "the cortex," although the cerebellum has a cortex as well. The cortex is connected to lower centers by vertically conducting tracts in the interior white matter. The two hemispheres are connected by a sickle-shaped band of white matter, the **corpus callosum.** The **thalami** (sing., **thalamus**) develop as egg-shaped centers in the walls of the diencephalon on either side of the third ventricle. The **hypothalamus** (*hypo,* below) consists of scattered nuclei in the lower

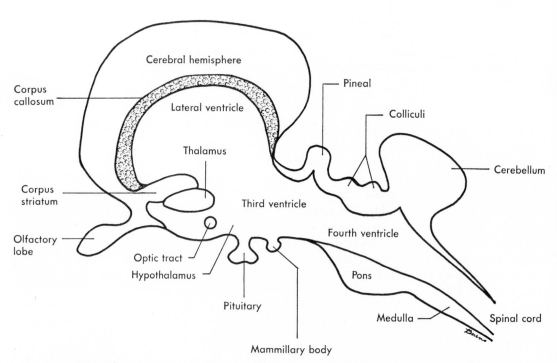

Fig. 6-8. Generalized mammalian brain. Sketch of a median view of one side of a generalized mammalian brain, showing some of its major features. For further explanation, see text.

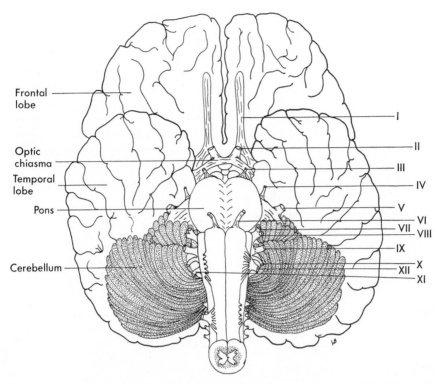

Fig. 6-9. Ventral view of brain. A drawing of the human brain as seen from below, showing the origins of the cranial nerves and other features. For further description, see text.

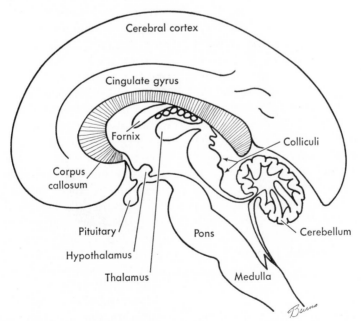

Fig. 6-10. Diagram of a human brain, seen from the medial plane (split down the middle). Some of the major features described in text are labelled in the figure.

walls and floor of the third ventricle. Above the cerebral aqueduct on the roof of the midbrain are the pea-shaped **colliculi** that are visual and auditory reflex centers. Below the aqueduct are the **cerebral peduncles,** made up of tracts connecting the brain and spinal cord. They are clearly visible on the ventral side of the brain as ropelike strands that emerge from the cerebral hemispheres and disappear again beneath the pons (Fig. 6-9). The **cerebellum** consists of the cerebellar hemispheres that develop on the dorsal surface of the anterior hindbrain. The cerebellum is connected to the brainstem by a great mass of tracts that "grasp" the brainstem and surround it on the lateral and ventral parts, the **pons.** The cerebellum, like the cerebrum, has surface gray matter and interior tracts. The **medulla** occupies the balance of the hindbrain, tapering down to the **spinal cord.**

FUNCTIONS OF THE MAJOR PARTS OF THE BRAIN
Cerebral cortex

Fig. 6-10 shows a central view of the human brain from a midsagittal (split down the middle) aspect, and should be compared with Figs. 6-7 to 6-9. The **cerebral cortex** is the highest set of integrating centers of the human brain. Through millions of synaptic connections in the gray matter of the cerebral cortex any stimulus input can result in any response output. Excitation originating in the receptors and carried to the cerebral cortex via cranial and spinal nerves and tracts is processed by lower centers, but may eventually reach the cortex. The cerebral cortex can "connect" any part of the brain with any other part, at least indirectly. Thus any response output may result from any stimulus input.

Corpus striatum

The **corpus striatum** in the walls of the cerebral hemispheres is an earlier development of a set of a master correlation and coordination centers in lower animals without a cerebral cortex or without a well-developed cortex. In these animals, particularly birds, the neural connections between stimulus and response for many patterns of instinctive behavior are found in the corpus striatum (basal ganglia). In man the corpus striatum regulates the sequence and timing of movements and processes certain facial expressions in emotion and "sequential acts" such as swinging the arms while walking.

Thalamus

The **thalamus** is likewise an integrating center. It also serves as a relay center for incoming sensory input to the cerebral cortex. In addition, many impulses going from one area of the cerebral cortex to another travel by way of synapses in the thalamus.

Hypothalamus

The **hypothalamus** contains many centers that are sensitive to conditions in the fluid **internal environment** of the blood and **cerebrospinal fluid,** the extracellular tissue fluid of the brain and spinal cord. The neurons of these centers act as receptors that are stimulated by changes in fluid salt content and osmotic pressure, chemical composition, and other conditions. Such changes represent **need-conditions** of the tissue or disturbances in internal consistancy and homeostasis (Chapter 2). The centers arouse and sustain internal and external responses until the need-condition is corrected and are therefore the basis of **drives.** The response adjustments that result may be as simple as a change in heart rate or may include complex learned behavior such as putting on a coat when cold.

Cerebellum

The **cerebellum** regulates balance and coordination of movement. It receives input from the muscles (tension receptors) and inner ear (balance and motion receptors).

Output from the cerebellum regulates muscle tone and adjustments in posture.

Medulla

The **medulla** contains many centers for the so-called "vital reflexes" of the body, which regulate, for instance, heart rate, breathing, and vomiting.

CRANIAL NERVES

Just as the spinal cord is connected to the receptors and effectors of the body by the spinal nerves, the brain is connected to the receptors and effectors of the head by the twelve **cranial nerves** that emerge from the brainstem in pairs (Fig. 6-9). Unlike the spinal nerves, however, the cranial nerves do not always have separate sensory and motor roots; some pairs contain only sensory fibers, some contain only motor fibers, and some are mixed. The first two (olfactory and optic) are not a true part of the peripheral nervous system, but are extensions of the brain itself, carrying sensory pathways or tracts. The cranial nerves are numbered in the order in which they emerge from the brainstem from anterior to posterior (Table 6-1). Students who wish to learn their numbers and names receive assistance from a classic bit of doggeral "poetry" of twelve words—each word starts with the same letter as the corresponding cranial nerve from the first to the twelfth: On old olympus, towering top, a French-speaking German viewed some hops.

FUNCTIONAL ANATOMY OF THE CEREBRAL CORTEX

The **cerebral cortex** undergoes greater development in man than in any lower animal. The cerebral hemispheres and covering cortex have expanded in size and area until the brainstem is almost completely covered except for the base of the brain. The increase in size of the cortex has resulted in a thickening to form sev-

Table 6-1. Summary of the cranial nerves*

No.	Name	Origin	Primary functions
I	Olfactory	Olfactory bulb	Afferent for smell
II	Optic	Diencephalon	Afferent for vision
III	Oculomotor	Midbrain	Afferent and efferent to all eye muscles except two
IV	Trochlear	Midbrain	Afferent and efferent to one eye muscle
V	Trigeminal	Pons	Afferent from skin and mucous membranes of head and from chewing muscles
			Efferent to chewing muscles
VI	Abducent	Pons	Afferent and efferent to one eye muscle
VII	Facial	Medulla	Afferent from taste buds of anterior two-thirds of tongue
			Efferent to muscles of face and salivary glands
VIII	Statoacoustic	Medulla	Afferent from the inner ear (hearing and balance)
IX	Glossopharyngeal	Medulla	Afferent from throat, rear of tongue, and taste buds of posterior one-third of tongue
			Efferent to throat and one salivary gland
X	Vagus	Medulla	Afferent from throat, viscera, and larynx
			Efferent to viscera
XI	Spinal accessory	Medulla	Efferent to viscera (via vagus), throat, larynx, neck, and shoulder muscles
XII	Hypoglossal	Medulla	Afferent and efferent to tongue muscles

*Adapted from Wenger, M. A., Jones, F. N., and Jones, M. H.: Physiological psychology, New York, 1956. Holt, Rinehart & Winston, Inc.

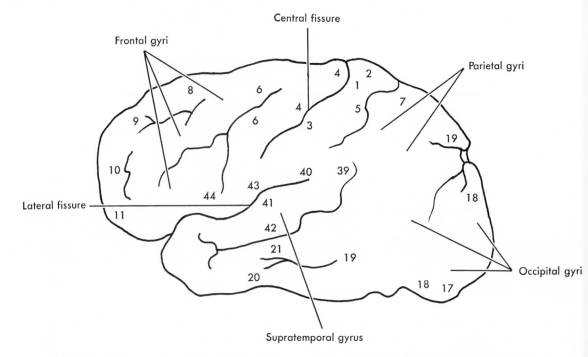

Fig. 6-11. Cerebral cortex, showing some of the major sulci and gyri and some of the principal numbered Brodman areas.

eral *layers* of cells and synaptic connections and a great increase in area as well, about 2½ square feet in man. The expansion of the cortex has occurred in the face of a limited cranial capacity, the size of the bony "box" of the skull. As a result, the cortex has developed folds to increase its area within the limited cranial volume, and much of the cortex is buried in the folds or sulci (sing., **sulcus**) of the brain (Fig. 6-11). The surface areas between the sulci are called gyri (sing., **gyrus**).

Each sulcus and gyrus is named, but only the major ones are important here. The **longitudinal fissure** divides the **cerebrum** into two **cerebral hemispheres.** (A fissure is a large sulcus.) The **central sulcus** divides each hemisphere into an anterior one third and a posterior two thirds of cortical area. The central sulcus lies between the **precentral gyrus** (area 4 in Fig. 6-11) and the **postcentral gyrus** (areas 3, 1, and 2).

The **lateral fissure** lies between area 41 and areas 44, 43, and 40.

The cortex is also divided into lobes. The **frontal lobe** is anterior to the central sulcus and includes about one third of each hemisphere. The **temporal lobe** lies below the lateral fissure—the cerebral hemispheres are shaped somewhat in the form of boxing gloves and the temporal lobe is like the thumb of a boxing glove. The **occipital lobe** is the posterior part of the hemisphere, and the **parietal lobe** lies between the occipital lobe and the central sulcus. There is no major sulcus to mark the dividing line between occipital and parietal lobes— the parietal lobe includes area 7 and the occipital lobe, area 19.

The thickness of the cortex is caused by six well-defined cortical layers (in most areas). Functionally, the cortex is *vertically organized,* with excitation carrier from cell to cell, largely in a vertical direction, reaching lower centers by way of the white matter of **projection fibers** and other cortical areas by way of both lower centers and **commissural fibers** that "loop" down into the white matter and back again. Various parts of the cortex differ in the relative thickness of the six cell layers. The **Brodman system** of cortical areas depends on the relative thickness of the cell layers and is a useful way to refer to a specific part of the cortex. In devising the Brodman system, a cross section of the cortex was taken in the postcentral gyrus. The first arrangement of cell layers encountered here was arbitrarily called area 1. With further cross sections, the first change in the relative thickness of the layers was called area 2, and so on, until all the cortex had been classified. Sometimes these anatomical differences correspond with known functional differences in the cortex and sometimes they do not. In any case the Brodman system is a useful way to refer to specific parts of the cortex.

More functionally, the cortex has also been classified into sensory projection areas, motor projection areas, and association areas. **Sensory projection areas** are those parts of the cortex in which pathways from the receptors, or sense organs, terminate. Thus, area 17 is the **visual projection area;** area 41, the **auditory projection area;** 3, 1, and 2 the **somesthetic** (skin senses) **projection area,** and so on. The **motor projection area** is the origin of fibers descending in the brainstem and spinal cord to the motor neurons of the cranial and spinal nerves that control the somatic muscles. It occupies area 4. The **association areas** are those that are not directly sensory or motor in function. Classically, they were presumed to "associate" incoming impulses to the sensory projection areas with outgoing impulses from the motor projection areas to permit responses to stimuli. Association areas are found in the cortex of all four lobes.

SUPPORTING AND NOURISHING TISSUE IN THE CNS

Nerve cells are not the only tissue making up the central nervous system. Specialized tissue is included in the central nervous tissue to perform functions of food and oxygen exchange with the circulation. Other varieties of specialized tissue surround and protect the brain and spinal cord, whereas still other cells support and bind together the nerve cells within the CNS.

Meninges

The CNS is surrounded by three layers of connective tissue called the **meninges.** The outermost layer, the **dura mater,** is a tough fibrous covering completely enveloping the brain and spinal cord. The dura mater is close to the skull, but there is some space between the dura mater and the vertebrae surrounding the spinal cord. Just inside the dura mater is a second, thinner, and more fragile layer of connective tissue, the **arachnoid layer.** The **pia mater** is the layer next to the spinal cord and brain and adheres closely to it. The space between the arachnoid and pia mater is filled with **cerebrospinal fluid** (see below). The pia mater contains many of the blood vessels that nourish the brain and produce the cerebrospinal fluid.

Cerebrospinal fluid

The brain and spinal cord are surrounded with cerebrospinal fluid, and the ventricles and spinal canal are filled with this same fluid. The fluid cushions the brain and spinal cord from the surrounding skull and vertebrae to minimize damage that could occur from blows to the head or spine. It is not known if the cerebrospinal fluid participates in the exchange of nutrition, oxygen, and waste between the blood and the nerve cells in the same fashion as the other extracellular fluids of the CNS. The cerebrospinal fluid is similar to the other extracellular fluids of the nerve cells in that certain substances will not pass from the blood to either fluid. Insulin, glutamic acid, and other substances that pass readily from the capillaries to extracellular fluid elsewhere in the body do not do so in the brain. Thus physiologist speak of a **blood-brain barrier** that becomes important to the study of the effects of various chemicals on the CNS and behavior.

Neuroglia

The various kinds of supporting cells in the CNS are collectively called **neuroglia** or, more commonly, **glial cells.** Their processes weave around and between the nerve cells and often attach to blood vessels. Their attachment to blood vessels may indicate a role in the blood-brain barrier (see above). Glial cells are involved in producing the myelin sheaths of axons in the tracts of the CNS. Recent work shows that some of them are mobile and can absorb damaged tissue. Glial cells may have other metabolic roles. They are clearly involved in the formation of **tumors** of the brain when they multiply in an abnormal fashion. There are ten times as many glial cells as nerve cells in the brain.

SUMMARY

The brain and spinal cord make up the central nervous system (CNS) in contrast with the peripheral nervous system connecting the CNS to receptors and effectors. The peripheral nervous system includes the peripheral somatic nervous system (PSNS) of sensory nerves coming from the receptors and motor nerves to the striate or somatic muscles. The peripheral nervous system also includes the autonomic nervous system (ANS) of motor nerves to the viscera. The PSNS and ANS both originate in cranial nerves from the brain and spinal nerves from the spinal cord; both kinds of nerves originate in pairs.

The ANS shows the unique features of (1) dual innervation of the viscera from the parasympathetic division (PNS) and from the sympathetic division (SNS), (2) peripheral inhibition, since PNS and SNS effects are opposite at the visceral effectors, (3) two fibers in the motor pathway of both PNS and SNS via preganglionic and postganglionic neurons, and (4) automaticity of effectors, the automatic activity of which is speeded or slowed by PNS or SNS excitation.

In the SNS preganglionic fibers are short, reaching nearby sympathetic chain ganglia or collateral ganglia from the thoracic and lumbar divisions of the cord; the postganglionic fibers are long and diffusely stimulated. In the PNS the opposite condition holds since the ganglia lie near the organs innervated. The PNS originates in cranial and sacral nerves and responds discretely. In both the PNS and SNS the preganglionic to postganglionic synapses use acetylcholine (ACh) as a transmitter, which is rapidly removed after acting because of the presence of the enzyme acetylcholinesterase (AChE). The neuroeffector junction in the PNS utilizes the same transmitter, but the postganglionic SNS fibers secrete epinephrine or norepinephrine, depending on whether their influence is excitatory or inhibitory; these secretions circulate to affect many effectors, reinforced by the presence of epinephrine and norepinephrine secreted by the adrenal medulla in response to SNS stimulation. The PNS stimulates the secretion of insulin from the pancreas by way of the vagus nerve.

The differences between SNS and PNS may be summarized by saying that the SNS is a adrenergic, sympatheticoadrenal, and thoracicolumbar system, whereas the PNS is a cholinergic, vago-insulin, and craniosacral system. Both systems are regulated by a part of the brain called the hypothalamus. The SNS acts diffusely on the viscera and stimulates relatively widespread PNS responses thereby so that there is a constantly changing balance between the two. The SNS acts on the viscera to prepare the body for physical exertion in an "emergency," causing increased heart rate and blood pressure, rapid breathing, and increased sweating (to cool the body). Measures of these reactions on the polygraph have been used to indicate emotional response to questioning in the so-called lie detector. The PNS has opposite effects on the viscera from those of the SNS. The PNS controls the discrete and sequential reactions of digestion and metabolism and is dominant during sleep. The PNS sometimes overreacts to SNS arousal in parasympathetic overcompensation.

The CNS determines the connections between incoming excitation from the receptors and outgoing excitation to the effectors. The CNS thus determines response to internal and external stimuli. These stimulus-response relationships are fixed in the reflex. In spinal cord reflexes, five types of elements are involved: (1) receptors, (2) sensory, or afferent, neurons, (3) association neurons, (4) motor, or efferent, neurons, and (5) effectors. Excitation from receptors in afferent neurons may reach the spinal nerves by either the dorsal or ventral rami, but enter the cord by the dorsal roots. The sensory neurons excite association neurons in the dorsal columns of the gray matter. The association neurons reach motor neurons in the ventral horns of the gray matter. The axons of the motor neurons leave the cord via the ventral roots to reach somatic muscles via either the dorsal or ventral rami.

If the SNS is involved, preganglionic neurons reach sympathetic chain ganglia via the ventral roots and the white ramus. Preganglionic neurons may synapse with postganglionic fibers in the chain ganglia when the postganglionic fibers rejoin the spinal nerves via the gray ramus to reach the smooth muscles and glands. Preganglionic fibers may pass through the chain ganglia to synapse with postganglionic neurons in the collateral ganglia before excitation reaches the visceral effectors. Excitation from re-

flexes reaches higher centers and is returned to spinal centers via the tracts of the white matter in the dorsal, ventral, and lateral funiculi of the cord. Reflexes are fixed and determined by the receptors excited, but more complex and variable response to stimuli involving higher centers can be depicted as following the "reflex plan" if many more association fibers, variability, and correlation of input and coordination of output are included.

The CNS, like other systems of the body, develops embryologically from a single cell. The single cell multiplies to form the "hollow ball" of a blastula, and a growth of cells inside then results in a gastrula. The inner layer, or endoderm, forms the viscera; the middle layer, or mesoderm, forms the somatic muscles; and the outer layer, or ectoderm, forms the skin and nervous system. The ectoderm forms the neural groove along the middorsal line of the embryo, and the groove "pinches off" from the surface to form the neural tube. The posterior part of the neural tube forms the spinal cord. Cells connecting the tube with the surface send processes into the tube to form the dorsal roots of the cord and processes out to the surface as sensory neurons. Neurons in the tube send processes out to the muscles to form the ventral roots and motor nerves.

The anterior portion of the neural tube forms the brain. Three primary enlargements develop, the forebrain, the midbrain, and the hindbrain. The forebrain develops into the endbrain and the diencephalon. The endbrain forms the cerebral hemispheres and corpus striatum, and the diencephalon develops the thalamus and hypothalamus. The midbrain develops the colliculi on its dorsal surface, and the tracts of the cerebral peduncles on its ventral surface. The hindbrain develops the cerebellum and pons in its anterior portion; the posterior part is the medulla.

The brainstem includes all parts of the brain except the cerebral hemispheres and the cerebellar hemispheres. The gray matter is internal to the white matter in the brainstem, but external in the hemispheres. The brain is hollow, as is the spinal cord. The lateral ventricles are in the cerebral hemispheres, the third ventricle is in the diencephalon, the cerebral aqueduct is in the midbrain, and the fourth ventricle is in the hindbrain. The gray matter covering of the cerebrum is the cerebral cortex and is the highest set of integrating centers, or nuclei, in the brain.

The corpus striatum or basal ganglia regulate instincts in lower animals and the timing and sequence of automatic movements in man. The thalamus is an integrating center and mediates incoming sensory input to the cortex as well as many connections between one cortical center and another. The hypothalamus regulates the ANS and reacts to changes in the internal environment to restore homeostasis, thereby serving as a center for drives. The colliculi are visual and auditory reflex centers. The cerebellum regulates balance and coordination in response to input from the inner ear and muscle receptors. The medulla contains the centers mediating the vital reflexes of heart rate, breathing, and so on.

The brainstem is most directly connected to receptors and effectors via the twelve pairs of cranial nerves, which may be sensory, motor, or mixed in function. They are named as well as numbered.

The gray matter of the cerebral cortex undergoes its greatest development in man. It is folded to increase its area and therefore forms gyri, sulci, and fissures. The longitudinal fissure divides the hemispheres, the central sulcus separates the frontal lobe from the parietal lobe, and the lateral fissure lies between the frontal and parietal lobes and the temporal lobe. The occipital lobe is the posterior portion of the hemisphere. Cortical thickness is divided into six cell layers. The relative thickness of these layers is the basis for the Brodman system of arbitrarily numbering different cortical areas. The cortex is vertically orga-

nized, excitation reaching lower centers by way of projection fibers and reaching other cortical areas by these and commissural fibers, including the corpus callosum that connects the two hemispheres. Areas of the cortex where sensory pathways terminate are called sensory projection areas and include those for vision (17), hearing (41), and somesthesis (3, 1, and 2). The cortical origin of motor pathways to the somatic muscles is the motor projection area (4). The remainder of the cortex of all four lobes form association areas.

The CNS is surrounded by three protective layers of connective tissue—dura mater, arachnoid, and pia mater. Cerebrospinal fluid is found between the arachnoid and pia mater and in the ventricles of the brain. Besides cushioning the brain, the cerebrospinal fluid may serve the same function of food, waste, and oxygen exchange as the other extracellular fluid of the CNS. Both fluids are not reached by some substances that readily circulate between the capillaries and other extracellular fluids of the body; physiologically there seems to be a blood-brain barrier. The various supporting cells of the CNS are referred to as neuroglia, or glial cells. These cells may have metabolic as well as supporting roles and may be involved in the blood-brain barrier. When they proliferate abnormally, they form brain tumors.

READINGS

Asimov, I.: The human brain, Boston, 1964, Houghton Mifflin Co.

Chapman, C. B., and Mitchell, J. H.: The physiology of exercise, Sci. Amer. **212**:88-96, May, 1965. (W. H. Freeman Co. Reprint No. 1011.)

Eccles, J.: The synapse, Sci. Amer. **212**:56-66, Jan., 1965. (W. H. Freeman Co. Reprint No. 1001.)

Gardner, E. R.: Fundamentals of neurology, ed. 4, Philadelphia, 1963, W. B. Saunders Co.

Houser, R. H.: Graphic aids to neurology, ed. 2, San Diego, 1948, Scientific Illustrators.

Smith, B. M.: The polygraph, Sci. Amer. **216**:25-31, Jan., 1967.

Wilson, J. V.: Inhibition in the central nervous system, Sci. Amer. **214**:102-110, May, 1966.

Part III

The senses

Chapter 7

Sensation and perception

OVERVIEW

This chapter introduces the third part of the text—the senses. Subsequent chapters on the senses will cover somesthesis, proprioception, the chemical senses, audition, and vision. Before discussing these sensory modalities, however, certain concepts that concern sensation and perception and their measurement should be mastered. These concepts are useful no matter which of the sensory modalities are discussed. The present chapter, then, covers topics that apply to all the senses.

The chapter begins by distinguishing between sensation and perception and shows how sensations can be studied through the human subject's response to perceptions as well as through animal experiments. A formal definition of a stimulus follows, together with the implications of that definition. Then the receptor is introduced and classified in several useful ways. Since receptors initiate sensation in response to physical energy, the measurement of sensations or psychophysics is the next topic discussed. Psychophysics is the relation between physical energy and sensations in man. The attributes or characteristics that all sensations share are discussed and their affects on nervous system activity pointed out. Adaptation, contrast, afterimages, compensation, and fusion are described. The chapter closes with a brief treatment of perception.

SENSATION, PERCEPTION, AND ENERGY

To the physicist, all events in the universe make up energy of various kinds, which he classifies as light, sound, temperature, mechanical events, chemical events, and so on. A great number of these events affect man, but man can sense only a few of them. He can be sunburned by ultraviolet light he cannot see, his hearing damaged by air pressure changes he cannot hear as sound, or he can be poisoned by chemical substances he cannot taste. Those events that man can sense are energy changes affecting his receptors in ways that stimulate sensory nerve cells. The nerve cells stimulate the CNS to cause sensations, which, in turn, are changed and elaborated by the CNS into perceptions.

Sensation

Receptors and sense organs stimulate the CNS when physical events affect them and stimulate their sensory nerve cells. The resulting nerve impulses provide the CNS with "information" about physical events occurring outside and inside the body. The input provides the *basis for discrimination* among stimuli in all animals and is the *basis for* conscious **sensations** that can be reported by man—the loudness of sounds, the hue of lights, and the rankness or sweetness of odors. The CNS reacts to sensory inputs in an integrated fashion. Stimuli are compared, contrasted with past stimulus events (memory), and reacted to in terms of the current internal state of the body—hunger, thirst, and so on. Responses that reflect discrimination between stimulus events result—the animal reacts to some stimuli, does not react to others, compares present and past inputs—and the responses reflect the current internal needs of the body, being appropriate to states of hunger, thirst, sex, etc. *Some* of the integrative activity of the CNS that *results* from sensation seems reflected in man's reports of conscious events—comparisons, images, memories, and feelings of hunger and thirst. Such reports constitute **perception,** the conscious accompaniment of events in the CNS that *result from* sensation inputs. Our knowledge of the physiology of the sense organs and CNS tells us much about sensation, but little as yet about the more complex CNS events involved in perception. The distinction is a useful one, however, because the study of sensation in man almost always involves some aspect of perception.

The distinction between a sensation and a perception is difficult to grasp in a more intuitive way. Adults rarely experience a sensation that has not been transformed into a more complex and meaningful perception. A sensation consists of the "raw input" of the receptor into the CNS before it is reacted to by the subject. It would be sensed, therefore, as the *input* from a receptor response to light, sound, touch, heat, pain, smell, or taste, per se—without identification of the stimulus, comparison, labeling (naming), classifying, etc. The latter processes belong under the rubric of perception. A sensation, then, lacks "meaning" in a semantic sense, or comparison with past events to classify it. One could momentarily experience a "pure" sensation on hearing a strange sound for the first time, before saying, "That sounds like. . . ." A sensation might result from filling the room with glaring red light before the subject said, "It's red."

If pure sensations are so rare and fleeting in man, how can the input of the sense organs be studied? In other animals, of course, electrodes can be placed on sensory nerves and in the brain so that the response of sensory nerves and the CNS to receptor activity can be recorded. In man the method of **introspection** is often used—the subject reports on his perception of a stimulus controlled by the experimenter. The experimenter varies the stimulus and the subject attends to one attribute of his perception that depends directly on the sensation input; changes in the intensity of a sound, for example, can depend on changes in sensation input rather than on the perceptual meaning of the stimulus. The subject detects differences in his sensations by comparing perceptions. The detection of the difference in pitch between tone A and tone B or whether a light is intense enough to be perceived at all, is an aspect of the subject's perception that depends directly on his sensations. It need not depend on his reactions to the meaning of the experiment.

Perception

Sensations do not impinge on a totally naive nervous system. In lower animals patterns of reaction and therefore patterns of perception are "built into" the CNS by inheritance (instincts). In higher organisms, including man, the functioning of the CNS is frequently altered by learning. Sensations, therefore, interact with the memory traces of past experience to form perceptions. The perception of a stimulus and the organism's reaction to it depend on past experience with similar stimuli and on the current stimulus pattern from other sources. For example, the sound of the dinner bell to a dog or a man will vary according to past associations of the bell with eating; the sound will also depend on hunger sensations perceived at the same time as the bell. The bell will sound different when one is hungry than it will after a full meal. Perception is the development of "meaning" that depends on past and present sensation input. As such, perception may be studied in its own right, as the development of meaning from past stimuli. It can be more narrowly related to current stimulus input. The more narrow approach includes how sensations act as cues to perception—the relation between perceived size and perceived distance of an object, for example. The chapters on the senses will include some study of perception. Only the relationships between perceptions and current sensation input will be discussed, however, because only these aspects of perception have been clearly related to physiological events.

Energy

Energy is the physical event that can initiate a sensation, and physical energy is therefore important to perception as well. The *rate* at which various forces act on the body must *change* to affect receptors most effectively. For example, man living at sea level is subject to 14.7 pounds per square inch pressure over his entire body, but no pressure receptor response or pressure sensations result. If he puts his finger in a glass of water, increased pressure on the submerged part of the finger results. He senses pressure at the instant he places his finger in the water because of the *change* from air pressure. The sensation is brief, however. The only continuing pressure sensation comes from the "ring" about the finger where water meets air, that is, the point of a *change* in the energy responsible for pressure.

STIMULUS

A **stimulus** is any physical energy that excites a receptor. This statement ends, by definition, the old argument over whether a tree falling in the forest makes a noise if there is no one there to hear it. The falling tree creates an energy change that is not a stimulus because it does not excite an animal receptor. (If a "noise" is a stimulus, the tree made no noise.)

Receptors

Receptors consist of tissues or organs that are specialized to respond to a specific *form* of energy. The sensory tissue involved is not only specialized for irritability, it is specialized to be more irritable to energy change of a specific variety and range of intensity (Chapter 2). The tissue is said to have a low **threshold** to the energy change for which it is specialized. The threshold for a receptor is the minimum energy that will stimulate that receptor. Receptors are specialized in man for five types of stimulus energy: **mechanical, thermal, chemical, acoustic,** and **photic.** Receptors specialized for mechanical stimulation include the skin receptors for pressure and pain, proprioceptive receptors in the muscles and joints that report limb position and movement, and receptors in the viscera that give sensations accompanying hunger (stomach contractions) and thirst (mouth and throat dryness). Thermal receptors in the skin report the temperature of the environment. Taste and smell are chemical receptors, that is, they respond best to substances in solution. For taste the substances are dissolved in saliva; for smell, airborne particles dissolve in the moist mucous surfaces of the nasal passages. Acoustic receptors are modified pressure receptors in the ear, which respond to the rapid variations in air pressure, called sound. Audition (hearing) shares with vision the function of reporting on events that occur at a distance from the subject. Visual receptors are photic receptors and respond to light, a part of the spectrum of electromagnetic energy. Receptors specialize in different ways in different parts of the body, but the examples given survey most of the sensory mechanisms of the body that give rise to sensations.

Some specialized receptors in the body do not cause sensations when stimulated. These include several kinds of receptor tissue that are involved in the reflexes of homeostasis. Such reflexes regulate the consistency of the internal environment and include receptor tissue that reacts to changes in that environment. There are receptors responding to blood pressure in the aorta (a large artery near the heart), specialized nerve cells in the medulla that react to the carbon dioxide content of the blood, and other specialized nerve cells in the hypothalamus that react to the osmotic pressure of the cerebrospinal fluid, to name a few examples. Such receptors initiate reflex reactions of the CNS, but apparently do not stimulate those areas of the brain whose activity leads to conscious sensations.

Adequate and inadequate stimuli

When a receptor is activated by the form of energy for which it is specialized, that receptor has received an **adequate stimulus.** This is true even if it is not the kind of receptor that can give rise to conscious sensations. For example, light is the adequate stimulus for the eye. When the receptor responds to a form of energy for which it is not specialized, it receives an **inadequate stimulus.** Pressure on the eyeball from a finger can cause a sensation of light, even though the eye is specialized to respond to light rather than to pressure. The eye has a low threshold to light and a high threshold to pressure, but the pressure threshold can be exceeded to stimulate the retina (sensory tissue of the eye).

Law of specific nerve energies

A receptor may be a separate group of specialized cells or a specialized ending on a nerve cell, as will be explained later. Adequate stimulation of a receptor results in a **generator potential** in the specialized tissue or ending. As explained in Chapter 4, a generator potential is an electrotonic change in the receptor. The generator potential, in turn, fires a **nerve impulse** in the sensory nerve fibers leading to the CNS. The nerve impulses result in a sensation. The form that the sensation takes—light, sound, taste, etc.—depends on the receptor or neuron stimulated. This statement is the **law of specific nerve energies.** The law holds because the neurons from different receptors go to different *places* in the brain. One sees light because the optic nerves lead to the visual areas of the brain, not because their nerve impulses are different from the nerve impulses reaching a different part of the brain from the ear. Electrical stimulation of the eye, the optic nerves, or the visual area of the brain causes a sensation of light. Stimulation of nerves leading to the auditory area causes a sensation of sound, even though the auditory impulses and visual impulses look the same on an oscilloscope. As Sherrington once stated, the nerve impulse is the "universal currency" of the nervous system.

CLASSIFICATION OF RECEPTORS

Sense organs and receptor tissue specialize to be irritable to a specific kind of physical energy: mechanical, thermal, chemical, acoustic, or photic. A given form of energy is the adequate stimulus for the receptor, which reacts to a limited intensity range of that form of energy. Specialization often involves changes in the *structure* of the receptor that adapts it to be sensitive to a given form of energy. Receptors and sense organs act as **transducers,** which are specialized to transduce, or change the nature of physical energy. All receptors transduce some form of physical energy into nerve impulses. The physical event that is the adequate stimulus initiates processes in the receptor, which result in nerve impulses. Some receptors have specialized in structure and function more than have others. Receptors can be classified (1) according to the form they have taken in specializing, (2) according to their location in the body, and (3) according to their adequate stimuli.

Classification by form

Receptors have developed as separate cells or as more or less specialized endings on neurons. Three classes are recognized (Fig. 7-1): (1) the **unspecialized nerve cell,** (2) the **specialized nerve cell,** and (3) the **specialized receptor cell.** The unspecialized endings on sensory nerves are found in great numbers just below the surface of the skin. They are also found in the viscera and muscles. This type of ending serves pain input, and similar neurons may go to areas of the brain that sense pressure and temperature as well. A number of more special-

ized endings on nerve cells are found beneath the surface of the skin, in the viscera and in joints of the skeleton. Some are known to serve pressure and others are probably temperature receptors. The sensory cells for smell are also specialized nerve endings. Finally, some of the most specialized receptors in the body take the form of separate cells. The specialized cells respond to a specific form of energy change and excite a sensory nerve cell which they "contact." The taste receptors are a prominent example of this kind of receptor. Elaborate sense organs such as the ear and eye have specialized receptor cells along with accessory structures to assure their stimulation. Although the variety of receptor

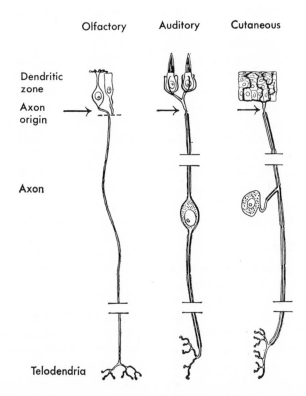

Fig. 7-1. Three classes of receptor structures, from left to right, are a specialized receptor structure on a neuron (a specialized nerve cell), a specialized receptor cell, and an unspecialized receptor ending on a neuron (unspecialized nerve cell). (From Bodian, D.: Science **137:**325, 1962. Copyright, 1962, by the American Association for the Advancement of Science.)

structures is wide, they can be usefully classified in these three ways.

Classification by location

Receptors are classified as **general senses** if they are found throughout the body and **special senses** if they are found only in the head. The general senses are often called **somesthesis** (Gr., body knowledge) and include **pressure, pain, warmth, cold,** and **kinesthesis** (sense of body position and movement from the muscles and joints). Pressure, pain, warmth, and cold receptors are found just below the surface of the skin over the entire body. A less extensive distribution of poorly specialized receptors that serve these four senses are found in parts of the viscera. The special senses in the head are more highly evolved and have more complex sensory mechanisms. In the course of evolution they probably developed in the head because this end of the animal encounters the environment first as the animal moves about. (It has also been suggested that this is why the brain is in the head!) The special senses include **olfaction** (smell), **vision, gustation** (taste), **audition** (hearing), and **vestibular sensitivity** (head position and movement). Vestibular sensitivity includes sensitivity to the position of the head, linear motions of the head, and turning movements of the head.

Classification by function

Receptors are also classified as **exteroceptors, interoceptors,** and **proprioceptors** by the location of their stimuli and as **nociceptors** if they signal injury. The classification is an overlapping one. It therefore becomes confusing unless the basis for classification is clearly understood. Exteroceptors are located at or near the body surface and signal events going on in the external environment. They include the **cutaneous general senses** of pressure, pain, warmth, and cold. The *cutaneous,* or skin, senses are the general senses located just beneath the surface of the skin and do not include the same general senses when they are located in the viscera. The special senses of vision, audition, olfaction, and gustation are also exteroceptors when they function to detect external events. Vision and audition are primarily exteroceptors. Olfaction is an exteroceptor when the subject smells a stimulus in the external environment and gustation is an exteroceptor when taste is used to explore the outside world.

Interoceptors are receptors that detect events going on inside the body. Olfaction and gustation are interoceptors when one smells and tastes during eating and digestion. Interoceptors are located inside the viscera, chiefly in the walls of the digestive and urogenital tract. They are *organic* rather than cutaneous receptors. The special senses of olfaction and gustation are therefore organic only when the stimulus comes from within the digestive tract, as in eating. The **organic general senses** of pressure, pain, warmth, and cold are included; these receptors are found in the viscera.

Proprioceptors are the *general* **kinesthetic** *receptors* located in the muscles, tendons, and joints and the *special* **vestibular** *receptors* found in the nonauditory inner ear. As previously explained, the kinesthetic receptors are included in the general senses because they are found throughout the body, whereas the vestibular receptors fall into the special sense category because they are found only in the head. Proprioceptors signal body position and movement.

Nociceptors are pain receptors wherever they are found. Man, therefore, has *cutaneous pain receptors, organic pain receptors,* and *kinesthetic pain receptors.* Cutaneous pain receptors are also exteroceptors, whereas organic pain receptors are interoceptors—both are nociceptors as well. Pain almost always signals injury, but it also locates the injury on the outside or inside the body.

ATTRIBUTES OF SENSATION

What characteristics of sensation are measurable and common to all sensory modalities? What happens in the sensory neurons, according to the law of specific nerve energies, when these attributes are varied? These are the questions attacked in this section, beginning with four measurable attributes that all the senses have in common: (1) **quality,** (2) **intensity,** (3) **extent,** and (4) *duration.*

Sensory quality

Sensory quality is that attribute which distinguishes one sensory modality from another. It also distinguishes *qualitatively* different attributes within a sensation, such as hues for vision and tastes for gestation. For senses that have more than one quality, there are **primary qualities** and **secondary qualities.** Primary qualities are the basic responses of the receptor whose combination produces all the other qualitative differences, or secondary qualities of sensation. Whether these basic responses depend on a single receptor or a combination of receptors, they cannot be analyzed further by the subject. To take an example from vision, the color red is primary and appears only red. The color orange is secondary, and primary yellow and primary red can be detected in orange just by looking at it.

The difference between primary and secondary qualities is most clearly seen by further examples from various sensory modalities. Somesthesis, or organic and skin sensitivity, has four primary qualities that appear to be four kinds of sensory modality: pressure, warmth, cold, and pain. Secondary somesthetic qualities such as tickle or itch are produced by combinations of these. The kinesthetic and vestibular senses are difficult to analyze in terms of sensory quality. Taste has four primary qualities: sweet, sour, bitter, and salt; all other tastes are combinations of these. Smell appears to have seven primary qualities: camphoraceous, musky, floral, pepperminty, etheral, pungent, and putrid. Audition has but one quality—pitch—so that secondary qualities do not result. Vision has four hue qualities; red, blue, yellow, and green; all other hues result from combinations of two or more of these qualities.

Quality indicates *what* sensory system or what *part* of a sensory system is functioning, whereas the other three attributes (intensity, extent, and duration) show only *how* it is functioning. Thus one speaks of the loudness of a pitch rather than the pitch of a loudness, or the brightness of a hue rather than the hue of a brightness. Intensity, extent, and duration modify quality, but quality does not usually modify the other three attributes in a systematic way.

Intensity

The sensed intensity of a stimulus increases with the intensity of the physical energy that stimulates the receptor. However, the relationship is not a linear one, as will be seen in the section on psychophysics. That is, equal increases in physical energy do not lead to equal increases in sensation intensity. At low intensities a small increase in stimulus energy makes as much difference in the intensity sensed as a large increase in the stimulus at high intensities—a whisper can be heard in a quiet room, but one shouts to be heard over the roar of a jet engine. Furthermore, quality and intensity interact. In hearing, for example, the ear is most sensitive to tones in the middle of the musical scale of pitch (a quality), and the eye is more sensitive to some hue qualities than it is to others. Pressure, pain, warmth, and cold all vary in sensed intensity, as do taste and smell. Auditory intensity is loudness and visual intensity is brightness. The attribute of intensity, then, is important for all the senses.

Extent

Extent is the "area" of the perceptual field covered by the stimulus. This means the *size* of the area of pressure, pain, warmth, or cold on the skin or in the viscera for somesthesis. The extent of the tongue occupied by a taste is another example. Extent has not been investigated for smell. There is, however, a dimension of auditory volume that is separate from loudness, although it interacts with both loudness and pitch. Visual extent is the proportion of the visual field occupied by a stimulus.

Duration

Duration is merely the time over which a sensation lasts in any of the sensory modalities.

Sensory attributes and the law of specific nerve energies

The statement has been made that all nerve impulses "look alike," whether in sensory neurons for somesthesis, proprioception, taste, smell, audition, or vision. Sensory modalities differ according to the *place* in the brain reached by sensory neurons serving different sensory modalities—the brain has visual projection areas, auditory projection areas, etc. Stimulating the eye with light or even pressure leads to a visual sensation because the sensory nerves lead to the visual area of the brain. Differences in modality are also differences in sensory quality so that these variations in quality may depend on the *place* in the brain reached by the fibers serving each modality. Somesthetic pressure and some proprioception reaches the somesthetic projection area; there is reason to believe that most pain and perhaps temperature excitation terminate in lower centers. Sensory modality seems to depend on the part of the brain stimulated.

Whether different qualities *within* a sense modality depend on stimulating different parts of their projection areas in the brain is not known. The taste receptors appear to send various *patterns* of excitation to the brain to signal salt, sweet, bitter, and sour. There seem to be seven different kinds of smell receptors for the seven olfactory qualities, but it is not known if their excitation reaches different places in the olfactory projection areas. There appear to be three receptors serving the four primary hue qualities for vision, but the reaction of the visual projection area to these is unknown. Auditory fibers excited by different pitches do reach systematically different places in the auditory area of the brain, however. There is some evidence for a "place theory" for sensory quality, but it is far from complete.

Intensity of the stimulus affects each sensory modality in the same way. As intensity is increased, more receptors and therefore more sensory neurons fire. Furthermore, each neuron fires more frequently until some of them, at least, are firing during their relative refractory period (Chapter 4). As a result, these neurons fire with a reduced spike since they do not recover their fully polarized condition. Which of these cues the brain uses in determining intensity has not been proved.

Extent would logically seem to have a single cue—the *area*, or extent, of the receptor field stimulated, and therefore the extent or proportion of the projection area in the brain being excited.

Duration would depend on the duration of excitation of the receptor and therefore on the duration of excitation to a projection area of the brain.

PSYCHOPHYSICS

Changes in the response of a receptor are caused by changes in the variety, intensity, extent, or duration of the physical energy stimulating that receptor. Energy changes are perceived as changes in quality, intensity, extent, and duration, respectively. By attending to the changes in perception that result from systematic changes of the stimulus, man can report the changes in sensation that accompany stimulus changes—the method of introspection. The physical energy can then be compared to the sensation reported by the subject. The relationship between energy change and sensation change is seldom linear; sometimes a small stimulus change makes a difference in sensation and sometimes it takes a large stimulus change to make a difference in sensation. The physical energy change required and the sensation that results must be measured separately and compared. This kind of measurement is **psychophysics.**

Thresholds

A threshold is a limiting (minimum or maximum) energy change, measured in terms of physiological recordings of receptors or nerve cells or in terms of reported sensation (in man). The questions to be asked include the following: (1) What is the minimum energy sensed (**absolute threshold**)? (2) What is the least *difference* in energy sensed, (**difference threshold**)? (3) What is the maximum energy sensed, that is, increasing the stimulus energy does not increase the sensation intensity (**terminal threshold**)? There are, then, three types of thresholds, each a measurement of physical energy as it affects sensation or receptor response. In visual intensity, for example, the absolute threshold for brightness is the dimmest light the subject can detect. The difference threshold is the smallest difference in brightness the subject can detect. The terminal threshold is the brightest light and the most intense sensation that the subject experiences; further increases in intensity do not make the light appear brighter to the subject. All three of these receptor and sensation responses have absolute and fixed values at a given moment. However, the sensitivity of the visual receptors varies from moment to moment. This will cause the absolute, difference, and terminal threshold values to vary from one measurement to the next. In addition, the subject makes *errors* in reporting his sensations, the experimenter makes errors in varying the stimulus and recording the results, and the stimulus light is not perfect. Fluctuations in receptor sensitivity and measurement error are involved. Some kind of average measurement is needed for the absolute, difference, and terminal thresholds. This means that any threshold is a derived *statistical* value rather than an absolute value for receptor sensitivity.

Absolute threshold. Frequently the absolute threshold is called "threshold," with the prefix absolute implied. The absolute threshold is most precisely defined as the minimum energy that results in a sensation (or stimulates a receptor) 50% of the time. As noted above, the 50% "average" value is used because the sensitivity of the receptor, the attention of the subject, and measurement errors fluctuate from time to time. Obviously, the more intense the energy, the greater will be the percentage of occasions that it will stimulate the subject—a more intense light will be detected more often, for example. The relationship between energy change and percent of responses by the subject is graphed as an **ogive** or umulative percentage (Fig. 7-2). The curve starts at an intensity that is always ineffective (0% response) and reaches an intensity that is always effective (100% response). The 50% point on the graph corresponds to the intensity the subject responds to half the time and is taken as the absolute threshold value.

Difference threshold. The difference threshold is defined as the least difference between two stimuli that can be detected 75% of the time. The reason for using 75% instead of 50% can be explained in Fig. 7-3. In determining a difference threshold the subject is making judgments about the *difference* between two adequate stimuli, A and B. The comparison illustrated in Fig. 7-3 is between the pitch of two tones. Two functions for differences between the stimuli are shown: (1) the percentage of occasions A is judged to have a higher pitch than B and (2) the percentage of occasions B is judged to have a higher pitch than A. Of course the two curves must be mirror images of one another; if A is judged higher than B 90% of the time at a 5 cycles per

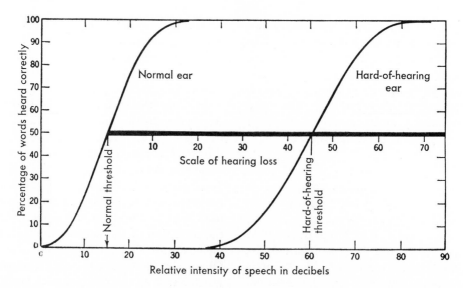

Fig. 7-2. Two threshold curves for hearing, plotted as ogives. The absolute threshold in decibles is indicated for each curve. (From Stevens, S. S.: Sensation and psychological measurement. In Boring, E. G., Langfeld, H. S., and Weld, H. P., editors: Foundations of psychology, New York, 1948, John Wiley & Sons, Inc.)

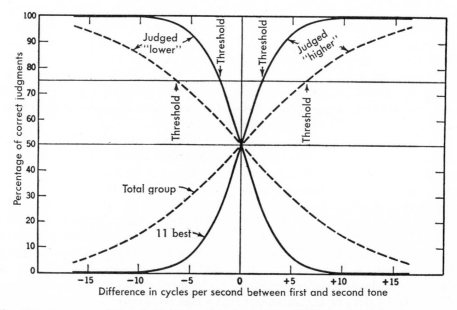

Fig. 7-3. Two sets of threshold curves for determining difference thresholds for pitch discrimination. Dotted curves are based on ninety-five normal subjects and the solid curve on the eleven subjects with the best pitch discrimination. The points used for determining the difference threshold for the latter group are indicated on their curves. For further details, see text. (From Stevens, S. S.: Sensation and psychological measurement. In Boring, E. G., Langfeld, H. S., and Weld, H. P., editors: Foundations of psychology, New York, 1948, John Wiley & Sons, Inc.)

second difference, then B *must* have been judged higher than A 10% of the time at an A minus B difference of 5 cycles. When the tones were just alike—zero cycles different—the subjects responded at a chance level. That is, A was judged higher half the time and B was judged higher half the time. At 10 cycles difference, the subjects were correct 100% of the time. The difference threshold is therefore fixed at halfway between chance (50%) and perfection (100%), or 75% correct judgments.

Terminal threshold. The other end of the scale from the absolute threshold is the terminal threshold. It is applied most readily to differences in the intensity and quality of stimuli. In terms of intensity it would be the stimulus intensity whose increase leads to no increase in sensation intensity half the time. As an example from quality thresholds, when increases in the frequency of a sound pass the range where the subject can hear them 50% of the time, the terminal threshold for pitch has been reached. However, there are two difficulties with the terminal threshold: (1) As the terminal threshold for intensity is approached, pain is sensed, and damage to the receptors may result. For practical reasons, the terminal intensity threshold is often measured in terms of the onset of pain. (2) Quality and intensity interact. For example, the sensory *range* for pitch increases with increased intensity so that both the absolute and terminal threshold values change—the subject can hear both lower and higher pitches at increased intensity.

Psychophysics and sensory attributes

Psychophysical methods can be used to determine thresholds for quality, intensity, extent, or duration in any sensory modality. Absolute, difference, and terminal thresholds can be determined for each attribute. In studying sensory quality, which stimulus value represents the absolute threshold and which represents the terminal threshold is

rather arbitrary; together they represent the *range* of qualities responded to by the receptor. In vision the hue quality is represented by a range of electromagnetic wavelengths from 400 to 750 mμ; beyond those limits the eye does not respond. Pitch, in hearing, corresponds to sound frequencies ranging from about 20 to 20,000 cycles per second; other frequencies do not stimulate the auditory receptors, regardless of their intensity. Qualitative thresholds for somesthesis, proprioception, and the chemical senses have received little study, but their measurement is at least theoretically possible.

Intensity thresholds have been studied in most sensory modalities. In vision, absolute, difference, and terminal thresholds for brightness have been established. These thresholds have also been measured for auditory loudness, intensity of each quality of taste, warmth, and pain, as well as for weight lifting (proprioception). The dimension of extent has been given the most attention in studies of visual size discrimination. Absolute thresholds of visual extent are the basis of the tests of visual *acuity* necessary in fitting eyeglasses. Difference thresholds for visual extent have been published as size judgments, but a terminal threshold merely means filling the visual field. The dimension of auditory extent (volume) has been scaled as it relates to pitch and loudness. Difference thresholds for extent of pressure sensations have been investigated. Absolute and difference thresholds for kinesthesis have received study by measuring the least angle of arm movement detected by the subject and the least difference between two angles sensed.

The measurement of duration is much the same for each modality and requires little attention here. Absolute and difference thresholds are the only ones studied; logically there can be no terminal threshold for duration of a stimulus as long as the subject is awake.

Weber's law

Weber's law deals with the attribute of intensity and states that the more intense the stimulus, the greater an increase in intensity must be before the increase can be sensed. In other words, the more intense the stimulus, the greater is the difference threshold. Further, the law states that this relationship is constant. If the base intensity is I, and the increase in intensity detected 50% of the time—the difference threshold—is ΔI, then $\Delta I/I = C$ when C is a constant. To use a simple example, if 1 candle must be added to 10 candles to detect an increase in the light in a room, 10 candles would have to be added to 100 candles to detect an increase. The constant in this case is 1/10, or 0.1. Everyday experience attests to the general correctness of Weber's law. For example, you can whisper to a companion and be heard during a quiet solo passage at a concert, but you must shout to him to be heard above the applause after the solo is over. The background noise has increased only moderately, but a greater increase in the intensity of your voice is needed to be heard. How great an increase is embarrassingly evident if the applause suddenly dies away and you find yourself making an announcement to the entire audience!

Weber's law can be used to compare the sensitivity of different sensory modalities. The more sensitive the modality, the lower its absolute threshold and the smaller its difference threshold, ΔI. The smaller the ΔI, the smaller is the constant, C, because $\Delta I/I = C$. For example, the Weber fraction for visual brightness is about 0.016; for auditory intensity, about 0.088; for cutaneous pressure, 0.136; and for taste, 0.200.

While Weber's law is correct in stating that the difference threshold increases with increases in base intensity, the constancy of the ratio does not hold at very low and very high intensities, particularly the former. In some cases the Weber fraction is largest

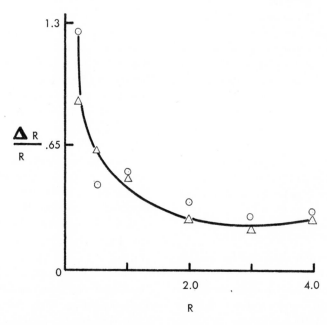

Fig. 7-4. Weber ratios for testing intensity differences in salt solutions. Expressions "R" and "△R" are equivalent to expressions "I" and "△I" in the text. (Modified from Holway, A. H., and Hurvich, L. M.: Amer. J. Psychol. **49:**37-48, 1937.)

at the low end of the intensity scale, minimum at moderate intensities, and greater than the minimum at high intensities (Fig. 7-4). The fraction cited in comparing the sensitivity of different sensory modalities is the minimum value, where the curve dips lowest. The Weber fraction holds better for some sensory modalities than it does for others; in vision and hearing the fraction is constant over more than 99.9% of the usable range of stimulus intensities. For modalities such as taste and pressure it is quite variable.

Fechner's law

Fechner stated that the relationship between stimulus intensity and sensation intensity is a logarithmic one, when sensation intensity is scaled in difference threshold units (Fig. 7-5). He was wrong in assuming that an intensity of 20 difference threshold units is only subjectively twice 10 difference threshold units, but that is of no concern here. The most important point is that the relationship between sensation intensity and stimulus intensity becomes nearly linear (one to one), when the stimulus values are given in log units. This is done because the increase in intensity needed to add one difference threshold unit gets larger and larger as intensity increases (as Weber's law states). Further, the rate of increase is logarithmic. By using a log scale for the stimulus values, the large increments at the high end of the scale are translated into smaller numbers. For example, the log of 10 is 1, the log of 100 is 2, the log of 1000 is 3, and so on. Plotted in the fashion shown in Fig. 7-5, the relation between stimulus intensity and sensation intensity usually turns out to be a straight line, which is esthetically satisfying at any rate! Expressed mathematically, the relationship between sensation intensity in difference threshold units (S), the intensity of the stimulus (I), and a constant (K) turns out to be $S = K \log I$. Just as in Weber's law, the smaller the value of the constant, K, the more sensitive the sensory modality.

A general psychophysical law: Steven's scale

Although Weber's law is correct enough to be useful for some senses such as vision,

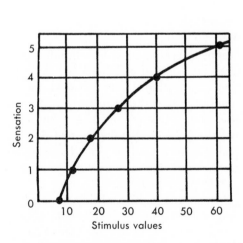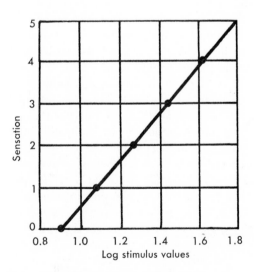

Fig. 7-5. Relationships between stimulus intensity and sensation intensity. For details, see text. (From Woodworth, R. S., and Schlosberg, H.: Experimental psychology, rev. ed., New York, 1954, Holt, Rinehart, & Winston, Inc.)

it is too inaccurate for others such as taste. Fechner's law is more generally useful because it shows the form of the relationship between stimulus magnitude and sensation intensity to be a logarithmic one. A logarithmic function relating two measurements is one kind of *power function* because the formula that describes the function contains an *exponent* to the base 10 (a logarithm). It turns out that another kind of power function best describes the relationship between stimulus magnitude and either sensation intensity or the electrical response of receptors and nerve cells. If the stimulus magnitude is phi (ϕ) and the sensation intensity or receptor and nerve cell response is psi (Ψ), the relationship between them is $\Psi = K\phi^n$.

K is a constant that depends on the relative size of the units used in measuring phi and psi. The exponent, n, varies according to the sensory modality; it may differ as much as tenfold for the different senses. The law depends on the validity of the measures used to determine stimulus magnitude and sensation intensity or nerve cell response. That is, the measures must accurately reflect changes in stimulus magnitude and sensation intensity and not be contaminated by events over which the experimenter has little control. A measurement is called a *scale,* and the scales required by the law are ratio scales, that is, scales with a true zero magnitude and equal units (see below). The state of the art of measurement in physiological psychology often confines us to "indicators" of magnitude which have neither a true zero nor equal units. In the area of sensation, however, ratio scales are often possible for both measures of stimulus magnitude and measures of sensation intensity, or sensory nerve cell response. To evaluate the validity of measures used in sensation and other areas of physiological psychology, therefore, some knowledge of scales of measurement seems useful.

Scales of measurement

A scale is a set of rules for measurement. Physicists have developed scales for measuring physical events. Psychologists use these scales as objective scales of stimulus magnitude and develop parallel scales that measure subjective quality, intensity, extent, and duration. In both physics and psychology measurement scales differ in accuracy and type, depending on how the data measured were obtained. Four varieties of measurement scales can be distinguished: (1) **nominal scale,** (2) **ordinal scale,** (3) **interval scale,** and (4) **ratio scale.**

Nominal scale. A **nominal scale** merely differentiates stimuli from one another. In physical terms it means sorting objects or events into *categories.* A post-office worker is using a nominal scale when he sorts letters into boxes labelled New York, Chicago, or Los Angeles. Psychologically, the scale assumes reliable (that is, repeatable) demonstration of the ability to *discriminate stimuli*—objects or events—from one another. The scale implies no order of magnitude; for example, the numbers on football players' jerseys are a nominal scale that enables the coach to repeatedly identify his men at a distance. The numbers do not imply that one man is a better football player than another. The nominal scale implies the ability of the subject to (1) determine the presence of the stimulus so that it can be assigned a "label," (2) determine what other stimuli are *equal* to the first stimulus so that they can receive the same label, and (3) determine what other stimuli are *different* from the first so that they may receive different labels. The basic psychological operation involved in a nominal scale is *discrimination.*

Ordinal scale. The ability to *rank* the stimuli as well as to discriminate between them is assumed by the **ordinal scale.** The size or meaning of the difference between stimuli may vary, but their *order* may not.

To use this kind of scale one must be able to repeatedly place objects or events in the same order, which also implies the ability to discriminate between them. If the members of a college class were lined up in order of height for a photographer to take their picture, the photographer would be using an ordinal scale of height. The *units* on his scale would probably not be equal; the tallest man might be two inches taller than the next man, and the third man four inches shorter than the second man. Most psychological scales are ordinal scales. Subjects can rank the United States presidents before 1925 on a scale of importance to history, for example. Washington might come first in importance, next Lincoln, and then Wilson. This does not mean that the difference in importance between Washington and Lincoln was greater than that between Lincoln and Wilson—the number of "units of importance" between ranks probably would differ if they could be measured. In a similar fashion, most classroom tests are ordinal scales. If you get a 95 on a test, Joe gets a 90, and Jim gets an 85, this does not mean that Joe knows as much more than Jim as you know more than Joe. Even if the scores are percentages of the items correct, the 5 percentage points might represent questions of different difficulty in the two cases. A, B, C, D, and F grades are also an ordinal scale. All that the ordinal scale requires, then, is *discrimination* and *ranking*.

Interval scale. An **interval scale** is one in which the *units* of measurement are equal, but the zero point is arbitrarily selected. Interval scales require the ability to discriminate, rank, and define equal intervals on the scale. A good example of a physical interval scale is the Fahrenheit thermometer, on which the units of temperature change are equal to one another because they are based on the expansion of a column of liquid up a scale of equal distance units (degrees) with heat. However,

the zero point was arbitrarily chosen as the freezing point of an ice and salt mixture. Temperatures below zero are common in Fahrenheit measurement, but they do not imply the absence of temperature, or inverse temperatures. Interval scales in psychophysics are based on the difference threshold. When a subject can discriminate between the pitch of three tones, place them in order of pitch difference, and determine when tone A is as much higher pitched than B as B is higher than C, then the basis for an interval scale is present. If the subject can just discriminate between A and B, he is at his difference threshold for pitch. If he can likewise just discriminate between B and C, he is also at his difference threshold. These two just noticeable differences, or JNDS, are subjectively equal units and form an interval scale.

Ratio scale. Scales requiring discrimination, order, equal intervals or units, *and* equal ratios are called **ratio scales.** A ratio scale has a true zero point because it has *equal ratios.* On a ratio scale four is twice two and eight is twice four. If this was not known, one would be unable to fix the zero point on the scale; the zero point on the scale makes equal ratios possible. Most physical scales are ratio scales. Scales of length, for example, are ratio scales because zero distance can be defined. The Kelvin temperature scale has an absolute zero, defined as the absence of all molecular motion. Weight measures are also an absolute scale. In psychophysics, absolute scales for sensation quality, intensity, extent, or duration are possible whenever the subject can reliably judge that one stimulus is twice another in one of these attributes, that is, when he can perceive *equal sensed ratios* as well as discriminate differences, rank the stimuli, and perceive equal intervals. If the subject can repeatedly demonstrate his ability to judge that one weight feels twice as heavy as another, a ratio scale of sensed weight can be set up to parallel the physical ratio scale of weights. Ratio scales have been worked out for loudness (sones), pitch (mels), warmth, pain, all four taste qualities, lifted weights, and brightness, among others.

SENSORY PHENOMENA

So far sensation and perception have been treated as though constant measurements were being taken of a single quality for a single modality, for example, the response of the eye to blue light. What happens to the sensitivity of a receptor if it is stimulated at a constant rate over a period of time? What happens when one sensory quality is stimulated for a time and then the stimulus for a different quality is substituted (for example, stimulating the eye with blue light for a time and then substituting yellow light)? What happens when two different qualities are presented at the same time—how does the eye respond to blue and yellow light, both presented at once? Various kinds of sensory reactions to continued stimulation and changes in sensory quality are the subject of this section.

Adaptation

Energy change of a specific physical nature and amount was defined as the adequate stimulus for a given receptor—light of a specified intensity and wavelength range for the eye, air pressure changes of a specified frequency and amplitude for the ear, and so on. Increases in energy within these limits results in increases in the perceived intensity of the stimulus. In some receptors *constant* energy input over a period of time results in a *decrease* in perceived intensity. If the decrease in perceived intensity results from a decrease in receptor sensitivity, the phenomenon is called **adaptation**. For example, the smell of flowers is quite noticeable on entering a florist's shop, but it nearly disappears after remaining in the shop for twenty minutes

or so. This happens because the receptors have become insensitive to the flower odor. The extent to which receptors adapt differs from one sensory modality to another. Adaptation to a constant stimulus is nearly complete for smell under most conditions, resulting in no stimulation after a period of time. Taste adaptation is usually about half complete. Adaptation to moderate stimulus intensities is complete for temperature. Some adaptation occurs in vision and hearing. Very little adaptation occurs for pressure, pain, kinesthesis, or the vestibular senses. If pressure adapted, one would "lose touch" with his environment. If pain adapted, one would become unaware of injurious stimuli. If kinesthesis adapted, one would lose sensations of position and movement. If the vestibular senses adapted, one would lose his balance. On the other hand, vision and hearing must change sensitivity to increase their intensity range so that they can respond to intense lights and sounds without damage from overstimulation, yet respond to faint lights and sounds when not adapted. Once smell or taste receptors have signaled the new stimuli they encounter, they can become insensitive to them without depriving the brain of useful information. Temperature receptors adapt after the body has made the adjustments to temperature change that keep the internal environment constant. If the body cannot cope with cold or warm stimuli in this manner, the receptors continue to signal this fact to the brain.

Habituation. Despite the fact that some receptors are always adapted, the brain receives more information from the remaining receptors than it can cope with at any one time. Of course, some receptors act only to set off coordinated reflexes of various kinds and one is not aware of these inputs as such. However, the responses to them stimulate other receptors that "feed back" to contribute to the brain's information load. This load of inputs is more than the higher centers of the brain can cope with all at once.

Consequently, one is not *aware* of many inputs until he turns his attention to them. This fact is called **attentional adaptation,** or **habituation.** The reader is unaware of the pressure of the clothes on his back or the background noises in the room until his attention is turned to them. The receptors have not adapted because he is aware of the pressure and sound stimuli when he turns his attention to them. Habituation therefore depends on the function of higher brain centers. These centers deal with only a limited number of the inputs bombarding the brain at any given time.

Consequences of adaptation: contrast and afterimages

When a sense organ adapts to a stimulus of a given *sensory quality*, its sensitivity to other sensory qualities may be unimpaired or even enhanced. Continued stimulation of the eye with red light, for example, decreases sensitivity to red, yet *increases* sensitivity to green. A continuous sweet stimulus raises the taste threshold to sweet but *lowers* the threshold to sour. This phenomenon is called **contrast.** When both stimuli are present at once, **simultaneous contrast** occurs. For instance, if the subject looks at a card painted half red and half green, the red area next to the green will look redder than the remainder of the red area, and the green area next to the red will look greener than the remainder of the green. Devotees of Chinese sweet and sour spareribs are enjoying simultaneous contrast— the sweet taste is accented by the presence of the sour taste and vice versa.

If the stimuli that mutually enhance one another are presented in succession rather than simultaneously, **successive contrast** will occur. If you look at a red card until your visual receptors have partially adapted and *then* look at a green card, the green card will look greener than it otherwise would because the eye has increased sensitivity to green. In a simular way a lemon tastes sourer after eating a candy bar.

Afterimages occur when the receptors continue to respond after the stimulus ceases acting on them. **Positive afterimages** usually result from *brief, intense* stimulation. The receptor continues to respond for a time just as it did during stimulation. For example, if you stare briefly at an unshaded light bulb and then look at a blank wall, you will continue to see the filament of the bulb for a time.

Negative afterimages result from *prolonged, moderate* stimulation of a given quality. The receptors adapt to that quality and the threshold of another quality is lowered so that the second quality is preceived when the first is no longer sensed. When the stimulus is removed, the receptors continue to respond, not with the same quality, but with an *opposite* quality. Thus, if you stare at a green card for a minute or two and then look at a gray wall, you will perceive the image of a red card on the wall.

Compensation and fusion

If two stimuli of different quality are presented to the same receptor, either **compensation** or **fusion** may occur. Compensation occurs when the two stimuli interact to neutralize the response of the receptor. For example, the odors of basalm and beeswax are quite distinct when smelled one at a time. If both stimuli are presented at once, the subject smells nothing. Fusion occurs when the two stimuli interact so as to cause a *qualitatively* different sensation. For example, a mixture of red and yellow stimuli can result in a sensation of orange.

CUES TO PERCEPTION

As previously stated, perception occurs when sensations interact together and with traces of past experiences in the central nervous system. Physiologically, little is known of how the nervous system integrates incoming sensations with the traces left by past sensation inputs. There is some knowledge of how incoming sensations interact in perception, at least so far as *cues* to the *location* of the stimulus are concerned. In hearing, for example, the difference in the response of the two ears because of their position on either side of the head serves as a way of locating the *source* of a sound stimulus. The two eyes respond differently as a visual stimulus approaches or recedes, and each eye also makes certain adjustments that act as *cues* to the distance of an object from the viewer. In forming perceptions the brain also makes certain "inferences" about the **constancy** of stimuli. For example, a visual stimulus increases in apparent *extent* (size) as it comes closer to the subject. The subject could assume that its *apparent* size was increasing because it was actually getting bigger or because it was getting closer. The latter assumption is nearly always made; objects are assumed to stay constant in size. They are also perceived as remaining constant in shape. A coin held at an angle to the eye makes an oval image on the retina—it is assumed that the oval image is caused by its position, not by a change in shape. Such assumptions are called the *constancy phenomena,* and the extent to which they are learned and are inherited perceptual tendencies has been the subject of much research.

SUMMARY

Physical energy excites receptors when they are sensitive to the given form and intensity of energy. The resulting sensations are "raw inputs" elaborated by the CNS into perceptions whenever several sensation inputs and CNS traces from past experience are integrated. Sensations are studied in man when a subject reports on those aspects of perception that depend on sensation. The inputs from stimuli are controlled by the experimenter in the method of introspection.

Stimuli are physical events to which receptors respond. Receptors are specialized to respond to specific forms of energy change. Some specialized receptors excite those parts of the brain whose activity results in conscious sensation; some receptors cause only homeostatic reflexes. There are receptors specialized to respond to mechanical, thermal, chemical, acoustic, or photic energy. When a receptor is activated by the form of energy for which it is specialized, it has received an adequate stimulus; if it is excited by another form of energy, it receives an inadequate stimulus. Either stimulus causes a generator potential that fires sensory neurons.

The modality of the resulting sensation depends on what part of the brain the nerve impulses reach, according to the law of specific nerve energies. Receptors transduce physical energy into nerve impulses. Receptors may be classified by form as unspecialized nerve cells, specialized nerve cells, or specialized receptor cells. They may be classified by location in the head only, or whole body, as special senses or general senses. The general senses are somesthesis (pressure, pain, warmth, and cold), and kinesthesis. The special senses are olfaction, vision, gustation, audition, and vestibular sensitivity. Receptors can be classified by the functional location of their stimuli as exteroceptors, interoceptors, and proprioceptors; pain receptors are also called nociceptors. Exteroceptors include cutaneous senses; interoceptors include organic senses.

The attributes common to all sensation are quality, intensity, extent, and duration. There are both primary and secondary qualities in sensory modalities that have more than one quality. Quality is signaled to the CNS by the arrival of nerve impulses at a given *place* in the brain when different modalities are involved, and perhaps by impulse pattern for different qualities within a modality. Intensity increases reach the CNS with the firing of more nerve cells at a faster rate with reduced spikes. Increased extent stimulates a larger area in the brain; increased duration stimulates for a longer period.

Comparison of changes in the physical

stimulus with resulting changes in sensation is called psychophysics. Thresholds can be measured for all four attributes of sensation. The absolute threshold is the minimum level of stimulation that can be detected 50% of the time. The difference threshold is the minimum stimulus difference that can be detected 75% of the time. The terminal threshold is the sensation intensity that cannot be exceeded 50% of the time.

Weber's law states that the relation between the difference threshold for intensity and the stimulus level from which the increase was taken is constant for a given modality. The constant ratio is smaller the more sensitive the receptor, but the ratio increases at very high and very low intensities. Fechner's law states that the relation between stimulus intensity and sensation intensity is a logarithmic one. The general psychophysical law gives a power function, relating stimulus magnitude and sensation intensity when ratio scales are used.

Four types of measurement scales can be distinguished: nominal, ordinal, interval, and ratio scales. Nominal scales require discrimination, ordinal scales require discrimination and order, interval scales require discrimination, order, and equal intervals, and ratio scales require all these plus a true zero.

Some sensory modalities become less sensitive when stimulated at a constant rate for a period of time, a phenomenon called adaptation. Sensory inputs that do not adapt completely may not be attended to, a phenomenon called habituation. True adaptation to one quality in a modality may enhance sensitivity to another quality in that modality—sensory contrast. If the two stimuli are presented simultaneously, simultaneous contrast results: if they are presented successively, successive contrast results. Afterimages result when the sensation outlasts the stimulus. Positive afterimages are a continuation of the same sensation and result from brief, intense stimulation. Negative afterimages are a sensation of opposite quality from the stimulus and result from prolonged moderate stimulation. Presenting two stimuli of different qualities at once to a sense organ may cause compensation when they cancel each other out to cause no sensation, or fusion when they result in a sensation having a new quality.

When sensations interact in cues to perceiving the location of the stimulus, the nature of the cues to location may be sought in some attribute of the sensation. The brain makes assumptions about the constancy of the shape, size, etc. of the stimulus—the constancy phenomena—in utilizing these cues.

READINGS

Boring, E. G.: The physical dimensions of consciousness, New York, 1963, Dover Publications, Inc.

Boring, E. G., Langfeld, H. S., and Weld, H. P.: Foundations of psychology, New York, 1948, John Wiley & Sons, Inc.

Case, J.: Sensory mechanisms, New York, 1966, The Macmillan Co.

Mueller, C. G.: Sensory psychology, Englewood Cliffs, N. J., 1965, Prentice-Hall, Inc.

Chapter 8

Somesthesis

OVERVIEW

This chapter concerns the least specialized of the sensory modalities—sensations of pressure, temperature, and pain that come from the skin surface, muscles, and viscera throughout the body. Collectively these sensations are called somesthesis. The chapter begins by classifying somesthetic sensations in contrast with the proprioceptive senses of position and movement. Some of the methods used in studying somesthesis are discussed. The primary and secondary sensory qualities follow, with proofs for the primary qualities. The problems involved in specifying receptors that determine primary qualities are examined. The next section summarizes what is known of the somesthetic receptors and the sensory phenomena that result from stimulating them. Pressure, temperature, and pain inputs receive attention. The nerve pathways serving somesthesis are traced from the receptors to the brain. The chapter begins by defining somesthesis in contrast to proprioception, and it ends by contrasting the somesthetic nerve pathways to those serving proprioception. A general plan for both inputs begins the section on nerve pathways. Fiber grouping by somesthetic modality in the spinal cord is contrasted with fiber grouping by body location in the brain. Secondary sensory pathways are traced. A more functional classification of somesthetic and proprio-

ceptive inputs ends the chapter, with implications for general arousal and attention that is specific to one sensory input.

SENSATIONS FROM THE BODY

The sensations that seem to come from the body are of two general kinds: (1) those of *condition,* such as pressure, pain, or temperature sensations in some part of the body, and (2) those of *position* and *movement* of some part of the body. The sensations of *condition* are the subject of this chapter, but the sensations of position and movement will be briefly classified by contrast.

Somesthesis

Somesthesis (Gr., body knowledge) is sensations of pressure, pain, and temperature and their complex combinations that come from all over the body. Somesthetic sensations are further classified according to which of the three layers of body tissue are stimulated. Sensations from the skin (ectoderm, Chapter 2) are called **cutaneous** somesthetic sensations, sensations from the muscles (mesoderm) are **muscular** somesthetic sensations, and sensations from the viscera (endoderm) are **visceral** somesthetic sensations. In each case sensations of pressure, warmth, cold, and/or pain are involved.

The cutaneous sensations originate from

130

exciting receptors located just beneath the surface of the skin. These receptors have received the most study because they are most accessible to the investigator and because they relate to conditions at the surface of the body where the outside world is encountered. Somesthetic receptors stimulate reflex responses from pressure receptors that affect posture, warm and cold receptors stimulate hemeostatic reflexes that maintain body temperature, and pain receptors initiate protective reflexes that prevent injury. Along with other exteroceptors such as vision and hearing, these receptors initiate complex adjustments to changes in the environment that are often accompanied by awareness of that environment—"touch" (pressure) sensations in finding the way past obstacles in a dark room, temperature changes that lead one to put on or take off a coat, pain sensations that prevent one from stepping into a shower when the water is too hot, and so on.

Somesthetic sensations from the muscles also initiate reflexes. Pressure sensations in limbs and muscles set off complex coordinated reflexes that make a movement depend on the present position of a limb. Input from temperature receptors changes the blood flow to a muscle as needed. Pain reflexes in muscles can cause contractions (cramps). These simpler adjustments are usually accompanied by awareness and are followed by more complex responses to the conditions signaled by the receptors.

Visceral somesthetic sensations come from the gut (digestive organs) and the blood vessels. Pressure sensations are often felt in digestion and initiate reflexes necessary to that process. Pressure receptors initiate the reflexes that empty the bladder and bowels. Temperature stimulation seem to be restricted to the mouth and esophagus, but it can prevent swallowing or cause vomiting of a dangerously hot or cold substance, in combination with pain. Visceral pain is poorly localized, but it still serves a warning function, particularly in the case of headache (from blood vessels in the head) or stomach pain. All these sensations are interoceptive.

Somesthetic sensations—cutaneous, muscular, or visceral—can serve to arouse and sustain behavior when adverse or uncomfortable sensations are involved. This is particularly true of pain. Some somesthetic sensations can therefore act as drives since a drive is any mechanism that arouses and sustains behavior. Pressure, warmth, cold, and pain sensations are included here. Pressure sensations from the bowel and bladder arouse and sustain behavior until evacuation reflexes are permitted to act. Our adjustments to pain and to excessive heat or cold also act as drives. Internal or external warmth, cold, or pain will sustain a high level of response activity until a comfortable temperature is found or until pain is relieved.

Proprioception

Proprioception involves sensations of *position* and *movement* rather than sensations of condition (warm, cold, pressure, or pain). Although somesthesis is a general sense, involving receptors found over the entire body, proprioception involves both a general sense and special senses found only in the head.

The special senses of proprioception are the **vestibular senses.** Their receptors are found in the nonauditory labyrinth of the inner ear and will be considered in detail in Chapter 9. The vestibular senses respond to the position and movements of the head. Besides initiating reflex reactions of balance, coordination, and eye movements, they are indirectly responsible for sensations of dizziness and nausea.

The general proprioceptive sense is **kinesthesis.** Kinesthetic receptors in muscles regulate muscle tone via the **stretch reflex** (Chapters 5 and 13) that partially contracts muscles according to the degree to which they are stretched. These receptors send impulses to the **cerebellum** to regulate balance and coordination, but they do not directly initiate conscious sensations. Other kinesthetic receptors in the joints, tendons, and connective tissue of muscle send impulses to the cerebral cortex and result in sensations of position and movement of the limbs. Their nervous connections will be noted later in this chapter by contrast with those of somesthesis. The study of muscle tonus, coordination, etc. will be deferred to Chapter 9.

METHODS OF STUDY

What is known of somesthetic input comes from three study approaches: (1) introspective, (2) anatomical, and (3) physiological.

Introspective study involves the familiar approach of stimulating a human subject under controlled conditions and asking him to report his sensations. The sensations of warmth, cold, pressure, and pain from the surface of the skin have been studied in this way. Sometimes the introspective technique has been combined with the anatomical technique, as when points on the skin sensitive to these four stimuli are mapped, and then the skin of that area is removed, stained, and sectioned for study of skin receptors under the microscope.

Anatomical study involves the tracing of tracts and centers in the brain served by sensory nerves coming from somesthetic and proprioceptive receptors. Introspective studies are subject to error because they involve only those receptor mechanisms concerned in conscious sensations and because subject reports cannot be confirmed except by other subject reports—there is no way of comparing the conscious sensations of two subjects. Anatomical studies can tell us only what receptors and tracts look like—not how they work in organizing responses. Furthermore, tracing anatomical tracts in the brain that serve sensation reveals only the most direct input pathways.

Pathways involving many synapses and diffuse inputs cannot be traced by ana-

tomical means because they are so diffuse that they show only the many *possibilities* for input. Which ones are actually involved in receptor input can be detected only by physiological means. The favorite physiological method for this purpose is the *method of evoked potentials.* The receptors are stimulated electrically, or by using their adequate stimuli, in an anesthetized animal. Electrodes are placed in various tracts, brain areas, and brain nuclei to detect where the input *actually goes.* New anesthetics have been developed that do not depress the excitability of the brain, yet paralyze response on the part of the animal, so that reactions of the brain to sensory input can be studied with the brain in a more or less normal condition. It is assumed that if the adequate stimuli for pressure, temperature, etc. are used, the appropriate inputs are being stimulated. Unfortunately, the animal cannot be asked to report on what other inputs are stimulated at the same time. To that extent, our data are uncertain.

The physiological methods remain, however, the ones least subject to error. The newest and most promising of these methods involves implanting electrodes in the brain of animals who are allowed to recover and can be "plugged in" to record electrical activity of specific parts of the brain while the animal is responding normally to stimuli controlled by the experimenter. This is the most "true-to-life" situation and ultimately will probably give us the most information on the way the sensory systems of the brain transact their business and control the behavior of the normal animal. Unfortunately, there is not yet as much information using the newer methods as we would like.

SOMESTHETIC QUALITIES
Primary qualities

The primary qualities of somesthesis are pressure, cold, warmth, and pain. Introspectively, these are the irreducible qualities of somesthetic sensation, although combinations of these sensations, or intermittent stimulation, can produce more complex sensations. The bulk of the evidence suggests that each of the four primary qualities represents a separate sensory *modality*, that is, a pressure sense, warmth sense, cold sense, and pain sense. However, some hold that one or the other of these inputs, particularly pain, may represent a pattern of inputs rather than a separate modality. In any case it is evident that each of the four modalities except pain is served by several kinds of receptors.

Secondary qualities

Secondary qualities can result from either intermittent stimulation of one primary quality or the combination of two or more primary qualities. As examples of intermittent stimulation, a tickle sensation results from intermittent pressure stimulation, and an itch is caused by intermittent pain stimulation. A combination of primary pressure and cold sensations results in a secondary sensation of wetness from dry stimuli; weak pressure and warmth produce an oily sensation.

Proof for four modalities of skin sensitivity

Visceral and muscle somesthesis are not ordinarily accessible to stimulation in human subjects who can report on their sensations while being stimulated. Most of the evidence rests on experiments with cutaneous sensitivity, and the evidence emphasizes the *punctuate* or point-to-point distribution of spots on the skin that are most sensitive to either pressure, cold, warmth, or pain. Reliable distributions of sensitive spots to each primary quality have been found, despite the many kinds of receptors found in the skin.

Skin mapping. The skin may be marked off in tiny 1 mm. squares on different parts of the body, using a stamp pad and ink to give a small area marked like graph paper.

Each square is then stimulated with a hair (for pressure), a warm or cold rod (for temperature), and a needle (for pain). By grading the intensity of each stimulus, absolute thresholds can be established for each square. Although nearly all spots will respond to pressure, some will have a higher threshold than others. Different spots will be *differentially sensitive* to cold, warmth, and pain as well. One spot may have a high threshold to cold and a low threshold to warmth, whereas another may show the opposite effect. This suggests that one spot is closer to a warm receptor and the other closer to a cold receptor. Furthermore, those parts of the body that are most sensitive to cold stimulation may not be the same parts that are most sensitive to pressure or pain. For example, the face is exquisitely sensitive to cold, but relatively insensitive to pain. A simple demonstration of punctuate sensitivity may be made by drawing a pencil point lightly across the skin; pressure, warmth, cold, and various secondary qualities such as tickle and itch will be aroused, in turn, as the stimulus passes over different points on the skin. By drawing the pencil over the fingertip, more pressure sensations will be felt; drawing it across the cheek results in more cold sensations. Again this indicates the different distribution of receptors for the four cutaneous sensations.

Spark gaps. The stimuli used so far arouse pressure sensations because they distort the skin surface. Sparks from a high-voltage source may be "jumped" to the skin to electrically stimulate receptors there. If the amperage (rate of current flow) is kept small, the subject does not sense a shock. Instead, from different points on the skin he will sense pressure, warmth, cold, or pain as well as combinations of these—warmth, cold, or pain can therefore be stimulated independently of pressure sensations.

Excitation and conduction time. If different kinds of receptors serve the four primary qualities, they should also differ in how rapidly the receptor responds and in how fast the different sensory neurons conduct to the CNS. Reaction time to the four kinds of stimuli should change as a result and this seems to be the case. Adaptation time also differs for the four stimuli, indicating receptors that adapt at different rates. Most of the nerve fibers serving pressure are large fibers of the A group (Chapter 4) that conduct rapidly, and reaction time to pressure stimuli is therefore faster than to warm, cold, or some pain stimuli. The pressure receptors adapt more rapidly than the others. Reaction time for cold is slightly faster than that for warmth—the fibers for both seem to be of the B group—but the cold-sensitive receptors are closer to the surface of the skin than are the warm receptors and may therefore be affected sooner by their adequate stimulus. Both adapt, but not as rapidly as pressure. Cold adapts more slowly than warmth. Pain may be served by both A and C fibers. The C fibers predominate, however, and conduction speed and reaction time for pain are usually slowest of all. Pain also adapts more slowly than the other three qualities.

Different effects of cocaine and asphyxia. Cocaine affects fibers without myelin sheaths more than myelinated fibers. C fibers are anesthetized first, then B, and then A. The drug abolishes dull pain (C fibers) first, then temperature (B fibers), then touch (pressure from A fibers), and finally sharp or prick pain (smaller A fibers—see below). Asphyxia, or lack of oxygen, has the opposite effect. It affects myelineated fibers first. Sensations from a limb can be asphyxiated (abolished through lack of oxygen) by cutting off blood flow with a tourniquet. Asphyxia abolishes pressure (touch) first, then temperature, and then pain. As circulation is restored, pain returns while the limb is still numb (no pressure sensations). Anyone who has had a limb "go to sleep" from poor circulation caused by an awkward position can testify

that "pins and needles" (pain) sensations return before the limb senses touch.

Nerve pathways. The cutaneous somesthetic modalities are carried in different parts of the tracts of the spinal cord. The exact anatomy will be considered near the end of this chapter. As further proof for four modalities, however, tract location differentiates between two groups of sensory modalities. Nerve impulses resulting from pressure stimulation are carried in tracts of the dorsal and ventral funiculi of the cord; nerve impulses serving temperature and pain are carried in tracts in the lateral funiculi. Cranial nerve input for pressure goes to one nucleus and pain and temperature to another.

Problems of further modality specification

Despite the proofs for four somesthetic modalities, problems are involved in further specifying the receptor and neural mechanisms underlying the four primary somesthetic qualities. These problems include identifying projection areas in the brain and receptor specificity.

Projection areas. Separate sensory projection areas in the cerebral cortex have been identified for the sensory modalities of audition, smell, and taste (Chapter 6). If pressure, warmth, cold, and pain are separate sensory modalities, their pathways should end on separate projection areas in the cerebral cortex. As far as is known, impulses for all four of these stimuli arrive at areas 3, 1, and 2 on the postcentral gyrus of the cortex—the somesthetic projection area. This is true despite the fact that pain and temperature inputs are separated from the pressure inputs in the spinal cord (see above). There is evidence, however, that pain (and perhaps temperature) projects to deeper layers in the cortex than does pressure. Further, the pain pathway has many more collaterals to excite subcortical centers than pressure. These collaterals excite secondary sensory areas for somesthesis (area SII) that lie outside the primary somesthetic projection area (SI).

Receptors. If pressure, cold, warmth, and pain are separate senses, their receptors should have specialized in at least four different ways to be most sensitive to four different kinds of physical energy. Differences in specialization would be likely to cause differences in the appearance of the receptors. Are there four or more different kinds of sensory transducers beneath the skin to correspond to four somesthetic modalities? Anatomical studies show that there are many different-looking receptors

beneath the skin. The function of some are understood, but the functions of others are in doubt. The most common receptor ending, an **anastomosis** of free nerve endings (Chapter 7), is the least specialized, however. It is difficult to prove four classes of specialized receptors in some areas of the body that are sensitive to the four somesthetic qualities because *only* free nerve endings are found in these areas. For example, the pinna (external ear) is sensitive to pressure, cold, warmth, and pain, yet it contains only free nerve endings. Perhaps there are four kinds of free nerve endings

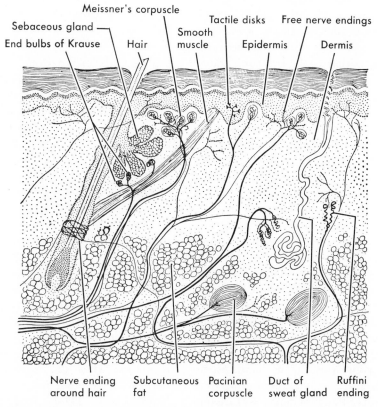

Fig. 8-1. Composite diagram of the skin and its receptors. Epidermis, dermis, and subcutaneous fat layers are shown, with receptors to be found in each layer. Not all endings shown are found in any one skin area (see text). (From Gardner, E. O.: Fundamentals of neurology, ed. 4, Philadelphia, 1963, W. B. Saunders Co.; modified from Woolard, H. H., Weddell, G., and Harpman, J. A.: J. Anat. **74:**413-440, 1940.)

that differ biochemically or in some other way that is not apparent under the microscope. Perhaps these endings differ in their "connections" to different parts of the brain. Evidence is lacking on these points. There are more specialized receptors in more sensitive areas of the skin, and the specialized nature of some of them is understood. It may be that these specialized receptors have evolved from different kinds of free nerve endings.

STRUCTURE OF THE SKIN

The structure of the skin must be considered to see how receptors have specialized for pressure, cold, warmth, and pain (Fig. 8-1). The skin consists of two layers, the tough outer **epidermis** and the thick fibrous inner **dermis.** Beneath these two layers is an insulating layer of **subcutaneous fat,** a layer that is thicker (and therefore softer!) in women than in men. The top layer of the epidermis (corneum) is made up of dead cells because living cells cannot survive exposure to air, water, or the temperatures and pressures of the external environment. These dead cells are continually flaking off—you can see a white streak made up of these cells by raking a fingernail across your arm. The outer dead layer of epidermis is continually replaced by living cells from the inner layer of epidermis (malpighian layer). Some of the more superficial receptors (thought to serve light pressure or touch) are found in the inner layer of epidermis, principally **free nerve ends** and **tactile disks.** Most of the cutaneous receptors are found in the dermis, whose rigid surface accounts for fingerprints and palm prints in the hand. **Meissner's corpuscles,** and **basket endings** are thought to serve touch. whereas **Krause end bulbs** may be cold receptors and **Ruffini endings** may serve warmth. **Pacinian corpuscles** ("deep pressure" receptors) are found at the surface of the subcutaneous fat layer. The form of the receptors shown in Fig. 8-1 is an idealized one in each case;

many mixed and unidentifiable forms of **encapsulated** nerve endings are found, and some areas of the body have only free nerve endings.

PRESSURE
Receptors

Several kinds of specialized endings appear to serve pressure sensitivity. Most of them are located near the surface of the skin, but some are located deeper beneath the skin and in the viscera, joints, and connective tissue of muscle. The adequate stimulus for each receptor seems to be a kind of mechanical deformation. Basket endings encircle the base of each body hair and are sensitive to movement of the hair, as you can discover by bending a single hair on your arm with the point of a pencil.

Meissner's corpuscles are found in hairless regions that are particularly sensitive to touch (light pressure), such as the fingertips. This distribution suggests that they are specialized pressure-sensitive receptors. They are dermal layer receptors. Free nerve endings are found in the epidermis over the entire body. In slightly more touch-sensitive regions they become more or less specialized tactile disks. These superficially located free ends and tactile disks do not serve pain because the superficial epidermis can be peeled off without pain sensations; their superficial location suggests that they are pressure receptors. They are found in the less pressure-sensitive areas of the skin where more specialized looking receptors appear to be absent.

Pacinian corpuscles are "deep pressure" receptors. They are located beneath the dermis and respond only to more gross skin deformation. These receptors are also found in the mesenteries, sheets of transparent connective tissue from which the intestines hang beneath the stomach. Here they are sensitive to the movements of the stomach and intestines in digestion. Pacinian corpuscles are found in the walls of hollow viscera, such as the bladder and colon, for sensations accompanying the need to urinate or defecate. They are found near joints where they signal position and movement of the limbs.

Pressure receptor as transducer

The pacinian corpuscle is the largest of the encapsulated endings and is visible to the naked eye. Its size lends it to study of how the physical energy of pressure is transformed or transduced into nerve impulses, a different form of energy. The encapsulated ending looks like an onion with a myelinated nerve fiber invading the core of the onion. Distorting the pacinian corpuscle sets up a generator potential (Chapter 4) of nonpropagated current flow in the ending, and this generator potential causes repetitive firing of the sensory neuron. The onion-shaped capsule around the nerve end can be destroyed down to its innermost layer without impairing the generator potential. However, the capsule itself will not produce a generator potential if the neuron is destroyed. The capsule probably serves to spread pressure over a larger area of the nerve ending to increase the size of the generator potential; several points on the nerve ending will *summate* when stimulated at the same time. That is, they will show increased response over pressure on a single point. The capsule may spread the stimulation in a like fashion. Greater pressure on the capsule results in a larger generator potential and a faster rate (frequency) of neuron firing to signal intensity.

Pressure sensitivity

The pressure sensitivity of different points on the surface of the body can be tested by using weighted rods on different contact areas. The rod (esthesiometer) is placed lightly on the skin, and weights are added until the subject reports a pressure sensation. In an older method, bristles of increasing thickness can be pressed against the skin until they bend. The thinnest bristle the subject can sense under this much pressure gives a rough guide to the threshold. Some parts of the body are found to be much more sensitive than others (Table 8-1). The tongue probably has the lowest absolute threshold, and the fingertips are also sensitive. These parts have more specialized receptors than parts of the body with higher thresholds, such as the back of the forearm or the loin.

Two-point threshold. Sensitivity to pressure can also be tested by using the **two-point threshold.** This is the smallest distance between two points that can be recognized as distinct by the subject. It is therefore a difference threshold rather than an absolute threshold. However, it should indicate sensitivity because it is closely related to pressure receptor *density* in the area tested, that is, how many receptors per square centimeter of skin surface. If two adjacent receptors are stimulated by the two points, the sensation will be that of a single point. To recognize two distinct points, stimulated receptors must be separated by unstimulated receptors. The more pressure receptors in a given skin area, the closer together they lie, and the closer two points can be when recognized by the subject as separate. The results obtained by

Table 8-1. Stimulus thresholds for pressure*

	Grams per mm.²
Tip of tongue	2
Tip of finger	3
Back of finger	5
Front of forearm	8
Back of hand	12
Calf of leg	16
Abdomen	26
Back of forearm	33
Loin	48
Thick parts of sole	250

*From Woodworth, R. S., and Schlosberg, H.: Experimental psychology, rev. ed., New York, 1954, Holt, Rinehart & Winston, Inc., p. 274.

using the two-point threshold agree closely with those from absolute threshold measurements in testing the relative sensitivity of various parts of the body to pressure.

Localization. The ability to locate a pressure stimulus on the skin surface, or localization, should also indicate receptor density. The closer together the receptors in an area of the skin, such as the fingertip, the more nerve fibers reach the CNS from pressure receptors in that area, and the larger is the cortical projection area devoted to that part of the body. To simplify, the brain has more separate receptor inputs in that area and is therefore more able to locate precisely the point stimulated. Experiments on localization show that where the absolute and two-point pressure thresholds are lowest, localization is most accurate.

In contrast with the fairly accurate localization of pressure sensations on the body surface, visceral localization is very poor. Visceral sensations are felt as diffuse. This is partly caused by fewer pressure receptors in the viscera, but not altogether—localization of bladder pressure is quite accurate, for example. One reason suggested for poor visceral localization is the lack of confirmation by other senses. Pressure stimuli on the skin can be confirmed by sight or touch often enough so that the subject learns to relate small differences in skin stimulation to small differences in the point stimulated. Obviously one cannot see pressure stimulations being applied to the stomach or intestine. On the other hand, one can sense the pressure relief in the bladder that results from urination.

Adaptation. Adaptation is partly a function of the receptor and partly a function of the stimulus. Continuous pressure stimulation of a part of the body will result in a gradual decrease in sensation, and sometimes the adaptation will be complete so that no pressure is sensed. This is true of light pressure sensations such as those that commonly result from wearing eyeglasses or rings, the presence of which can no longer

be felt after a time. The greater the area over which a constant pressure is applied, the faster the adaptation because the pressure and skin distortion per unit area is less. An intense stimulus applied over a small or large area adapts more slowly—it takes quite a while. An intense pressure stimulus continues compressing the tissues under it for some time; thus the receptors are continuously presented with changes in stimulus energy and have no chance to adapt. It also takes a long time after a pressure stimulus is removed before the skin recovers its original shape so that distortion of the pressure endings continues to change after the stimulus is removed. The receptors continue to fire, giving a pressure sensation like a positive aftersensation. As a result, removal of a ring or a wristwatch may leave the sensation that one is still wearing it because the skin is still distorted for a time. This may be one reason why rings and watches are so often mislayed.

TEMPERATURE

Cold and warmth appear to be separate sensory modalities, although experiments on one of these senses commonly involves the other. This is the case in studying cutaneous temperature sensitivity because local reactions in the blood vessels of the skin to a warm stimulus will change the threshold to cold, and vice versa. In response to a warm stimulus, blood vessels near the surface will dilate to cool the area, the threshold for subsequent warm stimuli will be raised, and the threshold for cold stimuli lowered. In response to a cold stimulus the same vessels will constrict to preserve body heat, thereby raising the threshold to subsequent cold stimuli and lowering the threshold to warm stimuli. The skin temperature at which neither warm nor cold sensations are experienced is called **physiological zero**; physiological zero shifts as a result of blood vessel reactions in the skin and also as a result of adaptation in the receptors themselves. The adequate stimulus for cold is a temperature at the skin surface of 35° to 39° C. or below; the adequate stimulus for warmth is a temperature of 34° to 35° C. or above. These temperatures overlap because of changes in physiological zero. The adequate stimulus temperature depends on what skin temperature you start with. The sensation of *heat* is a secondary quality composed of warmth and pain stimulation; the "stinging cold" occasionally experienced in cold climates is a combination of cold and pain.

Skin mapping

Cold and warm spots on the skin can be mapped with small cold and warm stimulus points such as the punctuate stimuli used for pressure. They show a fairly reliable distribution, but are not quite as fixed as the most pressure-sensitive points. The receptors for warmth and cold are farther beneath the skin than the more superficial pressure receptors, and localization may suffer as a result. In addition, temperature

Table 8-2. Concentrations of warm and cold spots*

	Spots per cm.²	
	Cold	Warm
Forehead	8.0	0.6
Nose	8.0 (side)–13.0 (tip)	1.0
Upper lip	19.0	——
Chin	9.0	——
Chest	9.0	0.3
Upper arm, volar side	5.7	0.3
Upper arm, dorsal side	5.0	0.2
Bend of elbow	6.5	0.7
Forearm, volar side	6.0	0.4
Forearm, dorsal side	7.5	0.3
Back of hand	7.0	0.5
Palm	4.0	0.5
Fingers	2.0–9.0	1.6–2.0
Thigh	5.0	0.4
Lower leg	4.0–6.0	——
Sole of foot	3.0	——

*Based upon data from Rein, H.: Z. Biol. **82:**513-535, 1925; and Strughold, H., and Porz, R.: Z. Biol. **91:**563-571, 1931.

changes are more diffusely spread through the skin than the mechanical distortion of pressure. Table 8-2 shows that cold is more sensitive than warmth in terms of sensitive spots per square centimeter. The areas of the body most sensitive to cold are usually those most sensitive to warmth, although there are reliable exceptions to this rule. In general, the face is one of the most sensitive areas to both kinds of stimuli.

Receptor location

Cold and warm "pulses" can be applied to the outside of the prepuce (foreskin) of the penis, and their arrival at the underside of the prepuce can be measured with appropriate instruments. With this procedure the rate at which the change in temperature moves through the thickness of the prepuce can be calculated. By timing the report of a cold or warm sensation by the subject, the depth of the cold and warm receptors can be estimated. The results suggest that the cold receptors lie about 0.1 mm. below the surface and that the warm receptors are more diffusely spread about 0.3 mm. below the surface. The experiment also shows that each type of receptor responds to the *absolute temperature* at its depth rather than a gradient of temperature change from "outside" to "inside"—the pulse may be sent through the prepuce from either the "outside" skin surface or the "inside" mucous surface without a change in threshold. The data for depth of receptor agree with experiments on tongue stimulation with warm and cold stimuli in the dog and cat when a cold or warm pulse is used as a stimulus and the time required for nerve impulses to begin is computed.

Receptors

There appear to be both specialized and unspecialized receptors for cold and warm stimuli. Krause end bulbs (Fig. 8-1) are found at the proper depth (0.1 mm.) to serve as cold receptors, judging by the experiments on the prepuce that were just described. These receptors are found in mucous membrane regions and in other areas sensitive to cold, such as the face. In one experiment tissue was removed and studied under the microscope after having been mapped and the cold spots marked. Krause end bulbs were found nearer cold spots than spots less sensitive to cold. The experiment has been repeated on the prepuce of the penis where the depth of the receptors has been more precisely determined. In a more daring experiment the transparent cornea of the subject's eye was stained (with methylene blue) and studied under a microscope while it was being stimulated. Only Krause end bulbs and free nerve endings are found in the cornea. In the corneal areas most sensitive to cold, Krause end bulbs could be seen.

Ruffini endings are at the proper depth (0.3 mm.) to serve as warm receptors. They are found most profusely in warmth-sensitive parts of the body. Mapping warm spots and then studying the skin under them with a microscope has been done in the same way as that described for cold. The prepuce and other warmth-sensitive parts of the skin have been studied in this manner. The results are not as clear-cut as those for cold spots. However, when Ruffini endings are found, they usually lie near spots on the skin that are the most sensitive to warm stimuli.

If Krause end bulbs are cold receptors and Ruffini cylinders are warm receptors, they are not the only endings serving warm and cold. In some nonmucous areas such as the palm of the hand, there are many encapsulated endings. In these areas, however, the encapsulated endings are too varied for classification. Other areas such as the pinna (external ear) have only free nerve endings. These areas *are* sensitive to cold and warmth, but less so than areas with specialized receptors. In areas supplied only by free nerve ends, perhaps the free endings near the surface are cold receptors and those deeper beneath the

skin are warm receptors. Free nerve endings may be arranged in layers, the most superficial ones for pressure, deeper ones for cold, still deeper ones serving warm, and the deepest endings serving pain. However, there are theorists who believe that the *pattern* of input from nerve endings determines all four somesthetic qualities.

Temperature phenomena

Experiments involving action potential recording from nerves serving the tongue of the cat and from nerves serving the skin have been done using cold and warm stimuli. These experiments have shown that the nerve endings serving cold and warmth respond to *absolute temperature*—the gradient of temperature change through the tissue is unimportant. Fig. 8-2 shows the rate of firing of a "cold neuron" and a "warm neuron" from the cat tongue in response to rapid cooling or warming of the tongue to the temperatures indicated. These neurons responded *only* to temperature and did not fire in response to pain or pressure stimulation.

Fig. 8-2 can be compared to some well-known temperature phenomena. The terminal threshold for cold is usually found to be 18° C., where pain is experienced, but cold can still be sensed at that point and Fig. 8-2 shows cold neurons firing down to 10° C. Pain from hot stimuli is encountered at 45° to 50° C., which agrees well with the data presented. Physiological zero is around 35° C., and *both* cold and warm fibers fire at that temperature, as shown in the illustration. On the skin, warmth is sensed above 35° C., where cold fibers do not fire; cold is sensed below 35° C., where the cold fiber is firing at a higher rate than warm fibers.

Cold receptors can be inadequately stimulated by very warm temperatures of 43° to 51° C., for example, the flash of cold sensation after placing one's hand in hot water that precedes heat and pain sensations. The phenomenon is called **paradoxi-**

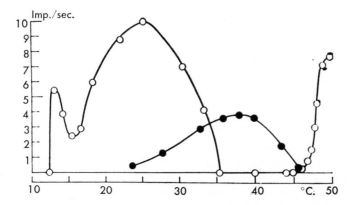

Fig. 8-2. Impulse frequency in a single cold fiber (open circles) and a single warm fiber (filled circles) as their receptors are stimulated by temperatures ranging from 10° to 50° C. (From Zotterman, Y.: Ann. Rev. Physiol. **15**:357, 1953.)

cal cold. Fig. 8-2 shows that cold neuron firing dominates that temperature range. Less reliably, warm receptors are stimulated by temperatures in the 25° to 31° C. range, producing **paradoxical warmth.** This is often masked by stronger cold responses. Anyone who has placed his hand on an iron railing in freezing temperatures can testify to the flash of heat sensation (warm plus pain) that precedes a stinging cold sensation (cold plus pain).

If the skin is cooled to 15° C., the cold sensation persists after the stimulus is removed, even though the tissue is warming. As also shown, the cold neuron firing frequency is higher at 25° C. than at 15° C. Both cold and warm aftersensations are positive and represent continued neuron firing after the stimulus has been removed. These data agree with the common finding that cold is easier to stimulate than warmth (lower temperature threshold). Cold spots are more stable and adapt more slowly.

Adaptation

All the temperature figures given for cold and warm response are subject to change because of adaptation in the receptors and because of blood vessel constriction or dilation. As previously pointed out, continuous warm stimulation adapts the warm receptors and causes blood vessel dilation to raise the threshold for warmth and lower the threshold for cold. Continuous cold stimulation will adapt the cold receptors and constrict blood vessels under the skin to raise the threshold for cold and lower the threshold for warmth. These adjustments to temperature can cause physiological zero to vary from 20° to 40° C. The change in physiological zero can be a general one, involving the whole body as one adapts to temperature change in passing from an air-conditioned room to hot outdoor temperature, or in passing from a heated house to the winter cold outdoors. The change in physiological zero can be restricted largely to the part of the body exposed to an adapting temperature. For example, the right hand can be temperature-adapted in a bowl of 40° C. water and the left hand temperature-adapted in a bowl of 20° C. water at the same time. Then if *both* hands are plunged into 30° C. water, the right hand will feel cold and the left hand will feel warm.

Muscular and visceral sensitivity

Little can be said about muscular or visceral sensitivity. There appear to be no temperature-sensitive receptors in the muscles, and visceral sensitivity is restricted to the mouth and esophagus. Temperature sensitivity may serve a protective function, setting off vomiting when very hot or cold substances are swallowed.

PAIN

Pain is one of the most difficult sensory modalities to study as a sensation because the affective perceptual reactions to it are so overpowering. Pain "hurts" so much that the subject has difficulty in responding to it as a sensation. Yet pain has received much study because of the importance of the topic to the practice of medicine. Pain is useful as a diagnostic tool since it usually is set off by tissue damage. At the same time an understanding of pain is necessary to the control of pain for surgery and dental procedures. Pain, furthermore, is the most potent stimulus known to arouse and sustain behavior; it is therefore important to the study of *drives*. Pain stimuli set off somatic and visceral reflexes. The body's first "line of defense" against injury are the somatic withdrawal reflexes; the visceral, glandular, and autonomic "emergency responses" of the sympathetic nervous system form a second line of defense. The third is sensation, which leads to drives and the perception of pain. Pain will be considered first as a sensation. After the receptor, stimulus, and measurement phenomena have been studied, perceptual reactions to pain will be treated briefly as pain phenomena.

Pain as sensory modality

Pain is a sensory modality and not just a change in quality that results from overstimulation of pressure or temperature receptors. There are several lines of evidence for this point of view. One of the most convincing comes from the adaptation of pain sensations. If pain receptors are stimulated so that they adapt and cease responding, the sensations do not turn into pressure, warmth, or cold. Extreme pressure, warmth, or cold can produce pain, but the pain sensations will "coexist" with pressure, warmth, or cold and will not turn into more pressure, warmth, or cold as they adapt. Furthermore, pain can be aroused by sparks "jumping" from a voltage generator to the skin without arousing sensations of pressure, cold, or warmth. Pain impulses are carried in the lateral funiculi of the cord. Cutting these tracts relieves pain without disturbing touch sensations that are carried in the dorsal and ventral funiculi of the cord. As shown earlier, drugs such as cocaine effect unmyelinated pain fibers before they anesthetize the myelinated fibers carrying touch sensations; yet cutting off circulation to a limb will effect pressure sensations more than pain.

Receptors

Free nerve endings are known to be pain receptors, although not all free nerve endings are pain receptors. Areas of the skin having only free nerve endings are sensitive to temperature and pressure. It is probable that the anastomoses of free nerve ends that serve pain lie deeper beneath the skin than those serving pressure. As evidence for this the superficial epidermis can be peeled off without causing pain—only pressure endings seem affected. Also, a light touch to the cornea results in sensations of pressure rather than pain; the cornea contains only Krause end bulbs and free nerve endings. Temperature receptors are farther from the skin surface than some pressure receptors. The difference between the deeper free endings serving temperature and those serving pain is not clear; perhaps the pain endings lie still deeper or differ biochemically.

There has been some debate over the possibility of two pain receptor systems. Recall of the sensations experienced the last time you "barked" a shin will reveal a "bright" first pain, followed by a "raw," burning second pain. It has been suggested that the first pain comes from lightly myelinated A-delta fibers that supply free nerve endings in the dermis and near the epidermis and conduct more rapidly than the C fibers that supply deeper free endings in the dermis (Chapter 4). Pain stimulation without mechanical distortion of the skin in animals gives both A-delta and C action potentials in the nerve serving that area of skin. This suggests that two pain systems have been stimulated. Other investigators believe that the first pain is merely a mixture of pressure and pain sensations, the pressure being carried by A-delta and the pain by C fibers. In one experiment square wave electrical stimuli and fine needles were used to stimulate skin pain without skin distortion (pressure), and the subjects reported only second pain. In another experiment an investigator bared a nerve in his own finger and stimulated it electrically only to fire the lower threshold A-delta fibers. A stinging pain resulted. But when the stimulus was altered to fire C fibers as well, a severe, long-lasting, aching pain resulted. The bulk of the evidence, then, suggests two pain systems.

Pain sensitivity and localization

The distribution of pain endings and therefore pain sensitivity varies widely from one part of the body to another. Pain sensibility is found in the hollow viscera, joints (aches), and muscles (cramp pains), although more is known of cutaneous pain because it is the most accessible to stimulation. Cutaneous pain sensitivity varies from **analgesic** (insensitive) areas such as Keisow's area on the inner cheek opposite the second molar tooth to exquisitely sensitive areas such as the "hollows" (fossae) of the body (armpit, back of knee joint, etc.). Table 8-3 gives a sample of the sensitivity of various cutaneous areas. Cutaneous pain localization is excellent; it is better than pressure localization. Muscular pain localization is accurate as the experience of cramp pain in muscles shows. Visceral pain localization is poor, except for the pain receptors on the covering of bones. "Bone bruises" are quite accurately localized, for example. Visceral

Table 8-3. Distribution of pain sensitivity[*]

Skin region	Pain "points" per cm.²
Back of knee (popliteal fossa)	232
Neck region (jugular fossa)	228
Bend of elbow (cubital fossa)	224
Shoulder blade (interscapular region)	212
Volar side of forearm	203
Back of hand	188
Forehead	184
Buttocks	180
Eyelid	172
Scalp	144
Radial surface, middle finger	95
Ball of thumb	60
Sole of foot	48
Tip of nose	44

[*]From Strughold, H.: Z. Biol. **80:**367-380, 1924.

pain is often confused with skin or muscle pain, as will be seen later (referred pains). It is not known whether visceral pain localization is poor because of a sparse supply of pain endings in the hollow viscera, or whether pain is poorly localized because the location of the injury producing pain cannot be confirmed by the other senses. When one has a stomachache, he cannot look to see whether the stomach or the intestine is inflamed. The location of a "bone bruise" or pain from a cut finger can be confirmed by touch and by sight.

Adequate stimulus

The adequate stimulus for pain is unknown. Perhaps there are several kinds of adequate stimulus. Tissue damage is not the adequate stimulus per se—stimuli such as sunburn and certain kinds of electrical currents can cause tissue damage without causing pain. Yet pain can be caused by mechanical, thermal, electrical, or chemical stimuli. One theory holds that the histamine released by damaged tissue is the adequate stimulus for pain. Certainly injections of histamine are exquisitely painful. Tissue damage changes the osmotic pressure of the tissue fluids—their content of solids—and this may act as an adequate or inadequate stimulus to the free nerve endings. The adequate stimulus may be the mechanical distortion or stretching apart of the branching "fingers" of the free nerve endings. There are several lines of evidence for this point of view: (1) If tiny balls of different sizes are pressed into the skin, pain begins when the ball is pressed in to its radius, irrespective of its size. This means that the amount of mechanical distortion is equal for each ball. (2) A cut causes little pain if the skin is immobolized with collodion (a kind of glue) to prevent distortion of the skin by the knife. (3) The viscera may be cut and burned without pain, but stretching, twisting, and especially distention cause severe pain. As will be seen later, headache is probably caused by the distention of cerebral arteries resulting from an increase in local blood pressure.

Pain thresholds

Pain thresholds can be measured by the algesiometer, an instrument similar to the esthesiometer used for pressure thresholds. A sharp needle is substituted for a dull point. The needle can be loaded with varying weights until pain is sensed. Sensitivity measurements, as absolute thresholds for various parts of the body, agree well with the distribution of pain "spots" shown in Table 8-3. The instrument of choice for measuring the effect of drugs, adaptation, etc. is the Hardy-Wolff-Gooddell apparatus. This device uses the inadequate stimulus of heat, radiated from a lamp to a black spot on the subject's forehead. The black spot absorbs all the radiant energy, and a shutter times the exposure (3 seconds). Brave subjects have established absolute and terminal (skin burn) thresholds. Difference thresholds have been established, and an equal-unit "dol" scale of 2 JNDs per unit has been established.

Adaptation. Pain adapts, although this is

hard to demonstrate. Muscle relaxation, lack of blood vessel changes (throbbing), and immobility are necessary to the constant level of stimulation that results in adaptation. For example, a needle driven deep in the arm can be tolerated after a time if the subject remains immobile and relaxes the arm. The chief difficulty in lack of pain adaptation is a "vicious circle" of self-stimulation that prevents adaptation: pain causes reflex muscle contraction; the rigid muscle contraction reduces the blood flow to the area (ischemia) like a tourniquet; this causes more pain, more reflex contraction, and so on.

PAIN PHENOMENA
Referred pain

Referred pain occurs whenever pain sensations that originate in one part of the body are perceived as coming from another part of the body. Usually, visceral pain is referred to skin or muscle. A common example is heart pain that is referred to the shoulder muscles (hence the name *angina pectoralis* for the pectoral muscles). In most cases the sensory neurons from the area of originating the impulses and those from the referred area enter the same dorsal spinal root or cranial nerve. This fact has led to speculation that a "short circuit" of the nerve impulses occurs, for example, impulses from the heart stimulating the same projection area of the brain as impulses from the shoulder. Others have speculated that poor visceral localization leads the subject to locate the pain in an area more frequently stimulated and accurately localized.

Hyperalgesic pain

Hyperalgesic pain is a very painful burning sensation that surrounds an injured area. The sensation is familiar to all who have had a severe but localized wound. The threshold to pain in this area may be increased, but once stimulated the pain sensations are persistent, strong, and unpleasant. They resemble the second pain previously described. The persistent and unpleasant quality is probably caused by the absence of competing pressure and temperature sensations from the area since their function was impaired by the injury. The deep-lying second pain endings are the only ones functioning, the superficial first pain endings near the epidermis being impaired. Competing sensations do relieve the insistent quality of pain; persons in pain clench their fists and jaw and apply pressure near the injured part to "smother" the pain input in other sensations.

Causalgia

Causalgia is a severe and burning pain that spreads from a focal point to wider and wider surrounding areas. Often there is no apparent injury, even in the focal point. The phenomenon is believed to be caused by *reverberating circuits* in the CNS (Chapter 6) rather than to receptor activity. In the pain pathways of the CNS there are many self-activating "circles" of nerve cells that could keep the pain pathways active for a long time in the absence of receptor input. The activity could spread to involve more widespread pathways.

Headaches

Headaches are probably caused by pain receptors in the cerebral arteries. When these arteries dialate, the nerve endings may be distorted; the soft tissue around them has limited "give" because it is surrounded by the bony box of the skull and therefore cannot swell.

Analgesics

Analgesics are drugs that relieve pain without causing unconsciousness. Aspirin, opiates (in small doses), and various synthetic drugs are included. Experiments have shown that analgesics raise the pain threshold, as measured with the Hardy-Wolff-Gooddell apparatus.

Pain as perception

Attention is a factor that changes the response to pain in many situations. Most persons have had the experience of being injured during an exciting event, such as an athletic contest, combat, or another emergency, and not becoming aware of the pain or injury until later. The anatomy of the pain pathways will show that pain input can be blocked on many levels to permit competing sensations to dominate. Under hypnosis pain sensations can be completely blocked—even reflex response to pain is impaired. On good subjects, hypnosis can be used instead of anesthetics for major surgery. Many reactions to pain seem to be learned ones—dogs raised in isolation show only reflex reactions to pain and do not learn to avoid painfall stimuli. On a higher level, injuries that relieved soldiers of combat were perceived as less painful than similar injuries in civilian surgery. Pain thresholds, as tested on the Hardy-Wolff-Gooddell apparatus, vary considerably from day to day in normal subjects and are still more variable in psychotics. In one study, opiates appeared effective in 75% of the cases by relieving anxiety and producing a "bemused state" (whatever that is). In 35% of the cases a placebo (fake drug) was successful in relieving pain reactions.

The diffuse nature of the pain pathways results in several perceptual phenomena. Cutting the pain pathways in the cord (anterolateral cordotomy) relieves intractable pain, yet the pain many return, in whole or in part, after a period of years. Amputees who have lost a limb report pain referred to the absent limb—phantom limb pain—at intervals for many years. Rarely, there are cases of congenital insensitivity to pain —people born without the ability to sense pain. These individuals must always be on guard to avoid seriously injuring themselves on hot or sharp objects without being aware of it. Some of them lack reflexes to pain. All show apparently normal nerve endings when sections of their skin are studied

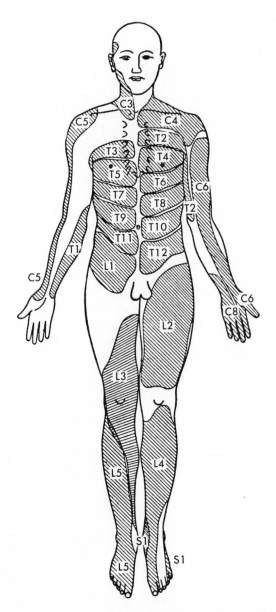

Fig. 8-3. Dermatomes of man. Successive dermatomes, labelled by spinal segment, are shown on alternate sides of the body to display the extent to which they overlap. (Based on data from Foester, O.: Brain **56**:1-39, 1933; redrawn by Lewis, T.: Pain, New York, 1942, The Macmillan Co.)

under a microscope. Other subjects have been found that lack only the subjective response to pain—they sense and react to pain as they do pressure or temperature, as a simple sensation. These subjects are like the isolated dogs mentioned above. They can, however, be taught to fear pain.

Pain as a sensation seems to be organized on lower levels of the brain than other somesthetic sensations; yet the perceptual reactions to it include the highest parts of the brain. Removing the cortex of one cerebral hemisphere does not interfere with the perception of pain, although it may raise the threshold. Pain caused by cortical stimulation or damage is rare, but it is common when the thalamus is stimulated or damaged. Severe intractable pain may be relieved by **prefrontal lobotomy,** an operation that severs the nerve fibers going from lower centers to the frontal lobes. The operation does not change pain thresholds, but the subject shows little subjective response to pain unless his attenttion is directed to it. He reports that he senses the

pain but it "doesn't bother him." When he attends to the pain sensations, his subjective response is increased, however.

NERVE PATHWAYS

Further understanding of somesthetic sensibility depends on knowing the anatomy of the sensory pathways involved. As an aid to understanding these pathways, their common features will be presented first, together with some notes on terminology. Then three major tracts in the spinal cord that differ by modality will be described, together with three nuclei that serve the same purpose for cranial nerves. Finally, the centers that serve these pathways in the thalamus and cortex will be described. With this knowledge the chapter can be concluded with a functional classification of two major sensory systems.

Dermatomes

Each dorsal root in the spinal cord contians sensory neurons serving pressure, temperature, and pain receptors from the sur-

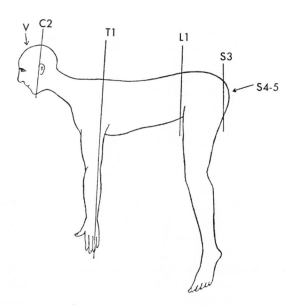

Fig. 8-4. Major dermatome boundaries in man in the quadruped (four-legged) position. (From Monrad-Krohn, G. H.: The clinical examination of the nervous system, ed. 12, London, 1964, H. K. Lewis & Co., Ltd.)

face of the skin. The area served by a single dorsal spinal root is called a **derma-tone** and is named for the spinal root. For example, L-1 would be the dermatome on either side of the body, served by the first lumbar spinal root (Chapter 6). Since there are thirty-one pairs of dorsal spinal roots, there should be thirty-one pairs of dermatomes for the body and neck (except for the lack of a first cervical dorsal root). The face and most of the head is served by the fifth cranial nerve, the trigeminal nerve. Somesthetic, visceral, and muscular input is also serially arranged, according to the dorsal spinal roots and cranial nerves. The dermatomes were evolved before animals walked on four legs, as can be seen from their major boundaries in man shown in Figs. 8-3 and 8-4. Development of limbs carried the dermatome boundaries out from the body. The sizes of the dermatomes for pressure sensibility shown in Fig. 8-3 are larger than those for temperature and show more overlap; the dermatomes for pain are still smaller.

"Three-neuron" plan

Typically, a somesthetic **first-order neuron** runs from the somesthetic receptor to the spinal cord, where it enters the dorsal root, ascends, and synapses within 2 to 3 segments of the cord with **second-order neurons** in the gray matter of the dorsal horn. (Kinesthesis and some pressure inputs are exceptions, see below.) The second-order neuron crosses to the opposite side of the cord, enters the white matter, and ascends to join with other neurons in the **medial lemniscus** of the brainstem. It ends on the **posteroventral nucleus** of the thalamus, synapsing with **third-order neurons.** Third-order neurons run from the thalamus to the somesthetic sensory projection area on the postcentral gyrus of the cerebral cortex (areas 3, 1, and 2—Chapter 6). In the trigeminal nerve serving the face, first-order neurons carry impulses to the sensory nuclei of the fifth nerve, second-order neurons

cross the brainstem to join the medial lemniscus, and third-order neurons run from the thalamus to the cortex.

Fiber grouping

The second-order neurons, ascending the cord as tracts, are grouped by *modality*. Kinesthesis (joint sensibility, etc.) and fibers from specialized pressure receptors are carried in the dorsal funiculus. Fibers from less specialized (higher threshold) pressure receptors send impulses up the ventral funiculus. Pain and temperature tracts are found in the lateral funiculus. In the medial lemniscus the fibers are rearranged according to their dermatomes of origin so that in the thalamus and cortex fibers project in a **topographical organization** (Fig. 8-5). On the postcentral gyrus of the cortex the most caudal parts of the body are found at the beginning of the gyrus (in the longitudinal fissures), first the genitals and buttocks, next the feet and legs, then the body, the arms, and finally the face—compare Fig. 8-4 with Fig. 8-5.

Spinal tracts

Spinal tracts are typically named for their origin, their destination, and sometimes the funiculus of the cord in which they lie. Thus the lateral spinothalamic tract begins in the spinal cord, ends in the thalamus, and lies in the lateral funiculus of the cord. We are concerned with three somesthetic tracts; two of them are named in this fashion.

Dorsal columns (Fig. 8-6). First-order neurons carrying kinesthetic impulses from the joints that signal limb position, the more sensitive cutaneous pressure receptors, and the pacinian corpuscles (deep pressure) are carried in the **dorsal columns.** These neurons enter the cord and ascend the dorsal funiculus without crossing, to end on the **gracile** and **cuneate nuclei** of the medulla. Second-order fibers from these nuclei cross and take up a ventral position in the medulla to form the **medial lemniscus.**

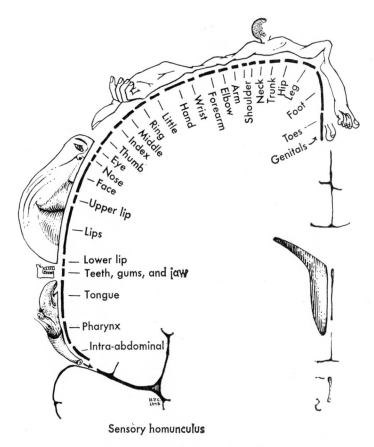

Sensory homunculus

Fig. 8-5. Sensory homunculus laid out on a cross section of one cerebral hemisphere. The length of each black line represents the proportion of sensory cortex devoted to the part of the body shown by the labels; the caricature of the head and body above the lines is in about the same proportion. (From Penfield, W., and Rasmussen, T.: The cerebral cortex of man, New York, 1950, The Macmillan Co.)

Ventral spinothalamic tract (Fig. 8-6). First-order neurons from more crude pressure receptors synapse with second-order neurons in the dorsal gray columns of the cord. The second-order neurons cross and ascend the ventral funiculus of the cord in the **ventral spinothalamic tract,** which joins the medial lemniscus in the midbrain.

Lateral spinothalamic tract (Fig. 8-7). First-order neurons from pain and temperature receptors synapse with second-order fibers in the dorsal grey columns of the cord. The second-order neurons cross to the opposite side of the cord and ascend the lateral funiculus as the **lateral spinothalamic tract.** Thus, in an operation to relieve intractable pain in the right leg, part of the left lateral funiculus of the cord could be cut above the level of entrance of these neurons. This would cut off pain and temperature sensation without disturbing kinesthesis or pressure that is carried in the dorsal and ventral cord. The lateral and ventral spinothalamic tracts join in the medulla and both join the medial lemniscus in the midbrain.

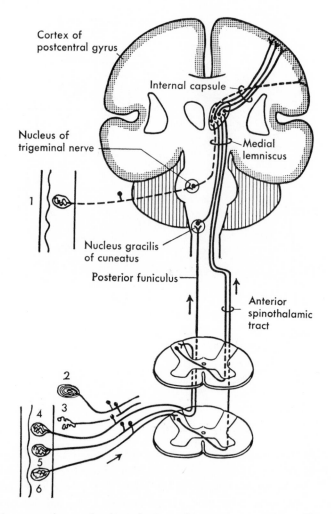

Cortex of
postcentral gyrus

Internal capsule

Nucleus of
trigeminal nerve

Medial
lemniscus

Nucleus gracilis
of cuneatus

Posterior funiculus

Anterior
spinothalamic
tract

Fig. 8-6. Afferent pathways for kinesthesis and pressure sensations. Though not shown separately, the mesencephalic nucleus of the trigeminal nerve is the anterior part of the nucleus shown, while the main sensory nucleus is the posterior part. In the spinal tracts, anterior is equivalent to ventral in the text, and posterior to dorsal. (From Gardner, E. O.: Fundamentals of neurology, ed. 4, Philadelphia, 1963, W. B. Saunders Co.)

Cranial nerve nuclei

In the spinal cord the modalities are separated into three different spinal tracts. In the brainstem the modalities are separated into three different cranial nerve nuclei, and the separation is a little more complete. Only kinesthetic input reaches one nucleus, only pressure input the second, and only temperature and pain input the third.

Mesencephalic nucleus of fifth nerve (Fig. 8-6). First-order neurons of the fifth nerve from kinesthetic receptors end in the **mesencephalic** (midbrain) **nucleus of fifth nerve.** Second-order neurons that originate here cross the brainstem to join the medial lemniscus.

Main sensory nucleus of fifth nerve. First-order neurons in the fifth nerve from pressure receptors reach the **main sensory**

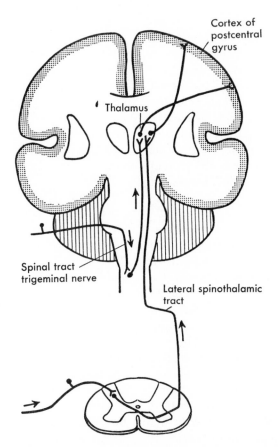

Fig. 8-7. Afferent pathways for pain and temperature. The uncrossed pathway for pain is not shown. (From Gardner, E. O.: Fundamentals of neurology, ed. 4, Philadelphia, 1963, W. B. Saunders Co.)

nucleus of that nerve. Second-order neurons originating here cross the brainstem to join the medial lemniscus.

Spinal nucleus of fifth nerve (Fig. 8-7). First-order neurons from pain and temperature receptors enter the brainstem and descend in the medulla as the **spinal tract of fifth nerve.** These neurons end on the **spinal nucleus** of that nerve in the lower medulla. The second-order neurons that originate here cross to join the medial lemniscus in the midbrain.

Thalamic and cortical projection

As described in the beginning of this section, the fibers from all the somesthetic inputs are rearranged in the medial lemniscus according to origin rather than modality. The thalamic nuclei are therefore arranged topographically, and the third-order neurons and cortical projection are also topographically ordered. There is evidence, however, that pain *sensation* is largely organized at the thalamic level, and pressure and kinesthetic sensations are organized at the cortical level.

Two sensory systems

Functionally there is evidence for two somesthetic-kinesthetic systems. The **medial lemniscal system** serves kinesthesis and more discriminative pressure sensations. Its neurons include the dorsal columns of the cord and the mesencephalic and main sensory nuclei of the fifth nerve. The **spi-nothalamic system** serves less discriminative tactile sensations in the cord and pain and temperature sensations in both the cord and brainstem. The ventral and lateral spinothalamic tracts are included in the cord, and the spinal tract and nucleus of the fifth nerve are included in the brainstem. The two systems are separate as far up as the midbrain, where the spinothalamic tracts join the medial lemniscus.

Medial lemniscal system

The medial lemniscal system serves discriminative touch receptors and kinesthetic input for limb position. At the cortex these two inputs are in the same location for each part of the body. Sensation seems to require cortical excitation, and the two inputs may compete by mutually inhibiting one another at the cortical level. The system seems capable of the efferent control of afferent input, an important mechanism for attention that will be encountered later in other senses. Fibers run from the cortical projection area down the brainstem to the mesencephalic and main sensory nuclei of the fifth nerve and to the gracile and cuneate nuclei of the spinal cord. These fibers seem able to *block* the input of parts of the system, when attention is being directed to other sensory inputs.

Spinothalamic system. The spinothalamic system seems to be the more primitive of the two. It serves less discriminative pressure, pain, and temperature. The system includes impulses reaching the brain via the spinothalamic tracts and the spinal nucleus and tract of the fifth nerve. Much of the input of the system for sensation seems to be organized in the thalamus, although the system projects to the cortex, probably for perceptual reasons. The second-order fibers of the tracts involved give off collaterals (branches) to an important part of the brain called the **ascending reticular activating system (ARAS)**. The ARAS consists of many short neurons in the core of the brain-stem. They send impulses to all parts of the cortex and keep it active. Unless the ARAS is excited, either by the spinothalamic system or descending impulses from higher brain centers, the individual goes to sleep. Direct arousal of the brain by the spinothalamic system would be expected since is carries pain input that signals tissue damage and an emergency situation.

Secondary sensory projection areas

The classic somesthetic projection area on the postcentral gyrus is not the only cortical area to receive somesthetic input. The classical area is called SI. Below it is another topographically organized area called SII, which probably receives input from both the medical lemniscal and spinothalamic systems. Unlike SI, which receives input from the opposite half of the body only, SII receives input from both sides of the body. There is also a "face area," SIII, in front of the other two. It seems to receive input from SII and only represents the head regions. SII may be important to selective attention. There is some evidence that SII is active when the animal is responding to input to SI. On the other hand, it may just be a sensory system with an older history in evolution.

SUMMARY

Bodily sensations are classified as somesthesis, the "condition" senses of pressure, cold, warmth, and pain, or as the position and movement senses of proprioception. Somesthesis may be cutaneous, muscular, or visceral. In addition to initiating important reflexes, somesthetic inputs give rise to complex responses accompanied by awareness of the input. Since they arouse and sustain behavior, somesthetic sensations, especially pain, can act as drives. By contrast, proprioception from the special vestibular senses responding to head movement and from general kinesthesis receptors that initiate the stretch reflexes do not lead directly to awareness. However, kinesthetic (movement sense) input from receptors in the joints, tendons, and connective tissue of muscles is sensed as limb position and movement.

The methods for study of somesthetic input include introspective, anatomical, and physiological techniques. Introspective technique lacks objective confirmation, anatomical technique shows only the most obvious pathways, and physiological experiments with animals lack introspective information. Physiological methods, using implanted electrodes in the otherwise normal animal, seem to be the most promising approach.

Introspectively the primary qualities of somesthesis seem to be pressure, cold, warmth, and pain. Secondary qualities result from intermittent stimulation or combinations of primary inputs. The evidence that the primary qualities are separate modalities depends largely on experiments with cutaneous sensitivity. Experiments with skin mapping for punctuate sensitivity in different parts of the body, arousing pain without pressure from spark gap stimulation, excitation and conduction time for the four senses, the different effects of cocaine and asphyxia on the four senses, and their separate pathways in the spinal cord all point to four modalities. Identifying specific receptors and projection areas in the brain for four separate modalities is more difficult. All project to the postcentral gyrus of the cerebral cortex, although pain probably projects to lower levels and involves more subcortical centers. Specialized receptors have been tentatively identified in some areas, but in others free nerve endings serve all four inputs; these may differ biochemically or in their connections to the brain.

The structure of the skin has much to do with cutaneous somesthesis. The outer layer of dead cells in the epidermis has no receptors, the inner layer of epidermis has a few free nerve ends (probably for pressure), the dermis contains most of the receptors, and subdermal cutaneous fat contains the "deep-pressure" pacinian corpuscles. Pressure receptors also include basket endings of the body hair and probably Meissner's corpuscles in hairless areas. As a sample sensory transducer, the pacinian corpuscle seems to function by spreading pressure over its included nerve ending so that the nerve ending can produce a larger generator potential to fire nerve impulses.

Pressure sensitivity can be gauged with an esthesiometer or by the two-point threshold. Either method demonstrates wide variation in pressure sensitivity over the body, from the sensitive lips and fingertips to the relatively insensitive back of the forearm or loin. The data for localization agree with the sensitivity differences. Muscle pressure localization is good, but visceral localization is poor. Cutaneous adaptation for pressure depends on a constant degree of skin distortion; the tissue slowly recovers shape after pressure is removed, and therefore aftersensations are positive.

Although cold and warmth seem to be separate modalities, they interact because local blood vessel reactions to either stimulus changes the threshold to the other. Physiological zero is the range of skin temperature where neither cold nor warmth is sensed and varies as a result of these vascular reactions. Cold results from temperatures below 35° to 39° C., warmth from temperatures above 34° to 35° C., depending on physiological zero. Heat and stinging cold include pain sensations. Skin mapping shows a fairly reliable punctuate distribution with more cold spots than warm; most of the areas more sensitive to cold are also more sensitive to warmth. Timing cold and warm "pulses" travelling through the prepuce shows that cold receptors are nearer the surface than are warm receptors and that both respond to absolute temperature rather than to temperature gradients through the skin. There are both unspecialized (free nerve endings) and specialized receptors for cold and warmth. The specialized cold receptors seem to be Krause end bulbs, the specialized warmth receptors, Ruffini cylinders. Some temperature-sensitive areas have only free nerve endings; others have encapsulated endings too varied to classify. Data on rate of firing of "cold" and "warm" neurons in the cat tongue agree with introspective findings: absolute thresholds, terminal thresholds, physiological zero, paradoxical cold and warmth, and adaptation phenomena are consistent with these data. Muscle sensitivity to temperature seems absent, and visceral response is limited to the mouth and esophagus.

Pain is difficult to study as a sensation because of the strong reflex and affective reactions to it. Since pain does not change quality as it adapts, it is not just overstimulation of another modality. Other proofs for pain as a separate sensory modality include spark-gap stimulation, separate pathways in the cord, and the effects of drugs and asphyxia. Some, but not all, free nerve endings are pain receptors. There appear to be two pain input systems—a rapidly-conducting first-pain system of small A fibers and a slower second-pain C fiber system. Pain sensitivity varies from high in the fossae to analgesic areas in the cheek. Cutaneous and muscle pain localization is good, but visceral pain is poorly localized and leads to referred pains. The adequate stimulus is unknown, although there are several theories. The viscera are pain sensitive only to distention; cerebral blood vessel distention causes headache. Pain adapts, although muscle relaxation is necessary to keep the stimulus constant. Pain phenomena include hyperalgesia, causalgia, headaches, and analgesic drug effects. Perceptual studies show that many of the affective responses to pain are learned. The diffuse pathways often cause anterolateral cordotomy effects to be temporary, and phantom limb pain

occurs in amputees. Congenitally insensitive persons have been found, but their skin nerve endings seem normal. Pain sensation seems subcortical; pain perception is probably cortical. Prefrontal lobotomy reduces affective response to pain.

Cutaneous somesthetic nerve pathways begin with the dermatomes that are served by the dorsal spinal roots and the fifth nerve. Pressure dermatomes are the largest and overlap most, temperature less so, and pain least so. The input for the muscles and viscera is similarly organized. The input is arranged in a three-neuron plan, with synapses in the cord between first- and second-order neurons and synapses with third-order neurons in the posteroventral nucleus of the thalamus. Input is organized by modality in the cord, but mingles by location in the medial lemniscus of the brainstem below the thalamus. Accurately localized pressure and kinesthesis are carried in the first-order neurons of the dorsal columns of the cord to the gracile and cuneate nuclei of the medulla; crude pressure input ascends the cord in the ventral spinothalamic tract of the ventral funiculus; temperature and pain sensations are carried in the lateral spinothalamic tract of the lateral funiculus of the cord. Two of these tracts are named for their origin, destination, and location (funiculus). The corresponding inputs for the fifth nerve are the mesencephalic (kinesthesis), main sensory (pressure), and spinal (temperature and pain) nuclei of the brainstem. The input to the brain is primarily crossed, each side of the brain serving the opposite side of the body. Functionally, two somesthetic and kinesthetic systems seem involved, the medial lemniscal system and the spinothalamic system. The former serves kinesthesis and discriminative pressure, the latter less discriminative pressure, pain, and temperature. The lemniscal system seems capable of efferent inhibition of afferent input at the mesencephalic and main sensory nuclei of the fifth nerve and at the gracile and cuneate nuclei. The spino-thalamic system includes the spinal tract and nucleus of the fifth nerve. This system seems the more primitive of the two, with much of the input organized at the thalamic level. The tracts give off many collaterals to the ascending reticular activating system (ARAS). The ARAS consists of many short neurons in the core of the brainstem that act to arouse the whole cortex to activity. When the ARAS is not aroused by the spinothalamic system or by descending impulses from higher brain centers, sleep ensues.

The primary cortical somesthetic projection area is called SI. Another topographically organized somesthetic area, SII, lies below it and receives bilateral input from the ARAS. A "face area," SIII, lies in front of the other two and is supplied by SII. SII may be important to selective attention—it seems active when the animal is responding to SI input. It may be just a supplemental or older system, however.

READINGS

Gardiner, E.: Fundamentals of neurology, ed. 4, Philadelphia, 1963, W. B. Saunders Co.

Livingston, W. K.: What is pain? Sci. Amer. **188:** 59-66, March, 1953. (W. H. Freeman Co. Reprint No. 407.)

Loenstein, W. R.: Biological transducers, Sci. Amer. **203:**98-108, Aug., 1960. (W. H. Freeman Co. Reprint No. 70.)

Melzack, R.: The perception of pain, Sci. Amer. **204:**41-49, Feb., 1961. (W. H. Freeman Co. Reprint No. 457.)

Montagna, W.: The skin, Sci. Amer. **212:**56-66, Feb., 1965. (W. H. Freeman Co. Reprint No. 1003.)

Chapter 9

Proprioception

OVERVIEW

The two sets of receptor inputs that are sensitive to *position* and *movement* of different parts of the body are the subjects of this chapter. Collectively, such input is known as proprioception. One set of proprioceptive receptors is found in the muscles, tendons, and joints, where they respond to muscle tension and the position and movement of the limbs. These receptors are classed as kinesthesis (Gr., motion knowledge). The other set of receptors are in the inner ear, or vestibule. The vestibular senses respond to the position and movement of the head. Conscious sensations are not a direct result of most proprioceptive inputs. Reflex responses *to* proprioception *result* in sensory input that *is* vital to orientation. Furthermore, the reflexes set off by proprioceptors are very important to normal behavior—literally, a coordinated movement cannot be made without them.

The kinesthetic input will be considered first. Joint sensitivity results in conscious sensations of limb position because the input reaches the highest levels of the brain. The nerve pathways involved were covered in Chapter 8. The reflex input that is the basis for coordinated movement will be discussed next; this input goes to the cerebellum and is not consciously sensed. The tendon jerk and stretch reflexes are used to show how posture and coordination depend on sensory input from the stretching of muscles. The sensory mechanisms in the muscle spindle and muscle tendons are examined. Their roles in muscle coordination are seen in the clasp-knife reflex. Mechanisms for varying the sensitivity of the muscle spindle by contraction of its fibers are explained. Applications of the sensitivity mechanism to reciprocal innervation and to motor learning conclude the first half of the chapter.

The vestibular senses are next. The semicircular canals respond to head rotation, and the sacs to linear (straight-line) movements of the head. The nerve pathways for reflex response to these two inputs are summarized. First, the semicircular canal receptors and their adequate stimuli are explained, and then the reflex responses to them are examined. The receptor mechanisms of the sacs and their reflex responses follow. The chapter closes with some practical applications of knowledge about the vestibular senses.

KINESTHESIS
Joint sensibility

The receptors that give conscious sensations of limb position and movement are found mainly in the joints. Some sensations of limb position and movement come from the connective tissue covering tendons and muscles and from the pull on the skin as a limb is moved or placed in an extreme position. However, if you close your eyes, rest your right arm on the table, grasp the index finger with your left hand, and flex it back and forth, the resulting sensations of movement will come primarily from the joints of the right index finger. Local anesthetics that paralyze receptors in the skin and muscles impair position sense very little since the joint receptors are not involved. The joint receptors, as well as all the other receptors contributing to sensations of limb position and movement, appear to be pressure receptors of one kind or another. Unlike pressure receptors in other parts of the body, they adapt very little under continuous stimulation, as when the body is maintained in one position for a long time. This is important because constant sensory input must keep us aware of body position at all times so that movement can begin from a known posture. In the joints most of the pressure receptors involved are pacinian corpuscles, a receptor discussed in Chapter 8. The pathway by which their excitation reaches the cerebral cortex was also discussed in Chapter 8. This pathway shares the dorsal columns of the spinal cord with pathways going to the cerebellum for reflex control of movement. The importance of the dorsal column kinesthetic pathways can be seen in victims of tabes dorsalis (destruction of the kinesthetic input by syphilis). The victim lacks knowledge of the position of his limbs from joint sensitivity and must watch his feet to walk. Even then, his walk is poorly coordinated; he "throws" his legs out and his feet slap the ground at every step because kinesthetic input is not available.

The pathways from the joint receptors to the cerebral cortex are long; the input involves long conduction and synaptic delay times. Such an input can guide and direct slow and voluntary movements such as those involved in a sorting task. The input can also report on body position before, during, and after a more rapid movement. However, the pathways are too slow for rapid correction of a movement, once it is initiated. In a golfer's swing, for example, the golfer may be aware when the movement is initiated that he is going to hit the ball incorrectly, but any attempt to consciously correct his swing will only make matters worse. It appears that the movement is "programmed" by higher centers that set off a series of *reflex* reactions in lower centers. These reflex reactions automatically control a rapid sequence of movements once they are initiated. The feedback from conscious sensations in limb position and movement before, during, and after the swing may be used to correct the reflex "program" for the next try. The input cannot be used to correct the swing while it is in progress. The sensory mechanisms for reflex programs of rapid movements and for automatic postural adjustment are the topic of the remainder of the section on kinesthesis.

Tendon jerks

If the tendon of a muscle is struck with a rubber hammer or with the heel of the hand, the muscle will react with a rapid and brief contraction—a **tendon jerk.** If a subject is seated with his legs dangling, striking the patellar tendon (just below the kneecap) causes a rapid contraction of the quadriceps (thigh) muscle and a kicking motion of the leg—the so-called "knee jerk" reflex. The quick contraction is a response to stretching the muscle by hitting the tendon to which it is attached. Similar tendon jerks can be stimulated in both flexor and extensor muscles over the entire body by striking their tendons. The tendon jerk is a reflex that is stimulated by receptors in the muscles that are sensitive to the *stretch* of the muscle. Striking the tendon results in rapid stretch of the muscle to which it is attached. The same muscle responds by contracting in a reflex fashion.

The tendon jerk is, then, a reflex. In

studying reflexes in Chapter 6, five elements made up the usual reflex: (1) receptors, (2) sensory neurons, (3) association neurons, (4) motor neurons, and (5) effectors. It was also pointed out that synaptic delay was responsible for most of the time required between stimulus and response. Tendon jerks require less time between stimulus and response than other reflexes because fewer synapses are involved. Measurements of the time required show that no association neurons are involved in the tendon jerk. It is a **monosynaptic** reflex that has only one set of synapses between the sensory and motor neurons. The sensory neurons make direct functional connections with the motor neurons so that only four reflex elements are involved (no association neurons participate in the tendon jerk).

Stretch reflex

The stretch reflex involves exactly the same elements as the tendon jerk—the same receptors, sensory neurons, motor neurons, and effectors. The **stretch reflex** is the reflex contraction of extensor muscles to a more gradual stretch from the pull of gravity (for example, as it bends the knee), rather than the abnormally rapid stretch of tendon jerks. Extensor muscles are stretched as a limb is flexed by either the force of gravity or antagonist flexors. When stretched by the force of gravity bending a limb, the extensor muscles react by contraction and straighten the limb. Since the onset of the stretch is more gradual, stretch receptors begin to fire a few at a time as their thresholds are reached. The contraction response that straightens the limb is therefore smooth and gradual as more and more groups of muscle fibers respond. For example, as the knees bend under the weight of the body, the tendon of the quadriceps (thigh) muscle is stretched over the kneecap. The muscle reacts to stretch by contraction, which straightens the leg. With normal shifts in posture, the

amount of stretch on various extensor or antigravity muscles changes. Their reflex contraction varies in proportion to the amount of load imposed upon them to enable the body to remain upright. If you shift your weight from your right leg to your left, the extensors of the left leg will be stretched more and will increase their contraction to compensate for the change in posture. Stretch reflexes are therefore important to normal postural adjustments.

As pointed out in Chapter 5, muscles are always stretched to some degree and are therefore always partly contracted in response, giving rise to **muscle tone,** the partial contraction of healthy muscle that varies with position (stretch). The postural changes in stretch reflex adjustment are simply increases or decreases in muscle tone. Flexor muscles are not needed for upright posture since they bend rather than extend the limbs. They have a higher threshold to stretch than extensor muscles, have less tone as a result, and do not show reflex contraction to gradual stretch, although they will react to the more rapid stimulus of tendon jerks. In man the flexors of the arms oppose gravity rather than the extensors; for example, bending the elbow opposes gravity. The arm flexors show all the characteristics of extensor muscles in the rest of the body, including postural stretch reflexes.

Muscle spindle

The receptors that excite the stretch reflex are found in specialized muscle cells called the **muscle spindles.** These specialized "sensory" muscle cells are attached to connective tissue that reaches the tendons on either end of the muscle. The stretch-sensitive muscle spindles are therefore "in parallel" with the other fibers of the muscle. If the *other* muscle fibers contract, stretch of the spindle fibers is *decreased* because the spindle fibers are indirectly "attached" to either end of the muscle and

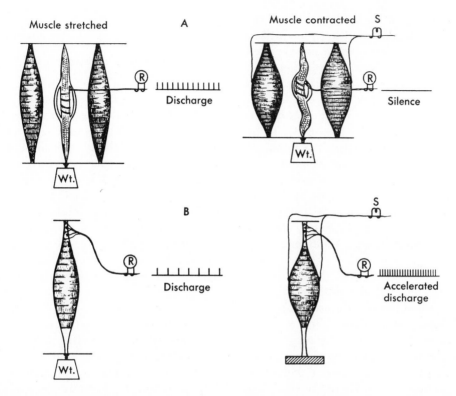

Fig. 9-1. Relationships among muscle spindle fibers, Golgi tendon organ, and muscle fibers. **A,** Muscle spindle arranged "in parallel" with muscle fibers so that muscle contraction relieves the pull on the muscle spindle. **B,** Golgi tendon organ arranged "in series" with the muscle so that either stretch or contraction stimulates the tendon organ. (From Patton, H. D.: Reflex regulation of movement and posture. In Ruch, T. C., Patton, H. D., Woodbury, J. W., and Towe, A. L.: Neurophysiology, ed. 2, Philadelphia, 1965, W. B. Saunders Co.)

the muscle has shortened. As a result, stretch reflex stimulation often ceases when the muscle contracts and relieves the pull on the spindle fibers (Fig. 9-1). Since there is normally some stretch stimulation to muscles, especially the antigravity extensors, the muscle spindle receptors are continuously exciting a few motoneurons to contract muscle fibers even when the muscle is at rest. It is the resting level of muscle spindle firing that accounts for muscle tone. As previously pointed out, tone varies with the amount of stretch imposed on the muscle.

Golgi tendon organ

The **Golgi tendon organ** is another receptor mechanism that is stimulated by stretch. This receptor is located in the tendon of the muscle, however. It is stimulated by stretch from *either* an external pull on the tendon *or* the pull that results from muscle contraction (Fig. 9-1). The intrafusal fiber or muscle spindle receptors are "in parallel" with the muscle; they are stimulated by stretching the muscle and lack stimulation when the muscle contracts. The Golgi tendon organ is "in series" with the muscle fibers and responds to pull on the tendon, whether the pull is applied by external force to the tendon or the tendon pull results from contraction of the muscle itself. The tendon organ has a much higher threshold than the receptors in the muscle spindle. Furthermore, stimulation of the Golgi tendon organ results in reflex *inhibition* of the fibers of the muscle. In contrast to the monosynaptic stretch reflex, the inhibitory reflex resulting from tendon stimulation includes interneurons. The sensory neurons excite Renshaw cells (Chapter 4), which inhibit the motoneurons. The pathway is therefore longer and the inhibitory response slower than stretch reflex excitation.

Silent period

When the tendon jerk reflex is stimulated, there is a **silent period** of muscle inhibition that follows contraction. After a strong synchronous contraction in response to stretch, the muscle goes completely flaccid for the better part of a second before recovering normal tone. There are three reasons for the silent period. (1) When the muscle shortens abruptly during contraction, stretch is relieved on the muscle spindles, and they stop reflexly exciting the muscle cells. The muscle therefore relaxes. (2) The Golgi tendon organs are stimulated by the sudden two-way pull on the tendon from both the stretch stimulus and muscle contraction. The Golgi endings inhibit the motoneurons by the reflex described above; this also relaxes the muscle. (As pointed out, the inhibitory pathway is longer than the excitatory pathway so that inhibition takes longer and follows excitation.) (3) The motoneurons have inhibitory **recurrent collaterals.** A recurrent collateral is a branch of the axon of the neuron that turns back toward the cell body. The recurrent collaterals of the motoneurons contact Renshaw cells, which inhibit these same motoneurons in a kind of "circular reflex." When the motoneurons fire, they inhibit themselves from firing again for a brief period via this pathway. During the silent period, motoneurons to muscle cells are inhibited, and the muscle relaxes.

Clasp-knife reflex: shortening and lengthening reactions

The relative roles of the muscle spindle and the Golgi tendon organ are clearly seen in the clasp-knife reflex of a decerebrate animal. A decerebrate animal is one in which the higher parts of the brain—the cerebrum and upper brainstem—have been cut away. Indirectly these regions of the brain exert a constant inhibitory influence on the motoneurons of extensor muscles. When the inhibitory brain areas are removed, the extensor stretch reflexes are exaggregated, and the animal's limbs are stiffly extended; there is increased extensor tone. If one attempts to flex a limb in a decerebrate preparation, the muscle spindles are stretched, the stretch reflexes are further stimulated, and the extensor muscles increase their contraction to resist flexion. When the pressure on the limb is increased beyond a certain point, the resistance to flexion "melts away," and the limb flexes readily—a **lengthening reaction** of the resisting extensor muscles. The lengthening reaction is caused by the increased pull on the tendon of the resisting extensor muscles, when the pressure to bend the limb is increased. The extensor muscle pulls one way on the tendon to resist the flexion, and the experimenter is applying pull on the other end of the tendon in attempting to bend the limb. The two-way pull on the extensor tendon exceeds the high threshold of the Golgi tendon organs, which fire a reflex to inhibit the extensor motoneurons and relax the extensor muscles. This allows the extensor muscle to lengthen, permitting the limb to be flexed. When the extensor muscle relaxes, pull on the tendon ceases, and the Golgi tendon organ is no longer stimulated to inhibit extensor contraction. At the same time, bending the limb further stretches the extensor muscles. Receptors in the muscle spindles again stimulate the stretch reflex, and the extensors contract again in the **shortening reaction.** Resistance to flexion reappears, and the limb resists flexion in its new position. The experiment may be repeated over and over until the limb is in a fully flexed position.

The initial "melting away" of resistance to flexion is called the clasp-knife reflex because the action of the limb resembles the resistance felt in closing a spring-loaded pocketknife. The limb or the blade of the knife first resists, then *actively assists,* flexion. The resistance is caused by the stretch reflex stimulation of the muscle spindles. The "melting away" of the resistance is caused by inhibitory reflex stimulation of the Golgi tendon organ. The active assistance of flexion is caused by other connections of the Golgi tendon organ—it *stimulates* the *flexors* of the limb to assist flexion at the same time that it *inhibits* the *extensors.*

Structure of the muscle spindle

The **muscle spindles** contain the receptors that stimulate the tendon jerk and stretch reflexes and provide the initial extensor resistance in the clasp-knife reflex. Study of the structure of muscle spindles shows that they contain other important sensory and motor mechanisms as well. Fig. 9-2 is a sketch of the muscle spindle and its nerve supply. The cell is slender, with an expanded sensory or "equitorial" region. The striated end parts of the cell, or "polar" regions, are motor in function. The end regions resemble other muscle cells. The more central sensory area consists of a nuclear bag full of cell nuclei, surrounded by a myotube area of lymph spaces. The nuclear bag is invaded by **annulospiral,** or **primary,** endings that are responsible for the stretch reflex—they respond to the pull on the sensory region that occurs when the muscle spindle is stretched by stretch of the whole muscle. The myotube part of the sensory region contains

secondary, or **flower-spray,** endings. These endings *inhibit* the other muscle fibers in a multisynaptic reflex, just the Golgi endings do. There is some evidence that the secondary endings are stimulated by outside pressure on the myotube endings when surrounding muscle cells contract. The secondary endings seem less important than the primary endings—some muscle spindles lack secondary endings. Finally, the striated motor ends of the muscle spindle can contract and are therefore invaded by small motoneurons, the **gamma efferents.** As will be seen later, contraction of the muscle spindle can stimulate the primary sensory endings of the same spindle.

Relative roles of Golgi, annulospiral, and flower-spray endings (Fig. 9-3)

There is evidence for three roles for the three receptors in normal coordinated behavior. (1) The Golgi tendon endings register *total* tension on the tendon, whether the tension is caused by an external pull from limb movement or a pull resulting from contraction of the muscle. They inhibit muscle contraction to relieve tension on the tendon, when the pull is so great as to endanger the muscle structure or the tendon and its attachment to bone. As a "safety valve," they have a high threshold, acting when there is an overload on the muscle and tendon. (2) The annulospiral endings react to the *length* of the sensory part of the muscle spindle. The extensor muscles are contracted according to their length whenever stretching the muscle stretches the muscle spindle. This action fires the monosynaptic stretch reflexes that are responsible for extensor tone and postural adjustments. The annulospiral endings are also excited when the muscle spindle contracts, as will be explained later. (3) The flower-spray endings seem to be stimulated by pressure on the fluid-filled myotube region, where these endings are found. The pressure is probably provided by surrounding muscle fibers when they

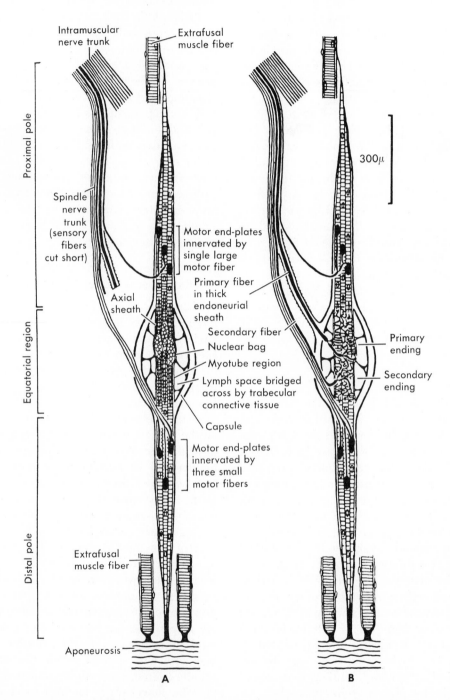

Fig. 9-2. Muscle spindle and its nerve supply. **A** shows only gamma efferent motor fibers to the contractile ends of the spindle. **B** shows also the sensory supply to the primary and secondary endings. (From Barker, D.: Quart. J. Micr. Sci. **89:**143-186, 1948.)

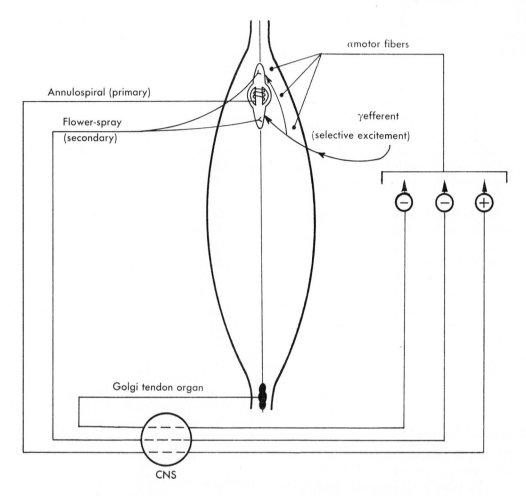

Fig. 9-3. Diagram showing excitatory (+) and inhibitory (−) inputs from the muscle spindle and Golgi tendon organ as they affect alpha (α) motor fibers to the muscle. The gamma (γ) efferent supply to the muscle spindle is also shown. For functional relationships, see text.

contract, shorten, and "bulge" in isotonic contraction that shortens the muscle. It may be that their inhibition of the muscle as it shortens helps bring the movement to a smooth conclusion.

Role of the gamma efferent fibers: contraction of the muscle spindle

The muscle spindle contracts when excited via the motor nerves going to its polar regions—the gamma efferent fibers. Contraction of the muscle spindle at its ends

exerts a pull on the central sensory area. Stretching the muscle spindle also pulls on the central part of the spindle. A pull on the sensory area by either force fires the annulospiral endings, which excite other fibers in the muscle. The stretch reflex is, then, a muscle contraction in response to the length of the sensory part of the spindle, whether caused by stretch of the whole muscle or contraction of the ends of the muscle spindle. In isotonic muscle contraction the whole muscle shortens, relieving stretch to the muscle spindle. If the gamma efferent fibers excite muscle spindle contraction while the muscle shortens, they "take up the slack" and maintain pull on the sensory region. The annulospiral endings remain excited and reinforce muscle contraction by their input. Contraction of the muscle spindle can therefore reinforce isotonic contraction of the muscle by shortening the spindle as the muscle shortens, keeping tension on the annulospiral endings. Contraction of the muscle spindle via the gamma efferent fibers can also reinforce isometric contraction, when the muscle does not shorten. By increasing tension on the annulospiral endings, reflex muscle contraction adds to "voluntary" contraction, without change in the length of the muscle. In general, the gamma efferent mechanism acts as a "biasing" mechanism or "gain control," regulating the sensitivity of the stretch reflex; when more gamma efferents excite muscle spindles, more annulospiral endings are excited, and muscle contraction is greater.

Reciprocal innervation

Reciprocal innervation has been defined as the nervous mechanism that allows an antagonist muscle to relax as the agonist contracts (Chapter 5). For example, an extensor muscle must relax and not react to being stretched when the opposed flexor muscle bends a limb. If the antagonist extensors reacted with a stretch reflex when flexors contracted to bend the leg at the knee, the movement would be difficult or impossible. It is now possible to explain how reciprocal innervation occurs. When the flexor motoneurons are excited, the gamma efferents to the flexor muscle spindle are also excited. As previously explained, they take up the slack in the muscle spindle so that tension is maintained on the annulospiral endings. This input reinforces flexor contraction. The same annulospiral input from flexor muscle spindles that excites flexor motoneurons *inhibits* the

antagonist extensor motoneurons. The antagonist extensors relax to permit flexion to occur. The same reciprocal relations exist for flower-spray and Golgi tendon endings. While these inputs inhibit the motoneurons to the stimulated muscles, they excite the motoneurons of antagonists. Any flower-spray or Golgi input from a muscle that inhibits the muscle excites its antagonists; any annulospiral input from a muscle that excites that muscle inhibits its antagonists. As a result, when a muscle relaxes, its antagonist contracts; when a muscle contracts, its antagonist relaxes. Both may relax or contract when these mechanisms are not brought into action, of course.

Crossed extension

When one limb is flexed, the opposite limb is extended in a reflex to maintain posture and balance and to permit movements such as walking (Chapter 5). The primary, secondary, and Golgi inputs are involved in the same way as in reciprocal innervation. The pattern of reflex input from those endings that supports homolateral (same side) flexion supports contralateral (other side) extension, and vice versa.

Resting discharge

The primary and secondary endings of the muscle spindle are not silent when the muscle is at rest. Some stretch to the muscle always exists, and there is a **resting discharge** of input from the primary annulospiral endings to maintain muscle tone (see above). The secondary endings also slow a resting discharge, which reflexly inhibits some of the motoneurons of the muscle. These levels of resting discharge are modified by intermittant firing of the gamma efferents. As a result the motoneurons to a muscle are the site of a constant interplay of excitatory and inhibitory influences. Influences come from the discharge levels of the receptors in the muscle spindles of the muscle, the discharge levels of muscle spindles in other muscles (both antagonists

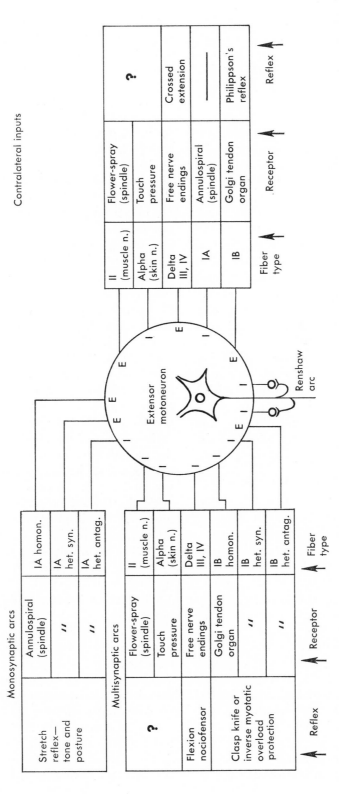

Fig. 9-4. Afferent inputs to a motoneuron that are confined to one segment of the cord. Influence of each input is shown as excitatory (E) or inhibitory (I). (From Patton, H. D.: Reflex regulation of movement and posture. In Ruch, T. C., Patton, H. D., Woodbury, J. W., and Towe, A. L.: Neurophysiology, ed. 2, Philadelphia, 1965, W. B. Saunders Co.)

and agonist), inputs to other reflexes, and influences from higher centers. The number of motoneurons firing at any given moment depends on the interaction of many excitatory and inhibitory influences (Fig. 9-4).

Input to the cerebellum

The primary and secondary muscle spindle inputs and the Golgi tendon organ input set off spinal reflexes. These inputs also reach higher centers. The role of higher centers, particularly the cerebellum, will be discussed in Chapter 14. Such centers are responsible for overall coordination of the body through their influence on the excitatory and inhibitory reflexes involved in muscle tone, stretch reflexes, and reciprocal innervation. These are the centers whose activity is "programmed" by the higher parts of the brain, when a rapid coordinated movement such as swinging a golf club at a ball is executed. As explained at the beginning of this section the movement is "set" once it is programmed and initiated by the highest parts of the brain. The movement is nevertheless dependent on the flow of input from the muscle spindles and the flow of output to the gamma efferent fibers.

Muscle spindle and motor learning

It now appears that the muscle spindles may be necessary for learning "voluntary" as well as reflex-controlled acts. They participate, therefore, in every move made. About one third of all the motoneurons in the ventral roots of the cord are gamma efferent motoneurons going to the muscle spindles rather than larger motoneurons to other muscle fibers. The gamma efferents regulate the sensitivity of the muscle spindles to stretch and therefore regulate most of the sensory "feedback" from movement that goes to spinal and higher reflex centers. The input from the muscle spindles seems to "decide" whether or not the muscle contracts in response to excitation from higher centers in so-called "voluntary" movements. If the gamma efferents contract

muscle spindles, excitation to motoneurons of the muscle is added to their excitation by higher centers—the muscle contracts. If the spindles do not contract and send excitation to the motoneurons, the excitation from higher centers may not be enough to cause the muscle to contract. In one experiment the role of the muscle spindles could be seen in teaching an animal to lift his leg at the sound of a tone to avoid a shock to his paw—a so-called **conditioned response** (**CR**) (Chapter 17). When the activity of the motoneurons is recorded during training, firing of gamma efferents to the muscles that lift the leg can be detected for several trials *before* the animal learns to lift his leg to avoid shock. It would therefore seem that excitation from contracting the muscle spindles must be added to excitation from higher centers in making the avoidance response.

Drugs can be used to block the junction between motoneurons (including the gamma efferents) and muscle fibers. Some of these drugs have no effect on the CNS and do not block smooth muscle responses such as those of the pupil of the eye. Under the influence of such a drug, the animal cannot lift his leg to avoid shock. But can he learn the response so that he can avoid shock when no longer under the influence of the drug? When presented with a tone, then a shock, for 500 to 1000 trials, he shows some signs of learning, even though he cannot move. Recordings from the brain show changes in CNS activity that are typical of learning. Responses to the bell that are typical of learning are also seen in the pupil of the eye (unaffected smooth muscle). However, when the drug is removed, the animal is unable to avoid the shock by lifting his leg to the bell, even though he is otherwise normal. The brain has learned, but the gamma efferents have not, so to speak. After 50 to 200 trials of training without the drug, the avoidance response is learned; the gamma efferents may now add their excitation to that from higher levels of the CNS, and the motoneurons for the response are excited. This suggests that excitation of muscle spindles may play a critical role in motor learning. (There are experiments cited in Chapter 17 that contradict this, however.)

VESTIBULAR SENSES
Labyrinth

The **vestibular** senses respond to head position and movement and set off many reflexes that enable us to maintain an upright posture. The receptors are located in the nonauditory part of the **labyrinth** of the inner ear, a structure shown in Fig. 9-5. The labyrinths are located in the temporal bones, internal to the pinna, or external ear, on each side of the skull. Each labyrinth is surrounded by fluid **perilymph** and the nonauditory parts are filled with fluid **endolymph** so that the whole structure is cushioned by fluid. The labyrinth walls are a membranous (membrane) structure. The nonauditory part of this structure can be classified into two sets of receptor structures on both structural and functional grounds: (1) the **semicircular canals**, which respond primarily to rotation of the head, and (2) the **sacculus** and **utriculus** (collectively called **sacs**), which respond primarily to head position and linear motions of the head. The three semicircular canals have a common opening near their ampullae (sing., ampulla), the bulge on each canal at one end. There they communicate with the utriculus, which, in turn,

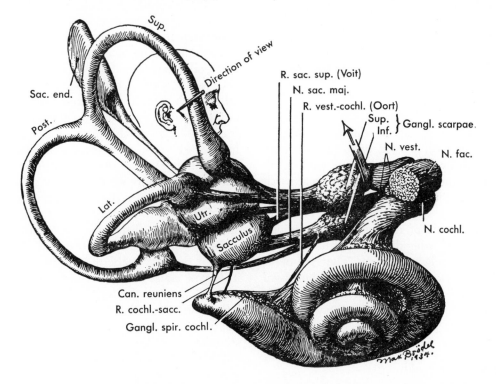

Fig. 9-5. Membranous labyrinth and its nerve supply. **Sup., Post.,** and **Lat.,** Anterior (superior) vertical, posterior vertical, and horizontal (lateral) semicircular canals; **Utr.,** utriculus; **N. sac. sup., R. sac. maj.,** and **N. vest.,** parts of the vestibular nerve supply. The ampulla is the bulblike swelling on one end of each semicircular canal. Other structures are auditory in function. For other details, see text. (From Hardy, M.: Anat. Rec. **59:**404, 1934.)

opens into the sacculus. The ampullae, the sacculus, and the utriculus are individually served by branches of the strato-acoustic, or eighth, nerve.

Nerve pathways

Nerve fibers that respond to stimulation of the semicircular canals and sacs pass in the eight nerve to the four **vestibular nuclei** of the medulla. Here they initiate *reflex* responses to head position and movement. The **medial longitudinal fasciculus** carries excitation from the vestibular nuclei to nuclei serving cranial nerves III, IV, and VI for reflex eye movements and to XI for reflex head movements. The **vestibulospinal tract** carries excitation down the spinal cord to the extensor motoneurons to vary posture as a function of head position. Other pathways reach the cerebellum for more general balancing reactions. Excitation can also reach vomiting centers in the medulla (to cause motion sickness or sea-sickness).

Sensations

Conscious sensations do not result directly from stimulation of the nonauditory labyrinth by head position and movement. Most of the strong sensations that result from changing head position are caused by reflex *responses* to the change. For example, sensations of dizziness from spinning around and around as children often do come from reflex responses. The eyes move reflexly back and forth so that the visual field seems to "swim" by. Reflex changes in extensor muscle tone cause the subject to feel that he is falling. These and other reflexes will be considered in detail later.

Semicircular canals

The semicircular canals lie in three planes of space at right angles to each other. There is a **horizontal, anterior vertical,** and **posterior vertical canal** in each labyrinth (Fig. 9-5). The horizontal canal inclines at about 30 degrees; the anterior and posterior vertical canals are at right angles to it and to each other. As a result, the anterior vertical canal on one side of the head is parallel with the posterior vertical canal on the other side of the head, and vice versa.

Ampulla. The bulblike swelling at one end of each semicircular canal where it joints the utriculus is called the **ampulla** (Fig. 9-5). Inside of the ampulla is found a ridge of sensory cells, the **crista** (Fig. 9-6). These sensory cells have hair-cell endings that thrust into an overlying gelatinous (jellylike) mass called the **cupula**. Together, the cupula and crista occupy most of the internal space of the ampulla. This means that any circulation of fluid through the semicircular canals will push against the cupula, bend the hair cells, and stimulate the fibers of the eighth nerve.

Rotational stimulation. Rotation of the head in any plane of motion will stimulate one semicircular canal more than the others because they are at right angles to one another; each canal is stimulated most by rotation parallel to it. The pattern of input from the three canals on either side of the head can be used to detect the direction of the rotation. For an example, consider stimulation of the horizontal canal by spinning around in a rotating chair. During *acceleration* from rest to a maximum rate of spin, sudden rotation of the canal will "move the canal around its fluid" because of the inertia of the rest of the fluid (Fig. 9-7, *A*). This will cause fluid pressure against the cupula, bending the hair cells, and stimulating the nerve fibers in the crista. When the rotating chair reaches a constant speed, stimulation will cease because the canal and the fluid will be rotating at the same speed and not in motion relative to each other. If the speed of rotation is too low for centrifugal force to be felt, no reflex reactions or sensations will result. When the rotation is suddenly *stopped* (decelerated), the horizontal semicircular canal will again be stimulated. The fluid will tend to keep

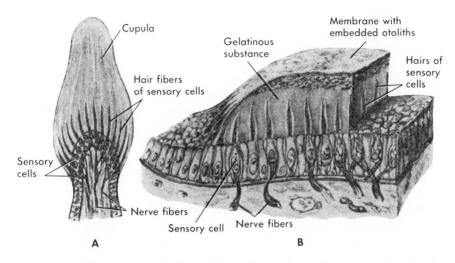

Fig. 9-6. Receptors of the nonauditory labyrinth. **A,** Crista; **B,** macula. For details, see text. (From Geldard, F. A.: The human senses, New York, 1953, John Wiley & Sons, Inc.)

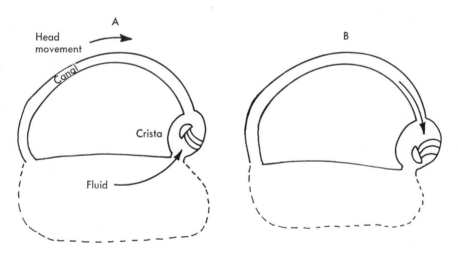

Fig. 9-7. Action of fluid motion on receptors in the ampulla of a semicircular canal. For details, see text.

moving in the direction the subject was rotating because of inertia of motion (Fig. 9-7, *B*). Fluid will press against the cupula from the opposite direction as compared to acceleration. Deceleration will give the same reflexes and sensations as if the subject had *begun* rotating in the opposite direction. Excitation from the semicircular canals depends on rotational *acceleration* and *deceleration* rather than on constant motion and occurs in relatively brief periods against a resting discharge level. Nerve fibers from the crista of the ampulla show a resting discharge level of about five impulses per second, a rate that is increased by ampulla-training acceleration and decreased by ampulla-leading acceleration.

Rotational reflexes. Rapid rotational acceleration will cause **rotational nystagmus,** or compensating eye movement reflexes. The subject's eyes will move back and forth. If the acceleration is to the *right,* the **slow component** of the eye movement will be to the *left,* aiding him to keep a fixed visual reference point as the visual field sweeps by. The **fast component** of the back-and forth eye movement will be to the *right* to pick up a new visual fixation point after his eyes have travelled as far as possible to the left. Sudden stopping (deceleration) will cause **postrotational nystagmus.** The stimulus pattern will be the same as if he began rotating in the opposite direction. Therefore, the slow component will be to the *right* and the fast component to the *left.* The student can test this assertion by spinning himself or another, stopping suddenly, and observing the postrotational eye movements in a mirror or directly on another subject. If you test yourself, the visual field will "swim by" in the direction of the slow component of the postrotational eye movements. To avoid rotational nystagmus, dancers often turn their heads in the direction opposite to a spin to avoid stimulating the semicircular canals and to maintain a fixed visual reference. Head movement and visual field change is restricted to one quick motion for each revolution.

Rotation also changes extensor tone. Extensors in the limbs toward which the subject is rotating (acceleration) contract to maintain balance against the shift in weight to that side. When a person stops suddenly, it is as if he were rotating in the opposite direction. This is why, after stopping, he tends to fall in the direction he was spinning; if he *was* spinning to the right, his reflexes are now responding to a left-hand spin.

Sacs

The **utriculus** communicates with the semicircular canals and the **sacculus** communicates with the utricule. The sacs are thus filled with the same fluid endolymph as the semicircular canals. However, their sensory structures are primarily specialized to respond to *head position* and to *linear acceleration* and *deceleration* rather than to rotary movements. The utricule seems to be more important to behavior than the saccule; destruction of the utricule disturbs equilibrium and locomotion, but destruction of the saccule does not lead to these symptoms. The input of the sacs seems more important in lower animals such as fish, amphibians, reptiles, and birds than it is to man and other mammals. Man can maintain equilibrium with vision when the sacs are destroyed, but he cannot stand erect on one foot with his eyes closed, and he loses orientation without a horizon—when swimming under water, for example.

Macula. The patch of sensory tissue on the inner surface of each of the sacs is called the **macula.** Its structure is shown in Fig. 9-6. The sensory cells extend hairlike processes into the cavity of the sac; the hairs are enveloped with a thick jellylike substance. On the free surface of the jelly rest many tiny particles of calcium carbonate (limestone "rocks"), the **otoliths.** The bases of the sensory cells are enveloped by basketlike endings of vestibular nerve fibers. These fibers are stimulated by the sensory cells, when the hairlike processes are bent or pulled by movement of the "top-heavy" mass of jelly-like material. This should occur whenever the hair cells are not upright or when the head is moved suddenly. The structure is like molded gelatin, with weights on top and hairs thrust into it from the bottom; movement "jiggles" the structure, and anything but an upright position displaces it to one side.

Hair cells. The hair cells are stimulated upon being bent or pulled when the "top-heavy" mass of jelly that envelops them is shifted from an upright position. Motion affects the gelatinous mass like shaking or tilting a gelatin mold. The stimulation results from linear acceleration or deceleration of the head or from head positions that tilt the hair cells and their enveloping jelly from an upright position. Head positions that keep the hair cells and jelly in an upright position result in minimum stimulation. If the hair cell structure is tilted to the side, increased stimulation results. Maximum stimulation results when the hair cells are upside down, with the otoliths and jelly pulling upon them.

Head positions. Various head positions affect the **macula sacculi** and **macula utriculi** differently. The maculus, or sensory structure, in each of the sacculi is oriented toward the outside of the head—to the sides, or laterally. This means that if the subject is lying on his right side, the hair cells of the left saccule will be upright and receive minimum stimulation; the hair cells of the right side will be "upside down" and receive maximum stimulation. The hair cells of the utricle are oriented upward and will be stimulated by any change from the upright head position. (Maximum stimulation would occur only when standing on your head!) It is evident that different **patterns** of input from the saccule and utricle can serve as cues to head position. As previously noted, the utricule is much more important to orientation than the saccule.

Acceleration and deceleration. Sudden linear movement of the head stimulate the maculae, especially the utriculus. This can distort sensations of the upright position when visual cues are not a help. For example, in flying, sudden acceleration makes the pilot feel he is climbing and sudden deceleration that he is diving, when he is in straight and level flight.

Eye reflexes and head position. Changes in head position result in elevation of the eyes when the head is lowered, depression of the eyes when the head is raised, and rotation of the eyes when the head is tilted. All these reflexes aid the eyes in orienting toward a level horizon. The eye reflexes originate in visual input as well as in the maculae. They are mediated by the medial longitudinal fasciculus pathways to the nuclei serving cranial nerves III, IV, and VI for the eye muscles. (These pathways were described earlier in the chapter.) At the same time change from the normal erect head position stimulates the maculae to send excitation to the neck muscles to return the head to the erect position. Here the medial longitudinal fasciculus carries excitation to cranial nerve XI for excitation of the neck muscles.

Righting reflexes

In four-legged animals, when the neck muscles react so as to restore the upright position of the head, the neck is "twisted" if the body is not erect. This stimulates proprioceptors in the neck muscles, whose input reaches descending tracts in the cord going to the motor nerve supply of the body trunk. The body muscles are stimulated to restore the upright position of the body. The sequence involved in neck and body righting reflexes is most clearly observed by holding a cat upside down and dropping it from a position 4 or 5 feet off the floor. First the head turns toward the upright position, next the forelimbs, and then the hindlimbs. Twisting the neck has stimulated the upper body trunk and twisting the upper trunk has stimulated the lower trunk, all in sequence. At the same time extensor tone has been increased, and the animal will land with all four limbs stiffly extended to cushion the shock.

Postural reflexes. The head also "leads" (caused by visual and macular input) in regulating posture. In animals the forelimb and hindlimb extensor tone will vary with head position. If a cat lowers its head in looking under an object, forelimb extensors will relax and hindlimb extensors contract— the forepart of the body will be reflexly lowered and the hindpart elevated. If the head is raised above the normal position, preparatory to jumping up on an object, forelimb extensors will contract and hindlimb extensors relax. The forequarters will be raised and the hindquarters lowered in position for the jump. These reflexes can be demonstrated in cats with the higher parts of the brain removed as long as the connections between the sacs and the spinal cord motoneurons are intact.

Vestibular senses: practical implications

In general, the vestibular senses depend on normal conditions of gravity and acceleration to furnish accurate input for normal responses. They evolved in fish, orienting in a three-dimensional environment with little gravitational effect and little visual orientation. Evolution has adapted mammals to gravity, subordinated them to accurate visual input, and developed them to respond to the amount and kind of acceleration and deceleration found in normal body movement. When these acceleration limits are exceeded, the resulting input can cause extreme disorientation and nausea, especially when accurate visual input does not correct for their misinformation. As pointed out previously, the extreme acceleration or deceleration encountered in flying an airplane can cause a pilot in level flight to believe that he is climbing or diving if he is flying "blind," that is, without a natural visual horizon. Centrifugal forces change stimulation to the sacs in a climb, a dive, or a turn, although the semicircular canals seem little affected. A pilot may be upside down in a "loop" with sufficient centrifugal force to feel that he is upright. One of the most difficult problems in learning to fly is to disregard vestibular input and depend strictly on vision—either a view of the horizon or, more difficult still, instrument readings when flying "blind."

Lack of normal gravitation, as in the weightlessness of outer space, causes lack of body orientation. There is no "up" or "down," and orientation is altogether visual. Prolonged weightlessness has been reported to cause nausea and dizziness, although these symptoms may be overcome by training.

Finally, regular rhythmic motions that differ enough from those of walking can cause carsickness, or airsickness, or seasickness via the nausea centers in the medulla. The primary component causing the disturbance seems to be vertical motion rather than "pitch" (fore and aft motion) or "yaw" (side to side motion). The frequency and amplitude of the vertical motion seem to be the important variables—frequencies near 20 per minute and amplitudes of about 7 feet being most disturbing. Drugs have proved to be of some help, and fortunately most persons adapt, as when a sailor gets his "sea legs."

SUMMARY

Proprioception is sensory input for body position and movement. It includes kinesthesis from the general receptors in joints and muscles and vestibular sensitivity from the nonauditory labyrinth. Kinesthesis in the limbs gives rise to conscious sensations of position and movement when receptors in the joints (mostly pacinian corpuscles) are stimulated. These receptors adapt little so that one is always aware of limb position. Their pathways up to the dorsal columns of the cord reach the cerebral cortex. Many synapses are involved so that cortically originated "voluntary" response to joint receptors is slow. This input can regulate slow "voluntary" reactions, but it is too slow to correct a rapid movement in progress. Rapid movements are regulated by reflexes in lower centers of the brain and cord that are "programmed" by the cortex, cerebellum, and other higher centers.

Kinesthesis also includes sensory input from the muscles and tendons that does not cause conscious sensation. These inputs participate in the reflex "programs" mentioned above and are important to posture and coordination. One such reflex that can be shown in exaggerated form is the tendon jerk. Striking the tendon of a muscle causes a quick contraction of the muscle. This reflex is stimulated by receptors in the muscle, sensitive to the stretching of the muscle when the tendon is struck. The reflex is rapid because it is monosynaptic.

More gradual stretch of extensor muscles elicits an extensor contraction in the stretch reflex. The stretch reflex is elicited in extensor muscles when limbs are flexed by the pull of gravity; it straightens those limbs. It is therefore an antigravity reflex. Shifts in posture change the pattern of stretch reflexes in extensors in normal postural adjustment. All muscles are anatomically stretched to some degree, and their stretch reflex response causes the muscle tone that varies with position (amount of stretch). Arm flexors in man are antigravity muscles that react like extensors.

The receptors stimulating the stretch reflex are found in the muscle spindles. The spindle fibers are functionally attached to the ends of the muscle, and stretch on them (and therefore stretch reflex stimulation) is relieved by muscle contraction; they are "in parallel" with the muscle. The Golgi tendon organs are found in the tendons and are "in series" with the muscle since they react to tendon pull imposed by external force or by the muscle itself. They have a high threshold and inhibit the muscle via a multisynaptic reflex.

A "silent period" of muscle relaxation follows muscle contraction in the tendon jerk reflex. The phenomenon is caused by three consequences of the contraction response: (1) relief of stretch to the muscle spindles, (2) stimulation of the Golgi tendon organ, and (3) inhibitory recurrent collaterals from the motoneurons.

The clasp-knife reflex in the decerebrate preparation is caused by the muscle spindles and Golgi tendon organs. Attempting to flex the limb of the preparation meets resistance because of the stretch reflex. The resistant "melts away" when the Golgi tendon organ is stimulated in the lengthening reaction. The lengthening reaction

relieves stimulation of the Golgi ending and restimulates the spindles, causing the extensors to contract again in the shortening reaction. The extensor lengthening reaction is accompanied by flexor contraction caused by flexor motoneuron connections of the extensor Golgi endings.

The muscle spindle has both sensory and motor functions. In its central part, primary, or annulospiral, endings respond to pull with the stretch reflex. Secondary, or flower-spray, endings inhibit the muscle; they are probably stimulated by pressure from the contraction of surrounding muscle fibers. The striated ends of the muscle spindle can contract to stimulate the primary endings. They receive motor fibers, the gamma efferents. The gamma efferents can stimulate the stretch reflex. They can therefore "take up slack" on the spindle in isotonic contraction of the muscle to maintain stretch reflex excitation of the motoneurons. They can reinforce isometric contraction by increasing stretch reflex input.

The reciprocal innervation of antagonist flexors and extensors is caused by kinesthetic input. The annulospiral input that excites a muscle inhibits its antagonist. The flower-spray and Golgi inputs that inhibit a muscle excite its antagonist. When a muscle contracts, simultaneous contraction of its gamma efferents stimulates annulospiral endings to inhibit the antagonist muscle. The same reciprocal relations hold for the crossed extension reflex. All three inputs also reach the cerebellum and other subcortical centers to regulate rapid reflex coordinations "programmed" by higher parts of the brain. Experiments seem to show that muscle spindle input is vital to learning even "voluntary" responses—in one experiment, muscle spindle excitation must be added to that from higher centers before a learned response can be performed.

The vestibular senses are special senses located in the nonauditory part of the membranous labyrinth. The nonauditory labyrinth is surrounded by perilymph and contains endolymph. Its semicircular canals respond to head rotation and its sacculus and utriculus to position and linear motion of the head; both are served by part of the eighth nerve that goes to the four vestibular nuclei of the medulla. The vestibular nuclei mediate reflexes rather than conscious sensations. The medial longitudinal fasciculus carries excitation to nerves III, IV, and VI for reflex eye movements and to XI for reflex head movements. The vestibulospinal tract carries excitation to spinal extensor motoneurons for postural adjustment, and other pathways reach the cerebellum for complex coordination. The anterior vertical, posterior vertical, and horizontal semicircular canals in each temporal bone are at right angles to one another, and each responds most to movement in its own plane. Three-dimensional movement is thus provided for.

The ampulla of each canal contains a crista of sensory cells, with hair endings thrust into an overlying gelatinous cupula. Fluid circulation in the semicircular canals pushes against the cupula to stimulate the hair cells. Rotary acceleration or deceleration of a canal, rather than a constant rotation, is the adequate stimulus. During rotation in a horizontal plane the horizontal canal is stimulated. During acceleration rotational nystagmus is produced, with the eyes showing a slow component of movement opposite to the direction of rotation and a fast component in the same direction. Deceleration reverses the direction of slow and fast components in postrotational nystagmus. Extensor tone is increased on the side toward rotation during acceleration and increased on the opposite side during deceleration.

The sacs include the sacculus and utriculus, the latter being the more important. The sensory structure in each is the macula, consisting of hair cells surrounded by a jellylike material with otoliths on its free surface. Displacement of the jelly by linear acceleration and deceleration, or head positions in which the hair cells are not upright, stimulates the hair cells. In the utriculus the hair cells are oriented vertically and in the sacculus they are oriented laterally so that each head position and movement has a different pattern of stimulus input. Departures from the vertical head position cause compensating eye movements to maintain the horizon and reflex reactions of the neck muscles to return the head to the erect position. Proprioceptors in the neck muscles stimulate reflex reactions of the body muscles to restore the upright position in the righting reflexes. Forelimb and hindlimb extensors in animals adjust to head position in postural reflexes.

In general, the vestibular senses depend on normal gravity and body movements. The extreme accelerations, decelerations, and centrifugal forces in flying can cause disorientation unless there are visual cues to go by. Lack of gravitation in outer space can cause lack of orientation. Large and regular vertical movement can cause car sickness, seasickness, and airsickness via nausea centers in the medulla.

READINGS

Buddenbrock, W. von: The senses, Ann Arbor, Mich., 1958, University of Michigan Press.
Mueller, C. G.: Sensory psychology, Englewood Cliffs, N. J., 1965, Prentice-Hall, Inc.

Chapter 10

Chemical senses

OVERVIEW

The chemical senses are so named because they are normally and adequately stimulated by substances in solution. They include gustation (taste), olfaction (smell), and the common chemical sense. The common chemical sense is the simplest and will be disposed of first; it is stimulated by dissolved irritants in the eyes, nose, throat, and other mucous areas. The sensory mechanism seems identical with pain; however, the "stinging" quality of ammonia in the eyes or pepper in the mouth seems different to the subject from somesthetic pain.

Gustation will be taken up next. Most of the taste receptors are confined to the tongue. Their primary qualities are sweet, salt, sour, and bitter. What is known of the adequate stimuli for these four taste qualities will be summarized. The nerve pathways for taste will be described. With receptors and nerve pathways understood, experiments on the physiology of taste can be discussed. Phenomena of taste thresholds, adaptation, contrast, compensation, fusion, and so on conclude the section on gustation.

Olfaction is the final topic of the chapter. Following some introductory remarks, the receptors and their nervous connections will be described. Some of the unique difficulties in accurately stimulating olfaction and the methods used to overcome these difficulties will precede discussion of olfactory qualities and the sensory mechanisms underlying them. Theories of olfactory sensory mechanisms will be summarized, with the stereochemical theory being clearly the most acceptable. Remarks on olfactory phenomena such as adaptation, compensation, and anosmia (smell "blindness") conclude the chapter.

COMMON CHEMICAL SENSE
Quality

The **common chemical sense** refers to the sensitivity of the mucous membranes of the body to dissolved irritants. The term is most frequently used in referring to the "stinging" quality that is aroused in the mouth by "hot" foods such as chili peppers. However, vaporizing substances such as ammonia cause stinging sensations from the eyes and nose, which are also caused by the common chemical sense. In the eyes and nose the irritants cause tears and nasal secretions, as anyone who has smelled ammonia or peeled an onion can testify. Nasal sensitivity seems the greatest (a few thousandths of a percent for some gases), eye sensitivity is intermediate, and sensations from the mouth may require a solution of 3 to 5% of some of the most irritating substances. Common chemical sensitivity is not confined to the nose, eyes, and mouth. Any

175

mucous membrane, as in the anus and genitals, has common chemical sensitivity.

Common chemical sensations are related to pain by the subject, but they seem subjectively different from pain in quality, being described as a "stinging" or "burning" sensations. Common chemical sensations from the mouth may be pleasant in mild arousal—when one "tastes" peppermint or a dry martini, common chemical stimulation is the "stinging" part of the "flavor." It has been argued that the common chemical sense differs from pain since the sensory quality seems different to the subject and since drugs affect these sensations in a different way (for example, cocaine anesthetizes skin pain much more readily than the common chemical sense). The change in sensory quality can probably be explained by variations in the stimuli causing common chemical sensation from those causing skin pain; dissolved mucous irritants *should* cause an altered sensation from skin pain stimuli, just as skin pain from a burn differs from that caused by a cut. Drugs can "deaden" skin pain more readily than can the common chemical sense. However, drugs may be less effective when the nerve endings are more directly stimulated by irritants on sensitive mucous surfaces. Finally, the anatomy of the receptors for pain and the common chemical sense are identical, as are their pathways to the brain. It may be concluded that the common chemical sense is pain sensitivity in the mucous membranes, that is, pain stimulated by irritants dissolved in the mucus covering the mucous membranes.

Receptors

The receptors are free nerve endings distributed to the tongue, nasopharynx, orbit, and other mucous surfaces. Like other pain endings their threshold is relatively high, but the CNS response fatigues slowly, and the receptors adapt little under most conditions of chemical stimulation. Receptor adaptation is rare because the dissolved irritant is not a "constant" stimulus; the chemical changes it initiates in the tissue are a process of active change. The "bite" of a peppermint stick will not change greatly, then, no matter how long you chew on it—and your eyes will not adapt to peeling onions!

Nerve pathways

The fibers from the mouth, tongue, orbit, and nasal passages that serve pain reach the brainstem in cranial nerves V, VII, IX, and X. They are distributed with other pain fibers to the spinal tract and nucleus of the fifth nerve. The input relays excitation to the thalamus and postcentral gyrus of the cerebral cortex (somesthetic projection area). As with other pain fibers, there are many collaterals to the reticular formation of the brainstem that arouse the brain to greater activity and contribute descending output to muscles. Pain input of any kind stimulates the nervous system to much activity.

GUSTATION

Taste sensitivity is caused solely by receptors on the tongue in adult man (children sometimes have taste receptors in the cheeks and pharynx, which later disappear). Strictly speaking, taste receptors give rise only to sensations of sweet, salt, sour, and bitter; the complex of subtle sensations called "taste" in everyday speech includes smell, common chemical sensitivity, and somesthesis. A food is said to taste bland when "stinging" common chemical sensations are not present. Foods taste flat when one has a head cold because it is impossible to smell food. Hold your nose and you cannot *taste* the difference between a slice of apple and a slice of raw potato—they can be distinguished only by their texture (somesthesis). Coffee tastes hot as well as bitter, and corn bread tastes "coarse" —both warmth and texture are somesthetic sensations. As used here, however, gustation refers only to sensations of sweet, sour, bitter, and salt from the tongue.

Methods and definitions

As usual, the names for the four primary taste qualities come from the reports of human subjects. In the usual experiment of this kind, various solutions are applied to the tongue of the subject, and he reports on what he tastes. (The tongue is washed with water between tests to avoid interference among successive stimuli.) Agreement among subjects is the criterion for naming taste qualities, and subjects largely agree on sweet, salt, sour, and bitter, or mixtures of these, as being all they taste under such circumstances. Animal experiments often involve washing the tongue of an anesthetized animal with the same solutions while recording from the seventh or ninth cranial nerve. As will be seen later, individual receptors for each of the qualities do *not* seem indicated by the data that result from nerve cell recording. However, the *patterns* of nerve cell firing are such that the CNS could detect four kinds of signals corresponding to four taste qualities (three in the case of the cat, which does not respond to sweet). Something is known of the properties of the adequate stimuli for taste, but little is known of how the receptor mechanism works. The nerve pathways turn out to be an anomaly, being partly separate and partly mixed with those for somesthesis.

Development

The development of taste sensitivity begins before birth, when sensory branches of nerves VII and IX invade the epithelial cells of the mucous membranes of the tongue. Under this influence (called **sensory appropriation**) the epthelial cells develop into specialized receptors. The development is complete at puberty, but the receptors begin to atrophy after about 45 years of age. These changes are related to the gonadal hormone; taste receptors atrophy after cas-

tration in animals, but they can be reestablished by injections of the missing sex hormones. Apparently taste matures at puberty and atrophies as the output of gonadal hormones falls off in middle and old age. This has important consequences for nutrition in older people, who frequently lose interest in food and do not eat enough. The taste receptors apparently require continuous renewal; sensory taste cells are replaced about every seven days, on the average, like other epithelial cells. Their replacement cells become receptors under the influence of the seventh and ninth nerves and the gonadal hormones.

Receptors

The taste receptors are spindle-shaped cells, each of which has a single hair. They occur in clusters of two to twelve, surrounded by supporting cells. The whole structure is called a **taste bud** (Fig. 10-1). The taste buds are most frequently found in the papillae of the tongue. The papillae are structures in the tongue, made up of a "moat" surrounding an "island". The taste buds thrust their hairs into the moat from the sides of the island and the walls of the moat. The moat serves to contain the solution to be tasted so that it can affect the hair cells; these receptors, in turn, set off nerve impulses in the taste nerve fibers. There are four types of papillae on the tongue (Fig. 10-2), but those in the center of the tongue do not contain taste buds. Only the tip, sides, and back of the tongue are taste-sensitive.

Qualities. Stimulation of the tongue with various solutions identifies four primary taste qualities when smell, temperature, somesthesis, and comon chemical sensitivity are ruled out. The four primary qualities are sweet, salt, sour, and bitter. The adequate stimulus for sweet is sucrose (sugar). The best salt response comes from NaCl (common table salt) solutions. Weak solutions of hydrochloric acid (HCl) provide the most adequate stimulus for sour. Bitter

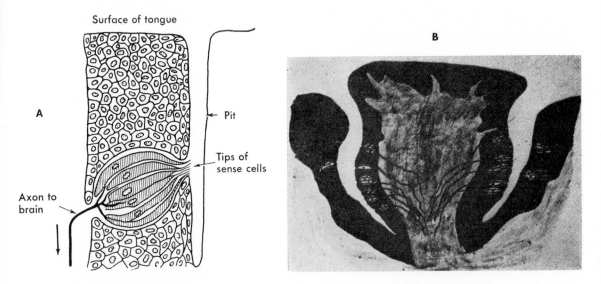

Fig. 10-1. Sensory structures for taste. **A,** Taste bud, with tips of the sense cells into the pit forming the "moat" of a papilla. **B,** Circumvallate papilla seen in diagrammatic cross section with taste buds lining the walls, their tips opening to the "moat" surrounding the papilla. (**A** from Woodworth, R. S.: Psychology, ed. 4, New York, 1940, Holt, Rinehart & Winston, Inc.; **B** from Geldard, F. A.: The human senses, New York, 1953, John Wiley & Sons, Inc.)

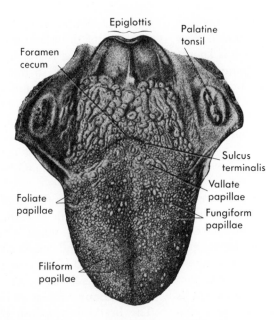

Fig. 10-2. Location of papillae on the tongue. (After Kahn: Das Leben des Menschen, W. Keller & Co.; from Neal, H. V., and Rand, H. W.: Comparative anatomy. Copyright, 1936, by McGraw-Hill Book Co. Used by permission.)

sensations result from stimulation with quinine solutions. In man the order of increasing sensitivity to the four primary qualities is sweet, salt, sour, and bitter when the test solutions named above are used. (If saccharin is used to stimulate sweet, this quality has the lowest threshold except for bitter.) All the more complex tastes are compounds of these four primary qualities; an experienced taster can detect which of the four are present and which are absent in a complex taste.

Detection is aided because the tongue is not equally sensitive to the four primary qualities at the tip, sides, and back. The tongue is most sensitive to sweet at the tip, bitter at the back, and sour at the sides. Salt sensitivity is widespread, but somewhat greater at the tip. Common reactions to three of the four tastes confirm the different sensitivity of parts of the tongue. In tasting a pleasantly sweet substance, a person "purses" his lips to concentrate the solution near the tip of the tongue. In response to a very bitter substance, a person gags, which acts to remove the substance from the back of the tongue. Very sour solutions cause an open-mouthed frowning expression, which removes the solution from the sides of the tongue. In addition to the subjective primary nature of the four qualities and the different sensitivity of various parts of the tongue, narcotizing the tongue with cocaine gives evidence for four primary qualities. As the drug takes effect, taste sensations disappear in the following order: bitter, sweet, salt, and sour. This is not the same as their order of sensitivity—the drug is affecting the four qualities differently—the tongue is not just losing sensitivity so that the less sensitive qualities are lost before the more sensitive ones.

Stimuli

The nature of the adequate stimulus for two of the primary qualities is clearer than for the other two. Sour and salt are stimulated by **ions,** or electrically charged atoms

or molecules, in solution. Less is known about what effects the sweet or bitter tastes. The biggest mystery is how the receptors react to solutions to cause nerve impulses.

The sour taste is stimulated by the positively charged hydrogen ion (H^+), an ion that dissociates well from weak acids in solution. The effectiveness of the H^+ ion is modified by the **buffer** action of the saliva. Saliva contains substances that neutralize either acid H^+ ions or basic OH^- ions. The more readily an acid gives off H^+ ions in solution, the more sour it tastes. However, organic ions are more sour than inorganic ions that dissociate to give off an equal number of H^+ ions. Furthermore, not all acids are sour, for example, amino acids are sweet, and picric acid is bitter. The H^+ ion may be the most important agent in a sour stimulus, but other factors are involved.

Both the positive and negative ions of salts are important to their salty taste. (A positive ion is called a cation and a negative ion an anion–Chapter 4.) In table salt ($NaCl$) the cation (Na^+) seems more important than the anion (Cl^-). Other anions joined with Na, for example, $NaSO_4$, taste salty, and other cations joined with Cl, such as KCl, taste salty, although the taste varies in quality and intensity. $NaCl$ is the most effective stimulus; the other salts taste less salty, and some have a mixed salt and bitter taste. Salts often taste bitter at threshold concentrations as well. The size of the salt molecule (its molecular weight) seems related to whether a salt will taste salty or bitter; the larger salts such as sodium acetate often taste bitter. As with sour, ions are the most important part of the salt stimulus, but other factors are involved.

Less is known about what makes a stimulus taste sweet. The sweetest substances are organic compounds that do not break up into ions. Most of the sugars taste sweet if the carbon chain of their molecule is not too long, with sucrose the sweetest. There are exceptions to these rules, however. Some of the inorganic lead and beryllium *salts* taste sweet, and a slight change in the molecular geometry of a sugar that does not change its carbon chain can change its sweetness. Increases in molecular size (molecular weight) can cause a compound to change from sweet to bitter. An increase in concentration of some sweet solutions can also change their taste; saccharin is the sweetest substance known when diluted but it tastes bitter in concentrated solutions. About all that can be said is that the geometry of the molecule is the most important factor that is known to determine sweetness.

Of all the primary tastes the least is known about bitter. Although quinine solutions are the stimuli generally used for bitter in the laboratory, alkaloids and some complex inorganic salts are also bitter. The bitter taste does not depend on ionization, but some ionizing metals are bitter in solution. As previously noted, some salts taste bitter at threshold concentrations, some salts with large molecules taste bitter, some sugars with large molecules taste bitter, and concentrated sweet stimuli can change to bitter. Molecular size and/or shape is important, but that was what was said about sweet. Little is really known about either stimulus.

Nerve pathways

The nerve pathways serving taste are partly unique to taste and partly shared with somesthesis. Taste fibers from the tongue go to their own primary nucleus in the brainstem. However, the second-order fibers that arise here join second-order somesthetic fibers en route to the thalamus. The third-order fibers from the thalamus to the cortex are also anatomically mixed with somesthetic fibers. Most of the first-order taste fibers are carried in the seventh (anterior tongue) and ninth (posterior tongue) cranial nerves. Upon reaching the brainstem, they form a tract, the **tractus solitarius;** the excitation is passed on by the nucleus of that tract. The second-order fibers

join the medial lemniscus and end on the **arcuate** (face) **nucleus** of the thalamus, along with second-order somesthetic fibers representing the face. The third-order fibers project with somesthesis from the face on area 2 of the postcentral gyrus. They are adjacent to the part of the precentral motor area (area 4) controlling the chewing muscles. Sensory input from somesthetic sensations of the mouth, taste, and motor control of chewing are as close anatomically as they are functionally.

Physiology of taste

The physiology of the taste receptor is largely a mystery. Substances must be in solution to stimulate the hair cells—one cannot taste a piece of stainless steel because it does not dissolve in saliva—but little else is known about how the hair cells respond. Experimenters have stimulated individual hair cells with micropipettes, and recordings have been made of the electrical responses of individual hair cells and individual afferent neurons. These experiments will be briefly described. What is confusing is that some single receptors fire neurons in response to more than one of the primary qualities. There are *not* four kinds of receptors, each responding to one and only one of the four primary qualities. Some more complex *pattern* of input signals each quality. Furthermore, some receptors respond to temperature as well as to taste! Some chemical event in the receptor initiates nerve impulses in response to solutions. There is evidence that this event is absorptive and not enzymatic—that some weak chemical bonding to a specific site on the receptor is involved. Since individual hair cells respond to more than one primary stimulus quality, these hair cells may have more than one receptor size. In the end, perhaps a match can be found between the shape and charge of the molecules or ions that stimulate taste and the physical shape or charge of the receptor sites. This has been done for smell but not for taste.

Micropipette experiments. A glass tube can be heated and drawn out to a fine point that is smaller than a hair cell. (This is the same process described for making microelectrodes in Chapter 4.) When the tip of the tube is manipulated under a microscope, it can be placed on a single hair cell. Solutions can be forced through the tube in minute amounts to stimulate a single hair cell. Recordings of the electrical response of the hair cell or the neuron serving it show that the cell responds to more than one of the primary qualities.

Nerve fiber recording. In agreement with the micropipette experiments, single fibers from the ninth nerve of the cat respond to more than one stimulus solution washed over the tongue. Of course only the smaller fibers go to a single receptor—the larger ones go to two or more receptors. However, the only information the brain receives is nerve impulses; it cannot distinguish between two receptors served by the same fiber. The pattern of fiber response is shown in Table 10-1. Four classes of fibers were found; those responding to salt or acid (salt fiber), acid alone (acid fiber), quinine alone (quinine fiber), or acid, quinine, and water (water fiber). The code to the CNS would involve detecting salt when the salt fibers fired, sour when both salt and acid fibers fired, and bitter when the quinine fiber fired. (The cat does not sense sweet, but fibers responding to sweet have been found in the dog and rat.) Doubt has been

cast on the water fiber since the saliva is a little salty, and the response of the water fiber to salt may depend on the state of adaptation of the tongue. On the other hand, it may be a receptor that responds to all four qualities and could act as a receptor that signals increases in the concentration of any solution. It is evident in any case that the primary qualities depend on *patterns* of input rather than single receptor stimulation. In the rat, for example, receptors have been found that are sensitive to both sweet and salt. One set of these receptors is more sensitive to sweet than to salt, and the other is more sensitive to salt than to sweet. The *relative* amount of input in these two sets of receptors may determine whether the rat senses salt or sweet. Further refinements of the input pattern are possible. Individual fibers in the rat differ in their response to various salts. For example, individual salt fibers differ in their response to NaCl and KCl, but give similar reactions to NH_4Cl and NaCl. Yet rats can distinguish NH_4Cl from NaCl in behavioral tests. Finally, the receptor input pattern must be quite *labile* (changeable), as tests on taste adaptation in man show quite clearly. By different conditions of adaptation before the test, salt (NaCl) can be made to taste salt, sweet, sour, or bitter!

Receptor cell recording. Recording from microelectrodes planted in single taste receptors merely confirms the data from nerve cell recording. Individual cells respond to

Table 10-1. Response of single fibers of taste nerves in the cat[*]

Stimulus	Water fiber	Salt fiber	Acid fiber	Quinine fiber		Theoretical sensation
H_2O (salt 0.03M)	+	0	0	0	$\longrightarrow$	Water
NaCl (0.05M)	0	+	0	0	$\longrightarrow$	Salt
HCl (pH 2.5)	+	+	+	0	$\longrightarrow$	Sour
Quinine	+	0	0	+	$\longrightarrow$	Bitter

[*]From Cohen, M. J., Hagiwara, S., and Zotterman, Y.: Acta Physiol. Scandinav. **33:**316, 1955.
Single fibers of nerve IX either do respond (+) or do not respond (0) to solutions washed over the tongue, showing *patterns* of response to primary qualities (see text).

more than one of the four primary taste stimuli. This confirms the dependence of the CNS on *patterns* of receptor and nerve fiber input and shows that each taste receptor probably has different *sites* that are selectively sensitive to different taste stimuli.

Temperature response. Single afferent neurons in the cat respond to temperature as well as to taste. One investigator found that only two of twenty-eight units that he studied responded to taste alone. Some responded to taste and to cooling, others to taste, warming, and cooling, and still others to temperature changes only. Perhaps this is why taste thresholds are so intimately dependent on temperature.

Duplexity theory of taste

In agreement with the temperature response of taste cells, one investigator has devised an ingenious way of detecting which taste and temperature inputs are most closely related in sensation. He stimulated the two *sides* of the tongue with different solutions and asked the subject where the taste seemed to be located. When salt, sour, or cold stimulated one side of the tongue, and bitter, warm or sweet stimulated the other side, the subjects localized the sensations at the sides of the tongue. The sensations seemed separate. But when salt, sour, or cold were presented in pairs, or when bitter, warm, or sweet were paired, the sensation seemed to come from the center of the tongue. These results suggest that the tongue sensations formed two groups: (1) bitter, sweet, and warm and (2) salt, sour, and cold. The neural basis of the phenomenon is unknown, but might be related to the receptors described in the preceding paragraph, receptors that respond to both temperature and taste.

Taste phenomena

Taste receptors are affected by temperature and prior adapatation. Temperature affects the sensitivity of the receptors and therefore their input pattern and the taste that is perceived. Further, some receptors respond to both temperature and taste (see above). Adaptation to one taste can enhance or depress sensitivity to another taste, giving contrast or compensation effects. Unlike some of the other senses, the primary qualities do not fuse to give a "new" taste. There is so little fusion in taste that an experienced observer can always detect which of the four primary qualities are present and which are absent.

Taste thresholds. The threshold for taste varies according to the area of the tongue stimulated, as previously described. The tip of the tongue is most sensitive to sweet and salt, the sides to sour, and the back to bitter. For any of these areas, reliable absolute thresholds can be established for each of the four primary tastes, provided that the tongue is rinsed between stimuli to prevent adaptation effects. The temperature of the stimulus solution must also be held constant. Absolute thresholds vary with the duration of stimulation as well. Difference thresholds have also been reliably measured, and an equal-interval scale of taste units called "gusts" has been established. The Weber ratio for taste resembles that for olfaction, diminishing from about 1 to about 0.2 for each of the four qualities as intensity is increased. At any given intensity it is smaller for bitter than for sour, smaller for sour than for salt, and smaller for salt than for sweet—the order of decreasing taste sensitivity of the four qualities (using quinine, hydrochloric acid, sodium chloride, and sugar solutions). As explained in Chapter 7, the more sensitive inputs usually have lower Weber ratios.

Temperature. Extreme hot or cold temperatures decrease sensitivity to all the primary taste qualities except sour. If you add sugar to a very cold glass of iced tea, it will be too sweet when it reaches room temperature—but the same is true of sugaring a very hot cup of coffee. Taste is most sensitive in a range of temperatures (17°

to 42° C. or 62° to 107° F.) that are near body temperature (37° C. or 98.6° F.). Within this range of temperatures the four taste qualities react differently to temperature change. Sour sensitivity remains constant. With increasing temperature salt and bitter become less sensitive. Sweet is most sensitive at 35° C. (near body temperature) but less sensitive at colder or warmer temperatures. If you sugar coffee when it is very hot (outside the 17° to 42° C. range), it will be too sweet when lukewarm (37° C.), but not very sweet when cool (17° C.). Soup that is salted when fairly hot (42° C.) will become too salty as it cools.

Adaptation. Taste, like most other senses, shows loss of sensitivity with continuous stimulation. Taste adaptation can be made complete for a given stimulus and area of the tongue under laboratory conditions. Adaptation is most rapid at stimulus temperatures where the receptors are most sensitive. This makes us reasonably sure that it is the receptor and not the CNS that is adapting because stimulus temperature affects the receptor, not the CNS. It has also been found, as expected, that the stronger the stimulus for any quality, the longer the adaptation time and the longer the period required to recover normal sensitivity. However, complete adaptation occurs only in the laboratory. A substance being tasted under normal conditions is shifted over different areas of the tongue—new receptors are continually being stimulated. Presumably, even an all-day sucker would remain somewhat sweet at the end of the day. Partial adaptation is common, however. Experts have estimated that a person is 25 to 40% adapted most of the time to the various taste qualities encountered. Of course taste adaptation can be prevented by taste **contrast,** or mutual taste enchancement, when "opposite" qualities are involved. Adaptation results in the opposite effect—taste **compensation**—when adapting to one taste quality raises the taste threshold to another quality. This seldom occurs except with primary tastes under laboratory conditions. In practical affairs taste contrast is usually the rule. Adaptation to one complex of taste qualities is prevented by contrast with another complex taste of different qualities. This is the reason that gourmets drink wine with food; the taste of the wine prevents adaptation to the taste of the food and the taste of the food prevents adaptation to the taste of the wine, permitting maximum enjoyment of both. The wine is selected to match the intensity of the food stimulation so that one taste does not mask the other taste. For example, mild white wine goes with the bland taste of fish, and stronger tasting red wine is chosen to match the more intense flavor of beefsteak.

Cross-adaptation. "Pure" taste stimuli react differently from the more complex everyday tastes. Adaptation to one stimulus for a primary quality may even raise the threshold for another stimulus to the *same* quality (**cross-adaptation**). In other cases the phenomenon does not occur. All the sour-tasting acids that have been tested show cross-adaptation, but twenty-four salts show no cross-adaptation at all. The results for bitter and sweet stimuli are variable.

Contrast. Mutual enhancement occurs when stimuli for certain of the four taste qualities are presented together (**simultaneous induction**) or successively (**successive induction**). Contrast effects of this kind depend on the intensity of the stimuli and on the specific stimulus substances used. In general, salt and sweet stimuli enhance each other as do sweet and sour tastes. The latter effect is evident in the taste of Chinese sweet and sour spareribs. Under laboratory conditions salt or sugar can be shown to enhance the other two qualities as well as each other. Quinine enhances sensitivity to all qualities but sweet. Hydrochloric acid (sour) has no effect, except to enhance sweet. The effects depend on using sugar, quinine, hydrochloride acid, and salt as stimuli and require optimum concentrations.

Compensation. Certain tastes raise one another's threshold, especially salt and sour. Salted grapefruit or salted beer tastes neither as salt nor as sour as expected, for example. Compensations of this kind require stimulus intensities well above the normal threshold.

Fusion. As previously pointed out, there is little fusion in taste. In hearing, notes can blend in a chord or hues can blend to form a new color in vision. In taste, a trained observer can usually detect which of the four primary qualities are present because they do not blend to produce novel tastes (secondary qualities).

Complex phenomena. Taste blindness (**ageusia**) for one or more of the primary tastes is unknown, although individuals differ widely in their taste thresholds. Perhaps the patterned nature of the nerve impulse "code" for the primary qualities prevents complete taste blindness from loss of some inputs. A taste deficiency for one specific substance (phenylthiocarbamide, or PTC) has been found, however. About a third of the population seems insensitive to this substance except in very high concentrations. The defect seems inherited as a simple mendelian recessive characteristic (Chapter 2). PTC tastes bitter to normal persons, but has no taste for nontasters. Yet nontasters show a normal threshold for other bitter substances; therefore, the defect is specific to PTC and does not apply to bitter sensitivity in general.

Taste can be viewed as a factor in the control of motivated behavior rather than as a simple sensation. Since this aspect of taste involves complex brain functions in addition to the receptor input, detailed discussions will be left to Chapter 15. It is enough to note that ingestive behavior is often controlled by taste. For example, animals avoid bitter substances (which are usually nonnutritive) and accept sweet substances (which are usually nutritive). Specific hungers, or "appetites", that develop as a result of dietary deficiencies also control ingestive behavior. For example, increased avidity for salt can be produced in animals by adrenalectomy or insulin injections that increase the body's need for salt (Chapter 3). The result is a difference in preference behavior that does not seem to depend on any change in taste thresholds. The experimental animal selects lower concentrations of salt solutions in preference to pure water than does the normal animal. Tests of the threshold for salt taste, using nerve cell recordings, show that the experimental animal's threshold is unchanged. The problem is one of palatability rather than taste sensitivity. Palatability changes involve higher brain centers and the whole problem of the dynamics of motivation.

OLFACTION

Smell is much more difficult to study than is taste, but it is probably a more important sense, even in man. As previously explained, odor forms a large part of the "flavor" of food, which tastes "flat" when the olfactory passages are blocked, as in a head cold. Smell probably accounts for as much as two fifths of the "taste" of food. This seems reasonable; smell has been estimated to be 10,000 times more sensitive than taste, as measured by stimulus concentrations. (However, the technical difficulties of studying odor thresholds can generate threshold differences of 150 times, depending on the methods used.)

Olfaction is important in another way. It acts independently of taste as an exteroceptor. As an exteroceptor, or distance receptor, smell joins vision, audition, and somesthesis in exploring the environment. Smell is not as important in this sense to man as it is to four-legged animals—in man the nose is not as close to the ground whence most odors eminate. However, human reactions to odor may be subjectively as important to man as to animals. The perfume industry spends millions of dollars on odor research, and men as well as women spend more millions on preparations that either add smell to their bodies or remove it! Man subjects the air to substances in spray cans that cover unpleasant odors or, in some cases, make us anosmic so that we can smell neither pleasant nor unpleasant odors. The wine industry is as interested in the smell of their product as its taste and devotes as much energy to that end. Even used car dealers have found they can raise their prices and sell cars whose interior has been sprayed to give that "new car smell."

In the face of all this activity it is only recently that a useful theory of olfaction has been possible, and a list of seven primary olfactory qualities developed. Earlier efforts had been blocked by difficulties of stimulus presentation and receptor study. The olfactory receptors are so sensitive (as little as 0.00004 mg. of mercaptan per cubic meter of air is detectable) and so inaccessible (above the nasal passages) that control of stimulus concentrations is very poor. Recording from receptors or nerve tracts is equally difficult. In animal research it is difficult surgically to "get at" the receptor or nerve tracts serving olfaction because of their location. As a result less is known of the electrical characteristics of receptor or afferent neuron response to smell than is the case for taste—our knowledge is largely anatomical.

Earlier studies of smell resorted to cataloging the thresholds of various substances in an attempt to find odor groups whose thresholds were alike. It was assumed that these would form the primary odor qualities. Stimulus control difficulties impeded this approach. Recently, however, a theory based on examination of the physical shapes of odorous molecules has generated an acceptable list of primary qualities and some knowledge of how these molecules must affect the olfactory receptor. More is probably known now about receptor mechanisms in olfaction that is known about somesthesis or taste; our knowledge is more complete about vision and audition than smell, however.

Receptors

The olfactory receptors are located high in the nasal cavities (Fig. 10-3). They are

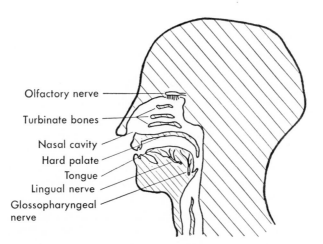

Fig. 10-3. Nasal passages. (From Pfaffman, C.: Studying the senses of taste and smell. In Andrews, R. C., editor: Methods of psychology, New York, 1948, John Wiley & Sons, Inc.)

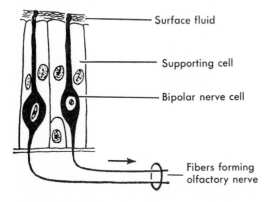

Surface fluid

Supporting cell

Bipolar nerve cell

Fibers forming
olfactory nerve

Fig. 10-4. Olfactory epithelium. (Illustration is upside down with respect to Fig. 10-3). Nerve fibers project to the olfactory bulb. (From Gardner, E. O.: Fundamentals of neurology, ed. 4, Philadelphia, 1963, W. B. Saunders Co.)

specialized hairlike endings on bipolar nerve cells (Fig. 10-4). The bipolar cells are surrounded by yellow-brown supporting cells, the whole being called the **olfactory epithelium.** The olfactory epithelium is located on either side of the **nasal septum** that completely separates two olfactory passages, one for each nostril. The two smell-sensitive areas are also called the **olfactory cleft.** Each covers about 2.5 cm.² (1 in.²) on either side of the nasal septum. The olfactory cleft is located in the "roof" of the nasal passages, high above the baffle-shaped **turbinate bones.** Inspired air reaches this olfactory epithelium via eddy currents created by the turbinate bones, especially with vigorous sniffing. Expired air stimulates the olfactory epithelium via the rear access to the **nasopharynx** (for interoception). The olfactory epithelium is covered with mucus that bathes the odor-sensing hair endings of the bipolar nerve cells. Presumably odorous vapor must dissolve in mucus to reach the hairlike endings of the olfactory receptors because the hairs barely reach the surface of the mucus covering them.

Nervous system

The axons of smell-sensitive bipolar cells pass through tiny holes in the bone that forms the roof of the nasal cavity and the floor of the brain case (Fig. 10-3). The fibers end in the **olfactory bulbs,** which are the swellings on the ends of the **olfactory tracts,** located on the base of the brain (Fig. 6-9). The short bipolar nerve cells are the true olfactory nerves that form cranial nerve I (the olfactory bulbs and tracts are part of the brain). The bipolar cells end in complex synapses in the olfactory bulbs, called **glomeruli.** Pathways in the olfactory tracts lead from here to the **prepyriform area** of the ventral surface of the cerebral cortex. This projection area is the oldest part of the cortex, phylogenetically, since the cerebral hemispheres originated as a correlating center for smell. Olfaction also shows its antiquity in being the only sensory input that does not relay excitation in the thalamus or related centers. Other pathways lead from the olfactory bulb via the olfactory tract to a "loop circuit" under the corpus callosum, involving the amygdaloid nucleus and hypothalamus. These paths are secondary, however, and olfactory sensitivity does not depend on them. Excitation traveling back and forth in loop circuits in the olfactory bulbs may act to "amplify" the effect of receptor activity exciting the central nervous system.

Stimulation

Many ingenious efforts have been made to stimulate the sensitive olfactory receptors in a controlled and quantitative manner. One of the earlier methods used was an **olfactometer.** The instrument was based on a hard rubber cylinder that was impregnated with odorous material. The cylinder fitted loosely over a graduated tube, the other end of which fitted the nostril. Thrusting the tube into the cylinder exposed less of the odorous cylinder to incoming air; as the tube was withdrawn, a greater length of the cylinder was exposed to air entering the tube. In this manner absolute and difference thresholds could be obtained. A crude scale of "olfacties," or subjectively equal odor increments, was also produced. The effects of presenting the stimulus to one nostril or two, adaptation, and the presentation of different stimuli to the two nostrils were studied. Rather variable data result from the subject's uncontrolled "sniff" volume, however.

Other investigators have used a **blast olfactometer.** An odorous liquid is contained in a small bottle with two outlets. One goes to a hypodermic syringe that permits a known volume of air pressure to be added to the bottle. The other outlet, closed by a pinchcock, goes to the subject's nostril. When the pinchcock is released, a known volume of odorous air is blasted up the nostril. The volume depends on the amount of air pressure, which is controlled by the syringe. Threshold determinations by this method are disturbed by cutaneous sensations from the air "blast." The subject may detect the presence of the stimulus, or differences in its intensity, by somesthesis rather than odor.

A more fruitful approach to odor investigation is the interaction of odors with one another. This approach uses the **mixing olfactometer.** Air is bubbled through several odorous substances via different tubes. The tubes are led to a mixer that can select any combination of them. The result is diluted by a known flow of outside air and led to a nose cone for smelling. Proportions of odorous mixes can be rather precisely controlled.

The most elaborate attempt to control odor, however, is the **olfactorium.** This is a small room, the whole atmosphere of which is under control and can be rapidly changed. A freshly bathed subject (to eliminate body odors), wearing an odorless plastic garment, occupies the room and reports his odor sensations while the room air is rapidly charged with odor-bearing air of known characteristics.

Thresholds. The findings for absolute and difference thresholds for odor vary according to the method used, and olfactory data are not usually very reliable. An absolute threshold as low as 0.00004 mg. per cubic meter of air has been obtained for mercaptan, one of the most odorous substances known. This is about one molecule in 50 trillion. However, a 20 cc. sniff would contain 10 trillion molecules of the substance. Odor sensitivity does not compare with visual or auditory sensitivity for the amount of molecular energy involved in the absolute threshold, but the threshold is lower than that for taste or somesthesis. Unlike other senses with low absolute thresholds, the difference threshold is rather high for smell. Although the absolute threshold for odor is much less than that for taste, the difference thresholds are comparable, and the Weber ratio is about the same. Determinations of $\Delta I/I$ depend on intensity. For one example, the ratio varies from about 1.0 at low intensities to about 0.2 at high intensities for India rubber.

Sensory mechanisms

To some extent an odorous substance must be (1) volatile, (2) soluble in water, and (3) soluble in fat. A *volatile* substance evaporates molecules into the air so that they may reach the olfactory receptors. Some powerful odors such as musk are not very volatile, but since one is so sensitive to them, relatively few molecules need reach the receptors for detection. Volatility is a necessary but not sufficient condition for odor; pure water, for example, is highly volatile, but odorless. Most of the organic compounds are both odorous and volatile, whereas most inorganic compounds are neither. Exceptions include the halogens (fluorine, chlorine, iodine, bromine), certain sulfides (for example, hydrogen sulfide smells like rotten eggs), nitrogen oxides, and ammonia. *Water solubility* is also related to odor. Presumably, odorous molecules must dissolve in the mucus covering the receptors to reach them, and mucus has a high water content. Exceptions can be found among the alcohols, however. *Fat solubility* may be related to odor because the cell membranes of the receptors contain fat and would be most sensitive to compounds that dissolve in cellular fat. Most fat-soluble compounds are odorous if they are also water-soluble. Yet exceptions can also be found to this rule; acetone is odorous, but has low fat solubility. Fat and water solubility may, like volatility, be a necessary but not sufficient condition for odor. Very odorous compounds may require less solubility because relatively few molecules need reach the receptors.

Theories of olfactory receptor mechanisms

There are several theories of how the olfactory receptor works, but only the most recent version predicts odors with reasonable accuracy. Olfactory theories fall in two groups, viewing the receptor mechanism as being either *vibrational* or *chemical* in nature. Vibrational theories assert that the receptor acts because of the way odorous substances absorb, refract, or scatter light. For example, most odorous compounds strongly absorb infrared wavelengths; this has led to the theory that infrared ray absorption by the stimulus is the essential part of the receptor process. Most odorous substances also absorb ultraviolet light, and this has led to a similar theory about ultraviolet light. A third vibrational theory notes that many odorous substances reflect light of a different wavelength than they receive (the Raman shift). However, all the vibrational theories are embarrassed by several important exceptions to the rule each proposes—odorous substances that do not show appropriate vibrational characteristics. Chemical theories view the receptor event as chemical in nature. Older versions, however, were not able to classify odorous substances according to their chemical nature in any manner that did not have important exceptions. Enzyme theo-

ries came later, proposing that odorous substances interferred with or facilitated reactions in the receptor that require a catalyst (Chapter 2). Later work showed that no known enzyme system can account for the odors of very dilute mixtures. The latest version of an old chemical theory, however, is the most promising. It is based on the *physical shape* or *electrical charge* of odorous molecules and is call the **stereochemical theory.** The theory does not specify the chemical event that is initiated in the receptor by the odorous molecule. The theory does state that the molecule must physically "fit" one or more of five *receptor sites,* or "holes," on the receptor hair endings or else be attracted by *positively* or *negatively charged* sites on the receptors. The seven sites, when individually stimulated, give rise to seven primary odor qualities. Stimulation of combinations of the primary sites gives rise to secondary, or mixed, odors. This occurs when a molecule will fit more than one site, depending on how it is oriented, or when a molecule is flexible enough to adapt itself to more than one site.

Olfactory qualities: stereochemical theory. The idea that odorous substances give off molecules that must fit variously shaped "pores" in the receptors is an old one. In modern form it began with the observation that the molecules of most odorous sub-

Table 10-2. Primary odors and familiar stimuli that resemble them[*]

Primary quality	Familiar stimulus
Camphoraceous	Mothballs, camphor
Musky	Angelica root oil
Floral	Roses
Minty	Peppermint candy
Ethereal	Dry cleaning fluid
Pungent	Vinegar
Putrid	Rotten egg

[*]Based on data from Amoore, J. E.: Ann. N. Y. Acad. Sci. **116:**457-476, 1964.

stances had carbon chains (Chapter 2) four to eight carbons long. It was noted that a slight change in molecular geometry made a big difference in odor. The organic chemistry literature was searched for data on odors. These are given in Table 10-2, together with familiar stimulus examples. Information was then collected on the physical shapes of molecules stimualting the seven primary odors. In five cases odors that smelled alike had molecules that were shaped alike. In the other two cases they had a similar charge. **Pungent** molecules had a deficiency of electrons, a positive charge, and would be attracted to a negatively charged (excess electrons) site. **Pu-**

Receptor site   Odorant molecule   Site plus molecule

Ethereal

Camphor-aceous

Musky

Floral

Minty

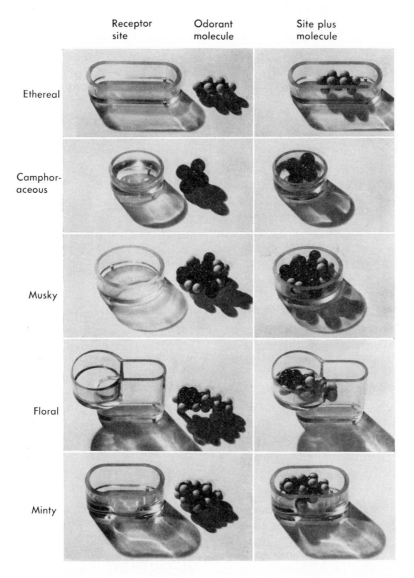

Fig. 10-5. Models of olfactory receptor sites and molecules that "fit" them in the stereochemical theory of odor. (From Amoore, J. E.: Ann. N. Y. Acad. Sci. **116**:457-476, 1964.)

trid molecules had excess electrons, were negatively charged, and are presumably attracted to a positively charged (deficient electrons) site. Models were made of the molecules stimulating primary odors and the shape of the receptor sites that would fit such molecules predicted and modeled (Fig. 10-5). The **ethereal** site is a narrow slot, the **camphoraceous** a hemispherical basin, the **musky** a larger eliptical flat-bottomed pan, the **floral** keyhole-shaped, and the **minty** wedge-shaped. Tests of the theory have been made, predicting primary or mixed odors from the shape or charge of over 200 compounds, with only one prediction that seemed incorrect. With the use of a mixing olfactometer to compare odors, subjects cannot tell the difference between substances whose molecules fit the same receptor site. New organic molecules have been synthesized to fit receptor site models and the resulting odor correctly predicted. Complex odors have been synthesized by mixing primary odors and the complex predicted. The theory has an impressive amount of evidence in its support. The stereochemical theory is incomplete because it does not specify the chemical event that occurs at the receptor site. However, it has produced a list of seven very promising primary olfactory qualities and has described accurately the nature of their stimuli.

Olfactory phenomena

Adaptation. In common with most other senses, olfaction adapts rather readily. Adaptation is complete for most single odors, the time required depending on the intensity of the odor (usually varying from one to ten minutes under laboratory conditions). This fact reduces the effect of the most expensive perfume to an initial impression! On the other hand, even the odor of a fertilizer factory is unnoticable after twenty to thirty minutes. Adaptation to single odors can be dangerous, as when miners do not detect a gradual increase in methane gas or a leak in a household gas line permeates the air too gradually and the receptors adapt before it is noticed. Absence of smell stimuli for a time results in an increased sensitivity to various odors that amounts to 10 to 40%, depending on the test odor. Apparently one is partly odor adapted most of the time. This would include one's own body odor, when "even our best friends won't tell us." It is difficult to predict, however, what effect adaptation to one odor will have on another odor. Adaptation to one odor may raise or lower the threshold to another odor. It may also result in a change in quality for the second odor. For example, adaptation to camphor raises the odor threshold to eau de cologne, but this does not affect the threshold for benzaldehyde. **Compensation** between odors also occurs; for example, the odors of balsam and beeswax cancel one another. Odor often changes quality with changes in stimulus intensity. Ionone, a substance used in perfume, changes its odor from cedar-wood to violets with decreasing intensity. Perhaps adaptation effects in complex odors can be rationalized in terms of the stereochemical theory, but the attempt has not yet been made.

Anosmia. Complete lack of smell sensitivity is rare, but cases are known. It seems to be an inherited defect. **Anosmia** may also result from long-standing nasal irritation or from blocking of the nasal passages, as in a head cold. The anosmic individual can still "smell" substances injected into the bloodstream, which shows that some functions of the receptors are intact. The chemical nature of the receptor process is supported by this observation and the fact that certain odor thresholds (for example, exaltolide) vary with the estrogen level of the blood and therefore with the menstral cycle in women. Temporary, partial, or complete anosmia can result from water in the nose, anesthesia, and other conditions. Formalin (formaldehyde) in weak solutions vaporizes to cause anosmia. This, rather than adaptation, explains why the formalin you smell so strongly when you enter a biology laboratory (where it is used to preserve animals for dissection) becomes odorless so quickly. Some household deodorants use formalin together with a masking odor to "cover" the formalin smell until the receptors quit functioning. Other deodorizers, of course, use only a masking odor.

SUMMARY

The senses normally and adequately stimulated by substances in solution are the chemical senses. They include the common chemical sense, gustation, and olfaction. The common chemical sense is pain sensitivity to dissolved irritants in the mucous membranes. It is most frequently stimulated by spicy foods in the mouth, but irritating vapors can also stimulate the eyes, which are more sensitive, and the nasal passages, which are still more sensitive. The nerve pathways are identical with those for skin pain, but the sensory quality seems different because the usual stimulus is different from that for skin pain. Adaptation is rare because chemical stimulation is a process that is seldom constant, and the receptor has no chance to adapt.

Gustation is limited to receptors on the tongue. The sensations commonly called "taste" include common chemical sensitivity, somesthesis from the mouth, and olfaction as well. The tongue receptors give rise to primary sensations of sweet, salt, sour, and bitter, in ascending order of sensitivity, when stimulated by solutions of sucrose, sodium chloride, hydrochloric acid, and quinine, respectively. The taste receptors are in papillae on the tongue, "moatlike" and "islandlike" structures with taste buds lining their walls. The receptors are developed from ordinary epithelial cells under the influence of sensory appropriation from nerves VII (anterior tongue) and IX (posterior tongue) and under the influence of the gonadal hormones. The tongue is most sensitive to salt and sweet at the tip, sour at the sides, and bitter at the back;

the center is insensitive. These four primary qualities do not fuse to give novel secondary sensations.

Sour is primarily stimulated by the H^+ ion. Salt sensations are mostly caused by Na^+ cations and/or Cl^- anions. Sweet substances are organic molecules with short carbon chains, and bitter substances include quinine, alkaloids, and complex inorganic salts. Salts often taste bitter at threshold, and concentrated sweet stimuli can taste bitter. Molecular size and shape are important in sweet and bitter stimuli. The nerve pathways for taste have their own primary nucleus—the nucleus of the tractus solitarius—but the second- and third-order neurons follow the somesthetic pathways to the cortex via the thalamus.

Experiments with microelectrode recording in the nerve pathway and with micropipettes stimulating individual taste receptors show that there are *not* four types of taste receptor, one for each quality. Some complex *pattern* of input signals each quality because individual case receptors respond to more than one quality. In addition, taste neurons serve two or more receptors, as shown in single-fiber experiments with cats. Some fibers may signal only intensity of any quality. Other neurons respond to both temperature and taste. In man taste stimuli to the sides of the tongue are perceived separately when salt, sour, or cold are paired or when bitter, warm, and sweet are paired; other pairings are localized in the center of the tongue.

Taste sensitivity is also dependent on stimulus temperature, thresholds for all four qualities being lowest in a range near body temperature. Within this range, difference thresholds for each quality result in Weber ratios that vary from about 1 to 0.2 as intensity is increased. Taste adaptation is most rapid in the same temperature range where the receptors are most sensitive, indicating that the adaptation is caused by the receptor and not the CNS. Complete adaptation is not found outside the laboratory because the substance being tasted is moved about the mouth from one receptor to another.

For complex tastes, adaptation may be prevented by taste contrast, drinking wine with food being an example. Different stimuli for the same qualities may or may not affect one another by cross-adaptation. Acids (sour) show cross-adaptation, salts do not, and bitter and sweet stimuli vary. Of the primary qualities, salt or sour enhances sweet if standard stimuli and concentrations are used. Salt and sour show taste compensation. There is little fusion in the primary taste qualities. Ageusia is unknown, although taste blindness for a bitter response to PTC can be inherited. Taste is a controlling factor in motivated behavior, although palatability is best studied in the chapter on motivation.

Olfaction is important as an exteroceptor to explore the environment as well as an interoceptor, where it forms part of "taste." Although it is not as useful an exteroceptor for man as compared to other animals, man's reactions to smell are equally important and are basic to the perfume, wine, and deodorant industries. However, research on smell has been hampered by the sensitivity of the receptor and its inaccessability. Little is known of the physiology of smell. The receptors are hairlike endings on bipolar nerve cells that are bathed in mucus. They are located to either side of the nasal septum on the roof of the nasal cavity above the turbinate bones. The sensitive areas are called the nasal cleft, or olfactory epithelium. Eddy currents of air created by the turbinate bones reach the receptor from the nostrils or the nasopharynx. Vaporized substances in the air stimulate the bipolar cell receptors. The axons of the bipolar cells reach the olfactory bulbs through holes in the bony roof of the nasal cavity and constitute cranial nerve I. Synapses, called glomeruli, transfer the excitation to second-order neurons going to the prepyriform area of the cortex. Reverberatory circuits may amplify the input.

Early attempts to stimulate the receptors in a controlled manner involved the olfactometer and blast olfactometer. Newer techniques include the olfactorium and mixing olfactometer. Threshold data vary widely according to the method used as well as the stimulus odor. Despite the sensitivity of the receptor, the difference thresholds are comparable to those for taste. Volatility, water solubility, and fat solubility seem necessary conditions for smell stimuli. The stimulus must reach the receptors as vapor, dissolve in watery mucus, and affect receptors whose membrane includes fat. Most organic compounds meet these conditions; most inorganic compounds do not.

Theories of how the receptor reacts have been vibrational or chemical in nature. The vibrational theories have been based on infrared or ultraviolet absorption or on the Raman shift. Chemical theories have proposed that enzymes are involved. The most promising theory is a new version of an old chemical explanation, the stereochemical theory. The theory states that an odorous molecule must physically "fit" one of five receptor sites or be attached to a negatively charged or a positively charged site. The seven primary odor qualities that result are ethereal, camphoraceous, musky, floral, minty, pungent, and putrid. The shapes of the receptor sites have been predicted from the shapes of the molecules. Subjects cannot tell the difference between odors whose molecules would fit the same receptor sites, and the odors of synthesized molecules have been predicted. Flexible molecules that would fit more than one site have mixed odors that are equally predictable. The theory is incomplete because it does not specify the chemical event that occurs at the receptor site.

In other olfactory phenomena adaptation to single odors is complete in less than a half hour, usually in one to ten minutes. An individual is usually 10 to 40% odor adapted under normal conditions. Adaptation to one odor may lower the threshold to another odor (contrast), raise the threshold to another odor (compensation), or change the quality of another odor. These effects have been unpredictable so far. Complete anosmia occurs, but this is rare. It may be inherited or caused by damage to, or blocking of, the nasal passages. Since even anosmics can "smell" substances in the bloodstream, the receptor events are probably chemical in nature. Temporary anosmia can also be caused by vaporized formaldehyde.

READINGS

Amoore, J. E., Johnston, J. W., and Rubin, M.: The stereochemical theory of odor, Sci. Amer. **210**:42-49, Feb., 1964. (W. H. Freeman Co. Reprint No. 297.)

Buddenbrock, W. von: The senses, Ann Arbor, Mich., 1958, University of Michigan Press.

Haagen-Smit, A. J.: Smell and taste, Sci. Amer. **186**:28-32, March, 1952. (W. H. Freeman Co. Reprint No. 404.)

Mueller, C. G.: Sensory psychology, Englewood Cliffs, N. J., 1965, Prentice-Hall, Inc., (Chaps. 5 and 6).

Pfaffman, C.: The afferent code for sensory quality, Amer. Psychol. **14**:226-232, May, 1959. (Bobbs-Merrill Reprint No. P-275.)

Chapter 11

Audition

OVERVIEW

The sense of hearing, or audition, is the subject of this chapter. Audition is the most complex sensory input studied so far (vision is equally complex if not more so). To understand audition requires some knowledge of (1) the nature of the *physical energy* that provides the sensory stimulus and (2) the anatomy of the auditory mechanism. With this background (3) the *physiology* and (4) the *psychophysics* of hearing can be understood. Finally, such topics aid study of (5) the complex phenomena of hearing. These are the topics of the chapter and their order of presentation.

The stimulus energy will be explained first in its simplest form, a sine wave of periodic changes in air pressure. The sine wave "tone" has simple characteristics of amplitude, frequency, and phase. More complex tones are also periodic waves of sound energy. Complex periodic waves are subject to a frequency analysis that reduces them to sine waves; aperiodic waves ("noise") cannot be consistently reduced to sine waves. The anatomy of the receptor mechanism that responds to sound energy is the next topic. The parts of the outer, middle, and inner ears change air pressure waves into vibrations of receptor cells in the organ of Corti. The nerve impulses that result are carried to the brain along the pathways described next. The organization of the input is fur-

ther improved by output pathways from the brain back to sensory nuclei and receptors.

The physiology and psychophysics of hearing study how such sensory and nervous mechanisms permit the brain to analyze pitch and loudness. Pitch detection may depend on nerve impulse frequency for low tones. For high tones, pitch is analyzed by the location of stimulus effects on hair cells along the length of the organ of Corti. A different set of hair cells respond to increased vibrations of the organ of Corti in detecting loudness. The "generator potential" set up by both sets of hair cells (the cochlear microphonic) probably causes sensory nerve impulses. Disturbance of any part of the auditory mechanism can cause auditory defects. Different kinds of auditory defects result from impairment of outer, middle, and inner ear mechanisms. The psychophysics of hearing involves the following major attributes of sound: (1) quality (pitch), (2) intensity (loudness), (3) extensity (volume), (4) duration, and (5) density. Thresholds and adaptation phenomena are discussed. The chapter concludes with a discussion of the following complex auditory phenomena: (1) aural harmonics, (2) combination tones, (3) consonance and dissonance, (4) masking, (5) speech phenomena, and (6) auditory localization.

PHYSICS OF SOUND

Any solid body will vibrate when struck, however brief its motion. The vibrations of some solid objects are regular, consistent, or periodic. This is true of a **tuning fork,** for example (Fig. 11-1). The regular movements of the tuning fork have a characteristic frequency or rate as well as a characteristic amplitude or extent. The motions of the tines of the tuning fork cause it to strike molecules of air. The air molecules collide with one another to transmit energy from molecule to molecule as the molecules vibrate back and forth. The energy radiates in all directions from the vibrating source. Since the vibrating source has a consistent frequency and amplitude of vibration, so do the air molecules. Air pressure is determined by how close together the molecules are. Since the air molecules are colliding with one another and then moving apart in a regular fashion, waves of air pressure *change* constitute sound. Pressure changes of consistent frequency and amplitude *are* the sound that radiates outward from the sound source.

Sine wave

Certain uniform bodies vibrate with a simple motion. The sound waves they produce—alternatively compressed and rarefied air molecules—have a simple pattern of air pressure change. The molecules alternately strike one another in a compressed area and are driven apart in a rarefied area. Since air pressure is merely the density of air molecules, pressure at a given point will be first above, then below, normal pressure. A graph of the pressure changes of air with distance from the vibrating source gives a

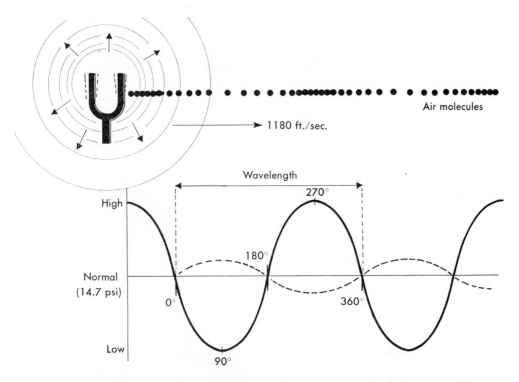

Fig. 11-1. Characteristics of sound energy. Vibrations of a tuning fork cause collisions of air molecules that radiate air pressure variations in all directions at 1080 feet per second, variations that can be plotted as a simple sine wave. The sine wave has characteristics of amplitude, wavelength, frequency, and phase.

simple sine wave of air pressure change at any given instant (Fig. 11-1).

Amplitude. The amount of compression and rarefaction of the air molecules will depend on how hard the tuning fork is struck and therefore on how far the tines of the fork vibrate back and forth to condense and rarefy the air. **Amplitude** is the total amount of air pressure change from condensation to rarefaction. Changes in amplitude are detected by the ear as changes in **loudness.** The intensity of the stimulus is proportional to the square of the amplitude of the pressure change.

Frequency. Different tuning forks will vibrate at different rates, each having a characteristic **frequency** of vibration. Frequency, or rate of vibration, is usually stated in cycles per second, abbreviated as cps. A cycle is one complete back-and-forth vibration of the tuning fork and results in first a compression, next a rarefaction, and, finally, a return to normal pressure (Fig. 11-1). If the tuning fork vibrates rapidly, it has a high rate of vibration, or high frequency; if it vibrates slowly, it has a low frequency. The **wavelength** of a sine wave of pressure change is the distance over which a single cycle of air pressure change extends at a given instant. High-frequency, or rapid, vibrations result in short wavelengths. Low-frequency vibrations have long wavelengths. (The amplitude may remain the same for high- and low-frequency vibrations.) The relationship between frequency and wavelength is usually constant because sound waves travel at a fixed rate. In air, sound travels at 1080 feet per second at sea level. A compression and rarefaction wavelength of 1080 feet could pass a given point one time each second if the sound has a frequency of 1 cps. If the wavelength were 108 feet, the sound wave would pass a given point ten times per second, for a frequency of 10 cps. Frequency and wavelength can therefore be translated into one another. Frequency is usually the term used in sound. The ear detects differ-

ences in frequency as differences in **pitch.** In a denser medium than air (for example, water), sound travels at a higher rate since the molecules are closer together and need not travel so far to strike one another. As a result, wavelengths are shorter and frequencies are higher. For example, an outboard motor has a higher-pitched sound when one listens to it with his head under water. At high altitudes in air the molecules are farther apart and must travel farther to strike one another. As a result, sound transmission is slower and apparent frequencies are lower. The rate at which sound moves in air can be appreciated by watching someone chop wood a half mile away. The sound will require more than 2 seconds to reach you after the axeman swings—he may have raised the ax for a second stroke before you hear the sound of the first stroke.

Phase. A complete sound pressure wave goes from normal to compression to normal to rarefaction to normal again. The point reached by the alternating pressure wave at a given time and place can be specified in terms of 360 degrees as a complete cycle (Fig. 11-1). The beginning point could be taken as 0 degrees, with the first rarefaction peak as 90 degrees, normal as 180 degrees, compression as 270 degrees, and normal again as 360 degrees (Fig. 11-1). If one sine wave is in compression while the other is in rarefaction, the first would be at 90 degrees in the cycle and the second at 270 degrees. They would therefore be 270 minus 90 degrees, or 180 degrees, *out of phase* and exert opposite effects on air pressure at that instant.

Measurements of amplitude and loudness

Frequency is measured in cycles per second and phase in degrees; little has been said about measuring the amplitude of a sound wave. A complex average of the amount of pressure variation over each cycle is sometimes used by engineers, who integrate the square root of the mean square of pressure variation. This is done because a high-frequency tone with more rapid pressure variations contains more energy than a low-frequency tone of the same amplitude. However, most sound amplitude measurements are made to apply to human use. A physical intensity scale has therefore been developed that matches the characteristics of the human ear as closely as possible—the **decibel scale**. The zero point of the scale approximates the absolute threshold of the human ear—an energy level of 0.0002 dyne/cm.^{2} for a 1000-cycle tone. (A dyne is the amount of energy required to accelerate 1 gram at 1 cm./sec.^{2} The zero point is near the point at which one would "hear" the random motion of molecules caused by heat!) Decibels of increase in intensity are a scale based on the **bel** scale. The bel scale is chosen because it is a logarithmic scale in which the physical units increase in size at higher intensities (Chapter 7). The human ear requires a larger

increase in sound intensity for the same loudness difference, with more intense stimuli. If zero bels is 0.0002 dyne/cm.^{2}, 1 bel is $10^1 \times 0.0002$ dyne/cm.^{2} and 2 bels is $10^2 \times 0.0002$ dyne/cm.^{2}, and so on. However, a smaller unit is required to match the difference threshold of the human ear; therefore the decibel, or "tenth" of a bel, is used. To be technical, the number of decibels between two sound intensities, I_1 and I_2, is $10 \log I_1/I_2$. The decible intensities of certain common sounds are given in Fig. 11-2.

Types of sound wave

The major characteristics of sound waves have been explained so far in terms of air pressure changes from a simple vibrating body that produces a simple **sine wave** of pressure variation with time or distance. The change is *simple* and *periodic* and results in a **simple tone** (Fig. 11-1). A complex body may vibrate with more than one frequency—the pressure waves of sound that result may be periodic or aperiodic. If the complex vibrating body has many parts, each with its own characteristic frequency and amplitude of vibration, several sine waves of pressure variation may be produced at once (Fig. 11-3). As these sine waves come in and out of phase because of their differing frequencies of vibration, they will alternately reinforce and cancel each other, as far as air pressure changes are concerned. A complex but repeated wave pattern will result—a **complex periodic wave** that is heard as a **complex tone**. However, if the component parts of the vibrating body begin and end vibrating at different times, the complex wave will not repeat itself—it will be **aperiodic**. Aperiodic complex vibrations constitute **noise**, especially when many high-frequency (high-pitched) components are in the complex. As a result, noise is harsh-sounding and variable in character.

Frequency analysis. Frequency analysis consists of analyzing a complex periodic tone into its component sine waxes of pres-

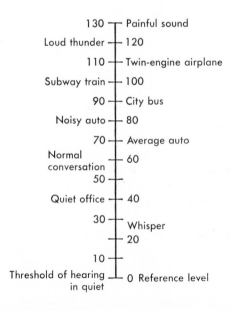

Fig. 11-2. Decibel intensities of some common sounds. (From Chapanis, A., Garner, W. R., and Morgan, C. T.: Applied experimental psychology, New York, 1949, John Wiley & Sons, Inc.)

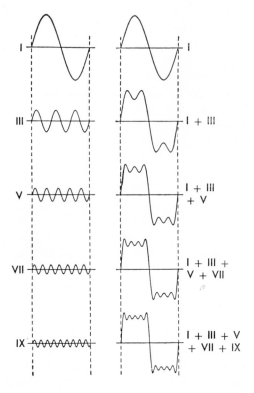

Fig. 11-3. Components of a complex sound wave. As the sine waves shown on the left are added to the fundamental wave at the top, increasingly complex periodic waves shown at the right result. (From Newman, E. B.: Hearing. In Boring, E. G., Langfeld, H. S., and Weld, H. P., editors: Foundations of psychology, New York, 1948, John Wiley & Sons, Inc.)

sure change (Fig. 11-3). These sine waves have frequencies that are related to one another in a lawful way. The physical basis for the frequency analysis is best understood in terms of a simple example such as the sound produced by plucking a violin string.

Harmonics

If a violin string is plucked, it will vibrate up and down, alternately compressing and rarefying the air molecules. The sine wave of pressure change that results will have a wavelength of twice the length of the violin string (Fig. 11-4). The length of the string can only represent either the compression or the rarefaction half of the cycle of pressure change at any given moment as it vibrates back and forth. This simple vibration represents the largest movement of the string, and the resulting frequency is called the **fundamental,** or **first harmonic,** frequency. However, the string also has a smaller "double vibration" —it vibrates in halves (Fig. 11-4). The double vibration will produce a sine wave of half the wavelength and twice the frequency of the fundamental tone. The double vibration is the **first overtone,** or **second harmonic.** The string also vibrates in thirds to produce the second overtone, or third harmonic, and so on. The frequencies of these sine waves are a function of their wavelengths. If the fundamental, or first, harmonic has a frequency of n, the first overtone, or second harmonic, has a frequency of 2n, the second overtone, or third harmonic, has a frequency of 3n, and so on. This relationship between the fundamental frequency and the overtone frequencies is called **Fourier's law.** Of course these simple sine waves combine into a complex periodic wave in the manner shown in Fig. 11-3.

Resonance

If the violin string is stretched between two points in open air, the amplitude of the fundamental frequency and overtones would bear a simple relation to one another. The first overtone would be greater than the second, the second greater than the third, and so on; the complex periodic wave of pressure change would be formed accordingly. However, the string is stretched across the body of a "sound box," or resonance chamber, the violin. Each part of the violin has a frequency with which it naturally vibrates when struck. The size of the air chamber in the violin also reinforces sound waves—those whose wavelength is a multiple of the length of the sound cham-

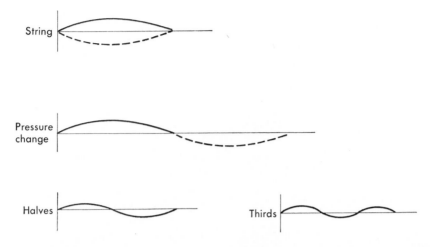

Fig. 11-4. Vibrations of a violin string. The string vibrates at a fundamental frequency whose corresponding wavelength is twice the string's length. Overtones occur when the string also vibrates in halves, thirds, and so on (see text).

ber. The parts of the violin can be struck with air molecules at their natural frequency. When this occurs, they will vibrate, or **resonate**, to amplify that frequency. This will increase the amplitude of certain overtone frequencies. Although the fundamental frequency will be the largest component of the complex wave, various overtones will be increased in size in a pattern unique to the violin. The relative size of various overtones will be different for the same fundamental note played on a trumpet. This variation in overtone pattern is recognized by the human ear as a difference in **timbre**. The violin has more parts that resonate with lower overtones; the trumpet has more parts that resonate with higher overtones. Their air chambers differ in a similar way. As a result, the overtone pattern of the violin has a louder pattern of low overtones than the trumpet. This is why the same note played on the two instruments "sounds different" in timbre.

Beats

Two fundamental frequencies may be sounded from two sources that differ by 1 cps in frequency. They will be in compression at the same time once each second and in rarefaction at the same time once each second. This is, one compression each second will be *in phase*, or reinforced in amplitude, and so will one rarefaction each second. (At other times the two sound waves will partially cancel each other by being out of phase. You can prove this to yourself by drawing two sine waves over a distance representing 1 second—one wave of two cycles and one of three cycles.) The tone that results when two sources differ by 1 cps will sound louder and softer once each second—one **beat** per second—because of one large pressure variation each second. If the two tones are two cycles apart, they will beat twice per second, and so on. This phenomenon is used by a piano tuner in tuning a piano string to exactly match the frequency of a tuning fork. He sounds the piano note and tuning fork together. As he tightens the string to bring its frequency up to that of the tuning fork, the difference in frequency diminishes, and the number of beats per second decrease. If he "overshoots," the number of beats per second will increase as the frequency of the piano note rises over that of the tuning fork, and

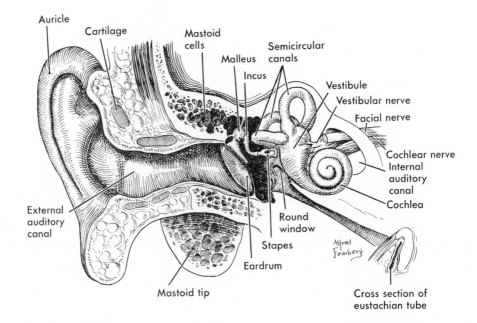

Fig. 11-5. Semidiagrammatic drawing of the ear. For description of the parts shown here, see text. (From Davis, H., and Silverman, S. R., editors: Hearing and deafness, rev. ed., New York, 1960, Holt, Rinehart, & Winston, Inc.)

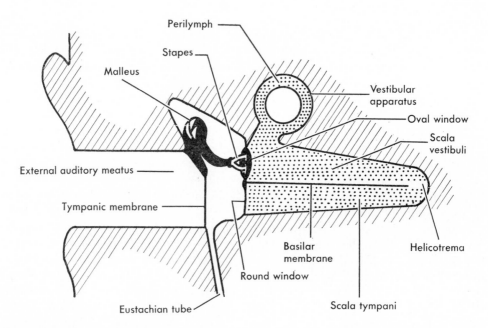

Fig. 11-6. Schematic drawing of the ear. (Redrawn from von Békésy, G.: Pflüger Arch. Ges. Physiol. **236**:58-76, 1935.)

the frequency difference between them increases. Beats can be heard on other occasions in everyday life; for example, the exhaust notes of two trucks travelling at nearly the same engine speed can be heard to beat.

ANATOMY OF THE AUDITORY MECHANISM

Analysis of the air pressure variations that form sound has shown the complexity of this form of stimulus. What kind of receptor apparatus can transduce differences in sound frequency, amplitude, and overtone patterns into nerve impulses in such a way that the brain can detect the corresponding differences in pitch, loudness, and timbre? As a receptor, the auditory apparatus changes air pressure vibrations into vibrations of a fluid medium. The fluid vibrations, in turn, set off nerve impulses by acting on the hair cells of the organ of Corti, a modified "touch receptor." The timing and spatial distribution of the nerve impulses provide the brain with the cues to pitch, loudness, and timbre. Further understanding of how all this is accomplished depends on knowing the parts of the auditory apparatus and how they relate to one another.

Outer ear

The **outer ear** consists of the **pinna** (auricle), **external auditory meatus,** and the **tympanum,** or eardrum (Figs. 11-5 and 11-6). The pinna is what you probably refer to as your ear—the convoluted flap that extends from the side of the head. It functions to collect air vibrations and funnel them into the external auditory meatus. Man has lost most of his muscular control of the pinna (except "wiggling" the ears as a parlor trick), but lower animals such as dogs and donkeys move the pinna in orienting to the source of sound—they "prick up" their ears. The external auditory meatus is the canal that curves through the mastoid bone of the skull to conduct vibrations to the tym-

panum, which seals off its inner end. The tympanum is a membrane that vibrates in response to the pressure waves of sound. It is cone-shaped like a loudspeaker and pivots on a fold at its lower rim.

Middle ear

The **middle ear** contains the three bony **ossicles** that are vibrated mechanically by the rapid movements of the tympanum. The ossicles conduct vibrations to the fluid-filled inner ear. The **malleus,** or hammer, is connected to the eardrum. It moves the **incus** (anvil), which, in turn, moves the **stapes** (stirrup). The three bones are firmly connected by ligaments and vibrate almost as a unit. The stapes fits into the **oval window** of the fluid-filled inner ear and is sealed in place by a membrane. The lever system of the ossicles has little mechanical advantage, but the smaller area of the oval window and stapes, as compared to the eardrum, provides a good impedance match between air and the more resistant fluid medium of the inner ear. The small variations in air pressure, distributed over the larger eardrum, are concentrated on the smaller oval window to vibrate the fluid of the inner ear because fluid is more resistant to movement than is air. To prevent this sensitive mechanism from being "overdriven" by loud sounds of low frequency, two muscles act to limit the motion of the ossicles. The **tensor tympani** pulls on the malleus to tighten the tympanum, and the **stapedius** pulls on the stapes to limit its motion at the oval window to loud sounds. These muscles, especially the stapedius, contract in a reflex reaction to loud sounds. The reflex may reduce sound intensity by as much as 20 db. As a chamber the inner ear is sealed off from outside changes in atmospheric pressure. The **eustachian tube** connects with the rear of the oral cavity (mouth) and is opened to equalize pressure with the outside air in the acts of swallowing or yawning. Any pressure difference is felt in the eardrums, which explains why they seem to "pop" if you swallow or yawn after a change in altitude. Outside air pressure changes with altitude, but middle ear pressure cannot change unless the eustachian tube is opened.

Inner ear

The **inner ear** contains the **cochlea,** which is coiled (2¾ turns) like a snail shell. There are three chambers in the cochlea (Figs. 11-6 and 11-7). The **scala vestibuli** begins at the oval window and is the "upper" chamber. It communicates with the "lower" **scala tympani** at the apex of the cochlear coil via a small opening, the **helicotrema.** The membrane-covered **round window** is found at the other end of the scala tympani. Both

the scala vestibuli and scala tympani are filled with fluid **perilymph.** The third chamber of the cochlea is the **scala media,** or **cochlear duct.** It is filled with fluid **endolymph,** and does not communicate with the other two scala. The scala media is triangular in cross section (Fig. 11-7), with **Reissner's membrane** separating it from the scala vestibuli as a "roof." The bony **modiolus** forms part of the "floor" of the scala media, and the membranous **basilar membrane** completes the division from the scala tympani. The function of these parts of the cochlea is best appreciated in a schematic diagram such as Fig. 11-6. Air vibrations (sound) are transmitted from the eardrum to the stapes via the other ossicles. The

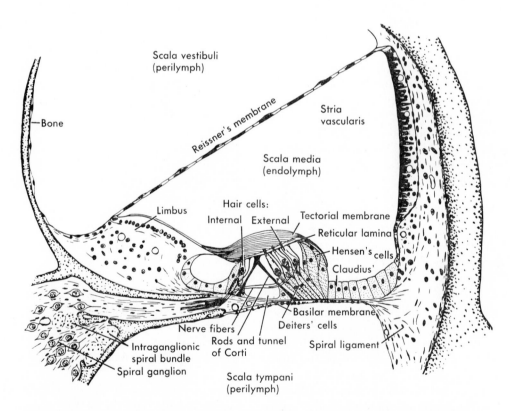

Fig. 11-7. Cross section of the cochlear duct (guinea pig). For further description, see text. (From Davis, H. R., Benson, R. W., Covell, W. P., Fernandez, C., Goldstein, R., Katsuki, Y., Legouix, J.-P., McAuchiffe, D. R., and Tosaki, I.: J. Acoust. Soc. Amer. **25:**1180, 1953.)

footplate of the stapes vibrates in and out of the oval window. Pressure changes in the perilymph of the scala vestibuli result. The pressure changes are transferred to the endolymph of the scala media, through the flexible Reissner's membrane. The pressure changes in the scala media affect the scala tympani via the basilar membrane. Since fluid is incompressible, pressure changes in the scala tympani cause the membrane over the round window to bulge in and out. There is little movement of fluid through the helicotrema caused by pressure changes in the perilymph, except in response to very low-frequency sound.

Organ of Corti. The **organ of Corti** is the receptor structure that rests on the basilar membrane. It transduces vibrations of the basilar membrane into nerve impulses when the **hair cells** are bent by the motions of the basilar membrane. The hairs of the hair cells are bent because they are thrust into an overlying **tectoral membrane.** The organ of Corti extends along the basilar membrane from its base to its apex. It is organized in a **tonotopic** fashion, with hair cells near the base of the basilar membrane (near the round and oval windows) being more affected by tones of high frequency and hair cells near the apex (toward the helicotrema) being more affected by tones of low frequency. The reasons for this organization will be explained later. One feature of anatomy that contributes to tonotopic organization should be mentioned now, however. Although the cross section of the cochlea narrows from base to apex of its coil, the width of the modiolus narrows faster than the width of the whole cochlear duct. As a result, the basilar membrane *widens* as one traces it from the base to the apex of the cochlea. Neurons from the hair cells leave the organ of Corti all along the basilar membrane, from base to apex. Some neurons from near the base of the basilar membrane respond more readily to high-pitched tones; some from near the apex respond more readily to low-pitched tones.

Nervous connections of the ear: the classic pathway

The nerve cells that invade the hair cells of the organ of Corti are the bipolar variety (Chapter 4). Their cell bodies are found inside the coil of the cochlea along its entire length as the **spiral ganglion** (Fig. 11-7). Their axons form the acoustic branch of the eighth, or **statoacoustic, nerve.** The first-order neurons reach the **dorsal** and **ventral cochlear nuclei** of the medulla on either side of the brainstem (Fig. 11-8). Second-order neurons from the dorsal nucleus cross the floor of the fourth ventricle (acoustic stria). Second-order neurons from the ventral nucleus either ascend without crossing or cross (and sometimes synapse) in the trapezoid body that forms a bulge across the ventral hindbrain behind the pons. Other important connections are made to a nucleus of the medulla, called the **olive.** The ascending fibers form the **lateral lemniscus.** Synapses for reflex movements (such as turning the head to respond to sound) are made in the **inferior colliculus.** The lateral lemniscus ends in the **medial geniculate body,** near the thalamus. From here neurons reach the **auditory projection area** (area 41) on the temporal lobe (Chapter 6). Input from the cochlea of each ear reaches the projection area of both hemispheres. However, the tonotopic organization of the cochlea is preserved at the cortex, with high, middle, and low tones stimulating different parts of the projection area.

Auditory area II (Fig. 11-9). A second projection area on the cortex is supplied by fibers reaching it via the nonspecific nuerons of the brainstem reticular formation. These pathways are supplied by collaterals from the lateral lemniscus as well as side branches of other sensory pathways. Like most areas of the cortex supplied by the reticular formation, A II seems to concern arousal and attention as well as serving as an alternate auditory pathway. Other cortical areas known to be involved in hearing

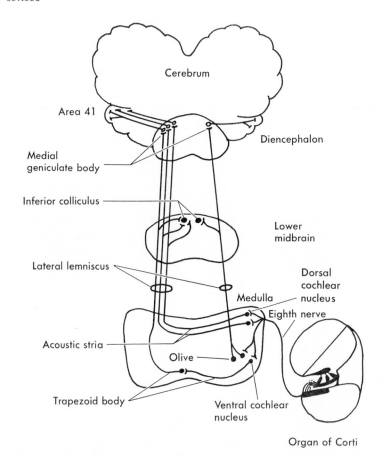

Cerebrum

Area 41

Diencephalon

Medial
geniculate body

Inferior colliculus

Lower
midbrain

Lateral lemniscus

Dorsal
cochlear
nucleus

Medulla

Eighth nerve

Acoustic stria

Olive

Trapezoid body

Ventral cochlear
nucleus

Organ of Corti

Fig. 11-8. Auditory nervous pathways. For description, see text.

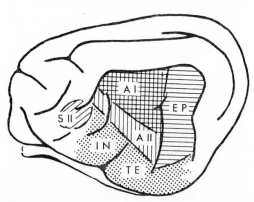

Fig. 11-9. Areas of the cat brain showing auditory function. For further description, see text. (From Ades, H. W.: Central auditory mechanisms. In Field, J., editor: Handbook of physiology, vol. 1, Baltimore, 1959, The Williams & Wilkins Co.)

are shown in Fig. 11-9. The auditory cortex does not seem to be important to either pitch or loudness discrimination in animals, but it is required to discriminate *patterns* of pitch variation from one another.

Efferent pathways. Recent research indicates an inhibitory pathway from the olive to the organ of Corti (the olivocochlear tract of Rasmussen). The tract can function to raise the threshold of the hair cells to sound vibrations. Electrodes, permanently implanted in the dorsal cochlear nucleus of a cat, recorded bursts of firing in response to repeated "click" sound stimuli in an awake and active cat. The classic sensory pathway was therefore active, and the animal was otherwise normal. When shown mice in a jar, the cat oriented visually, and impulses stopped arriving at the nucleus from the primary neurons. Since tests showed that the middle ear muscles (stapedius and tensor tympani) were not involved, the site of inhibition should lie where the primary sensory neurons invade the hair cells or in the hair cells themselves. (The inhibitory output pathway ends in these regions.) The principle of efferent inhibition of sensory input is an important one to the topic of attention. It was encountered in somesthesis and will be found in vision as well. Other efferent pathways reach the inferior colliculus, the nuclei in the lateral lemniscus, and the olivary nuclei (olive). Some of these may also inhibit sensory input. Perhaps some of the lack of response to sound when reading, for example, may result because one "turns off his ears." Other efferent pathways may serve to *selectively* inhibit input from wide areas along the organ of Corti, to sharpen the **tonotopic organization** of that input. In response to a high-pitched tone, for example, neurons from near the base of the basilar membrane fire more readily than others, but others along the length of the organ of Corti may respond as well. Inhibition would affect the latter neurons more, and the "local sign," or location cue for pitch, would be improved. Input would be largely restricted to that coming from the base of the cochlea, a cue for high-pitched sounds.

PHYSIOLOGY OF THE COCHLEA
Tonotopic organization of the cochlea

It has already been stated that high-pitched tones stimulate the organ of Corti most near the base of the cochlea, and low-pitched tones stimulate most nearer the apex of the cochlea. There are three factors responsible for this relationship: (1) the laws of fluid motion, (2) travelling waves in the basilar membrane, and (3) the relative width of the basilar membrane.

Fluid motion. In a fluid medium, low-frequency (long wave) vibrations reach maximum amplitude farther from the source than high-frequency vibrations. This may be illustrated by vibrating one end of a water-filled balloon with a tuning fork while holding it along the forearm. The lower the frequency of the tuning fork, the farther away from the tuning fork will maximum vibrations be felt on the skin. In the cochlea the lower the frequency of vibration of the stapes against the oval window, the farther away from the base of the cochlea will fluid displacement of the basilar membrane be at a maximum (Fig. 11-10).

Travelling waves. The basilar membrane is under no tension, and is of a limp and "leathery" consistency. When vibrated by fluid motion, it acts somewhat like a rope tied to a post at one end and vibrated up and down by hand at the other end, at slow or rapid rates. Low-frequency vibrations cause maximum movement farther from the source of the vibrations (hand or oval window); high-frequency vibrations, or fast movements, are maximum nearer the source of the movement.

Width of the basilar membrane. As previously described, the basilar membrane *widens* from base to apex of the cochlea. As a result the mass of the basilar membrane is least near the base of the cochlea and is less resistant there to rapid, high-frequency motion. Near the apex it is wider, has greater mass, and is therefore less resistant only to low-frequency motion.

Pitch mechanisms in the organ of Corti

The location of maximum displacement of the basilar membrane is more precise for high frequencies than for low—below 50 cps; for example, the whole basilar membrane vibrates as a unit. Yet pitch discrimination is excellent at low frequencies. Another mechanism beside tonotopic organization must function as a cue to the pitch of low-frequency sounds. The **volley theory** of pitch discrimination is the most promising explanation.

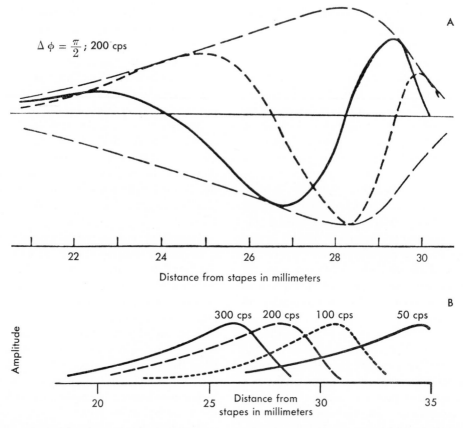

Fig. 11-10. A shows a travelling wave on the basilar membrane (really the cochlear partition). The solid line shows the pattern at one instant, dotted line a quarter-cycle later. The envelope shows the maximum displacement at each point along the basilar membrane at any time. **B** shows the amplitude of the basilar membrane (cochlear partition) for four different frequencies as a function of distance from the stapes. (From von Békésy, G.: J. Acoust. Soc. Amer. **19**:452-460, 1947.)

Volley theory. The higher the frequency of simple or complex tones, the more frequently auditory neurons fire. A 50 cps tone, for example, will stimulate nerve firing at a rate of 50 impulses per second, a 100 cps tone, 100 impulses per second, and so on. It is as if the neurons were fired by the hair cells in response to each pressure variation. A gross electrode on nerve VIII will record impulses "following" the frequency of the sound stimulus up to 4000 cps. But individual neurons in the nerve cannot fire at a rate higher than 1000 times per second; their absolute re-

fractory period is at least 1 msec. (1/1000 second) long, and they cannot fire during that period. The apparent contradiction is explained by the firing of neurons in "relays," or "volleys." While one neuron is firing, three others are recovering. By analogy, four riflemen, each firing once per second, could produce four shots per second. The "frequency following" ability of auditory nerve input is progressively reduced when recorded at higher levels of the auditory pathways. Synaptic interruptions in the pathway reduce the frequency that can be followed by "volleying" input—at the cortex, "following" is limited to frequencies below 2000 to 2500 cycles. Since the human pitch range extends to 20,000 cps, higher frequency input must depend on the tonotopic organization of the organ of Corti that has already been noted. Tonotopic organization is poor at very low frequencies, however, and frequency following could provide an important cue to pitch at low frequency.

Loudness mechanisms in the organ of Corti

The detection of loudness differences depends on more hair cells firing more neurons, with increases in the motion of the basilar membrane. This must occur irrespective of the location of the displacement along the basilar membrane and organ of Corti. The organ of Corti includes two "rows" of hair cells (Fig. 11-7). The inner row has a single column of hair cells, and the outer row has three or four columns of hair cells. The outer row appears to be a loudness detection mechanism, which responds to minimum intensity levels. There are two reasons for this supposition. (1) The outer row of hair cells is farthest from the "pivot points" of the basilar membrane and tectoral membrane (Fig. 11-7); as the basilar membrane and tectoral membrane "flap" up and down, they bend the hair cells in a lateral direction to fire nerve impulses. The outer row hair cells are bent more by this motion than the inner row hair cells. (2) Several hair cells are innervated by each neuron going to the outer row. This constitutes a *summation* mechanism; the generator potentials of several bending hair cells add their effects to fire a single neuron.

Pitch and the hair cells

The inner row of hair cells seems designed to respond to the *place* along the length of the organ of Corti that is most displaced by sound. There are three reasons for this assumption. (1) The "travelling waves" of displacement have a maximum area of motion along the basilar membrane that depends on wavelength and therefore frequency (Fig. 11-10). Travelling waves bend hair cells in a *longitudinal* direction along the *length* of the organ of Corti. Longitudinal bending affects inner row hair cells as much as outer row hair cells. (2) The inner row hair cells seem to have a higher threshold than the outer row hair cells. As a result, they would respond only to the area of *maximum* displacement of the basilar membrane. As noted above, this location depends critically on pitch. (3) As a rule, each of the inner row hair cells is innervated by a single neuron. They have a "private line" from each hair cell to the CNS. This improves discrimination by the CNS of which hair cells fire neurons—and therefore where the organ of Corti was most stimulated along its length.

Action by the CNS on the tonotopic input

The accuracy of frequency discrimination is the result of the action by the CNS on a relatively crude tonotopic input. The descending pathways from higher nerve centers that were previously described seem to act on auditory input to refine its tonotopic organization. The following facts were gleaned from studies of single-fiber recording to show the complexities involved:

1. Fibers from the basal area of the cochlea may respond to tones of any audible frequency, but apical fibers respond only to low-frequency tones. Basal fibers are most sensitive to high-frequency tones, however.

2. The range of frequencies to which a single fiber will respond broadens with increased intensity ("loudness") of the stimulus. Even at high intensity, however, these fibers show a sharp "cutoff" point as frequency is increased, a point found just above the frequency to which they are most sensitive. (The increase in threshold at lower frequencies is more gradual—Fig. 11-11).

Response area of a single auditory nerve fiber

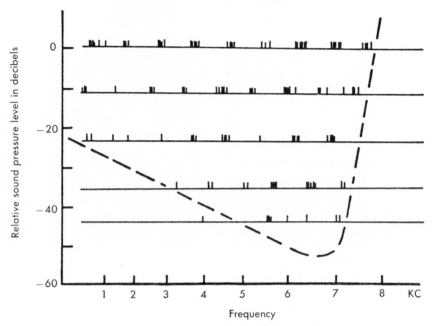

Fig. 11-11. Responses of a single auditory nerve fiber to tone pips of different frequencies and intensities. For further description, see text. Dotted line shows boundary of "response area" of this fiber. (From Tasaki, I.: J. Neurophysiol. **17:**97-122, 1954.)

3. The tonotopic organization of fibers improves as the site of recording shifts from nerve VIII to colliculi and geniculate bodies to the cortex. That is, the farther up the auditory pathway one records, the more frequency-specific the individual nerve fibers become. This is probably caused by the descending inhibitory pathways already described.

4. Some fibers in nerve VIII respond to all frequencies (loudness fibers from outer row hair cells?). Some respond only to complex tones and cannot be stimulated by a sine wave "pure" tone.

5. Some nerve VIII fibers respond "spontaniously," having an irregular "resting" level of firing. Some studies show that these fibers are inhibited by auditory stimulation, whereas others find no such effect.

6. A frequency-specific nerve VIII fiber, firing in response to a pure tone, may be inhibited by subsequent stimulation with a higher or a lower tone.

7. A brief click stimulus produces a burst of firing in a fiber with as little as one millisecond between spikes, which may outlast the stimulus by 20 to 30 milliseconds.

8. Continued stimulation by a tone produces an irregular discharge that continues at a diminishing rate (all the impulses from a given fiber were consistent in frequency; they followed the frequency of the stimulus or a multiple of it). The diminishing response probably results from auditory adaptation to a constant stimulus.

Cochlear microphonic

The individual hair cells bend in response to sound in a manner already described. The bending of the hair cells produces a change in a current that is continually flowing through them. This *change* in current flow probably constitutes a "generator potential" that fires the sensory neurons going to the hair cells. As originally recorded from the surface of the cochlea, such electrical changes were known as the **cochlear microphonic** because they differ from nerve impulses in certain important respects: (1) they are not "all-or-none" in character (Chapter 4), but increase in size as the stimulus increases in intensity (by contrast, a nerve cell fires or does not fire with a *rate* that depends on stimulus intensity), and (2) the electrical changes faithfully reproduce the *form* as well as the frequency of the sound wave stimulus. Nerve cell firing is an electrical change that is unlike the wave form of the stimulus. The cochlear microphonic potentials act like the electrical changes produced in a microphone by sound—they can be amplified to reproduce the sound through a loudspeaker. Microelectrode recording has shown that the cochlear microphonic originates at the cuticular surface of the hair cells.

Origin of the cochlear microphonic. A constant flow of current through the hair cells seems to be modified when the hair cells bend in response to sound-induced motion of the basilar membrane. The current flow presumes a voltage difference to power it. The voltage difference is one of about 80 mv. that exists between the scala media and the other two scala of the inner ear (Fig. 11-7). The scala media is positively charged with respect to the other two scala. The positive charge exists because the endolymph of the scala media has a much higher potassium (K^+) and only slightly lower sodium (Na^+) content than the perilymph of the other two scala. The endolymph is probably produced by the vascular "lining" of the bony outer wall of the scala media (the stria vascularis). Considered in this light, the stria vascularis acts somewhat like a battery in producing a potential difference. The current flow that results passes through the hair cells as well as other structures. The current flow is modified when the hair cells bend from basilar membrane vibrations in response to sound; at least there is evidence that this is the case. These fluctuations in voltage difference between the scala media and the other scala would reflect the form of the sound input wave, just as movement of the basilar membrane does. Destruction of the hair cells has been shown to abolish the cochlear microphonic as well as the response of nerve VIII cells to sound. The flow of current through the hair cells, as modified by their bending in response to sound, appears to stimulate the individual fibers of nerve VIII. The cochlear microphonic therefore serves as a "generator potential" to stimulate impulses in the sensory neurons.

Auditory defects

Defects in any part of the auditory mechanism from external ear to cerebral cortex may impair hearing, although cortical damage is more perceptual than sensory in its effects. Sensory impairment may be too subtle to detect by judging response to everyday sounds. As a result, some persons are partially deaf without being aware of it. They are unable to compare their own hearing with the hearing of others, unless the defect is so striking as to make it obvious that they do not hear what others do. The nature of a sensory impairment must often be detected by **audiometry,** in which the auditory threshold is tested at selected points over a range of frequencies (Fig. 11-12). The results are plotted as an **audiogram,** which is scaled so that normal sensitivity appears as a straight line across the top of the graph.

Outer ear defects. Defects in parts of the outer ear affect all frequencies fairly evenly. The external auditory meatus may become clogged with wax to impair conduction of sound waves to the eardrum. The eardrum may become infected, which impairs its flexibility. Punctures of the eardrum can result in some loss of its move-

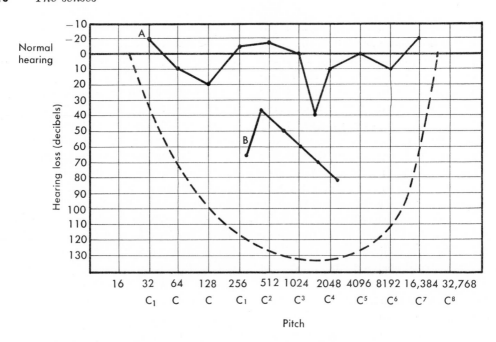

Fig. 11-12. Two fictitious but not unusual audiograms, plotted on the same graph. One shows a tonal gap **(A)** and the other is a tonal island **(B)** (see text). The broken line represents total loss of effective hearing.

ment in response to sound waves. Infections of the eustachian tube of the inner ear can also impair the eardrum's movement, when a pressure difference builds up between the middle ear and the outer ear across the eardrum.

Middle ear defects. Apart from eustachian tube infection, defects of the middle ear result in a greater loss of sensitivity to the lower frequencies. This is because such defects affect the ossicles that transmit mechanical motion from the eardrum to the fluid of the inner ear. The *extent* of motion of the ossicles is usually greater for low frequencies than for high frequencies; impairment of the ossicles limits their motion and therefore their ability to respond to low frequencies. The ligaments holding the ossicles together may lose elasticity. More commonly, the membrane that seals the footplate of the stapes into the oval window may harden (otosclerosis) to limit the motion of the stapes. These are examples

of **transmission deafness** that often accompany old age. In extreme cases surgery may free the junction of stapes and oval window. Another treatment is to cut a new window and cover it with a tiny flap of skin (fenestration). Two types of hearing aids are used to overcome the defects. One amplifies sound waves; its "loudspeaker" is placed in the external auditory meatus (air conduction). The other transmits sound vibrations to the mastoid bone behind the pinna so that vibrations reach the cochlea via bone conduction.

Inner ear defects. Inner ear defects usually arise from nerve damage or damage to the hair cells. This damage is called **nerve deafness,** and is usually localized so that it affects high frequencies more than low frequencies. Nerve deafness is the most common hearing defect of old age, and, when limited to more specific frequencies, it is called a **tonal gap,** or a **tonal island** (Fig. 11-12). Such defects can result from exposure to very intense sound—**exposure deafness.** The basilar membrane is over-driven by intense sound of a specific frequency range, which damages the hair cells in a specific region along the length of the organ of Corti where the travelling wave of motion of the basilar membrane is at a maximum. More generalized nerve deafness also results in a symptom called *recruitment.* The threshold for hearing is raised, but when sound exceeds that threshold, it suddenly seems very loud. The symptom can be explained by the summation mechanism of the outer row hair cells. When enough undamaged hair cells are stimulated so that several fire each neuron, many neurons suddenly begin to fire—the sound therefore seems loud.

Other auditory symptoms. A continual "ringing" sound, called **tinnitus,** is sometimes experienced. The cause is usually in the inner ear, continuous low-grade stimulation resulting from infection, the after-effects of loud sounds, etc. Dizziness frequently accompanies tinnitus because the vestibular apparatus is involved. **Diplacusis** occurs when the ears are "mismatched" for pitch. The two ears may hear a single tone as an octave to a semitone different in pitch. Differences in the loudness threshold in the two ears are common, but they are rarely large enough to cause difficulties. Because of the bilateral connections of the auditory pathways from the two ears in the CNS, summation occurs; the two ears together have a lower threshold than one so that binaural hearing is always more sensitive than monaural hearing.

PSYCHOPHYSICS OF HEARING

Hearing demonstrates the basic attributes encountered in the other senses: (1) quality (**pitch**), (2) intensity (**loudness**), (3) extensity (**volume**), and (4) duration. A fifth psychological attribute, (5) **density,** must be added, and the attribute of volume requires some explanation. Volume is not identical with loudness, but is the per-

ceived "size" of a tone. It qualifies as a psychological attribute because subjects can agree on comparative judgments of the sizes of tones, and an equal-interval scale can be constructed from their judgments. Apparent volume is dependent on a combination of pitch and loudness. Lower pitch and/or decreased loudness is perceived as an increase in volume. A low-pitched organ note sounds "larger" than a high-pitched flute note, but the organ note diminishes in apparent size as its intensity increases. Density is also a reliable psychological attribute that varies in the opposite manner with changes in pitch and loudness. Density is the apparent compactness or hardness of a tone—its lack of "loose," "thin," or "rare" characteristics. A high-pitched and/or intense sound appears quite dense, whereas a low-pitched and/or less loud sound is not very dense or compact. Density qualifies as a psychological attribute for the same reason that volume does; subjects agree enough in their judgment of tones when they compare them for density so that an equal-interval psychological scale of density can be constructed. Little need be said to define the attributes of pitch, loudness, or duration. Duration is self-explanatory. Psychologically perceived loudness varies with physical sound intensity in a manner to be described later. Psychologically perceived pitch varies with frequency in a manner that will also be described. Pitch is the *single* primary quality of sound, whereas other senses have several primary qualities—four somesthetic qualities, several primary colors for vision, and so on. The interactions of pitch with intensity will also be discussed.

Intensity thresholds

The absolute threshold of the human ear is so low that the sound source must be calibrated at intensities well above threshold. Depending on the method used to determine threshold and the stimulus frequency, the absolute threshold may be as low as

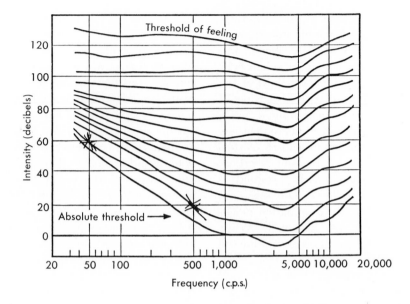

Fig. 11-13. Equal loudness contours. Lowest curve represents the absolute threshold for various frequencies. Points along each of the other curves sound equally loud to the listener (see text). (From Stevens, S. S., and Davis, H.: Hearing, New York, 1938, John Wiley & Sons, Inc.)

80 db below 1 dyne/cm². The lever system of the ossicles in the middle ear has a resonant frequency of 1700 cps, and the external ear canal (meatus) resonates at 4000 cps; these features largely determine the threshold curve for hearing, which is lowest in the 800 to 6000 cps range (Fig. 11-13). The threshold increases less rapidly for lower than for higher frequencies outside this range. The terminal threshold for loudness is much less dependent on pitch. The terminal threshold is usually set by the beginning of somesthetic sensations from the ear—the so-called threshold of feeling. The chief attribute of these sensations is pain, though tickling and itching are sensed as well. Besides being masked by somesthesis, further increments of sensed loudness require stimulus intensities that can permanently damage the organ of Corti. At low intensities the ear is most sensitive to tones in the 800 to 6000 cps range for the reasons given above. This means that a high- or low-pitched tone that sounds just as loud as a 800 to 6000 cps tone must be of greater physical intensity. High-fidelity music systems frequently have a switch on the amplifier that boosts the intensity of high and low frequencies. Its purpose is to allow music recorded at high intensity to be reproduced at low intensity without losing the "natural" loudness of the high and low frequencies.

Intensity discrimination

The difference threshold, or **difference limen** (DL), for intensity varies little with changes in frequency when the base intensity is above 30 db. At lower intensities the DL is minimal at about 2500 cps. With increases in intensity at any frequency, the DL for loudness increases more rapidly than Weber's law of a constant $\triangle I/I$ would lead us to expect. The difference threshold for loudness, in other words, increases more than the base intensity does. The increase, again, is least for frequencies near 2500 cps. Even here, near the frequencies most common to human speech, an experience common to most of us illustrates how Weber's law affects everyday life. Nearly everyone has raised his voice to speak to someone nearby over the loudness of applause at a concert only to find he was shouting to the whole auditorium when the applause died away suddenly. The $\triangle I$ increased when I diminished, and the results were embarrassing.

Frequency thresholds and frequency discrimination

The limits—absolute and terminal thresholds—for pitch in human hearing are usually taken as 20 to 20,000 cps. Below 20 cps. a "chugging" or a "fluttering" sound is heard, which acquires tonal character between 15 and 25 cps, depending on the complexity and intensity of the tone. Above 20,000 cps the most acute ear hears nothing, although unpleasant somesthetic "tickling" is sometimes experienced at high intensities. As noted before, little usually happens to sensitivity for lower frequencies with age, but upper frequency limits are progressively reduced during and after middle age.

The difference threshold for pitch changes with loudness. In the first place, the DL for pitch increases with decreasing stimulus intensity, that is, if you are off pitch, sing softly and others cannot tell the difference. The DL for pitch changes with frequency mostly below 4000 cps. Below this point, the lower the stimulus frequency, the more sensitive the ear to pitch differences; the DL for pitch decreases rapidly down to 2000 cps and slowly thereafter. This means that an off-pitch bass would be easier to detect than an off-pitch soprano. Finally, an odd interaction between apparent pitch and loudness occurs for pure sine wave tones, but not for complex periodic tones. With increases in intensity, pure tones higher than 2500 cps increase in apparent pitch,

whereas those below 2500 cps decrease in pitch. No one knows why this is the case, but it has little effect on music because musical tones are complex periodic waves; the overtones seem to keep the apparent pitch constant, whatever the loudness.

Adaptation and fatigue

The auditory threshold does increase following continuous stimulation, but the increase is very brief for sounds of moderate intensity and duration, usually less than half a second. This is why one does not notice auditory adaptation under normal circumstances. Greater intensities—a noisy office, for example—increase the threshold so that two minutes or so are required for recovery in a quiet environment. Continuous stimulation for several minutes at 110 db—about all one can tolerate without ear damage—will result in impairment lasting about half an hour. The threshold for both ears is raised by stimulating one. This means that at least part of the adaptation occurs in the CNS because the auditory nerve pathways are shared by both ears.

COMPLEX AUDITORY PHENOMENA
Aural harmonics

In discussing the nature of sound, it was explained that complex structures vibrate at more than one frequency, even when the base, or fundamental frequency, is a simple sine wave. Overtones or harmonics are thereby produced that determine the timbre of a sound. The auditory mechanism itself is no exception to this rule, although its overtones are simple ones when the stimulus intensity is moderate. The first overtone is usually more prominent than the second, the second more prominent than the third, and so on. The more intense the auditory stimulus, the greater the amplitude and number of these **aural harmonics** and the less consistent the overtone pattern described above. Aural harmonics, because of the characteristics of the auditory mechanism, are seen in the cochlear microphonic. Even if one stimulates the ear with a pure sine wave tone, the hair cells that probably cause the cochlear microphonic are being stimulated by a complex periodic wave. Aural harmonics are added to all sound wave stimuli and are responsible for combination tones and other complex auditory phenomena.

Combination tones

If two pure sine wave tones are sounded at once, the experienced observer will hear at least four. The most easily heard tone not present in the two stimulus frequencies is the **difference tone.** The frequency of the difference tone is the difference between the frequencies of the two sine wave stimuli. The difference tone should not be confused with beats, the changes in loudness whose frequency is also the difference between the stimulating frequencies. As one stimulating frequency is increased over the other, the loudness will wax and wane in beats as the two sounds come in and out of phase. As this occurs more and more often with greater separation between the frequencies, the resulting beats will be heard as a "roughness" that is quite unpleasant at high intensities. *Superimposed* on this roughness will be the difference tone. The difference tone is not caused by the beats. It is caused by the interaction of the aural harmonics of the two stimulating tones. It will be heard as a low growl when the two stimulating frequencies are about 50 cps apart, and it will increase in frequency as the two stimulus tones differ more and more in frequency. Under these conditions it sounds somewhat like a siren.

A **summation tone** can also be heard, although it is less prominent. The summation tone is also caused by the interaction of the aural harmonics of the two stimulating frequencies. Its frequency is the *sum* of the two fundamental stimulating frequencies. If, then, the observer is stimulated with two simple sine wave tones, one of 700 cps and one of 1000 cps, he will hear

four. The difference tone will be 300 cps and the summation tone will be 1700 cps.

Recording cochlear potentials will show other difference and summation tones. If h is the frequency of the higher-pitched tone and l the frequency of the lower-pitched tone, there will be two second-order difference tones of frequencies, $2h - l$ and $h - 2l$. Two second-order summation tones will be $2h + l$ and $h + 2l$. The general formula for the many summation and difference tones is $N = mh \pm nl$, where N is the frequency of a difference or summation tone and m and n are all possible integers. However, the first difference and first summation tones are all that are detected by the observer.

Consonance and dissonance

When two tones are sounded together, the combination usually sounds "pleasant" or "unpleasant" to most observers. The combinations that sound pleasant are **consonant frequencies**—they seem to "fuse" or blend well together. The combinations that sound "harsh" or discordant are called **dissonant frequencies.** Though musical styles change, the difference between the two frequencies (their interval) seems to be most important to producing consonance or dissonance. The most accepted explanation states that dissonance occurs when the higher overtones of the two fundamentals are so close in frequency as to beat at a rate that gives a "rough" sound. **Consonance** occurs when the upper overtones of the two fundamentals differ enough in frequency to be distinct. Even two pure sine wave tones could be consonant or dissonant because of the interaction of the aural harmonics they produce. Consonant intervals form the basis for the octave in music, and various combinations of these tones produce consonant chords.

Masking

A tone of high intensity may mask, or make inaudible, a tone of lower intensity. The low-intensity tone must be made louder in the presence of the high-intensity tone to be heard. The intensity required of the less intense sound to be heard is a measure of the **masking** effectiveness of the high-intensity tone. Masking effectiveness depends on the relative frequencies of the two tones. The effect is greatest when the two tones are close to the same frequency. However, the effect is lost when the tones are identical and partially lost when they are close enough together to *beat* audibly. Masking effectiveness is greater in the high-frequency direction; that is, a tone will mask another tone of higher frequency more readily than it will mask a tone of lower frequency. This is because the aural harmonics (higher-frequency overtones of the auditory mechanism) from a low-frequency tone interfere with the ear's response to the higher-frequency tone. This rule will not hold when the masking tone has an overtone that is the same as the masked tone, the overtone then reinforces the masked tone instead of interfering with it.

Speech

Speech is both tone and noise, that is, it has periodic vowel sounds, aperiodic sibilants (hissing sounds), and clicklike consonant sounds; the sibilants have high-frequency (noise) components. A range of 100 to 10,000 cps contains nearly all the frequencies and overtones, but most of the sound energy output is below 1000 cps for men or women. The sex differences include more output from 300 cps to 5000 cps for men than for women and slightly more in the reverse direction above 5000 cps. The major problem for communication equipment is intelligibility rather than reproducing this whole spectrum of frequencies at vast expense. A range of 200 to 10,000 cps is normally used in communication equipment.

Localization

Many complex factors may affect the localization of sound: head movements to vary the sound to the two ears, visual cues from objects that make common sounds, such as a telephone, the complexity of the sound wave, echoes, and so on. When pure tones or "click" stimuli are used, the head held still, and the subject blindfolded, certain cues emerge that may be important to the initial localization of a strange sound: (1) intensity difference, (2) phase difference, and (3) time difference. These cues are all caused by the difference in sensations from the two ears, when the sound source is to one side of the head or the other.

Intensity difference to the two ears occurs because the head casts a "sound shadow" if the sound comes from one side. The sound will be louder to the ear nearer the source, especially if it is a sine wave tone above 1000 cps. Lower-frequency or long-wave sounds "bend" around the head more readily and do not sound as different in intensity to the two ears as high-pitched short-wave sounds.

Phase differences occur when the wavelength of a tone is such that it reaches one ear in compression and the other in rarefaction, that is, the wavelength is half the distance between the ears. This occurs in the 800 to 1000 cps range. (Of course, this does not tell the subject which side of his head the source is on.) When the frequency is below 800 cps, the phase difference is less than 180 degrees and the subject can tell which ear is "leading" and which is "lagging" in the cycle of compression and rarefaction.

Time differences are also important if the sound has a sharp onset, as a "click" stimulus does. The sound reaches one ear before it reaches the other. Sound travels at 1080 feet per second, but the human ears can detect a difference between them in sound onset of little more than half a millisecond (0.65 msec.). This is sufficient to detect which ear was stimulated first.

All these cues probably depend on an intact cerebral cortex—at least in the cat sound localization is lost when the auditory cortical areas are removed. Intensity, phase, and time differences combine when using pure tones so that errors of sound localization are minimal below 500 cps and above 10,000 cps and maximal at 3000 cps. More complex periodic tones such as those of music act differently, however. The low frequencies have enough overtones in the 3000 cps range so that they are localized poorly. Only high-frequency tones are most accurately localized. This is why high-fidelity enthusiasts are taking such pains to place their tweeters, or high-frequency speakers, to minimize directional effects.

SUMMARY

The discussion of audition included the physical energy of sound, the anatomy of the auditory mechanism, the physiology of hearing, the psychophysics of hearing, and complex auditory phenomena, in that order. Physically, sound is the alternate compression and rarefaction of air molecules caused by a vibrating body. The simplest vibrating bodies, such as a tuning fork, produce periodic variations in air pressure that can be plotted as a sine wave of pressure change over distance and produce a simple tone. The graph has simple characteristics of amplitude and wavelength. Amplitude is the amount of air pressure change, interpreted by the ear as loudness. Since sound travels at a uniform rate of 1080 feet per second, wavelength translates readily into frequency. Frequency is interpreted as pitch by the ear. Various points along the complete normal to compression to normal to rarefaction to normal sine wave can be indexed in terms of phase, the points mentioned being 0, 90, 180, 270, and 360 degrees, respectively. If one sine wave is in compression while the other is in rarefaction, they are 270 minus 90 degrees, or 180 degrees out of phase.

The amplitude of a sound wave is measured on a log scale of pressure change, constructed to match the absolute and difference thresholds of the human ear and called the decibel scale. The zero point is an energy level of 0.0002 dyne/cm.^{2}, and

there are ten decibels in a bel, the exponent to the base ten multiplied by the zero point. In addition to simple periodic sine wave tones, sound includes complex periodic tones and complex aperiodic tones. Complex periodic tones are produced by bodies such as musical instruments that vibrate with more than one frequency to produce a complex repeated wave of pressure changes made up of several sine waves. The dominant and lowest frequency is the fundamental, or first harmonic; the other frequencies are overtones or higher harmonics that are simple multiples of the fundamental, according to Fourier's law. The overtones are caused by the resonance of parts of the instrument and its air chambers. Differences in the relative amplitude of various overtones in different instruments are interpreted by the ear as differences in timbre. When the sine waves produced by a vibrating body are not repeated in a regular pattern, they are aperiodic and heard as noise, especially if many high-frequency components are present. Two periodic waves can come in and out of phase the same number of times per second that they differ in frequency, to produce variations in loudness called beats.

The auditory mechanism transduces air pressure changes into fluid vibrations that cause the hair cells of the organ of Corti to fire nerve impulses. The outer ear funnels air pressure changes gathered by the pinna into the external auditory meatus, where they vibrate the tympanum like a drum. In the middle ear three bony ossicles, the malleus, incus, and stapes, transfer this motion to the fluid-filled inner ear, the stapes footplate being smaller than the tympanum to provide an impedance match between air and fluid. The motion of the ossicles to loud sounds can be dampened by reflex contractions of the stapedius and tensor tympani muscles. The eustachian tube, from the middle ear to the oral cavity, equalizes middle ear pressure with the atmosphere. The coiled cochlea of the inner ear has three fluid-filled chambers. The scala vestibuli and scala tympani are filled with perilymph and communicate via the helicotrema at the cochlear apex. The scala media or cochlear duct is filled with endolymph. Vibrations by the stapes at the oval window cause perilymph vibrations in the scala vestibuli, which are transmitted across Reissner's membrane to the endolymph of the scala media. These vibrations are transmitted across the basilar membrane that is attached to the bony shelf of the modiolus to form part of the "floor" of the scala media. The resulting pressure variations in the scala tympani cause the round window membrane to bulge in and out.

The organ of Corti lies along the length of the basilar membrane. Its hair cells are thrust into an overlying tectoral membrane, so that when the basilar membrane moves, the hairs are bent. In response the hair cells generate firing in the nerve cells that innervate them. The hair cells are organized in a tonotopic fashion, those nearer the base of the cochlea firing more often to high-pitched tones, those near the apex responding to low-pitched tones. There are three reasons for this: (1) high-frequency waves in fluid reach their maximum amplitude nearer the source than do low-frequency waves, (2) travelling waves of motion in the basilar membrane act in the same fashion, and (3) the basilar membrane widens from base to apex of the cochlea. The tonotopic organization is poor for low frequencies, but the neurons fire in "volleys" at these frequencies to "follow" the frequency of the stimulus input, according to the volley theory. The outer row of hair cells serve as a loudness mechanism since they are bent most by radial motions of the basilar membrane that are not as frequency-specific as are the longitudinal motion resulting from travelling waves. Several outer row hair cells are innervated by each neuron; therefore they summate. The inner row hair cells are affected most by longitudinal movements of the basilar membrane, have high thresholds,

and single nerve cell innervation; therefore they serve pitch by signalling the location of the maximum stimulus along the length of the basilar membrane. The CNS sharpens this tonotopic input by efferent pathways that inhibit input from areas not receiving maximum stimulation. The bending of hair cells fires nerve cells by altering a flow of current between the other two scala of the cochlea and the scala media (which is positive to the other two chambers). The current flow alteration is called the cochlear microphonic.

The cell bodies of the bipolar nerve cells make up the spiral ganglion; their axons form the acoustic branch of the stato-acoustic nerve. This nerve reaches the dorsal and ventral cochlear nuclei. Fibers connecting here, both crossed and uncrossed, make up the lateral lemniscus, with synapses in its nucleus and in the olive. Collaterals reach the inferior colliculus and the path relays in the medial lemniscus before reaching auditory area I in the cerebral cortex. Area II may be important to attention and is more diffusely supplied. An efferent path from the olive to the hair cells can inhibit auditory input.

The effect of defects in the auditory mechanism depends on where they occur. Cortical damage is more perceptual than sensory in effect. Outer ear defects such as clogging of the meatus or eustachian tube, or a ruptured eardrum, affect all frequencies. Ossification of middle ear bones that limits their motion or hardens the stapes to the oval window affects low frequencies most. Inner ear damage to nerves or hair cells affects high frequencies most. These symptoms may be detected by audiometry and plotted on an audiogram. Other symptoms are tinnitus and diplacusis.

Psychophysically, hearing demonstrates the basic attributes of quality (pitch), intensity (loudness), extensity (volume), duration, and density. Volume increases with low pitch and less intensity; density acts in the opposite fashion. The absolute loudness threshold is a function of pitch, being lowest in the 800 to 6000 cps range. The terminal threshold is fixed by the onset of somesthetic sensations at 100 to 120 db, where hair cell damage can occur. Above 30 db the loudness DL varies little with pitch; at lower intensities it is minimal at 2500 cps. The Weber ratio increases as loudness increases. The frequency limits for hearing are about 20 to 20,000 cps. The DL for pitch improves as loudness increases and is smallest for lower frequencies below 4000 cps. Auditory fatigue is brief for all but extreme loudness and seems to be partly a phenomenon of the CNS.

Complex auditory phenomena are often caused by overtones created by the hearing mechanism itself, or aural harmonics. Difference and summation tones are caused by this mechanism. Dissonance, on the other hand, is believed caused by the beating of two sets of overtones, consonance occurring when they do not beat. A lower-pitched tone can mask a higher-pitched tone more readily than the reverse; masking is less effective when overtones reinforce or beat. Masking is most effective when the frequency difference is small. Speech includes both tones and noise of 100 to 10,000 cps range. Sex differences are small. Auditory localization is binaural and depends on (1) intensity differences, (2) phase differences, and (3) time differences.

READINGS

Alpern, W., Lawrence, M., and Wolsk, D.: Sensory processes, Belmont, Calif., 1967, Brooks/Cole Division, Wadsworth Publishing Co., Inc.

Buddenbrock, W. von: The senses, Ann Arbor, Mich., 1958, The University of Michigan Press.

Kellog, W. N.: Porpoises and sonar, Chicago, 1961, Phoenix Books.

Mueller, C.: Sensory psychology, Englewood Cliffs, N. J., 1965, Prentice-Hall, Inc.

Stevens, S. S., and Newman, E. B.: The localization of actual sources of sound, Amer. J. Psychol. **48:**297-306, 1936. (Bobbs-Merrill Reprint No. P-335.)

van Bergeijk, W. A., Pierce, J. R., and David, E. E.: Waves and the ear, Garden City, N. Y., 1960, Doubleday & Co.

von Békésy, G.: The ear, Sci. Amer. **197:**66-78, Aug. 1957. (W. H. Freeman Co. Reprint No. 44.)

von Békésy, G.: Similarities between hearing and skin sensations, Psychol. Rev. **66:**1-22, 1959. (Bobbs-Merrill Reprint No. P-31.)

Chapter 12

Vision

OVERVIEW

The topic of vision, like audition, can be considered from three points of view: (1) the anatomy and physiology of the eye and its nervous connections, (2) the physical energy that provides the stimulus, and (3) the psychophysics of interaction between the stimulus and the visual mechanism that provides a sensation. The anatomy and physiology of the eye will be discussed before studying the nature of light because many aspects of the stimulus energy are easier to understand after learning how the eye reacts to stimuli and sends signals to the brain. A simplified explanation of the physical nature of light follows, including the most common units of light measurement. Then visual sensations can be surveyed by using units of physical measurement and units of psychological response in visual psychophysics. Finally, various visual phenomena will be described and their basis in visual physiology given when it is known. In visual psychophysics, how light reaches the eye determines the colors that are seen. Newton's laws of color and the visual dimensions of hue, brightness, and saturation explain the basis of color mixing by addition and subtraction. The visual phenomena discussed include adaptation, aftersensations, contrast, acuity, critical flicker frequency, the phi phenomenon, cues to depth and distance, the constancy phenomena, and color vision defects.

ANATOMY OF THE EYE

The eye is a sense organ and therefore an organization of different kinds of tissue, each tissue having a role to play in the eye's response to light. The tissues are organized into parts of the eye that contribute in unique ways to vision. The various parts of the eye will be discussed first and the function of each part noted. Then interaction of these parts in accommodation, convergence, and the pupillary reflexes will be described.

Extrinsic muscles of the eye

There are six muscles that originate in the bony orbit or eye socket and insert on the eyeball. Their function is to move the eyeball— to "point" it in various directions. The **extrinsic** eye muscles train the eye on objects in reflex and in learned responses to light, movement, and the input from other senses. The extrinsic eye muscles are named by contrast with the **intrinsic** muscles inside the eyeball that control the lens and the pupil.

Layers, or coats, of the eye

One way to understand some parts of the eye is to consider the eyeball as consisting of three layers—the sclerotic coat, the choroid coat, and the retina (Fig. 12-1). The **sclerotic coat,** or **sclera,** is the tough opaque outer fibrous tissue forming the "white" of the eye. It serves a protective and binding

219

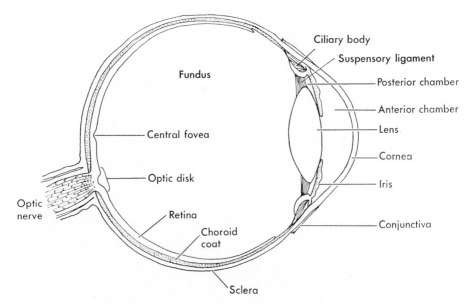

Fig. 12-1. Cross section of the eye in diagrammatic form, as seen from above. For a description of the structures named, see text.

function and, to some extent, prevents light from entering the eye except by way of the pupil. The sclera is continuous with the **cornea** at the front of the eye. Light first enters the interior of the eye through the transparent cornea. The cornea begins the focusing job that the **lens** completes by bringing light rays into focus on the retina.

The **choroid coat** is the middle layer of the eyeball. It contains many blood vessels that nourish the other tissues of the eye. It is pigmented, or dark-colored, on its inner surface to minimize the scattering of light by reflection inside the eyeball. The choroid coat is continuous with the **ciliary body**, or **ciliary ring**, a ring of smooth muscle that is attached to the **lens** by the **suspensory ligament.** Contraction of the ciliary ring relieves tension on the suspensory ligament and causes the lens to *thicken* of its own elasticity. Thickening the lens focuses light from nearby objects on the retina (see below). The ciliary body is also continuous with the **iris**, another smooth muscle structure that determines the color of the eye and surrounds the pupil. The iris contains

circular muscle fibers, which contract to constrict the **pupil** and radial muscles that contract to open the pupil (see below).

The **retina** covers only a part of the interior surface of the eyeball, the back portion. The retina contains the light-sensitive receptor cells as well as several kinds of nerve cells. It develops as an extension of the cerebral cortex of the brain that grows out from the brain on two large "stalks," the optic nerves, to invade the developing eyeballs. The retina therefore contains nerve cells and synapses in well-defined layers like the cerebral cortex. Much of its fine structure has been recently defined by the electron microscope.

The retina is arranged "inside out"; that is, the receptors lie nearest to the choroid coat, and light must pass through several layers of connecting nerve cells to reach the receptors (Fig. 12-2). The receptors are called **rods** and **cones**, which form a distinct layer in the retina. The most distinct of the other layers of the retina are the **bipolar cell layer** and the **ganglion cell layer.** The rods and cones pass excitation to

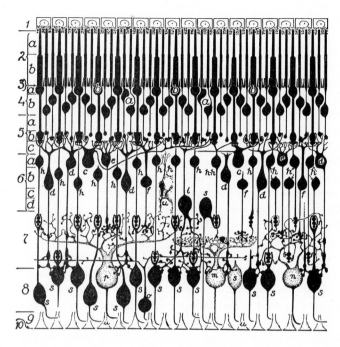

Fig. 12-2. Drawing of the structure of the retina as seen under the microscope (Golgi stain). Rods (**a**) and cones (**b**) are seen at the top, next to the pigmented layer (1) of the choroid coat (the interior of the eyeball is at the bottom of the figure). Bipolar cells (**d, e, f, h**) are the principal feature of the middle layers, but amacrine cells (**i, l**) and horizontal cells (**c**) can also be seen. Ganglion cells (**m, n, o, p, s**) dominate the inner layers. (From Polyak, S. L.: The retina, Chicago, 1941, The University of Chicago Press.)

the bipolar cells when stimulated by light. The bipolar cells, in turn, pass excitation on to the ganglion cells. The axons of the ganglion cells form the optic nerve that carries excitation from the eye to visual centers in the brain. In the retina itself there are interconnections among the receptors via **horizontal cells**, and **amacrine cells** interconnect the bipolar cells. Excitation and inhibition can thereby spread from one point to surrounding areas of the retina. This mechanism will become important later, when its function in sharpening visual input is discussed. Finaly, there are *efferent* fibers reaching the retina from the brain. These fibers probably synapse with amacrine and ganglion cells; their function appears to be inhibitory. The efferent fibers

may act to sharpen vision by blocking off extraneous input from other parts of the retina, or they may reduce visual input generally, but this is still speculation. (Efferent inhibitory fibers were found in the somesthetic and auditory systems as well.)

The **fovea** is a pit, or depression, in the retina that is in line with the pupil of the eye when the eye is directed toward an object (Fig. 12-1). The fovea is the point of clearest vision and is densely packed with receptors. The receptors are arranged radially around the pit, with connecting bipolar and ganglion cells radially connected to them. Therefore light does not have to pass through the ganglion and bipolar cells to reach the receptors in the fovea. Only cones are found in the fovea, but they are packed so densely together that they take on the elongated shape of rods. Since light reaches foveal cones directly and since they are so numerous, foveal vision is clearer than peripheral vision from other parts of the retina. Light rays from objects are focused by the lens on the fovea in visual accommodation.

The cones are the color-sensitive receptor cells of the retina. Stimulation of cones results in sensations of hue as well as brightness. Cones are most numerous in the fovea, but they rapidly become scarcer as one moves toward the periphery of the retina. In the most peripheral retina there are no cones; only rods are found. The cones have a relatively high threshold—cone vision is daylight vision. Light stimulates the cones by breaking down a chemical called **iodopsin** into intermediate compounds; light also causes the intermediate compounds to break down further into vitamin A and cone opsin (Fig. 12-3). Iodopsin is found in the sensory end of the cone, next to the pigmented epithelium of the choroid coat that furnishes the vitamin A. These details will be useful to a later discussion of the duplexity theory of vision.

The rods have a lower threshold than the cones and are sensitive only to brightness; they give sensations of varied shades of gray. This is why one does not have sensations of hue under conditions of night vision, when rod response predominates. At night there is often not enough light to stimulate cones. Instead of iodopsin the rods contain **rhodopsin,** a visual pigment, that is much more sensitive to light. Light breaks down iodopsin into intermediate compounds in stimulating rods; the intermediate compounds may further break down into rod opsin and vitamin A (Fig. 12-3).

Rods and cones excite bipolar cells, which, in turn, stimulate ganglion cells. It is the ganglion cell axons that leave the eye to form the optic nerve. At the point where the axons leave the eye there are no receptors; this point (the optic disk) is called the blind spot because it is insensitive to light. The blind spot lies on the nasal (nose) side of the retina; since light travels in a straight line, there is a blind spot in the temporal (peripheral-toward the temples) visual field. One is ordinarily not aware of this small area of blindness. To demonstrate its presence one can close the left eye, hold up a left finger at arm's length and focus on it

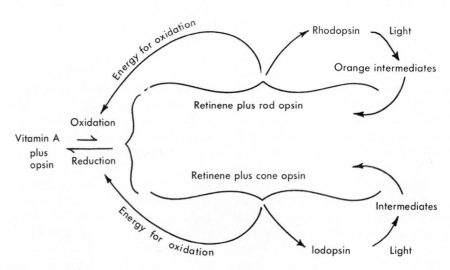

Fig. 12-3. Simplified synopsis of some of the major photochemical reactions in rod and cone vision.

with the right eye, and bring an upright right finger in from the periphery. When the right finger crosses the blind spot in the visual field, the right fingertip will seem to disappear.

Cavities and fluids of the eye (Fig. 12-1)

The **anterior chamber** of the eye lies between the cornea and the iris of the eye and communicates with the **posterior chamber** of the eye via the pupil. The posterior chamber lies between the iris on one hand and the ciliary ring, suspensory ligament, and lens on the other. Both anterior and posterior chambers are filled with **aqueous humor,** a watery fluid resembling the extracellular and lymph fluids of other parts of the body. Neither chamber communicates with the **fundus,** or large interior cavity of the eye, at least not directly. The fundus contains a jellylike substance called the **vitreous humor** that is much more viscous than the aqueous humor. Both fluids absorb some light rays and scatter others as do the lens and cornea. Despite its pigment coating the interior of the eyeball scatters some light, and still more light leaks through the opaque outer covering (sclera) of the eyeball. Considering all this,

it is a matter of some wonder that one sees as well as one does.

Mechanisms of accommodation

Light rays that reach the eye from objects more than 15 or 20 feet away are parallel as compared to light rays from nearby objects that *diverge* noticeably in reaching the eye. The normal eye is arranged so that the parallel rays from distant objects are bent just enough by the cornea and lens to be focused on the retina (Fig. 12-4). Light rays travel in a straight line except as they are bent by the cornea and lens. The image focused on the retina is therefore upside down and reversed. Rays from the lower half of the visual field stimulate the upper part of the retina and vice versa; rays from the left visual field stimulate the right half of the retina and vice versa. If the object is closer than 15 to 20 feet away, light rays from it *diverge* noticeably on their way to the eye. Such diverging rays must be bent more than parallel rays to be focused on the retina. This is accomplished by *thickening* the lens, a process called **accommodation.** The ciliary muscle contracts to constrict the ciliary ring, drawing it forward and de-

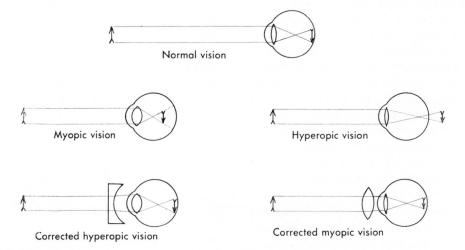

Fig. 12-4. Focus of light rays in normal, myopic, and hyperopic vision. For further details, see text.

creasing its diameter. This relieves tension on the suspensory ligament holding the lens. Under decreased tension the lens bulges of its own elasticity to become thicker, causing greater bending of diverging light rays as an object is brought closer to the eye.

A **myopic,** or nearsighted, person has a lens that is too thick or an eyeball that is too "long" in the front-to-back dimension. Parallel rays of light from distant objects are therefore bent too much and brought into focus before they reach the retina, where the receptors are found (Fig. 12-4). Rays reaching the retina are therefore scattered again and "blurred," and the myopic person cannot see distant objects clearly. Nearby objects can be focused since their light rays diverge and require either a thickened lens or elongated eyeball to be focused on the retina. The myopic individual must focus on objects closer to his eyes than an individual with normal vision, and the myopic person without glasses holds things "close to his nose." The condition is corrected by *concave* lenses, which make parallel light rays diverge. This compensates for the tendency of the myopic eye to bend light rays too much; parallel rays become diverging rays that can be focused on the retina of the myopic individual.

A **hyperopic** or farsighted, person has an eyeball that is too short or a lens that is too thin. In either case parallel rays of light from distant objects are not bent enough to be in focus when they reach the retina; these rays would focus "behind" the fovea if that were possible (Fig. 12-4). The hyperopic person can focus parallel rays of light from distant objects by thickening his lens in accommodation—the same response the normal eye makes to the diverging rays of nearby objects. The hyperopic individual is therefore accommodating all the time whereas the normal eye only accommodates to nearby objects. Further, there is "disagreement" between the reflexes that converge ("cross") the eyes to focus on nearby objects and the reflexes that thicken the lens. Abnormal stresses in the extrinsic muscles that "point" the eyes result in fatigue and headaches. The hyperopic person is unable to thicken his lens enough to focus on objects held close to his eyes; to read, he must hold a book at arm's length. The condition is corrected by convex lenses that partly bend the parallel rays from distant objects before the rays reach the lens. The lens completes the job to bring the light into focus on the fovea.

Presbyopia is the lack of accommodation of old age. For some reason nearly everyone becomes less able to accommodate, especially in the 60's and 70's. The range of accommodation is reduced; the lens is less elastic and cannot be thickened enough. The presbyopic person often must wear bifocals—glasses with thin lenses in their upper half for distant objects and with thick lenses in the lower half for nearby objects.

In **astigmatism** the eye may be partly farsighted, partly nearsighted, or both! This anomalous condition occurs because the lens or the cornea has an unequal curvature. The correct thickness for one cross section accompanies another cross section that is too "thick" or too "thin," that is, too curved or not curved enough. For example, a horizontal line would be correctly focused because the horizontal section of lens or cornea had the correct cross section, whereas a vertical line is blurred because the vertical section of cornea or lens is incorrect for focus. Lenses of opposite error in cross section correct the condition.

Cataracts result from clouding of the cornea. The cornea may be removed and thick eyeglasses substituted. The only "cure," however, is transplanting a cornea from another living eye. "Eye banks" of living corneas bequeathed in the wills of their deceased owners form the main supply of living corneal tissue.

Convergence and accommodation

The ciliary muscles of each eye contract to close the ciliary ring, allowing the lens to thicken of its own elasticity. This brings diverging rays of light from nearby objects into focus on the retina, as explained previously. It also serves as a cue to the distance of nearby objects since the nearer the object, the greater the ciliary contraction and the stronger the sensation of muscle strain. These sensations may be experienced by closing one eye, focusing on the fingertip held about a foot away, and then slowly bringing the finger as close to your eye as you can and still keep it in focus. If both eyes are used in this exercise, another set of muscle strain sensations will be experienced. In addition to the sensations from the *intrinsic* ciliary muscles, sensations from the *extrinsic* muscles that "point" the eyeballs will be felt. The closer the object, the more "cross-eyed" one must look at it to keep the fovea of each eye "pointed" at it in visual **convergence.** These two sets of muscle sensations serve as *cues* to the distance of objects up to several feet away. In the normal eye the two sets of reflexes are linked so that the correct amount of convergence of both eyes accompanies the correct amount of thickening of the lens of each eye. In the myopic or hyperopic individual correct focus does not accompany correct convergence because the lens or cornea of one eye or both is abnormal. Especially in the hyperopic person one eye sees a blurred image because it is out of focus, or double images are seen because the eyes are not converged properly. As a result the brain learns to suppress the input from one eye and depend on the input from another, a condition called **amblyopia.** It is especially common in children with undetected visual defects. If not discovered early enough, the input from one eye may be permanently suppressed, causing irreversible partial blindness in that eye as far as its use is concerned. If detected early, the impaired eye's function can be restored by forcing its use, partly or completely blindfolding the other eye for part of each day.

Pupillary reflexes

The pupil, the opening by which light reaches the interior of the eye, is surrounded by the colored iris. The contraction of intrinsic muscle fibers in the iris determines the size of the pupil and therefore the amount of light that reaches the retina. Contraction of the **radial fibers** of the iris opens the pupil to admit more light in dim illumination. Contraction of **circular fibers** of the iris constricts the pupil to admit less light under conditions of bright illumination. These are *reflex* reactions to light mediated by the autonomic nervous system. They help explain how the eye can react to very small amounts of light, yet function under brightnesses of hundreds of candlepower without damage.

NERVOUS CONNECTIONS OF THE EYE

As already noted, the retina itself is an extension of the brain, and many interconnections between nerve cells are made there. The axons of ganglion cells of the innermost layer of the retina converge on the optic disk, or blind spot, and emerge from the eyeball as the **optic nerve** (Figs. 12-1 and 12-5). The optic nerves from the two eyeballs are really *tracts* since they are part of the central rather than the peripheral nervous system. However, for convenience the ganglion cell axons are called the optic nerve before they reach the **optic chiasma** and are called the **optic tract** after they leave it, as can be seen in Fig. 12-5. Upon reaching the optic chiasma a hemidecussation, or "halfcrossing," occurs in the ganglion cells (in higher mammals). Fibers from the *nasal* (toward the nose) or medial halves of each retina cross, whereas fibers from the *temporal* (toward the temple) halves of each retina do not cross. As a result the crossing fibers from the nasal halves of the retina of each eye send excitation to the *opposite* cerebral hemispheres, whereas fibers from the temporal half of each retina that do not cross send excita-

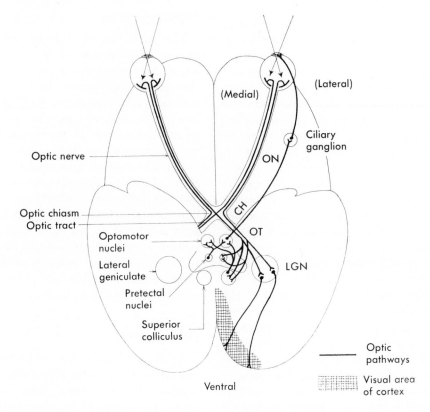

Fig. 12-5. Diagram of optic pathways. For description, see text.

tion to the cerebral hemisphere of the *same* side. The right optic *tract*, for example, would contain fibers from the nasal half of the left retina and the temporal half of the right retina. Now the nasal half of the left retina and temporal half of the right retina "see" the *left* half of the visual *field*. Damage to the right optic tract would therefore impair vision in the left visual field. By contrast, cutting the right optic nerve would merely blind the right eye. Damage to the crossing fibers of the chiasma (as sometimes occurs in pituitary gland tumors) would destroy fibers from the nasal halves of both retinas, impairing peripheral vision from the temporal halves of both visual fields (tunnel vision).

The optic tract of each side terminates in the **lateral geniculate body** or lateral geniculate nucleus (LGN). Like the sensory nuclei of the thalamus, the LGN serves mainly as a relay station for the cortex and is topographically organized. The optic tract also sends fibers to the **superior colliculi** and **pretectal nuclei.** The superior colliculi mediate reflex movements of the eyeball in convergence and in other eye movements. These responses are handled by connections with the **optomotor nuclei** of the third, fourth, and sixth cranial nerves. The pretectal nuclei, on the other hand, are concerned with the intrinsic muscles of the eye, the ciliary muscles of lens accommodation, and the reflex regulation of the pupil by the iris. Intrinsic eye muscle reactions are controlled via the parasympathetic fibers of the third nerve and via sympathetic fibers that relay excitation from the spinal cord.

The major function of the LGN is to supply the **striate cortex,** the primary visual projection area in the occipital lobes. This

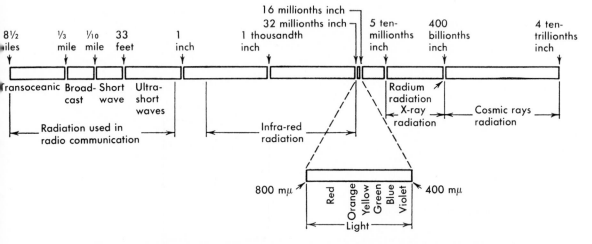

Fig. 12-6. Electromagnetic spectrum, showing the range of wavelengths that stimulate the visual receptors (light). (From Dimmick, F. L.: Color. In Boring, E. G., Langfeld, H. S., and Weld, H. P., editors: Foundations of psychology, New York, 1948, John Wiley & Sons, Inc.)

is the area called visual I and corresponds with Brodman's area 17. (The LGN also sends fibers to the association nuclei of the thalamus.) The cerebral cortex has a visual II in the prestriate area (areas 18 and 19) and a visual III in parietal and temporal areas. Visual II and visual III have been located mainly by recording from the cortex of anesthetized animals while stimulating the eye with light. The exact anatomy of these pathways is not known. They are presumed to include the association nuclei of the thalmus (diffuse thalamic projection system) and the brainstem reticular formation (ascending reticular activating system).

PHYSICS OF LIGHT

The physics of the light energy that stimulates the retina should be understood, at least in elementary fashion, before study of the physiology and psychophysics of vision. Light is a complex and poorly understood form of energy that is part of the **electromagnetic spectrum** of energy. This spectrum is a different form of energy than the air pressure changes perceived as sound; unlike sound, electromagnetic energy travels

readily through a vacuum and travels at a rate much higher than sound (the speed of light is 186,272 miles per second).

Physicists frequently speak of light in terms of flowing particles, or quanta, a quantum of light being the least measurable part of radiant energy. It will be more useful, however, to begin studying light as vibratory energy, forming a part of the electromagnetic spectrum of wavelengths.

The wavelengths of electromagnetic energy form a broad band, or spectrum (Fig. 12-6). The wavelengths include radio waves (18 miles to 1-inch wavelengths), infrared waves (1 inch to 32 millionths of an inch), light (32 millionths to 16 millionths of an inch), and x-rays and cosmic rays (down to 400 ten-thrillionths of an inch). From this one can see that visible light forms a small part of the electromagnetic spectrum and the wavelengths are very short.

Light reaching the eye from the sun is a mixture of all the visible wavelengths. If a small beam of sunlight from a point source is passed through a *prism*, the light will be bent, or refracted. A prism is a wedge-shaped block of glass that bends light rays as a function of their wave-

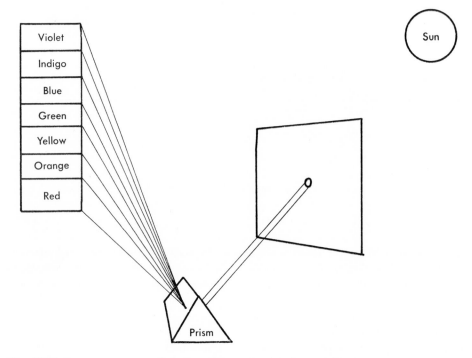

Fig. 12-7. Spectrum, as revealed through use of prism (see text).

lengths. The longer wavelengths of light are bent less than the shorter wavelengths so that an orderly array of wavelengths is produced by the prism (Fig. 12-7). The resulting **visible spectrum** will be seen as bands of different **hues**, from violet through blue, green, yellow, orange, and red, as shorter to longer wavelengths are separated. Any single wavelength is spectrally pure and fairly **saturated,** that is, distinct in hue. (Some mixtures of wavelengths produce gray-looking hues, or colors low in saturation.) Single wavelengths are **homogeneous;** mixtures of wavelengths are **heterogeneous.** Increasing the *amplitude* of either a single wavelength of light or any mixture of wavelengths produces increases in **brightness.**

Light, then, varies in wavelength, intensity, or amplitude, and homogeneity, or wavelength mixture. Changes in wavelength are perceived by the eye as changes in hue; changes in amplitude or intensity are perceived as changes in brightness;

changes in the homogeneity of light can result in saturation differences.

Measurements of light

Wavelengths are measured in **millimicrons (mμ).** A millimicron is one thousandth of one millionth of a standard meter, or one millionth of a millimeter. A range of 400 to 750 mμ is commonly taken as the limits of the visible spectrum, although some intense stimuli outside these limits can be seen. Homogeneity or heterogeneity may be specified in terms of the proportions of each component wavelength in mixtures of light waves. Measurements of intensity are more complex and are based on the rate of flow of "particles" of light rather than on the amplitude of a vibratory light wave.

Brightness of a source. The brightness of a light source is calibrated in terms of the flow of light from an international **candle,** a standard source about as bright as a candle with a 1-inch flame. The candle radiates luminous **flux,** or flowing light particles, in all directions. The density of these particles—how close they are together—diminishes as light scatters with increasing distance from the source. (A standard candle radiates 4Π **lumens** of luminous flux.) One lumen of light would cover a square inch 1 inch from the candle or a square mile 1 mile from the candle.

Illuminance. Measurements of brightness differ for light falling on a surface from measurements of light coming from a surface. **Illuminance** is the name given measurements of light falling on a surface. A **footcandle** of light (one lumen) would fall on a square foot of surface placed 1 foot from a standard candle.

Luminance. **Luminance** is the brightness of a surface that is either emitting or reflecting light. The usual standard is the **lambert,** defined in lumens per square centimeter of area.

Light stimuli

Light reaching the eye from any point or surface varies in intensity, wavelength, and heterogeneity of wavelengths. The resulting sensation appears to vary in brightness, hue, and saturation, respectively. Light reaching the eye from the sun is uniform in brightness; sunlight lacks hue and saturation because it is a heterogeneous mixture of all visible wavelengths. Light reaching the eye from other objects has undergone changes in intensity and component wavelengths; therefore it is changed in brightness, hue, and saturation.

A physical object may **transmit, reflect, absorb, refract,** or **radiate** light. In each case it is the light reaching the eye that determines the hue, saturation, or brightness. A color filter may be placed between the source and an observer, which will absorb some wavelengths and transmit others. For example, it may transmit only the longest wavelengths, resulting in a red hue. The mixture of wavelengths transmitted determines saturation, whereas the amount

of light transmitted determines brightness. A prism, on the other hand, refracts or bends the light it transmits, resulting in a spectrum of wavelengths, as already pointed out. A surface such as a painted wall may absorb some wavelengths and reflect others. The wavelengths that are reflected to the eye determine the hue and saturation; those that are absorbed are not seen. The amount of light of any wavelength that is reflected would determine brightness. An object may also radiate light of certain wavelengths because of heat (incandescence) or chemical reactions (luminescence). The wavelengths emitted will be determined by the chemical properties of the object. An ordinary light bulb heats a tungsten filament and gives off more "yellow" wavelengths than others as a result. The hue of the luminescence of a "neon" light will depend on the type of gas used in it, different gases producing different wavelengths of light by chemical reactions. This property is often used in advertising signs.

VISUAL PHYSIOLOGY

Now that the anatomy of the eye, the visual pathways, and the physics of the stimulus have been discussed, the topic of visual physiology may be undertaken. Beginning with the reactions of the rods and cones to light, the known effects of visual stimulation can be traced to the highest part of the brain.

Duplicity theory

The initial assumption made about the way the rods and cones work as light receptors assigns them different intensity ranges and reactions to hue. The rods are supposed to be **achromatic,** or **scotopic,** receptors that do not give sensations of hue and have very low thresholds for functioning in low illumination (night vision). The cones are supposed to be **chromatic,** or **photopic,** receptors that have relatively high thresholds (about 10 microlamberts) and function under conditions of daylight vision. The evidence behind these statements can be summarized as follows:

1. Two different visual pigments in the eye, iodopsin and rhodopsin have been discovered, with iodopsin being much more sensitive to light.

2. Relative sensitivity to individual wavelengths differs under high illumination as compared to low illumination; the cones seem most sensitive in the yellow-green region of the spectrum (555 mμ), whereas the rods seem most sensitive in the green region of the spectrum (511 mμ).

3. The curves for spectral sensitivity, or sensitivity to different wavelengths of light for rods and cones, look like curves measuring the amount of light of the same wavelengths that is absorbed by rhodopsin and iodopsin, respectively. Presumably, the more a given wavelength is absorbed to break down rhodopsin, for example, the more sensitive the rhodopsin-containing rods would be to that wavelength.

4. The central part of the retina—the fovea, which contains only cones—provides the most acute vision in high illumination; the periphery of the retina (peripheral vision) contains only rods and is most sensitive in the dark adapted eye.

5. When looking at a gray field, hues are seen only in the central part of the visual field where the cones respond; spots of color in the periphery where the rods respond are seen as gray (see color zones, below).

6. Adaptation to darkness from daylight seems to occur in two stages. For approximately the first 5 minutes the eyes become more sensitive at a diminishing rate as more iodopsin is built up in the cones while there is not enough light to break it all down. Later, enough rhodopsin begins to be built up in the rods so that they begin responding. Since they are more sensitive than cones, the eyes again start increasing in sensitivity at a rapid rate, reaching maximum sensitivity after a half hour or so.

There is other evidence supporting the duplicity theory, but these seem to be the main points. The theory needs restatement, however. For instance, new evidence shows that there are three kinds of cones that respond differently to different hues and perhaps another kind of cone, or a mixed reaction of the retina, that responds to brightness alone.

Electroretinogram

In stimulating the eye of anesthetized animals the electrical responses of the retina are often used to indicate visual response to light. Some recording measures to be reported involve electrodes placed in the retina—in single ganglion cells of the retina or their fibers in the optic nerve. A more gross measure of the overall response of the retina is used often enough to deserve mention, however. This measure is the **electroretinogram (ERG)**. The ERG is usually recorded by placing one electrode on the cornea and another near the back of the eye. Four electrical waves are recorded when the eye is stimulated with light (Fig. 12-8); an A, B, and C wave is recorded when the light is turned on, and a D wave is recorded when the light is turned off. Gross recordings of this kind are, of course, compounded of the electrical responses of many cells. The A and B waves are compounded of an early component that has been identified with photopic receptors (cones) and a late component that is identified with scotopic receptors (rods). As a result an arbitrary amplitude of the A or B wave is often selected as a threshold measure for vision experiments.

Color vision theory

Over the last hundred years theories of color vision have been based on either a three-color or a four-color response of the eye. Three-color theorists (such as Young and Helmholz) have been impressed by the fact that three hues can be selected that mix to give white or gray; mixing these hues two at a time can reproduce all other hues. They

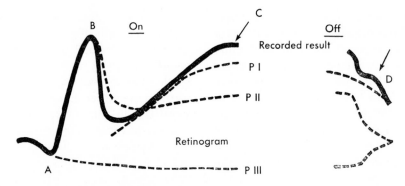

Fig. 12-8. Electroretinogram (ERG). Major *A, B, C,* and *D* waves recorded are presumably made up of the components P I, P II, and P III (see text). (From Bartley, S. H.: Psychol. Rev. **46:**337-358, 1939.)

proposed that the eye works the same way, having three kinds of cones that respond maximally to three different "primary" hues —a mixed response would signal other colors. Four-color theorists (such as Hering), on the other hand, were impressed by the unitary nature of red, green, yellow, and blue. When other hues are mixed to give red, green, yellow, or blue, their presence cannot be detected. By contrast, red and yellow can be detected in an orange or blue and green in an aqua. Four-color theorists also note that color-blind individuals are usually deficient in red *and* green vision or else blue *and* yellow vision, not other combinations. Since the red and green in question mix to give gray or white, as do the yellow and blue, they proposed a red-green (R-G) cone and a blue-yellow (B-Y) cone. Red light would polarize the R-G cone oppositely to green light; the same kind of reaction would occur in the B-Y cone to blue and yellow light. In this manner two kinds of cones could signal four primary visual responses to the brain.

Modern research suggests that both sets of theorists may have been right. To oversimplify the findings that will be reported, it appears that there are three kinds of cones, a "blue" receptor with maximum sensitivity near 450 mμ, a "green" receptor with maximum sensitivity near 525 mμ, and

a "red" receptor with maximum sensitivity near 555 mμ. On the other hand, recordings in the connecting cells of the retina suggest positive electrical reactions to red and yellow and negative reactions to green and blue. There is still another negative reaction of the retina in signalling the amount of light of any wavelength (brightness). It appears that the cones may react on a three-color basis, but the retina transforms the input into a four-color signal to the ganglion cells that lead to the brain. Such notions will become clearer as some of the experiments giving rise to them are explained.

Absorption spectrum of single rods and cones

The rods are stimulated when the rhodopsin they contain is affected by light; the cones are stimulated when their iodopsin is changed by light. However, neither rhodopsin nor iodopsin are equally sensitive to all wavelengths of light. It is reasonable to assume that rods in the dark-adapted eye would absorb more of the wavelengths that break down rhodopsin most readily; cones in the light-adapted eye should absorb more of the wavelengths that affect iodopsin most. In a general way experiments have shown this to be the case. The rhodopsin and iodopsin used were chemical extracts of the retina, however, and the tests of visual sensitivity involved the whole eye. Newer optical techniques permit stimulating *single* rods and cones in the freshly removed living human retina by using exactly controlled wavelengths. The proportion of light absorbed at each wavelength can be measured over the whole visible spectrum for each single rod or cone. Presumably the more a given wavelength is absorbed by a rod or cone, the more sensitive the receptor is to light of that wavelength. Fig. 12-9 reports some of the results obtained by this method under conditions given in the legend. Only a single kind of rod was found, and its absorption spectrum agrees rather well with sensitivity to various wavelengths in night vision; maximum absorption was at 505 mμ, whereas night vision is most sensitive at 511 mμ. The difference can probably be

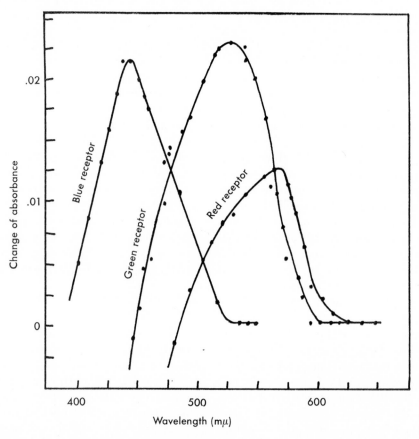

Fig. 12-9. Absorption spectrum of single rods and cones. Freshly excised human retina, including the fovea, was placed in a small container and axially exposed to single cell width light from a recording spectrophotometer, and the absorption spectrum measured while the cells were under 2000× microscopically projected observation. Wavelengths were varied from 650 to 380 mμ and back again, recordings being taken after dark adaptation and after bleaching the receptors by exposure to a flash bulb. Curves are averages of the conditions. (Redrawn from Brown, P. K., and Wald, G.: Science **144**:46, 1964. Copyright 1964 by the American Association for the Advancement of Science.)

accounted for by the wavelengths absorbed by the fluids in the cavities of the normal eye and light scattering, etc. in normal vision; the excised retina was stimulated directly. The cone data are of greatest interest, however. Three kinds of cones were found, as predicted by the three-color theorists: a blue cone with an absorption peak at 450 mμ, a green cone with an absorption peak at 525 mμ, and a red cone with an absorption peak of 555 mμ. These data compare well with some tests of human visual sensitivity that follow.

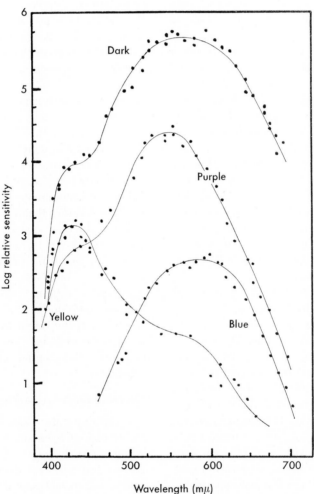

Fig. 12-10. Sensitivity of the human retina to spectral wavelengths. The curve labeled "dark" is for the dark-adapted eye, "yellow" is yellow-adapted, "purple" is purple-adapted, and "blue" is blue-adapted, bringing out the response of "blue," "green," and "red" receptors, respectively. For further details, see text. (Redrawn from Wald, G.: Science **145**:1009, 1964. Copyright 1964 by the American Association for the Advancement of Science.)

Sensitivity of the human retina

If there are three kinds of cones, tests of sensitivity by a human observer to various wavelengths involve a mixed response, more than one kind of cone responding to each wavelength to some degree. However, if there are three kinds of cones, blue, green, and red, the response of one cone might be emphasized by selectively *adapting*, or "fatiguing," both of the others to make them less sensitive. If the eye were stimulated with yellow, the green and red receptors would respond until they lost some sensitivity, but the blue receptor would not react and would be "rested" and quite sensitive. If the sensitivity of the retina to various wavelengths were tested under these conditions, the reaction of blue receptors would be at a maximum and blue would seem more intense when the green and red receptors were "fatigued." The experiment has been ingeniously performed; the conditions and results are presented in Fig. 12-10. The visual field was restricted to 1 degree to confine the image to the fovea, where only cones (color receptors) are found. When the eye was adapted to maximum cone sensitivity, a "dominator" curve of visual sensitivity by wavelength was found, with maximum sensitivity at 568 mμ, representing the mixed response of all three kinds of cones. Then the red and green receptors were adapted with a "surround" patch of yellow, and the apparent brightness of this stimulus was compared with a central test patch of different wavelengths by the subject. This brought out the relative sensitivity of blue cones, which showed peak sensitivity at 435 mμ—in good agreement with the 450 mμ absorption maximum for blue cones in the last experiment. Adapting red and blue cones with purple light brought out a green cone modulator curve with a maximum at 550 mμ, which compares with the absorption spectrum maximum of 525 mμ. Finally, adapting blue cones brought out a red modulator peaking at 585 mμ, which compares with the absorp-

tion peak of 555 mμ. Differences in the two experiments can probably be accounted for by the way the intact eye absorbs and scatters light in this experiment compared with the excised retina of the last experiment.

Retinal responses

So far there appear to be three kinds of cones affected differently by different wavelengths. What happens when these cones stimulate the bipolar and ganglion cells of the retina to send nerve impulses to the brain? Briefly, it appears that the cones cause the bipolar (and horizontal and amacrine) connecting cells to increase or decrease their polarity without firing; the change in polarity changes the rate of firing of the ganglion cells going to the brain in the optic nerve. In this manner it appears that three-color cone signals are changed into four-color signals in the ganglion cells —a red-green signal and a blue-yellow signal. In addition, another signal depends on brightness rather than on wavelength alone. Some of the color-coded cells fire when the visual stimulus is turned "on," representing excitation, and some fire when the stimulus is turned "off," representing inhibition (perhaps a "rebound effect" of firing that follows inhibition). Positive and negative responses of the retina to various hues may be represented by "on" and "off" type responses that signal excitation and inhibition.

Microelectrode recordings

A technique has been developed (Granit) for recording from single ganglion cells in living animals of various species. The cornea and lens are removed from the eye and a microelectrode is lowered through the fundus of the eye until it impales a single cell in the retina. Since the retina is "inside out," the electrode encounters a ganglion cell first rather than the underlying connector or receptor cells. The eye is then stimulated with various wavelengths of light, and the responses of the single gan-

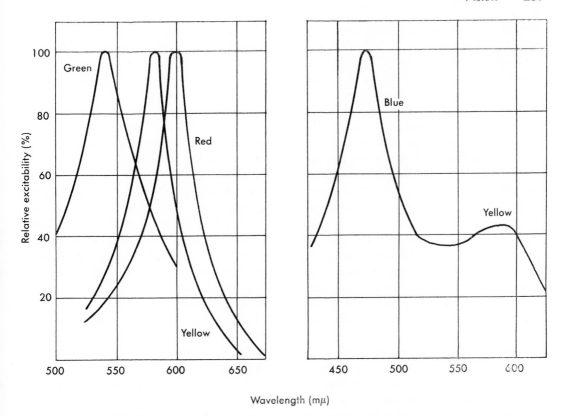

Fig. 12-11. Modulator and dominator curves in the frog retina. For further description, see text. (Redrawn from Granit, R.: Acta Physiol. Scand. **3:**137-151, 1941.)

glion cell are recorded. Some arbitrary number of impulses, for example, four, is chosen as response threshold, and the sensitivity of response of the ganglion cell to various wavelengths is tested. Many ganglion cells can be tested in a single eye in this manner. The response of each represents the signal being sent to the brain in that ganglion cell, a signal that results from the stimulation of several rods and/or cones, the interaction in connecting cells, and the outcome in ganglion cell firing. The eyes of several species have been tested in this manner and the results compared with what is known of the rods and the cones of the eye of each species.

Dominator and modulator curves. In retinas that resemble man's, ganglion cell

units have been found that respond to a broad spectrum of wavelengths and the resulting "threshold" curve for various wavelengths is called a **dominator curve.** The sensitivity of these ganglion cells to various wavelengths under light-adapted conditions is in good agreement with the threshold curve for human daylight (cone) vision; the threshold curve of other units under dark-adapted conditions resembles the sensitivity curve for night (rod) vision in man. Other ganglion cells have been found that respond to a narrower band of wavelengths. These are called **modulator curves** and are illustrated in Fig. 12-11. In the frog eye four modulators have been found, peaking in the blue, green, yellow, and red regions of the spectrum at wavelengths close to the four that appear primary to man.

Coupled and uncoupled receptors. In these experiments the ganglion cell that is firing in response to light may be reacting to more than one kind of cone, or even a rod and a cone, because of the many interconnections between the rods and/or cones and the ganglion cells that form the optic nerve (Fig. 12-2). If more than one receptor will fire the ganglion cell, the two receptors are said to be **coupled receptors.** If two cones of different sensitivities to different wavelengths control a ganglion cell, a modulator curve with two "humps" of ganglion cell response may be found (Fig. 12-11). For example, a blue-sensitive receptor and a yellow-sensitive receptor may each fire the ganglion cell. Its threshold modulator curve may then show two peaks of sensitivity, depending on which of the two receptors is controlling the ganglion cell. Coupling like this may explain why red and green or blue and yellow cancel each other out in human color vision, or why one is red-green color-blind or blue-yellow color-blind and not color-blind in some other fashion. Perhaps the three types of cones discussed previously are coupled to give results of this kind.

Retinal interactions. Microelectrode recordings from near the "connecting" cells (bipolar, horizontal, and amacrine) of the retina show **graded potentials** in transferring excitation from the rods and cones to the ganglion cells. That is, they increase or decrease their polarized condition to cause firing of ganglion cells, but they do not fire themselves. To simplify, it looks as if decreased polarization of the connecting cells causes the ganglion cells to fire upon onset of the visual stimulus; increased polarization of the connecting cells causes other ganglion cells to fire when the visual stimulus ceases in a "rebound" effect. Still other ganglion cells are influenced by both "on" and "off" cells and fire briefly when the stimulus is turned on and briefly again

when it is turned off. Whether a ganglion cell acts as an "on" cell, and "off" cell, or an "on-off" type depends on the conditions of stimulation at the minute. The interconnections between rods and cones on one hand and ganglion cells on the other are very diffuse so that the response of the ganglion cell depends on the *pattern* of retinal stimulation at the moment.

Retinal zones. If one records from a single ganglion cell in the retina, and the stimulus light is directed to receptors adjacent to it and farther from it, retinal "zones" of effect on the ganglion cell can be plotted (Fig. 12-12). The zone has a central area that is consistent in giving *either* an on or off response, but not both. It is surrounded by an area consistently giving the opposite response; that is, if the central area gave a consistent on response, the peripheral area gives a consistent off response. In between the central and peripheral areas is an intermediate zone that give *both* on and off responses. If the central area gave an on response, it was considered an *excitatory* area, surrounded by a peripheral *inhibitory* area (off response) with an intermediate zone of interaction (on-off response) between excitation and inhibition.

Color coding. One important feature of these on and off responses is that some of them are color-coded, whereas others depend only on brightness. The color-coded ganglion cells in goldfish give an on or off response, depending on the wavelenght used as a stimulus to the receptors. The on response covers a band of wavelengths, but is most sensitive to 650 mμ, for example, whereas the off response covers an overlapping band of wavelengths and is most sensitive at 500 mμ. Other color-coded cells with different on and off peaks have been found. Noncolor-coded cells are also found, giving both on and off responses to a wide variety of wavelengths over most of the visible spectrum. In these cells the wavelength giving peak sensitivity to the on response is the same as the wave-

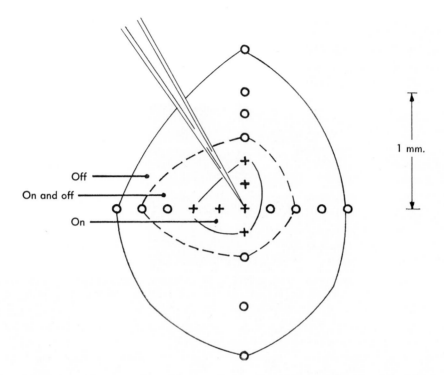

Fig. 12-12. Retinal zones, plotted by ganglion cell response at the tip of the electrode. For details, see text. (Redrawn from Küffler, S. W.: J. Neurophysiol. **49**:16, 1953.)

length giving the most sensitivity to the off response; these cells are therefore not color-coded. In either color-coded or noncolor-coded cells, the on response always has a lower threshold than the off response, as would be expected of an excitatory process as compared to an inhibitory process. Color-coded on and off responses in ganglion cells may provide a way for the retina to signal hue to the brain, whereas non-color-coded ganglion cells may signal brightness. Recordings from near the cells that "connect" the rods and cones with the ganglion cells suggests that such may be the case.

Graded potentials

As previously reported, excitation of the rods and cones sets up *graded* potentials of increased polarization or decreased polarization in the cells that transfer excita-

tion from rods and cones to ganglion cells. It is now known that these graded potentials are shown by glial cells. Glial cells, in the retina as in the brain (the retina is an extension of the brain) were thought to have only metabolic and supporting functions. However they are very close to the "connector" neurons and may influence them. Microelectrode recordings show that glial cells respond to light—whether the response is mediated by the receptors or not. However, they respond to light in a different way than either the rods and cones or the nerve cells. They give generator potentials (Chapter 4) that have been called S potentials (for slow potentials). Their resting potentials are reduced in the dark (dark adaptation), and their response is of two main types, depending on the effect of the hue of the light. The type L response is the same depolarization of glial

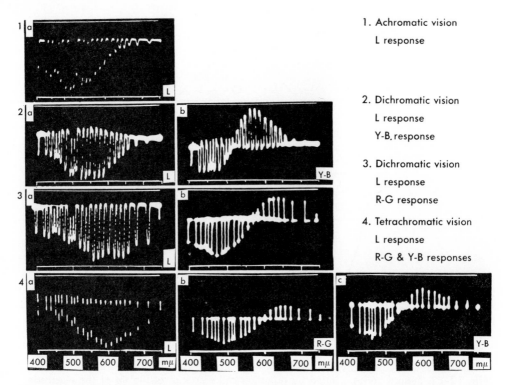

1. Achromatic vision
   L response

2. Dichromatic vision
   L response
   Y-B. response

3. Dichromatic vision
   L response
   R-G response

4. Tetrachromatic vision
   L response
   R-G & Y-B responses

Fig. 12-13. Graded slow potentials recorded from the retina as a function of wavelength of the stimulus. For details, see text. (From Svaetichin, G., and MacNichol, E. F.: Ann. N. Y. Acad. Sci. **74**:388, 1958.)

cells for all wavelengths of light. Only the *degree* of depolarization varies with wavelength in a way much like the sensitivity curve for brightness at various wavelengths (Fig. 12-13). This response may signal *brightness*. The type C response, on the other hand, is a depolarization or a hyperpolarization of a glial cell that depends on wavelength. Type C responses seem coded to either yellow and blue or red and green wavelengths rather than to other combinations of wavelengths—a four-color signal. (Positive potentials in a single cell represent a depolarization effect and negative potentials a hyperpolarization effect since the electrode is inside the cell.) If depolarization is excitatory, it may initiate an on response, and if hyperpolarization inhibits ganglion cells, it may initiate an off response. However, the experiments only

measure the degree of response of each glial cell to each of the visible wavelengths.

Sometimes an attempt is made to adapt the eye to a band of wavelengths to see if this changes the response of a cell. The subjects have usually been fish of various kinds believed to have color vision, but similar results have been found for the cat; the results can probably be generalized for all vertebrates. Three types of responses, then, have been found: (1) an L response, or luminosity response, (2) a R-G response, or red-green response, and (3) a Y-B response, or yellow-blue response. The L response is a change in glial cell polarization that depends on wavelength. It does not seem to be color-coded, however, since adaptation to specific wavelengths does not change the shape of the curve of polarization in a way that depends on wavelength;

that is, if the cell becomes less sensitive to one wavelength stimulus, it adapts to all of them. The L response may signal brightness to the ganglion cells; its curve is strikingly like that of sensitivity of the light-adapted eye to various wavelengths. The R-G and Y-B responses *are* color-coded and may signal hue to the brain. In each case the response at the shorter end of the spectrum (G or B) is negative, and the response at the longer end of the spectrum (R or Y) is positive. The G or B response will disappear after selectively adapting with green or blue light; the R or Y response can be eliminated with red or yellow light. Different process must therefore be involved; fatiguing the red process, for example, reduces the positive polarization response in the glial cells. If the positive (depolarization) Y or R responses are excitatory, they should cause "on" firing in ganglion cells, whereas the negative (polarization) G or B responses could cause "off" response in the ganglion cells. In this manner four-color signals could be sent to the brain.

VISUAL PHENOMENA

The phenomenology of vision will be discussed in this section; that is, the way in which hue, saturation, and brightness appear to interact in laboratory tests of color mixing, visual adaptation, aftersensations, contrast, acuity, some complex phenomena such as flicker and apparent movement, the cues to depth and distance, and color blindness. Wherever possible, each visual phenomenon will be related to visual physiology on the one hand and everyday experience on the other.

Newton's laws of color

Many years ago Sir Isaac Newton produced a visible spectrum of hues by separating the wavelengths of light coming from the sun. Using a narrow beam of sunlight from a pinhole, he interposed a prism that bent, or refracted, the beam of light.

Light refraction depends on wavelength; the shorter wavelengths were bent more than the longer wavelengths, producing an array of wavelengths—the visible spectrum. Different wavelengths are perceived by the eye as different hues so that bands of different hues were seen from violet through blue, green, yellow, orange, and red, with shorter to longer wavelengths over the 400 to 750 mμ visible spectrum (Figs. 12-6 and 12-7). Any single wavelength is fairly saturated, that is, distinct in hue, and the spectrum produced in this manner is of intermediate brightness. Having separated the wavelengths to produce the hues of the spectrum, Newton recombined individual hues, a process often called "color mixing." His experiments led to Newton's three laws of color, which can be rephrased as follows:

1. **Law of complements.** For each hue there is another hue that will mix with it in some proportion to cancel both hues and give a gray or white color. Whether gray or white is obtained depends on brightness.

2. **Law of supplements.** Noncomplementary hues will mix to give a hue that lies between them on the spectrum. For example, a chartreuse (yellow-green) and an orange will mix to give a green. Hues from the ends of the spectrum—violets and reds—mix to give purples, which are not spectral hues.

3. **Law of resultants.** The same hue may be produced by several mixtures. Mixing two hues produced in different ways alters nothing; mixtures that match one another mix without change in hue. For example, a green could be obtained with a single wavelength or by mixing yellow-green and orange-red. If the two greens matched, their apparent hue would not change when they were combined.

Visual response

The eye perceives changes in the physical amplitude, or rate of flow (flux), of light as a change in brightness, from black to gray to white, for example. Changes in the wavelength of light are perceived as changes in hue—reds, greens, blues and yellows, for instance. But colors that are of the same hue and brightness may differ in saturation—a green may appear as green as it can be or it may be a grayish green—equally bright, of the same basic hue, but "not as colored." The last statement is a bit misleading since gray, black, and white are colors, although they lack hue or saturation. *Saturation is the amount by which a hue differs from the total lack of hue perceived in a gray of equal brightness.*

Unique colors

It has been estimated that there can be about 7,295,000 discriminable colors (including grays), although industry uses about 5,000 in the Natural Bureau of Standards compilation. A careful study by Chapanis (1965) suggests that the number of color names actually used by human subjects is 52 to 55. Some of these color names represent differences in brightness; others, differences in saturation; and still others, differences in hue. It is not necessary to have even this many color names, however, because colors can be classified by their resemblance to seven colors that are unique. A **unique color** is one that can be psychologically described only in terms of itself. This is true because the component colors making up a unique color cannot be perceived. By this definition the seven unique colors are red, green, yellow, blue, white, black, and gray. A neutral gray may be composed of a mixture of black and white, but this cannot be perceived by looking at it. A green may be a mixture of a yellow-green and a blue-green, but neither the yellow nor the blue can be perceived in the green. By contrast, a nonunique hue, such as orange, recognizably contains red and yellow. A whole series of oranges can be described by reference to the relative amount of unique red or yellow they appear to contain. The same can be said for the blue and green in aqua, the red and

blue in purple, or the yellow and green in chartreuse. The three achromatic unique colors—black, white, and gray—represent differences in brightness. The four chromatic unique colors—red, green, blue, and yellow—represent differences in hue. Mixing gray with any of the four unique hues reduces saturation. The seven unique colors are the seven **primary qualities** of vision, the irreducable elements making up differences in visual hue, brightness, and saturation.

Color formula. The seven primary color qualities can be specified in terms of the physical stimuli producing them. Black, white, and gray are specified in terms of the intensity of a light stimulus that produces no hue sensations. The spectral wavelengths in millimicrons producing perceived red, green, yellow, and blue are 494c, 515, 582, and 476, respectively. (Unique red is not a spectral color; it is that mixture of wavelengths that is the complement of 494 mμ and is therefore called 494c.) The way in which the seven unique colors interact can then be described in the **color formula** given below:

Color = (Red or Green) + (Yellow or Blue) +
        (Black or White) + Gray

  or

$$C = \underbrace{(R \text{ or } G) + (Y \text{ or } B)}_{\text{Hue}} +$$

$$\underbrace{(Bl \text{ or } Wh)}_{\text{Brightness}} + \underbrace{Gr}_{\text{Saturation}}$$

The four chromatic qualities represent the visual experience of hue. The formula shows that they can be taken only one or two at a time, however. Unique red and green are complementary; they mix to give gray, which is given elsewhere in the formula. The same is true of unique yellow and blue. Other hue experiences are provided by mixing noncomplementary unique chromatic qualities—red and yellow to give orange, for example. The experience of brightness is taken care of by unique black to decrease brightness *or* unique white to increase brightness. Both are not used because they mix to give unique gray, given elsewhere in the formula. Unique gray adds the element of saturation to color experience. Adding gray to any of the four chromatic elements—red, green, yellow, or blue —may reduce their saturation without changing their brightness. A gray-looking red, for example, is low in saturation but may be of the same brightness (reflect as much light to the eye) as unique red, which has maximum saturation. An orange could be produced by mixing a red and a yellow and then be desaturated by adding gray. The seven unique colors are given in the equation and represent the primary color qualities.

Secondary color **qualities** can be produced by mixing two or more of the primary color qualities; red and yellow give orange, for example, or red and white produce pink. If two elements from the color equation are used, the result is a **duplex** color. Because of the limitation on using red and green, blue and yellow, or white and black at the same time, there are only eighteen duplex combinations possible, and only two of the dimensions of hue, brightness, and saturation can be involved. When three elements of the formula are used at once, a **triplex color** is produced, and all three dimensions (hue, brightness, and saturation) can change at once from one color to another, although they need not. There are twenty triplex combinations possible. **Quadruplex colors** use four elements of the color formula and are the most complex mixtures possible. There are eight quadruplex combinations possible.

Color pyramid. The seven primary visual qualities, their relation to hue, brightness, and saturation, and the limitations on their combination are clearly seen in the color formula. The way the seven qualities interact in duplex, triplex, and quadruplex colors is better seen in the double spa-

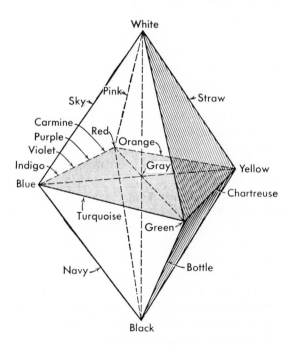

Fig. 12-14. Color pyramid. For details, see text. (From Dimmick, F. L.: Color. In Boring, E. G., Langfeld, H. S., and Weld, H. P.: Foundations of psychology, New York, 1948, John Wiley & Sons, Inc.)

tial pyramid of Fig. 12-14, the **color pyramid.** Fig. 12-14 also clarifies the interaction between hue and brightness. The seven elements of the color formula are represented as positions on the double pyramid to establish the three dimensions of hue, brightness, and saturation. The four points around the square base of the double pyramid represent the four unique hue qualities: red, green, yellow, and blue. Duplex colors made by mixing hues are intermediate between the hues involved; for example, orange lies on the edge of Fig. 12-14 between red and yellow. Note that the red and green of the color formula are opposite one another, as are the blue and yellow, with gray as the center point. This shows that the unique red and green and the unique blue and yellow are complements— mixing either pair gives gray which is at the center of the illustration.

All the hues that can be perceived lie on the edge of the base of the double pyramid and all hues directly opposite one another are complements; a line drawn from any hue through gray will end at the complement of that hue. The central gray point adds the dimension of saturation to the illustration—any hue, unique or not, can be desaturated by moving from the location of that hue at the base of the double pyramid toward the gray at the center. A hue can therefore be desaturated by adding gray or by adding the complement of that hue—either operation moves the location of the hue toward the gray in the center. Brightness is represented by the vertical axis of Fig. 12-14. Black is at the bottom of the double pyramid, white at the apex, with gray on a line between them since black and white mix to give gray. Fig. 12-14 also shows that unique blue can be changed into sky blue by increasing brightness (adding white) or into navy blue by decreasing brightness (adding black), in duplex colors that differ in brightness but not in hue. The pyramid shows that brightness and saturation interact, and the surface of the

pyramid represents the maximum saturation for any hue at a specified brightness. The greater the distance of a point on the surface from the line of no saturation running from black through gray to white, the greater the perceived saturation of the hue. This expresses the known fact that hues are most saturated at intermediate brightness. A pink, for example, cannot be as saturated as a unique red, and a bottle green cannot be as saturated as a unique green. An example from everyday experience is the increased saturation of hues in moderate brightness just after the sun goes down, compared to their saturation earlier in the day in bright sunlight or later at dusk, just before dark.

Comparing the color pyramid with the color formula will show that the seven unique colors are located at either the center (gray) or the six points of Fig. 12-14. All duplex colors are found on the edges between these points, on a line between a unique hue and black or white, or on the central axis between white and black. Triplex colors lie on triangular cross sections of the pyramid between the seven primary reference points. Quadruplex colors can lie anywhere not already named.

Color formula and pyramid: visual physiology. The sensations described by the color pyramid and formula are in agreement with some of the findings of visual physiology already given. The four hue responses and their complementary nature agree with the four-color coding of the retina, described in the experiments on slow potentials of the retina—green or blue giving negative potentials and red or yellow giving positive ones. The increased sensitivity of the eye to hue at intermediate brightness agrees with what is known of iodopsin function in the cones; too much brightness bleaches iodopsin into vitamin A to diminish the photochemical change that causes color sensation. The dark-adapted cone has maximum sensitivity to light, but when only a few of the most sensitive cones are responding under conditions of low illumination, less hue response is possible. Other correspondences could be pointed out, but these may suffice.

Color mixing

The four **unique hues** (red, green, yellow, and blue) can be used, two at a time, to reproduce any other hue. Just as unique red and green or unique yellow and blue mix to give gray (complementary colors), all four unique hues mix to give gray. These facts are in agreement with the four-color coding that the retina appears to use in signalling the brain. There are, however, only three kinds of hue-sensitive cones in the retina—a blue cone, a green cone, and a red cone; if all three were stimulated at once at the proper intensity, their response would probably "mix" to produce a visual sensation that *lacks* hue. It is therefore not surprising that three hues can be selected that are **primary hues** in the sense that (1) all three mix to give gray and (2) taking two of these hues at a time, any other hue can be produced by mixing them. There are a large number of trios of primary hues. When one selects any hue made of any mixture, one has determined the composition of the other two hues that will mix with it to cancel hue response, leaving a gray or white. The three hues thus determined can be used two at a time to produce all the other hue responses. The relative brightness and saturation of each of the three components will have to be adjusted to obtain a gray. Reproducing some hues that lie between two of the primaries will also require adjustment of relative brightness and saturation. Within these limits, however, there are many sets of three primary hues, or primary colors, as they are often called.

Color mixing by addition. A method of mixing colors that usually increases the *brightness* of the mixture over the brightness of its components is color mixing by addition. One such method would be over-

lapping spots of light to form supplementary hues. If a spot of light from a red spotlight were shining on a white reflecting surface, a red circle would be seen—red wavelengths would be reflected off the surface to the eye. If a yellow spot of light were shown on the wall, yellow wavelengths would be reflected to the eye. If both spots of light were shown on the reflecting surface to *overlap,* the overlapping area would look orange—a mixture of red and yellow. Furthermore, the orange area would be *brighter* than either the red or yellow areas since it would be reflecting light to the eye from *both* spotlights. Three spotlights could be used whose hues mixed to cancel each other out as a set of primary hues. In the area where all three spots overlapped, white would be seen rather than gray because of the increase in brightness; the brightness of all three spotlights would be mixed by addition. Of course the brightness of each spotlight could be reduced until the overlapping area looked gray.

Colors can be mixed by addition without increasing brightness if another method is used—the **color wheel.** If a red disk of paper is interleafed with a yellow disk of paper, a single disk can be produced that is half yellow and half red. If this disk is rotated rapidly by an electric motor, an orange disk will be seen. Red and yellow are, of course, supplementary hues that mix to give orange. The orange is no brighter than the red or the yellow, however, if the red disk and yellow disk reflect equal amounts of light. If three disks are selected that mix to cancel each other, they will mix on the color wheel to give a gray of the same brightness as the component hues. Used two at a time, other hues can be produced by varying the proportion of each hue on the disk. This is color mixing by addition without increasing brightness.

Color mixing by subtraction. Color mixing by subtraction always results in diminished brightness. Therefore, when three primary hues are mixed by subtraction, a very dark gray or black is usually seen. One method of mixing hues by subtraction is overlapping colored filters. A color filter *absorbs* all wavelengths of "white" light but those transmitted to the eye to be seen as a hue. Supposing that three primary hues were created by three filters, for example, a red of 650 mμ, a green of 530 mμ, and a blue of 460 mμ. If these filters were perfect, each would absorb all wavelengths but the one named in each case. If any two of them were overlapped in front of a light source of all visible wavelengths, no light would reach the eye; the second filter would absorb all the wavelengths transmitted by the first filter. However, filters usually transmit a *band* of wavelengths, the amount of light that is transmitted decreasing on either side of the wavelength for which they are named. The green filter of 530 mμ in the example would transmit more light energy at 530 mμ than at any other wavelength. However, it would pass some of the light at wavelengths that might range from 480 to 620 mμ, the amount transmitted being less and less in either direction from 530 mμ. Therefore, if the red (650 mμ) filter and the green (530 mμ) filter were overlapped, *each* would pass *some* wavelengths in the 580 mμ range (yellow) while absorbing most other wavelengths. A yellow hue of diminished brightness would result. If the blue (460 mμ) filter were now placed in front of the other two, it would absorb the residual 580 mμ yellow wavelengths so that no light would pass all three filters and a black would be seen. Mixing paint pigments has the same effect as overlapping filters. A paint pigment has the hue of the wavelengths it *reflects* (does not absorb). Therefore, mixing two hues of paint will result in an intermediate hue of diminished brightness consisting of the wavelengths that neither pigment absorbs (or both reflect). Subtractive color mixing is somewhat more complex than this in practice, but the basic principles explained here govern the process. It explains why the amateur, mixing water colors, often winds up with a gray or dark brown instead of the hue he was attempting to produce.

Color zones of the retina

The phenomena of hue and the mixing of hues hold when the retina receives widespread stimulation, especially in the foveal (central) region. All areas of the retina are not equally sensitive to hue and peripheral areas that lack color receptors (cones) do not see hue so that peripheral vision is "color-blind." If one brings a small spot of a definite hue in from the periphery of a gray visual field, it is seen as gray until it reaches a point where it can stimulate the more centrally located color receptors of the retina. Blues can be seen most peripherally, then yellows, then red, then greens. The wavelengths involved do not exactly match those of the color formula, but the difference may be accounted for by the nervous connections of the peripheral retina.

Purkinje shift

According to the duplicity theory (see visual physiology above) the cones are chromatic, or photopic, receptors that have a relatively high threshold. The rods are achromatic, or scotopic, receptors that have a very low threshold. The absolute threshold of either rods or cones depends upon wavelength. The rods "see only gray," but they are maximally sensitive at about 511 mμ (green region) and are less sensitive to other wavelengths. For example, they do not react to red wavelengths (above 680 mμ). The cones react to all wavelengths of the visible spectrum to some extent, but they are most sensitive at near 555 mμ (yellow-green region). The change in the relative brightness of various wavelengths in passing from photopic (daylight) to scotopic (night) vision and vice versa is called the **Purkinje shift.** For example, objects known to be green (such as grass) would appear as a brighter gray at night than objects known to be blue (such as a lake).

This is why movie directors can shoot black and white moonlight scenes in the day-time by using a blue filter. The blue filter shifts the relative brightness of objects to the blue and green areas of the spectrum and produces the relative brightness one is used to seeing at night.

Adaptation

In common with other receptors the rods and cones of the eye become less sensitive with continued stimulation. The adaptation of rods and cones differs, however, because of differences in their brightness threshold and in the *range* of brightness to which each responds.

Dark adaptation. During normal daylight vision few rods are responding. Their rhodopsin has been bleached into vitamin A by light, and there are few rods with enough rhodopsin left for light to affect. The cones are firing at intermediate sensitivity; their iodopsin is broken down by light to fire nerve impulses and is reconstituted in a continuous cycle. If the subject goes into a dark environment, both rods and cones increase their sensitivity by building up more visual pigment. The cones in-

crease their sensitivity first by building up iodopsin in the absence of light—the more iodopsin built up, the more sensitive the cones. The cones reach the limit of their sensitivity in 5 to 10 minutes of darkness. It takes this long for the more sensitive rods to build up enough iodopsin from vita-min A so that they can begin to respond to light. As they begin to function the thresh-old drops again, diminishing further over 20 minutes or so as rod vision increases in sensitivity. As a result there is a "break" in the threshold curve for dark adaptation; the first segment represents increased cone sensitivity to a limiting point, the second segment represents increasing rod sensi-tivity (Fig. 12-15).

Light adaptation. Under conditions of darkness or dim illumination the cones are not stimulated, and they build up a maxi-mum supply of iodopsin because there is insufficient light to break it down. The rods may have a moderate supply of rhodopsin since it is being reconstituted as fast as it can be broken down by dim light. Upon coming suddenly into bright light the threshold of most of the rods and cones are exceeded and most of the receptors of

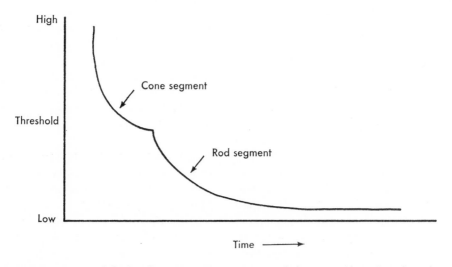

Fig. 12-15. Curve of dark adaptation. Two segments of the curve show first the adapta-tion of cones, then the adaptation of rods (see text).

the retina fire, causing a "blinding" sensation of light. The pupil constricts to reduce the amount of light entering the eye and protect the receptors from overstimulation. The rods cease to respond because all their rhodopsin is broken down into vitamin A. The cones have higher thresholds, however, and their iodopsin continues to be broken down and reconstituted; therefore these cells continue to respond with light sensations.

Hue adaptation. Continuous stimulation by a given hue appears to reduce the sensitivity of cones responding to that hue. The result is a decrease in the apparent saturation of the hue—the color appears grayer. Hue adaptation is the basis for visual aftersensations.

Aftersensations

Aftersensations are sensations that are caused by a stimulus, but they begin after the stimulus is removed. Visual aftersensations may be positive or negative. After stimulation ceases the eye may continue to react with the same sensation for a time—a **positive aftersensation.** Or, the eye may react with a quality or an intensity opposite to that caused by the stimulus after the stimulus is removed—a **negative aftersensation.** Examples will be given below for aftersensations of brightness (intensity) and hue (quality). Meanwhile, a good rule to remember is that *brief, intense* stimulation usually causes positive aftersensations, whereas *prolonged, moderate* stimulation usually causes negative aftersensations.

Brightness aftersensations. Stare at the filament of an electric light bulb for a few seconds, and then look at the wall. You will continue to see the filament for a time as a positive aftersensation. The receptors continue to respond for a time after they have been intensely stimulated. Prolonged moderate light stimulation raises the brightness threshold because of light adaptation, however (see above). As a result a room looks darker after coming in from the sun-

light than it will later—a negative aftersensation of brightness.

Hue aftersensations. Aftersensations of hue are usually negative. If one stares at a patch of color for a minute and then looks at a neutral gray wall, a patch of color will appear that is the *complement* of the stimulus patch. This is a negative aftersensation. There appears to be a balance among the color receptors that has been upset by adaptation to the stimulus hue; a hue of opposite quality results when stimulation ceases. For example, one sees a patch of yellow on a gray surface after staring at blue.

Contrast

Contrast effects are caused by adaptation of *areas* of the retina. As a result neighboring areas become more sensitive to the opposite process—either a complementary hue (quality) or the opposite brightness (intensity). The effect of adaptation of one area of the retina on neighboring areas is called **simultaneous induction.** Red looks more saturated against a blue background, for example, and white looks brighter against a black background.

Brightness contrast. The darker one stimulus patch is, the lighter an adjacent one will seem. For example, the same light gray patch may appear white against a black background and dark gray against a white background. When the gray is on a black background, the receptors responding to it become more sensitive because of lack of activity in neighboring receptors from the black surrounding it (dark adaptation). This makes the gray patch look brighter (whiter). When the surrounding receptors adapt to white (light adaptation), the more central receptors responding to the gray patch also become less sensitive, making the gray patch appear darker.

Hue contrast. A hue appears maximally saturated against a background of the *complementary* hue. Thus a red patch looks more saturated against a complementary green background than against a gray

background. The green background prevents the central area of the retina from
adapting to red and loosing sensitivity because of simultaneous induction. If two
complementary hues are placed side by
side, the line at which they meet will appear gray, perhaps caused by retinal color
mixing of the complementary hues. The
area of each hue that is near the complementary hue will seem more saturated than
outlying areas. Apparently the closer two
oppositely stimulated areas lie on the retina,
the greater the simultaneous induction effect and the less the resulting adaptation in
either area.

Visual acuity

Larger objects may be seen at a greater
distance than smaller ones. The only uniform measure of visual acuity is therefore
the *angle* subtended by the light rays as
they reach the eye from the object. A large
object at a great distance may form the
same **visual angle** at the cornea of the eye
as a small object seen a short distance away.
The smaller the angle at which an object
can be seen, the greater the visual acuity.
Visual angle may, however, be measured
in two ways: (1) the **minimum visible
angle** and (2) the **minimum separable angle.** (Of course the greater the *contrast*
between an object and its background, the
greater the visual acuity. The tests to be
cited use maximum contrast, for example,
black against a white background or vice
versa). The minimum visible angle is the
smallest angle subtended by light rays that
can be perceived as coming from an object
against a background of good brightness
contrast. The diameter of a black wire that
can be seen against a white background
at a standard distance is a good test of
minimum visible angle. The minimum separable angle, on the other hand, is formed
by the smallest distance *between* two objects that can be perceived at a given distance against a background of good brightness contrast. Two black wires against a

white background may be used and brought
closer together until the subject can just
detect the space between them. The minimum separable angle is usually greater
(about 1 minute) than the minimum visible
angle (about 1 second). The minimum separable angle is used in a rough fashion in
the most common test of visual acuity, the
Snellen test. This test uses rows of letters
of diminishing size, displayed from a distance of 20 feet. The horizontal bars of the
large E found at the top of the chart form
a separable angle, for example. In scoring
the test the distance at which a normal eye
sees a given row of letters forms the denominator of a fraction; the distance in feet at
which the subject must stand to see the
same letters forms the numerator. Thus
20/20 eyes are normal, 20/40 indicates subnormal acuity, and 20/10 is superior acuity.
The Snellen test is far from the best test of
visual acuity, but it is the most commonly
used. Almost anyone who has had a general physical examination or who has con-
sulted an eye specialist has seen a Snellen
chart.

Critical flicker frequency

Visual acuity is a test of spatial thresholds for the eye, but the eye has temporal
(time) thresholds as well. One way of
measuring a temporal threshold for the eye
is the **critical flicker fusion frequency**
(**CFF**). The CFF refers to the rate at
which a light must flicker on and off before
the eye fails to perceive it as flickering and
sees it as a steady light. The CFF depends
on the relative duration of the light and
dark cycles as well as the rate of flicker.
The CFF is increased with the intensity of
the stimulus, differs for various hues, and
tends to decrease with the age of the subject. For some reason there is a low positive correlation between the CFF and
standard tests of intelligence. The CFF is
higher in the periphery of the retina (peripheral vision) than in the fovea. This is
partly because receptors are more dense in

the fovea, and their afterfiring during the dark interval interferes with the perception of flicker. The cones, densest in the fovea, have a lower CFF threshold than the rods that are the only receptors in the extreme periphery of the retina. Ordinary neon or fluorescent lights flicker 60 times per second on their usual 60-cycle current supply, but one is unaware of this at their usual intensities. They may, however, be seen to flicker in peripheral vision where they stimulate rods.

Phi phenomenon

Another temporal threshold for the eye is that for movement as compared to displacement in space. If two lights spaced a few inches apart are slowly turned on and off so that one light is on while the other is off, each light will be perceived as turning on and off at its true location. If the rate of alternating flicker of the lights is increased, a point will be reached at which a single light is perceived as moving back and forth between the two locations. This is the **phi phenomenon** that forms the basis for animated street signs and motion pictures. The rate at which the lights must be alternated to produce the illusion of apparent motion depends on the duration of the light cycle and dark cycle of each light, the intensity and size of each light, and the distance between them. At a still higher rate the CFF for each light will be exceeded, and two steady lights at different locations will be perceived.

Cues to depth and distance

The perception of the distance of an object from the observer, or depth perception, depends on a number of sensations from the eyes, some of them visual and some kinesthetic. Two kinesthetic cues of muscle sensation have already been mentioned in this chapter—convergence and accommodation. Convergence is a **binocular cue** since sensations from the extrinsic muscles of both eyes must be compared to

judge how much the eyes are "crossed" in training them on a nearby object. Accommodation is a **monocular cue** since it depends on sensations of intrinsic muscle strain that are the same for each eye when the lens is thickened to focus on nearby objects.

Binocular cues. Convergence depends on strain sensations from the extrinsic muscles of the eyes when the eyes are "crossed" to focus nearby objects on corresponding points in the foveas of the two eyes. The closer the object, the greater the sensation. The geometry of seeing is such that the strain is perceived only within a very few feet. Since the eyes are only about 2½ inches apart in the head, muscular convergence of the visual axes of the eyes is only noticeable when the object is close to the eyes. The visual geometry of binocular vision is called **binocular parallax,** and it has consequences in visual as well as in kinesthetic sensations. Since the eyes are about 2½ inches apart, the visual angle, or angle of regard of an object, will differ for the left and right eye. Thus the left eye will see more of the left side of a three-dimensional object and the right eye more of the right side of the object. The difference between the image formed on the right retina and the image formed on the left retina is called **retinal disparity.** The closer the object, the greater the difference in what the two eyes see—the greater the retinal disparity. You can demonstrate this for yourself by holding up an index finger about 6 inches from your nose, closing one eye, and then opening it and closing the other; observe how much the finger appears to "jump" back and forth against the background. Then repeat the experiment with the finger at arm's length; it will appear to move less because the retinal disparity is less. The principle of retinal disparity is used to lend an illusion of depth in the **stereoscope.** Two pictures are taken at once: the two cameras (or twin lenses) are about as far apart as the two eyes. The resulting pictures are presented in a stereoscope, which presents the left picture to the left eye and the right picture to the right eye. A startling illusion of a single three-dimensional, or stereoscopic, photograph is obtained.

Monocular cues. Monocular cues to depth and distance are those that do not depend on the displacement of the eyes in the head; they are as useful to a one-eyed person as to one with two eyes. Monocular depth perception is not nearly as accurate as binocular depth perception within 15 to 25 feet, as can be rapidly discovered by trying to park a car with one eye closed. Beyond this distance one relys on monocular cues exclusively, since no convergence is needed to focus on distant objects and since the images formed in the two eyes are essentially identical. The most important monocular distance cue is *size*. The farther an object is from the observer, the smaller the visual angle subtended at the eye and the smaller the image on the retina. Since it is assumed that objects remain constant in size (size constancy, see below), the smaller the object looks, the more distant it is judged to be.

Linear perspective is a special case of the size cue and is the basis for perspective drawings that have a three-dimensional appearance. A series of objects of similar size that are equally spaced appear to diminish in size and become closer together as they recede from the observer toward the horizon (a row of telephone poles, for example). A roadway of constant width narrows at a constant rate as it recedes from the observer toward the horizon. Cues of this kind seem commonplace now, but they were not discovered by artists until a few hundred years ago. Prior to that time paintings lacked perspective.

Texture is another special case of the size cue. Irregularities in a rough surface, such as a plowed field, are progressively lost as one gazes from the near to the far end of the field, and the eye reaches its acuity limits in perceiving irregularities. The closer the area in the field focused upon, the rougher the texture; the more distant the area, the less irregular the texture appears.

Interposition is another monocular cue that seems obvious on reflection, although one is not usually aware of it. If a familiar form has part of its outline blocked from view by another familiar form, it is thought that the latter object is the closer. For example, a nearby hill cuts off from view part of the contour of a more distant hill, or a house may be completely seen but block part of the view of a more distant woods.

Relative movement is a cue that is less obvious, but no less important. Man is often moving and so are the many objects about him—automobiles, animals, etc. Given two objects passing an observer at the same rate, for example, two flying birds, the nearer one will sweep past the observer's field of vision at a faster apparent rate. In the same manner, if the observer is moving, nearby objects will change their position relative to his at a faster rate than will distant objects. For example, in walking by a tree in front of a house, the tree will sweep past the field of vision faster than the house. If you are riding in an automobile, look down at the blur of rapid motion of the ground near the car, the slower relative movement of signs or houses some distance from the road, and the almost negligible apparent movement of distant hills or clouds.

Light and shade help one to judge the depth and contour of objects because of our adaptation to overhead light sources, as from the sun. Therefore protuberances (bumps) have shadows on their lower surfaces, whereas cavities are shadowed in their upper portions. The effectiveness of this cue can be seen by taking a picture of an unfamiliar, irregular surface, photographed in strong overhead light, and turning it over. Photographers obtain dramatic effects by photographing familiar images, models, for example, using lightning that comes from below rather than from above.

Aerial perspective is a monocular distance cue because one is adjusted to some lack of transparency in the atmosphere. The air is not a perfectly transparent medium; even on a clear day it is obscured by particles of dust and water vapor. Such impediments obscure the outlines of distant objects more than nearby objects. The use of this cue is based on a habitual amount of obscurity, and it can cause one to underestimate or overestimate distances under unusual atmospheric conditions. In dry clear desert air the outlines of distance objects are quite clear, and distant objects can be perceived as being closer than they actually are. A distance hill of unknown size may be outlined so clearly as to appear only a mile or two away, when it is actually 10 to 20 miles from the observer. In a fog the opposite kind of error is often made. Objects seem to "loom up" through the fog as one approaches them since their distance was overestimated when their hazy outlines first appeared. (Water vapor makes air less transparent.)

Object constancy

Many cues to depth and distance as well as other kinds of visual orientation depend on the "assumption" that objects remain constant in size, shape, and brightness no matter what their distance, orientation, or illumination. **Size constancy** is the assumption that familiar objects remain constant at a known size. If the retinal image of a familiar object diminishes in size, the assumption is not that it has shrunk but that it is receding. The importance of this cue can be demonstrated under artificial conditions; for example, if a featureless dull white balloon is blown up and reduced in size against a featureless black background, an observer will perceive it as a constant-sized sphere that is advancing and retreating from his point of vantage.

Shape constancy is the assumption that familiar objects remain constant in shape;

if their retinal outlines change, it is because of their changed orientation. For example, a round coin produces an oval image on the retina when viewed at an angle, but it is still perceived as round. The shape constancy assumption enables the observer to orient himself in space with regard to familiar round, square, and rectangular objects.

Brightness constancy is the assumption that familiar objects have a known constant brightness, irrespective of how much light they are reflecting to the eye. A piece of coal has the same perceived brightness, for example, whether seen in shadow or bright sunlight. Brightness constancy enables the observer to make assumptions about changes in illumination by assuming that the brightness of an object is constant, but the light falling on its has changed.

Defects of color vision

Deficiencies in hue perception are often accompanied by changes in the perception of gray colors so that a color-deficient individual differs from a normal individual in his perception of both hue and brightness. Deficiencies in hue perception may involve complete inability to detect the difference between any hue and a gray that has the same apparent brightness to the subject. At the other extreme, the color deficiency may only mean deficiencies in the perceived saturation of some hues that can be detected with only the most sophisticated tests. The most common test for color deficiency is the **Ishihara test.** It consists of several pages of colored dots in a booklet. The dots are arranged so that they differ in color and brightness in two patterns that form two different numbers. One number will be seen by the normal eye, the other by the "color-blind" eye that has known deficiencies involving changes in the relative brightness of the colored dots. As was pointed out previously the normal eye requires at least three primary hues to make mixtures that match all the hues to which the eye responds. On this basis deficiencies of color vision are usually classified as monochromatism, dichromatism, or trichromatism, depending on the number of primary hues the subject requires to match all the hues that he can perceive.

Monochromatism is complete hue blindness. All hues appear as gray to the subject, and he cannot distinguish between any hue and a gray of equal subjective brightness. All colors that he sees lack hue and saturation, and he responds only to differences in brightness. The disorder is rare and is sometimes caused by complete lack of cone vision, with the resulting foveal blindness and poor adaptation to daylight conditions that is the consequence of total dependence on rod vision.

Dichromatism takes four different forms, but **protanopia** and **deuteranopia** are most common. Neither disorder allows the subject to distinguish between red and green, although blue and yellow vision is unimpaired. The protanope shortens the red end of the spectrum, and greens are seen as grays. Deuteranopes confuse reds and greens with bluish and yellowish grays. The other two types of dichromats (tritanopia and teternopia) are forms of yellow-blue blindness, probably quite rare.

Trichromatism is normal or near-normal color vision. **Protanomaly** and **deuteranomaly** are color-weak red-green forms of trichromatism. Both involved weaknesses in the saturation of reds and greens, with the peak of the photopic visibility curve shifted from the normal 555 mμ to 540 and 560 mμ, respectively. The third kind of trichromatism is **tritanomaly**, a rare yellow-blue weakness.

SUMMARY

The eye, as a visual sense organ, is controlled or "pointed" by extrinsic muscles and made up of specialized tissue in three layers—an outer sclerotic coat, an intermediate choroid coat, and an inner retina. The sclera is continuous with the cornea, and the choriod coat is continuous with the intrinsic muscles of the iris and the ciliary body, which holds the lens via the suspensory ligament. The retina contains several layers of nerve cells as well as the receptors (rods and cones) since it is an extension of the brain. Light must pass through the ganglion cell layer and the bipolar cell layer before reaching the rods and cones except in the fovea. Horizontal and amacrine cells interconnect retinal areas; ganglion cells form the optic nerve as they leave the eyeball at the blind spot. After a hemidecussation the optic nerve forms the optic tract. Only hue-sensitive, photopic, high-threshold cones are found in the fovea; their photosensitive pigment is iodopsin. The more peripheral low-threshold rods are scotopic and have rhodopsin for visual pigment. The anterior and posterior chambers of the eye contain aqueous humor; the fundus contains vitreous humor. In the normal eye parallel rays of light from distant objects are focused on the fovea by the cornea and lens; diverging rays from nearby objects are focused by thickening the lens in accommodation. The myopic eye has a lens that is too thick, or an eyeball too long, which is corrected by concave lenses; the hyperopic eye has an abnormally thin lens, or short eyeball, which requires a convex correcting lens. Presbyopia is the lack of accommodation that results from aging; astigmatism results from unequal curvature of lens or cornea; and cataracts result from a clouded cornea. Convergence and accommodation may become dissociated to cause amblyopia. Pupillary reflexes regulate pupil size in response to the amount of light reaching the eye.

Because of the hemidecussation that forms the optic tracts at the chiasma, damage to either tract causes loss of the opposite visual field, whereas damage to the crossing fibers causes "tunnel vision." The optic tracts terminate in the lateral geniculate nuclei (LGN) that send topographically organized fibers to cortical area 17, visual area I. The optic tract also sends fibers to the superior colliculi for reflex eye movement, to the pretectal nuclei for the intrinsic eye muscles, ciliary muscles, and iris reflexes, and to the optomotor nuclei controlling eye movements. Other fibers reach visual areas II and III via association nuclei of the thalamus and brainstem reticular formation.

Light energy consists of wavelengths from 400 to 750 mμ on the electromagnetic spectrum. Changes in wavelength cause perceived hue changes, mixtures of wavelength cause saturation changes, and amplitude differences change brightness. Brightness is also measured in flux, or rate of flow, from a point source of a standard candle. Light falling on a surface is illuminance; light coming from a surface is luminance. A physical object may transmit, reflect, absorb, refract, or radiate light; in each case light reaching the eye determines hue, saturation, and brightness.

Duplicity theory states that the rods are low-threshold achromatic scotopic receptors and the cones are high-threshold chromatic photopic receptors for night and day vision, respectively. The theory is based on differences between rods and cones in visual pigments, wavelength sensitivity, absorption spectra, foveal and peripheral sensitivity, and color zones as well as the break in the dark adaptation curve.

The electroretinogram (ERG) is the gross electrical response of the retina, recorded with electrodes on the cornea and near the back of the eye. The A and B waves have been identified with rod and cone response, respectively, and are often used in threshold measures.

Some color vision theory has assumed three color responses of the cones because sets of three primaries can be used to match all hues. Other theories assume opposing red-green and blue-yellow processes because of the psychological primary nature of these four hues, their paired opposition as complementary colors, and the usual red-green or blue-yellow color blindness. Research now suggests that there are three kinds of cones, but their interactions in the retina result in a four-color signal to the brain.

Measurements of the absorption spectra of single rods and cones supports duplicity theory and blue-, green-, and red-sensitive cones. Tests of human foveal sensitivity after adaptation to yellow (adapting red and green cones), purple (adapting blue and green cones), and blue (for blue cones) brought out sensitivity peaks for blue, green, and red cones that agree with the absorption spectrum data. Microelectrode recordings from biopolar and ganglion cells of the retina show a four-color response, however. When the threshold of firing of ganglion cells is tested for various wavelengths, a dominator curve for rod or cone vision emerges, depending on brightness and on how the ganglion cells are coupled to rods and cones. Selective adaptation reveals modulator curves with sensitivity peaks in the blue, green, yellow, and red regions of the spectrum in several species. Man's three color cones may be coupled in a red-green and blue-yellow manner. Microelectrode recordings from horizontal cells reveal slow potentials from light stimulation: (1) a luminosity response (L response) of partial depolarization, which is like the cone sensitivity curve and is not color-coded, (2) a red-green (R-G) response and (3) a blue-yellow (B-Y) response. The latter two responses are negative at the short end of the spectrum (G or B) and positive at the long end (R or Y); they are color-coded because either the positive or negative response can be abolished by selective adaptation. The responses probably come from glial cells in the retina. The R and G responses seem excitatory to the ganglion cells and the B and Y responses inhibitory. They may be related to the excitatory "on" responses of firing ganglion cells that accompany the onset of visual stimulation and the "off" responses of other ganglion cells that occur when stimulation ceases. Some of these cells are color-coded, and the on response always has a lower threshold than the off response. When retinal zones are plotted by recording from ganglion cells, the central area stimulated by light may show an on (excitatory) response surrounded by a peripheral off (inhibitory) response, with cells in between that fire to both on and off signals. In other cases there is a central off and peripheral on area.

Most visual phenomena agree with what is known of visual physiology. Newton's laws of color include (1) the law of complements, (2) the law of supplements, and (3) the law of resulants, which govern complementary colors, supplementary colors, and color mixing as far as hue is concerned. The dimensions of brightness and saturation must be added in addition to the psychologically unique hues red, green, yellow, and blue. Seven visual primary colors result—black and white for brightness, gray for saturation, and red, green, yellow, and blue for hue. The color formula $C = (R$ or $G) + (Y$ or $B) + (Wh$ or $Bl) + Gr$ shows how the primary qualities combine to form secondary qualities, whereas the double color pyramid demonstrates the interaction between brightness and saturation. Monoplex, duplex, triplex, and quadruplex colors result. Any hue may be reproduced by mixing two of any set of three primary hues that will combine as a trio of complements (brightness and saturation must be adjusted). Color mixing by addition may involve overlapping spots of light; where all three overlap, the result is a white of increased brightness. A color wheel may be used for additive color mixing without brightness change where complements give gray. Color mixing by subtraction involves overlapping color filters or mixing paints. This reduces brightness, and complements give dark gray or black.

All areas of the retina are not equally sensitive to hue, and color zones result.

Most peripherally the retina is not sensitive to hue; moving centrally reveals the boundary of zones sensitive to blues, yellow, reds, and greens, in that order. The Purkinje shift involves a change in sensitivity to wavelengths, daylight (cone) sensitivity being maximum at 555 mμ (yellow-green), whereas night (rod) sensitivity is maximum at 511 mμ (green). Dark adaptation involves increasing sensitivity of the cones for about 10 minutes as iodopsin is built up to their minimum threshold to light and then the beginning and continued increase in rod sensitivity as rhodopsin is built up—the resulting threshold curve has cone and rod segments. Light adaptation first involves incapacitating the rods as all their rhodopsin is bleached by light. The cone threshold is exceeded also, and the pupil constricts to limit light input to the range of maximum cone acuity. Adaptation to brightness, or hue, results in aftersensations that are positive if the same brightness, or hue, is seen or negative if the opposite brightness, or complementary hue, is seen. Contrast effects occur when different *areas* of the retina are stimulated by contrasting brightnesses or complimentary hues. The resulting simultaneous induction prevents adaptation. Visual acuity is measured in terms of the minimum visible angle or minimum separable angle, the former being smaller. A rough test of the latter is the Snellen test, scored as a ratio between the distances letters can be read by the subject and the normal eye. Temporal thresholds of the eye include the critical flicker fusion frequency (CFF) and the phi phenomenon. The CFF is the rate at which a light must flicker to be seen as constant. Phi is apparent movement caused by alternating the light and dark cycles of the two flashing lights placed near one another.

Cues to depth and distance are binocular within 15 to 20 feet and monocular at any distance. Convergence and the retinal disparity that results from binocular parallax are binocular cues. Monocular cues include accommodation size, linear perspective, texture, interposition, relative movement, light and shade, and aerial perspective. Orientation in space and to common objects demands the "assumption" of object constancy, including accommodation, size, shape, and brightness constancy assumptions.

Color vision defects affect both hue and brightness sensitivity; the Ishihara test of colored dots that form numbers is the most common test of color vision. Monochromats are completely color-blind and may have only rod vision. Dichromats include red-green blind protanopes and deuteranopes and two yellow-green blind types. Trichromats are normal, or nearly so, with protanomaly and deuteranomaly red-green "weakness" and tritanomaly yellow-blue "weakness."

READINGS

Alpern, M., Lawrence, M., and Wolsk, D.: Sensory Processes, Belmont, Calif., 1967, Brooks Cole Publishing Co.

Brindley, G. S.: Afterimages, Sci. Amer. **209**:84-91, Oct., 1963.

Buddenbrock, W. von: The senses, Ann Arbor, Mich.; 1958, The University of Michigan Press.

Case, J.: Sensory mechanisms, New York, 1966, **209**:84-91, The Macmillan Co., chap. 6.

Epstein, J. P., and Casey, A.: The current status of the size—distance hypothesis, Psychol. Bull. 58:491-514, 1961. (Bobbs-Merrill Reprint No. P-437.)

Fatechand, R.: The cells that organize vision, New Scientist 24:726-728, 1966.

Granit, R.: Receptors and sensory perception, New Haven, Conn., 1955, Yale University Press.

Hubel, D. H.: The visual cortex of the brain, Sci. Amer., **209**:54-62, Nov., 1963. (W. H. Freeman Co., Reprint No. 168.)

Kennedy, D.: Inhibition in visual systems, Sci. Amer. 209:122-130, July, 1963. (W. H. Freeman Co., Reprint No. 162.)

Kolers, P. A.: The illusion of movement. Sci. Amer. **211**:98-106, Oct., 1964. (W. H. Freeman Co. Reprint No. 487.)

Luckiesh, M.: Visual illusions, New York, 1965, Dover Publications, Inc.

MacNichol, E. F.: Three-pigment color vision, Sci. Amer. **211**:48-56, Dec., 1964. (W. H. Freeman Co. Reprint No. 197.)

Mueller, C. G.: Sensory psychology, Englewood Cliffs, N. J., 1965, Prentice-Hall, Inc.

Muntz, W. R. A.: Vision in frogs, Sci. Amer. **210**:110-119, March, 1964. (W. H. Freeman Co. Reprint No. 179.)

Rushton, W. A.: Visual pigments in man, Sci. Amer. 207:120-132, Nov., 1962. (W. H. Freeman Co. Reprint No. 139.)

Teeven, R. C., and Birney, R. C.: Color vision, Princeton, N. J., 1961. D. Van Nostrand Co., Inc.

Wald, G.: Eye and camera, Sci. Amer. **184**:32-41, Aug., 1950. (W. H. Freeman Co. Reprint No. 46.)

Wallach, H.: The perception of motion, Sci. Amer. **201**:56-60, July, 1959. (W. H. Freeman Co. Reprint No. 409.)

Part IV

Adaptive behavior

Chapter 13

Reflexes and motor organization

OVERVIEW

This chapter begins a new section on adaptive behavior. The book began by surveying certain aspects of anatomy and physiology of the nervous system to form a background for Part III on the senses. This section discusses adaptive responses to outside sensory information and central states of the body. The behavior is complex enough to require further study of the nervous system, with emphasis on central motor mechanisms rather than on sensory input. The student should reread Chapter 6 at this point to be sure that the major subdivisions of the central and peripheral nervous system are fresh in his mind. Chapter 6 will prepare him for the present chapter that surveys adaptive reflexes and their control by higher centers. Chapter 14 on brain dynamics will show how higher brain centers are organized to control adaptive behavior of a more complex sort than reflexes. Finally, chapters on motivation, emotion, learning, and stress will survey these kinds of complex adaptive behavior, describing their control by nervous and endocrine mechanisms.

This chapter begins, as did Chapter 6, with the reflex. Despite its relatively fixed pathways, response variability is seen because of the influence of higher centers; yet the reflex is under *stimulus control*. Various types of reflex preparations that isolate the

reflex from different higher centers are described—spinal, decerebrate, and decorticate preparations. Spinal mechanisms in the reflex response are explained by comparing a reflex with a muscle twitch (stimulation of a muscle by its motor nerve). The latent period, contraction time, and relaxation time of each are compared. The final common (nervous) path for a reflex movement will show facilitation or occlusion, depending on its inputs. These phenomena are also seen in direct and indirect reflex inhibition as well as excitation. Varieties of reflexes and their mechanisms are discussed—stretch, extensor thrust, flexion, crossed extension, and long spinal as well as higher-level reflexes (vital reflexes, postural reflexes, and placing and hopping responses). The motor organization of the nervous system is the last section of the chapter. This organization is arbitrarily divided into the pyramidal, extrapyramidal, and cerebellar systems for study. Each system is studied in (1) function, (2) pathways (in the nervous system), and (3) symptoms of damage. The chapter concludes with an integration of their contributions to behavior.

NATURE OF A REFLEX

As explained in Chapter 6 the usual reflex has five categories of "elements": (1) receptors, (2) afferent, or sensory, neurons, (3) interneurons, or association neurons,

(4) efferent, or motor, neurons, and (5) effectors (muscles or glands). These are categories rather than single elements. In the simplest reflex, for example, withdrawing the hand from a painful stimulus, many receptors, neurons, and effectors are involved. The pathways are relatively fixed from receptors to afferent neurons, interneurons, efferent neurons, and effectors and produce an automatic withdrawal response. The stimulation of pain receptors always leads to withdrawal; therefore the reflex response is under *stimulus control*. However, the exact movement involved in withdrawal will vary to some extent, depending on posture and on the position of the limb relative to the body. For example, the withdrawal movement will involve some different muscle groups when one burns the back of his hand on a stove as compared to burning the palm. Some different movements will follow, depending on whether one is leaning on that arm or not. The reflex reactions are *modified* by both spinal and higher centers to withdraw the hand efficiently and in a way that maintains balance and posture. Some different interneurons and therefore some different motor neurons and muscles are used, but the *form* of the reaction is determined by "fixed" pathways from the pain receptors through the CNS. To paraphrase Sherrington, the nervous system "thinks" in terms of movements rather than muscle contractions.

Stimulus control

The kind of stimulus that is used will determine the kind of reflex response that will occur. This is true because the different varieties of receptors are specialized to respond to different kinds of energy and specialized receptors activate specific kinds of reflexes. For example, the **flexion reflex,** already mentioned, involves contraction of the flexors of a limb in response to pain stimulation of the limb. The nervous "connections" between pain-specialized receptors and flexor muscles are "built into" the CNS. This is why one will always withdraw his hand from a painful stimulus and why a dog with an injured paw will hold that limb in a flexed (withdrawn) position, even if he has to walk on three legs to do it. On the other hand, the **extensor thrust reflex,** the opposite movement to flexion, will result from stimulating pressure and proprioceptive receptors in the limb. Different afferent neurons are fired, and therefore different interneurons, motor neurons, and effectors are activated. Pressure instead of pain stimuli to the sole of the foot, or spreading the digits, increases contraction of extensor muscles in the limb. In standing or walking the onset of this foot pressure from the weight of the body extends the limb to support the body. If the two reflexes are opposed and the stimuli for both are used at once, which response will occur? If both pain and pressure receptors in an animal's paw are stimulated will he flex or extend the limb? This depends to some extent on the intensity of the pain stimulus as compared to the pressure stimulus, that is, the number of receptors and therefore the number of other elements activated. In general, however, the flexion reflex will predominate. It overrides extension because it is a nociceptive reflex of survival value to the animal.

REFLEX PREPARATION

As already explained, the exact form of a "fixed" reflex response, such as the flexion reflex, will depend on higher centers in the brain that respond to the posture and movements of the animal. Other movements may be set off by the reflex stimuli to higher centers. To keep the reflex as constant as possible and to prevent most other responses, the CNS is **transected** (cut) above the level of the neurons involved in the reflex. For example, if a flexion reflex of the hindlimb is being studied, the spinal cord may be cut above the level of the sensory and motor roots involved in the reflex. This isolates the interneurons from higher centers. Input from the stimulus cannot cause widespread body movements via higher brain centers, and the reflex response will no longer be affected by higher centers that respond to position and movement. As a result the flexion response will be more consistant from one stimulation to the next. The effect of other variables on the reflex can be best studied when the response is otherwise consistant.

Spinal preparation

In the spinal preparation just described the spinal cord is severed above the level of the spinal cord involved in the reflex. Reflexes of the limbs are most isolated in this way. However, spinal preparations have severe practical disadvantages. It is most convenient for the physiologist to study **acute** preparations, that is, anesthetized animals kept alive only for the duration of the experiment (a day or two). Spinal animals cannot be studied as acute preparations because **spinal shock** ensues when the cord is severed, and the shock lasts for some time. All muscles supplied by motor neurons below the level of the lesion become flaccid (lose tone) and will not react to reflex stimulation. The recovery time involved depends on the development of the brain in the species being studied. Cat and dog—the usual subjects—require about 48 hours for all reflexes to recover, most monkeys about a week, and spinal (**paraplegic**) man about two to three weeks. Spinal shock is caused by the dependence of the motoneurons on constant excitation from the brainstem reticular formation (BSRF) and vestibular nuclei (Fig. 13-1). The vestibular nuclei normally bombard the spinal motoneurons with excitation via the vestibulospinal tract. This makes the motoneurons more excitable when incoming reflex stimuli are added. The BSRF excites motoneurons by a different mechanism. The BSRF sends excitation to the gamma efferent neurons that contract the muscle spindles for stretch reflexes. Con-

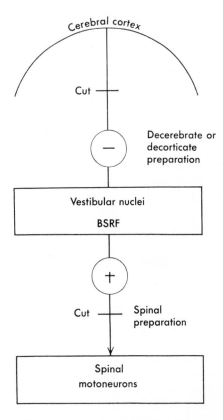

Fig. 13-1. Diagram showing the types of reflex preparation and the excitatory (+) and inhibitory (−) influences of various centers on each other and on the extensor motoneurons (see text).

traction of muscle spindles excites their annulospiral receptors, which, in turn, send reflex stimulation to the muscles (Chapter 9). The latter mechanism maintains the *tone*, or constant partial contraction, of healthy muscle. When spinal transection interrupts excitation of the muscle spindles, tone is lost, and the muscles become flaccid. If the experimenter waits for the animal to recover from spinal shock, the wait is long enough for infection to develop from the operation (2 to 3 days). The original operation must therefore be carried out under troublesome aseptic or sterile conditions, the incisions carefully closed, and the animal allowed to recover. Such a **chronic** preparation can be maintained for a long time with careful nursing, but it is troublesome to keep, and the animal must be operated upon a second time to expose the nervous system for experimental manipulations.

Decerebrate preparation

Spinal shock can be avoided so that acute preparations can be studied if the neuraxis is cut at the level of the midbrain. This does not isolate the cord from all higher centers, but does cut off most of the brain. The cut lies above the vestibular nuclei and most of the BSRF, leaving them functionally "connected" to the motoneurons. The motoneurons continue to receive excitation from these centers to maintain reflex excitability (Fig. 13-1). The animal will, however, display **decerebrate rigidity**, a state of *exaggerated* extensor tone that results in all four limbs being rigidly extended. Extensor tone is caused by stretch reflexes (see above), which depend on excitation from the vestibular nuclei and BSRF, particularly the latter. These two centers receive some constant inhibition from the cerebral cortex and basal ganglia. A midbrain transection cuts off inhibition to the vestibular nuclei and BSRF. When the vestibular nuclei and BSRF are released from inhibition by higher centers, their excitatory effect on motoneurons is increased. The effect on extensor motoneurons is the most marked, and the limbs are rigidly extended. The **spastic** condition of the extensors is permanent and provides an abnormal background of muscle tension in studying reflexes. The transection is usually made between the superior and inferior colliculi as landmarks, but it may be made higher for some midbrain reflex studies or lower to reduce decerebrate rigidity a little.

Decorticate preparation

The decorticate preparation is made by removing the cerebral cortex. The prepara-

tion is useful for studying reflexes of the diencephalon, or upper midbrain, since they are left intact. Examples could include reflexes of the hypothalamus or visual and auditory reflexes involving the colliculi. Decerebrate rigidity is present, of course, because cortical inhibition of the vestibular nuclei and BSRF is eliminated.

CNS MECHANISMS IN THE REFLEX

The response of a muscle to direct electrical stimulation of its motor nerve is called a muscle twitch. If the muscle is a limb flexor, it will respond to electrical stimulation of pain receptors in the limb with a flexion reflex. The reflex response of the muscle differs in important ways from the muscle twitch since the CNS is involved in the reflex response but not in the muscle twitch. Important CNS mechanisms were discovered in attempts to explain the differences.

Experimental arrangements

To study the characteristics of a muscle response independent of other muscles, the muscle under study is *excised*, or removed from the limb, with its nerve and blood supplies intact (Fig. 13-2). Strong stimulation at S_1 in Fig. 13-2 will fire all the motoneurons to the muscle and cause a muscle twitch—a full contraction of the muscle. If the muscle is a flexor, intense stimulation at S_2 will fire afferent pain fibers to cause reflex contraction in the same muscle. If one end of the muscle is fixed and the other hooked to a lever, a trace can be made on a revolving drum (**kymograph**) for both kinds of muscle response. The records shown in Fig. 13-2 for the muscle twitch and for the reflex response can be compared.

Latent period

The **latent period** is the time required for the muscle to *begin* to respond after the onset of the stimulus. It is the period that elapses between the stimulus and the onset

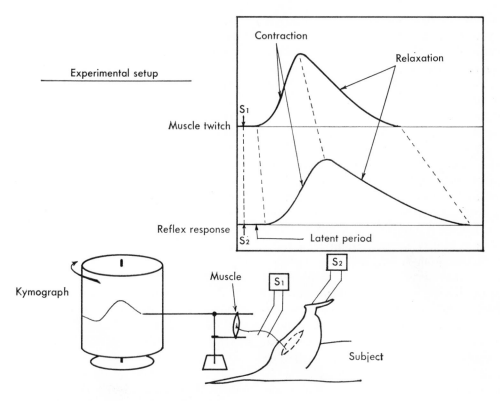

Fig. 13-2. Diagram of the setup for recording from a reflex preparation and records obtained from muscle twitch and reflex stimulation (see text).

of the muscle response. The muscle twitch may begin within $\frac{1}{100}$ second after the stimulus is applied; the reflex response does not begin until about $\frac{1}{5}$ second after the stimulus. There are two minor reasons and one major reason for the difference.

The *conduction time* for neurons involved in the reflex is obviously greater than for neurons in the muscle twitch. The impulse initiated at S_2 must traverse as much as 2 feet of nerve fibers before reaching the muscle; the impulse initiated at S_1 has only a few inches to go. Figuring that the conduction speeds involved range from 5 meters per second in the fastest sensory pain neurons to 120 meters per second in motoneurons, the difference in conduction time can amount to less than $\frac{1}{10}$ second. This does little toward explaining a dif-

ference between $\frac{1}{5}$ and $\frac{1}{100}$ second in the two types of responses.

Synaptic delay is involved in the reflex but not in the muscle twitch. That is, excitation from the sensory neurons for the reflex must cross synapses between nerve cells in the spinal cord; this is not true of excitation for a muscle twitch. In Fig. 13-2 the nerve impulse from S_2 must cross spinal cord synapses to excite the motoneurons; S_1 stimulation directly excites the motoneurons. However, direct measurement of synaptic delay shows that one nerve cell excites another within 0.5 msec. (half of $1/1000$ second) so that synaptic delay *as such* is a negligible factor.

Summation is the most important factor. It is probably *not* true that a single neuron fires another single neuron via their synapses in a reflex. To fire each motoneuron excitation must *converge* on it from several interneurons and many synapses are involved. When an interneuron acts on the cell body and dendrites of a motoneuron, the effect is over in 0.5 msec. or less. Since the interneuron has a refractory period of at least 1 msec., it will be that long before it fires again, and the effect of the first impulse has died away before the second arrives to supply more excitation. This means that excitation must *converge* on the motoneuron from several interneurons and that these impulses must arrive within 0.5 msec. of each other to summate and fire the motoneuron. When these repetitive impulses arrive via pathways of different length, having crossed different numbers of synapses en route, they arrive at different intervals after stimulation. Time is required before enough of them arrive at a motoneuron within 0.5 msec. of each other to summate and fire the motoneuron. To use an anology, it would require some time before ten men of different stride, walking together, all put their right foot down within a ⅕-second interval.

Contraction time

Contraction time is the time required for the muscle to reach full contraction after it has begun to shorten. It is much longer for the reflex than the muscle twitch, as can be seen in Fig. 13-2. The reasons for the greater contraction time of the reflex are classified under the term **recruitment**. Stimulation to the motor nerve for a muscle twitch at S_1 fires all the motoneurons simultaneously, so that all motor units are excited at nearly the same time. As a result nearly all the muscle cells begin to contract at the same time. Contraction time for a muscle twitch, therefore, is largely the time required for the muscle cells to shorten when excited. Stimulation at S_2 for a reflex involves summation at synapses, conduction time in neurons, and muscle contraction time (see above). Even if all the pain im-

pulses from S_2 arrive at the cord nearly together, interneurons will respond at different rates. Summation will require a longer time for some motoneurons than others, so that different motoneurons will begin firing at different time delays after the S_2 stimulus. As each motoneuron is added to the response, it is said to be recruited into the active **motoneuron pool** until all motor units are responding. As each motoneuron becomes active, its motor unit is added to the reflex response. The time required for this process increases the contraction time over that of the muscle twitch.

Relaxation time

Relaxation time is the time required for the muscle to reach its original length (that is, relax) after full contraction is attained. After stimulation at S_1, the muscle cells all contract nearly simultaneously. This means that all the muscle cells begin to relax at once. Relaxation time for the muscle twitch is therefore only the time required for the muscle cells to reach their original length after the mechanical relaxation process begins in all of them. Relaxation time for the reflex response is longer than this. The longer relaxation time can only mean that some muscle cells remain contracted after others have begun to relax. Some motoneurons must still be firing after stimulation at S_2 has ceased and after maximum contraction has been reached. This phenomenon is called **afterdischarge.** It is caused by two kinds of "circuits" in the interneurons of the CNS that continue to stimulate motoneurons after input excitation is over. These are the "loop" and "parallel" circuits illustrated in Fig. 13-3.

The **parallel circuit** results when there are several interneuron pathways of differing lengths and a number of synaptic interruptions that are interposed between the sensory and motor neurons for a reflex. In Fig. 13-3 stimulation of sensory neuron *A* fires pathways *1, 2,* and *3.* Pathway *1* in-

Parallel circuits

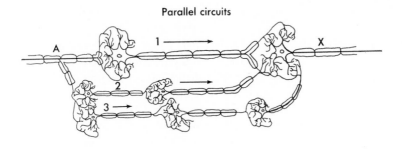

Loop circuits

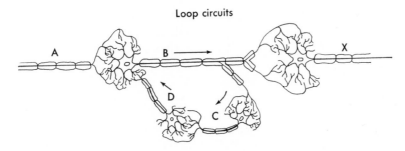

Fig. 13-3. Loop or reverberating and parallel circuits in the CNS. Semidiagrammatic.

volves the fewest synaptic interruptions and less summation so that it fires motoneuron X first. By the time excitation reaches neuron X via pathway 2, the motoneuron has recovered and is fired a second time. It recovers again and pathway 3, with still more synapses, fires it a third time. In this oversimplified example three output impulses result from one input stimulus. In the CNS hundreds of interneurons diverge and converge to form many parallel pathways.

A **loop**, or **reverberatory, circuit** or **closed chain** involves reexcitation of an interneuron over and over by way of a circular pathway. In Fig. 13-3 the input pathway A fires interneuron B, which fires motoneuron X. But neuron B has a collateral that fires neuron C, C fires D, and D fires B, which has recovered by now. B fires X and again reexcites the loop. In the example one input impulse at A can follow this loop and continue to fire the reflex response via X until some element in the loop becomes involved

in other CNS pathways; this might cause it to be refractory when the loop excitation reaches it. The example is simplified of course. Many interneurons would be involved in a loop circuit, and loop and parallel circuits probably interact in the interneurons of the CNS. Both kinds of pathways have been seen under the microscope, and both pathways represent ways in which reflex motor units could continue to respond for a time after stimulus input and maximum reflex contraction are over.

Final common path

A given reflex response may be excited in several ways. No matter what the input, however, the motoneurons controlling the responding muscles are the **final common path** taken by any excitation that elicits the reflex. These motoneurons receive excitatory and inhibitory influences from all levels of the CNS. The algebraic sum of the excitation and inhibition that reaches the motoneurons of the final common path will determine whether or not the response will occur and what will be its extent. The extent of the response will also be determined by how interneurons from several inputs converge and "overlap" as they reach the motoneuron pool for a reflex response. The result of this convergence and overlapping is called facilitation if it results in a greater response than expected and occlusion if the response is less than expected.

Facilitation. When two different stimuli to a reflex are applied at once, **facilitation** may occur, and the reflex contraction may be greater than the sum of the reflex contractions to each stimulus. Suppose that stimulating pain receptors in the paw causes a 1-gram contraction in a flexor muscle, stimulating pain receptors in the lower leg causes a 1-gram response in the same muscle, but stimulating both sites at once causes a 3-gram response. A 3-gram response is greater than the sum of two 1-gram responses, and therefore facilitation has occurred. Fig. 13-4 shows how interneurons can converge on motoneurons so that facili-

tation can occur. Suppose that motoneurons X, Y, and Z control different motor units in the reflex, each contributing 1 gram of muscle contraction. Suppose further that two of the synaptic "end-knobs" shown in Fig. 13-4 must be active to fire a motoneuron. This means that input A will fire motoneuron X for a 1-gram response, but it will only *facilitate* (not fire) neuron Y. Input B will cause a 1-gram response via motoneuron Z, but it will only facilitate Y. However, if inputs from A and B both arrive at once, motoneurons X, Y, and Z will fire for a 3-gram response.

Occlusion. When two different stimuli to a reflex are applied at once, **occlusion** may occur, and the reflex contraction may be *less* than the sum of the reflex contractions to each stimulus. Suppose an excised extensor muscle responds with a 2-gram contraction to either pressure on the footpad or spreading the toes (extensor thrust reflex). Yet applying both stimuli results in only a 3-gram contraction—less than the sum of two 2-gram contractions. In this case the motoneurons might receive input as shown in Fig. 13-4 under occlusion. Each of moto-

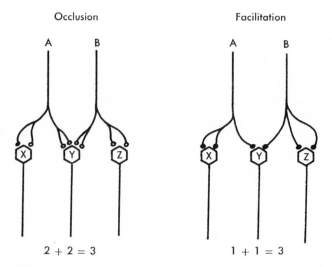

Occlusion   Facilitation

2 + 2 = 3   1 + 1 = 3

Fig. 13-4. Neural mechanisms for facilitation and occlusion. For explanation, see text.

neurons X, Y, and Z control different sets of muscle fibers, and each give a 2-gram contraction. Two "synaptic knobs" are required to fire each motoneuron. Input A (paw pressure) fires neurons X and Y for a 2-gram response. Input B (spreading digits) fires Y and Z for a 2-gram response. Inputs A and B "share," or both control, neuron Y. So when A and B fire together, only three motoneurons can respond—X, Y, and Z. This results in a 3-gram response, which is less than the sum of two 2-gram responses. The facilitation and occlusion diagrams are, of course, vast oversimplifications of the way that interneurons converge on the motoneuron pool of even the simplest reflex.

INHIBITION

Two reflexes may be opposed. This was true of the flexion and crossed-extension reflexes in the examples already given. If flexion in a limb is stimulated by a standard stimulus to pain fibers, a certain strength of flexion will occur. If, at the same time, extension is stimulated by spreading the toes of the same limb, flexion will still occur, but the strength or amount of flexor contraction may be reduced by the stimulus to extension. The amount by which flexion is reduced is the amount of **inhibition** of the flexor response caused by the extensor thrust stimulus. A more common example involves crossed extension. If flexion is stimulated in the right hindlimb, the left hindlimb will extend to support the weight of the animal (**crossed-extension reflex**). If pain fibers in both limbs are stimulated strongly, both hindlimbs flex and the animal will fall, showing that flexion overrides crossed extension just as it overrides the extensor thrust reflex. However, a weak pain stimulus to the right hindlimb will cause enough crossed extension to reduce left flexor reaction to pain stimulation of the left limb. Again, the amount by which left hindlimb flexion is reduced is the amount of inhibition. Since flexion and ex-

tension cannot occur in the same limb at once, the interneurons for the two responses are "wired" so that reflex pathways that excite flexion inhibit extension and vice versa, an arrangement called **reciprocal innervation.**

Phenomena

Inhibition is caused largely by inhibitory neurons, as will be explained shortly. Just as excitatory neurons converge on the motoneuron pool to excite a reflex response, so inhibitory neurons converge on the motoneuron pool of opposed muscles to inhibit them. The resulting inhibition can be measured as a reduction in the opposed response. Inhibition therefore shows all the reflex phenomena already discussed—latency, conduction time, synaptic delay, afterdischarge, summation, facilitation, and occlusion. The principles are the same in each instance, but the response measured is response reduction rather than response excitation.

Central inhibitory mechanisms

Inhibition can theoretically occur because of direct or indirect influence on the motoneurons. **Direct inhibition** results when a motoneuron is hyperpolarized by an inhibitory neuron and thereby made harder to excite, or else when the action of excitatory endings on the motoneuron is blocked (see below). **Indirect inhibition** occurs when the excitation to a motoneuron is reduced; some of the interneurons supplying it become involved in other pathways. Modern theorists believe inhibition is largely of the direct variety.

Indirect inhibition is presumably caused by lack of excitation. Whenever two opposed reflexes share a common path over a group of interneurons, then the path must divide to supply motoneurons for opposed muscle groups. When one reflex is active, the shared motoneurons may be refractory as excitation arrives via the sensory path for the opposed reflex. It is somewhat doubtful that this kind of inhibition occurs, but it is theoretically possible.

Direct inhibition occurs when reflex response of the motoneurons is directly prevented via interneurons that are excited by an opposed reflex response. Direct inhibition may be caused by **presynaptic** or **postsynaptic inhibition.** Postsynaptic inhibition occurs when the collaterals of interneurons for a reflex stimulate **Renshaw cells,** which, in turn, inhibit the motoneurons for the *opposed* reflex response. Renshaw cells are short Golgi II cells that release gamma-aminobutyric acid (GABA) to hyperpolarize the neurons and make them harder to excite (Chapter 4). The inhibitory influence occurs after the synapses and is therefore postsynaptic. Presynaptic inhibition occurs when the inhibitory neurons or their collaterals contact some of the *axon terminals* of cells that would otherwise excite the motoneurons. They may keep the transmitter substance of these filaments exhausted so that they cannot participate in depolarizing the motoneurons. Such synapses are called **axoaxonic synapses** by contrast with the normal **axodendritic synapses** (synapses between axon filament endings and dendrites and cell bodies).

VARIETIES OF SPINAL REFLEXES AND THEIR MECHANISMS

So far the flexion, crossed extension, and extensor thrust reflexes have been used as examples in explaining reflex mechanisms of excitation and inhibition. These are not the only examples of adaptive reflexes, and their utility will be further explained in the course of citing the adaptive reflexes that have received the most study.

Stretch reflex

The **stretch,** or **myotatic, reflex** was covered in some detail in Chapter 9 on proprioception. In response to stretch the muscles, especially extensors, react by a partial muscle contraction that maintains muscle *tone.* Annulospiral receptors in the muscle spindle fibers react to stretch of the muscle by firing some motor units of the muscle in a monosynaptic, or single synapse, reflex, the afferent neurons directly exciting the motor neurons. Sensitivity to stretch can be increased by contracting the muscle spindles themselves via the BSRF and gamma efferent fibers, muscle spindle contraction firing their annulospiral receptors just as muscle stretch does. In response to increased stretch, as when limb extensors are stretched by shifting weight to a limb to bend the knee, extensors react to straighten the limb and maintain an upright position. The reflex is therefore useful in postural adjustment as well as in maintaining muscle tone.

Extensor thrust reflex

The **extensor thrust reflex** has already been used as an example. This reflex also aids postural adjustment and reflex standing. Pressure receptors on the sole of the foot and proprioceptors that respond to spreading of the digits from body weight reflexly contract extensor muscles in the limb. The extensor contraction stiffens the limb to support the weight being placed upon it. The more pressure, the more extension, so that shifts in posture are accommodated.

Flexion reflex

The **flexion reflex** has also been cited. In response to pain stimulation to a limb, particularly the foot, flexor muscles withdraw the limb from the stimulus. The reflex is a powerful one, taking precedence over opposed reflexes in most circumstances. This reflex is also adaptive, removing the limb from injurious stimuli. It is therefore a nociceptive reflex, and has survival value for the animal.

Crossed-extension reflex

The **crossed-extension reflex** accompanies the flexion reflex and was used as an example when inhibition was discussed. Flexion of a limb is accompanied by extension of the contralateral limb. The contralateral limb thus supports the weight of the animal when a leg is withdrawn from an injurious stimulus. Limb flexion in walking is also accompanied by contralateral extension; the reflex is therefore adaptive for the alternating stepping movements required for walking.

Long spinal reflexes

The reflexes discussed so far have involved only one level of the spinal cord. Stimuli to a limb have resulted in flexion or extension responses of that limb or the contralateral limb, all supplied by the same segments of the spinal cord. **Long spinal reflexes** involve excitation entering one level of the cord and travelling up and down the cord to result in limb and body movements at other levels. Such reflexes have both spatial and temporal characteristics. The **reflex figure** of Sherrington demonstrates the *spatial* characteristics of long spinal reflexes. Flexion of the right hindlimb will cause reflex extension of the left hindlimb in the crossed-extension reflex of the same spinal segments. But excitation will also ascend the cord to cause extension of the left forelimb and flexion of the right forelimb. In four-legged animals this long spinal reflex is useful in maintaining balance and in the alternating movements of forelimbs and hindlimbs in walking. The **scratch reflex** is a long spinal reflex that demonstrates *temporal* characteristics. Tickling the flank of a dog—even a spinal dog—will result in scratching movements of the hindlimb on the same side. Scratching involves alternating flexion and extension of the limb, a temporal pattern of movement that is useful in walking as well.

HIGHER-LEVEL REFLEXES

Not all reflexes are mediated by the interneurons of the spinal cord alone. Many reflexes are organized by the interneurons

of the brainstem or even the cerebral cortex. The sensory or the motor side of these reflexes, or both, may involve the cranial nerves. Most of the reflex centers are to be found in the medulla of the brain since most of the cranial nerves originate in the medulla, but reflexes with centers at other levels of the brain will be cited as well. The higher-level reflexes are usually concerned with two kinds of adaptive behavior. (1) The "vital reflexes" maintain automatic adjustments of the visceral muscles and glands of the body to changes in internal states such as blood pressure and blood chemistry. The motor adjustments are largely via the autonomic nervous system; the reflexes maintain the consistency of the internal environment necessary for life. (2) Other higher-level reflexes involve postural adjustments and are superimposed on some of the postural spinal reflexes already mentioned.

Vital reflexes

Several of the vital reflexes are respiratory because breathing must be regulated to maintain blood oxygen within optimum limits. Blood oxygen for the cells must be constant in the face of the widely varying demands of rest, exercise, and other metabolic changes; therefore reflex regulation is necessary. Breathing is organized by threee reflex centers in the medulla (inspiratory, pneumotaxic, and expiratory). In normal quiet breathing, however, only the **inspiratory center** is involved. The inspiratory center is directly activated by a rise in the carbon dioxide (CO_2) content of the blood and tissue fluid. Blood CO_2 rises as blood oxygen (O_2) falls because the cells use O_2 and give off CO_2 (Chapter 2). Breathing rids the blood of CO_2 with every exhalation and increases blood O_2 with every inhalation.

When the blood CO_2 reaches a minimum level, one inhales and exhales to correct the CO_2-O_2 balance. This minimum CO_2 level stimulates the inspiratory center directly. The inspiratory center sends excitation via the phrenic nerves to the diaphragm and via the intercostal nerves to the rib muscles. When the diaphragm contracts, the "bottom" of the chest cavity is lowered, and the intercostal muscles raise the ribs; both events increase the volume of the chest cavity, and the lungs expand to fill it, taking in air. The resulting lung expansion stimulates pressure receptors in the lungs. The pressure receptors fire fibers in the vagus nerve, which inhibit the inspiratory center. The diaphragm and rib muscles relax, and the chest cavity "collapses" the lungs by its own elasticity, forcing exhalation. In normal quiet breathing, therefore, inspiration is active and expiration is passive.

If the blood CO_2 rises further because of exercise for example, the expiratory and pneumotaxic centers become active, and both inspiration and expiration become active processes. With high blood CO_2, the inspiratory center causes a deeper inhalation. The increased input via the vagus from lung pressure receptors fires the **pneumotaxic center.** The pneumotaxic center excites the expiratory center and inhibits the inspiratory center. The **expiratory center** stimulates the appropriate rib muscles for forced exhalation. Breathing therefore becomes more rapid to increase the rate of lung ventilation, lowering the blood CO_2 and raising its O_2. In a supporting reflex receptors in the **carotid sinuses** of blood vessels leading to the brain react to low blood O_2 by acting on the respiratory centers to increase the rate of breathing.

Circulatory reflexes

Circulatory reflexes aid in regulating the transport of O_2 and CO_2 by regulating the heart rate and blood pressure. The sense organs for circulatory reflexes are pressure-sensitive receptors found in the carotid sinus and aortic arch (arteries leading from the heart) and in the vena cava (a major vein returning blood from the body to the heart). These pressure receptors act on the sympathetic **cardioaccelerator** and parasympathetic **cardioinhibitory centers** to slow the pumping of the heart when the blood pressure rises or to speed heart action when blood pressure falls. The two centers are mutually inhibitory so that heart rate increases when blood pressure falls and decreases when blood pressure rises.

Blood pressure also rises when the arteries constrict and falls when they dilate. The **vasoconstrictor** and **vasodilator centers** of the medulla are also mutually inhibitory, react to the above pressure receptors, and interact with the cardiac centers to regulate blood pressure. Both sets of centers react appropriately to the blood CO_2 level, to keep the blood CO_2 level within bounds by changes in heart rate and blood pressure. The flow of blood from the lungs to the tissues and back is therefore regulated by the CO_2 and O_2 content of the blood itself.

Finally, the acid-base balance of the blood and tissue fluid is regulated by the heart rate and blood pressure centers. **Chemoreceptors** in the aortic arch and carotid sinus are sensitive to oxygen lack, excessive carbon dioxide, and increased H+ ion content.

All these events accompany high CO_2 and blood acidity. The heart rate and blood pressure receptors react reflexly to increase blood flow to and from the lungs, which lowers blood acidity until the chemoreceptors no longer react. Blood CO_2 largely controls both the respiratory reflexes on one hand and the heart rate and blood pressure reflexes on the other. Lung ventilation and transport of O_2 and CO_2 by the blood therefore interact in maintaining the O_2, CO_2, and acidity of the tissue fluid within homeostatic limits.

Postural reflexes

The higher-level postural reflexes are superimposed upon the adaptive postural reflexes of the spinal cord that were discussed previously. They involve inputs from the proprioceptors to the BSRF in the medulla and inputs from the special senses to higher brain centers. The regulation of extensor tone occurs largely in the BSRF and in the vestibular nuclei of the medulla. However, input from the basal ganglia, cerebellum, and cortex can alter BSRF and vestibular regulation of extensor tone in reaction to higher levels of motor organization. In the low decerebrate (medullary) preparation higher centers are removed so that regulation of extensor tone is confined to BSRF and vestibular responses to proprioception (including the cerebellum). The animal can stand if balanced, but shows decerebrate rigidity. Lowering the head relaxes the forelimb extensors and contracts the hindlimb extensors; the animal's posture is that of "looking under" something. Raising the head has the opposite effect; the cat's posture is that of preparing to jump to the top of a table. Turning the head from side to side changes extensor tone as if the animal were prepared to turn in the direction the head is pointed. The extensors on that side relax, and the extensors on the opposite side contract, preparing the animal for movement that follows head direction. The receptors for these reflexes are kinesthetic receptors in the neck muscles that respond to head position.

Righting reflexes restore the animal to an upright position. Perhaps you have seen someone hold a cat upside down by its limbs and drop the animal to watch it land on its feet. Close observation shows that the head turns first, then the forequarters, and then the hindquarters. These reflexes depend upon the *midbrain* and can be demonstrated in an animal with the brain transected above that level. Stimulation of the vestibular maculae by the inverted head position (Chapter 9) initiates this series of reflexes. The neck muscles respond to macular stimulation by twisting the neck to turn the head toward the upright position. Kinesthetic receptors in the neck muscles are stimulated and cause reflex twisting of the

forequarters in the same direction. Kinesthetic receptors in this region reflexly twist the hindquarters. The animal twists, then "unwinds" from head to tail in regaining the upright position while it falls. Righting responses in man are more dependent on visual stimulation. However, visual stimulation can also initiate the sequence in lower animals with the maculae destroyed.

Placing and **hopping reflexes** are mediated by the cerebral cortex and are absent in the decorticate animal. If the back of the paw of a blindfolded cat is pressed against the edge of a table, the cat will place his paw on the table—a placing response. If the standing cat is pushed sideways, it will retain balance by a hopping response, alternately flexing and extending all four limbs in "hopping" movements. These reflexes represent complex and organized cortical reactions to proprioceptive stimuli.

MOTOR ORGANIZATION

The brain integrates behavior in a very complex manner that is constantly modified by input from many sensory receptors. Since behavior moves the animal about, the sensory input changes. This is a *feedback* situation because input modifies behavior and behavior modifies input. To consider all the sensory inputs that initiate or modify movement at the same time would unduly complicate this section. To simplify matters all input except that from the proprioceptors will be ignored. Proprioceptive input from the semicircular canals, maculae, and kinesthetic receptors in the muscles are the most integral part of the feedback modifying movement. Such inputs must therefore be considered in motor organization. Appropriate response change to visual, auditory, tactile, and other sensory input will be assumed rather than discussed. To further make the section manageable, a more or less arbitrary distinction will be made between the following three "motor systems" of the body: (1) **pyramidal,** (2) **extrapyramidal,** and (3) **cerebellar.** Modern research shows that these catagories are artificial ones since no one system can operate normally without the others and their major functions overlap so much. However, each system can be said to make a major contribution to behavior, and it is less confusing to take them one at a time instead of all at once. Considered in this light the major contribution of the pyramidal system is the initiation of precise movement, whereas the extrapyramidal system provides for gross "background movements," and the cerebellar system supports balance and coordination.

Pyramidal system

The pyramidal system contains most of the fibers that run directly from the motor projection areas of the cerebral cortex to the motoneurons of the cranial and spinal nerves. These fibers are found chiefly in the **pyramidal tract.** Pyramidal tract fibers that originate in the cerebral cortex pass to the brainstem and spinal cord via the medullary pyramids. The pyramids can be seen on the ventral side of the brainstem, emerging from under the temporal lobes as prominent ropelike strands, diving beneath the pons, and emerging on the ventral side of the medulla to either side of the midline (Fig. 6-10). Fig. 13-5 shows the cortical areas originating pyramidal fibers by contrast with extrapyramidal fibers. The *single* cortical area that supplies most fibers to the system (31%) is the motor projection area of the brain, area 4 in the Brodman system (Fig. 6-11). However, all

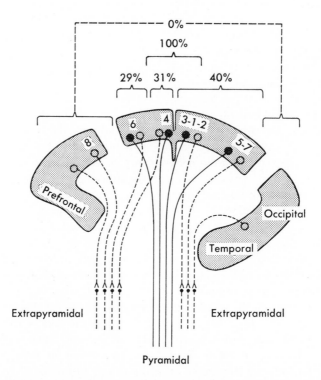

Fig. 13-5. Cortical origins of the pyramidal and extrapyramidal tracts. (Based on data of Russell, J. R., and De Meyer, W.: Neurology, **11:**96-108, 1961; from Ruch, T. C.: The cerebral cortex: its structure and motor functions. In Ruch, T. C., Patton, H. D., Woodbury, J. W., and Towe, A. L., editors: Neurophysiology, ed. 2, Philadelphia, 1965, W. B. Saunders Co.)

other cortical lobes but the occipital, prefrontal, and temporal contribute fibers to the pyramidal tract.

Topographical organization. The motor projection area of the brain, area 4, is topographically organized. Stimulation of the exposed brain in an anesthetized animal shows that each part of area 4 controls a selected set of the muscles controlling body movement. Starting down in the longitudinal fissure that divides the hemispheres in man, movements of the toes, then ankles, then knee can be found when the cortex is stimulated (Fig. 13-6). Continuing down

the precentral gyrus elicits movements in a toes-to-head direction, except that the face is erect rather than inverted. The illustration is also distorted in that muscle groups requiring most precise control, such as the lips and fingers, have a disproportionately large cortical area devoted to them. By contrast the large muscles of the body trunk are represented by a rather small cortical area. To understand this phenomenon realize that pyramidal neurons control spinal motoneurons rather directly and that each spinal motoneuron controls a *motor unit.* In Chapter 5 it was shown that

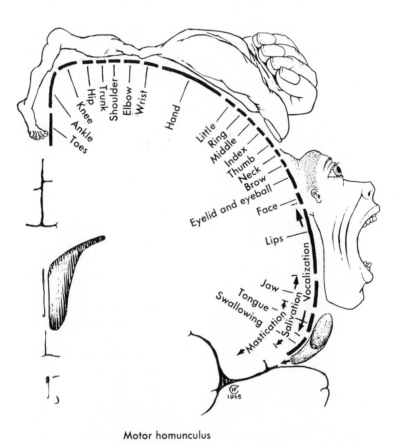

Motor homunculus

Fig. 13-6. Motor homunculus. A section of the precentral gyrus in diagrammatic form. Dark lines repersent the relative proportion of cortical tissue controlling the muscles of parts of the body on the labels. Surrounding the section is a caricature of the body in the same relative proportions. Compare with Fig. 8-5. (From Penfield, W., and Rasmussen, T.: The cerebral cortex of man, New York, 1950, The Macmillan Co.)

muscles requiring precise control of movement had fewer muscle cells supplied by each nerve cell than muscles controlling gross body movement. Precise control involves many degrees of contraction, and therefore only a few muscle cells are brought into contraction as each motor nerve cell is excited—a small innervation ratio. Such muscles require more motoneurons for their size than do muscles controlling gross movements. The motoneurons are stimulated via pyramidal neurons that originate in the cortex. Therefore more pyramidal neurons are found controlling movement of "precise" muscles than control "gross" muscles. As a result a greater area of cortex is devoted to precisely controlled muscles, such as those of the lips and fingers, in comparison with muscles of the body trunk.

Anatomy. The pyramidal tracts are largely *crossed,* that is, the left hemisphere of the brain controls the right side of the body and vice versa. Three tracts are involved: (1) the **corticobulbar tract** that supplies motor fibers of the cranial nerves, (2) the **lateral corticospinal tract,** a crossed tract of the lateral funiculus of the cord, and (3) the **ventral corticospinal tract,** an uncrossed track of the ventral funiculus of the cord. In each case the fibers run from the cortex to the level of the motoneurons and excite them via interneurons much like a reflex. Fig. 13-7 shows all three tracts. The corticobulbar tract contains fibers that originate in the face area of the precentral gyrus. The fibers descend the brainstem of the same side (with few exceptions) and cross at the level of the cranial motoneurons they supply. The lateral corticospinal tract is formed by approximately 75% of the pyramidal fibers that cross at the decussation of the pyramids in the lower medulla. The remaining uncrossed fibers form the ventral corticospinal tract. Most of these fibers cross in the ventral white commissure of the spinal cord at the level of the motoneurons they excite via interneurons.

There is evidence that the pyramidal tract gives off collaterals to the gracile and cuneate nuclei of the medulla. The influence is both excitatory and inhibitory. Since the gracile and cuneate nuclei relay pressure and fine touch sensations, these inputs are directly altered by movements initiated by the pyramidal system.

Symptoms of damage. If area 4 is selectively damaged by surgery, without damage to other areas, a **flaccid paralysis** results in the muscles represented by the damaged area. The muscles retain normal tone, but they are poorly controlled. The paralysis is severe only in the extremities; the animal is still capable of gross movements. The nervous system is capable of considerable retraining, and some control of the affected extremities can be learned by remaining brain areas. The younger the animal, the more true this is. Some loss of precise control of muscles, such as those of the fingers or lips, is permanent, however. Accidental brain damage is seldom restricted to area 4, so that flaccid paralysis is rarely seen without symptoms of extrapyramidal damage as well.

Extrapyramidal system

The extrapyramidal system seems largely organized for "background movement," the postural adjustments that accompany more precise movements. For example, in picking up a pencil from a table, gross adjustments in the position of the body trunk, shoulder, and upper arm would accompany the precise, pyramidally controlled movements of the lower arm and fingers. As can be seen in Fig. 13-5, many of the cortical fibers of the extrapyramidal system originate in area 6, the **premotor area,** although fibers are supplied by many other areas of the cortex. Intense stimulation of area 6 will lead to gross body movements, although the threshold is higher than that for area 4. Body areas nearer the midline seem to be represented by area 6 as compared to area 4—muscles of the trunk, hip and shoul-

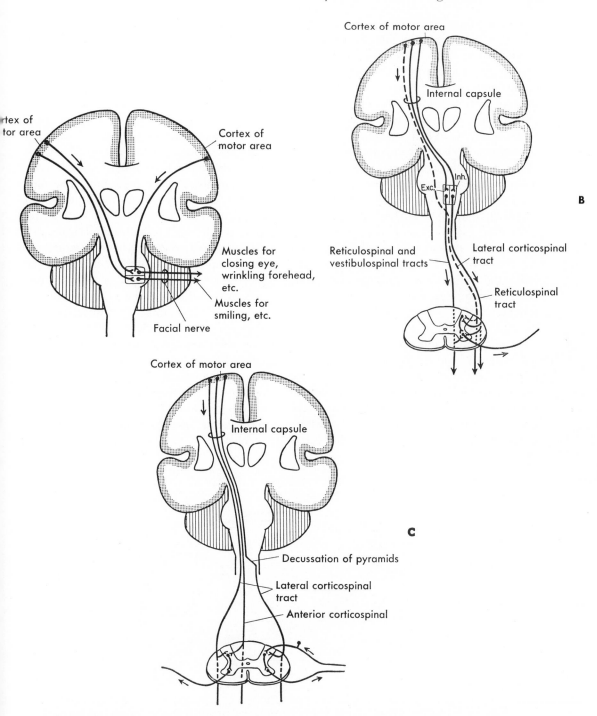

Fig. 13-7. Major motor tracts of the brain in diagrammatic form. **A,** Corticobullar tract. **B,** Lateral and ventral (anterior) corticospinal tracts. **C,** Reticulospinal and vestibulospinal tracts. (From Gardner, E. O.: Fundamentals of neurology, ed, 4, Philadelphia, 1963, W. B. Saunders Co.)

der, and upper extremities. Topographically, moving from area 4 into area 6 is like moving from areas with more control of the extremities to areas with more control of the body trunk. However, the mechanisms of extrapyramidal control over the muscles are quite different from the mechanisms of pyramidal control.

Anatomy. The extrapyramidal system consists of an array of relatively short and branching neurons, which descend through the brainstem to excite subcortical nuclei and include much of the brainstem reticular formation (BSRF) and the cerebellum. Some of the pathways—those leading from the cortex to the thalamus, the corpus striatum, the red nucleus (an important motor center in four-legged animals), and the cerebellum, for example—are anatomically distinct. Others can be followed only by the technique of stimulating the cortex and following the course of the resulting nerve impulses with implanted electrodes. All the extrapyramidal pathways that originate in the cortex form part of the **cortically originating extrapyramidal system (COEPS).** Other descending pathways of the extra-

pyramidal system originate in the nuclei named above as well as other nuclei of the brainstem. Some of the pathways involved are shown in Figs. 13-7 and 13-8. These pathways control "background movements" by adjustment of extensor muscle tone although this is an entirely different mechanism from the direct control of motoneurons exerted by the pyramidal system. The cortex and the caudate nucleus selectively inhibit a large excitatory area and a smaller inhibitory area in the brainstem reticular formation (BSRF). These two areas give rise to the **reticulospinal tract.** The reticulospinal tract supplies the gamma efferent motoneurons, which, in turn, excite the muscle spindle fibers in extensor muscles. When the muscle spindles contract, their sensory endings (annulospiral endings) fire stretch reflexes in the extensors. The BSRF inhibitory area has an inhibitory effect on the gamma efferents that stimulate stretch reflexes. The cortex and caudate nucleus selectively suppress these influences to cause a *pattern* of background movement. The BSRF inhibitory area also receives a pattern of inhibition from the

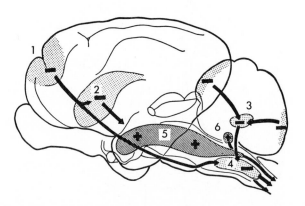

Fig. 13-8. Reconstruction of cat brain showing inhibitory and facilicatory interactions that relate to spasticity and decerebrate rigidity. Inhibitory pathways: **1,** corticobulboreticular; **2,** caudatospinal; **3,** cerebelloreticular; **4,** reticulospinal. Facilicatory pathways: **5,** reticulospinal; **6,** vestibulospinal. (From Lindlsey, D. B., Schreiner, L. H., and Magoun, H. W.: J. Neurophysiol. **12:**197-205, 1949.)

cerebellum. In this general way the cortex, caudate nucleus, and cerebellum control the BSRF, which, in turn, regulates the extensor stretch reflexes. By the mechanism of reciprocal innervation the contraction of extensor muscles is accompanied by the relaxation of their opposed flexor muscles and vice versa. As a result, the area of the BSRF that is labeled excitatory for extensors inhibits flexors and the inhibitory BSRF excites the flexors while it inhibits extensors. However, the main influence of the BSRF is to excite extensor muscles via the reticulospinal tract. This is why a decerebrate animal shows decerebrate rigidity, or spastic paralysis. The large excitatory BSRF area is being released from the inhibitory influence of the premotor cortex and caudate nucleus when these centers are cut away. Excitation to the extensor stretch reflexes via the reticulospinal tract is thereby increased. The extensors react with strong contractions, and the animal assumes a posture with all four limbs rigidly extended.

The extensor motoneurons are subject to direct rather than to indirect excitation via another pathway of the extrapyramidal system. The **vestibular nuclei** of the eighth nerve send excitation directly to the extensor motoneurons via the **vestibulospinal tract** (Fig. 13-8). The vestibular nuclei are normally subject to cortical inhibition. Their direct excitation of extensor motoneurons is therefore increased when the cortex is cut away in decerebration. This adds to the decerebrate rigidity caused by the BSRF. In the normal animal the vestibular nuclei receive a pattern of input from the semicircular canals and maculae, reporting on the position and movements of the head. In response the vestibular nuclei send a pattern of excitation to the extensor motoneurons via the vestibulospinal tract. The extensor muscles respond to adjust the posture of the animal to the position and movements of the head. This mechanism is the origin of the righting reflexes that were discussed earlier.

Some of the pathways of the extrapyramidal system are involved in a cortical feedback mechanism. Cortical feedback coordinates events in the premotor area and basal ganglia with initiation of movements

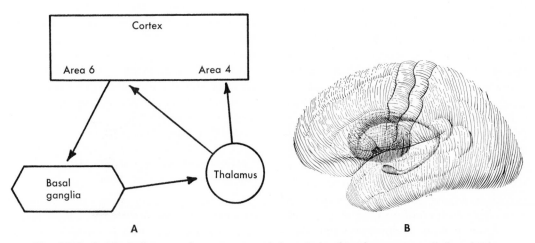

Fig. 13-9. A, Block diagram showing some of the relationships between cortical and subcortical motor centers (see text). **B,** Phantom of the striatum within the cerebral hemisphere. (From Krieg, W. J. S.: Functional neuroanatomy, Evanston, Ill., Brain Books.)

from pyramidal area 4. Neurons leaving premotor area 6 relay in subcortical nuclei and feedback to area 4. In this manner the "background movements" initiated by the extrapyramidal system are coordinated with the more precise movements initiated by the pyramidal system. The circuit involved is shown in Fig. 13-9. Excitation from premotor area 6 goes to the **basal ganglia** (striatum or putamen, caudate nucleus, and globus pallidus). The basal ganglia send excitation to the thalamus (ventrolateral nucleus) and the thalamus feeds back to both area 6 and area 4. This is a case of *negative feedback* since area 6 and the basal ganglia largely *inhibit* area 4. However, selective inhibition can coordinate the pyramidal and extrapyramidal systems just as well as selective excitation could.

Symptoms of damage. Damage to premotor area 6 or other parts of the COEPS results in **spastic paralysis** of the affected extensor muscles. This is similar in principle to the decerebrate rigidity already discussed. The excitatory BSRF and vestibular nuclei are released from cortical inhibition. As a result extensor muscle tone is increased, and the affected limbs are rigidly extended in four-legged animals. Extensor muscles are antigravity muscles since they bear the weight of the animal in reflex standing and prevent the limbs from flexing against the force of gravity. In two-legged primates (including man) the flexors of the arms and hands resist gravity rather than the extensors; bending the arm and fingers is done against the force of gravity. As a result the flexors of the arm and hand take on the antigravity role of extensors and are connected to the extrapyramidal system accordingly. Spastic paralysis of the arm and hand in man, therefore, involves a rigidly *flexed* arm, wrist, and hand. This position of arm, wrist, and hand is frequently seen in spastics when damage to the appropriate brain areas has occurred.

Damage to the cortical feedback loop or

its connections to other pyramidal centers has a more complex and variable outcome. Ceaseless jerky movements (chorea), continuous involuntary writhing of the hand (athetosis), or violent "flinging" motions of the limbs (ballismus) may occur. **Parkinson's disease** is a more common result. In this disorder, as in the others mentioned, *tremor at rest* is the most common symptom. Minor damage to the extrapyramidal system from circulatory disorders often occurs in elderly persons, and continuous fine tremors, especially of the hand, are often seen. These tremors usually disappear when a voluntary movement is made. This is why tremors at rest can be suffered by an old watchmaker, for example, without unduly affecting the precise movements necessary to his work. Some believe that the feedback loop and connections to other subcortical motor centers suppress continued activity of centers that cause the alternating muscle contractions of tremor. Tremor alone is not Parkinson's disease, however. In Parkinson's disease tremor at rest is accompanied by a disabling reduction in voluntary and associated movements (poverty of movement), by rigidity of posture and relative immobility, and by impaired facial expression of emotion (masklike face). Surprisingly enough, these symptoms are often relieved by further extrapyramidal damage. Surgical destruction of part of the cortical feedback loop just described can relieve the symptoms dramatically. The connections between the globus pallidus and lateroventral nucleus of the thalamus, or the nucleus itself, are destroyed by a carefully placed probe that freezes the cells.

Cortical control of movement: supplementary motor areas

The distinction between the pyramidal and extrapyramidal systems in both origin and function has been overemphasized to simplify matters for the student. When the cortical origin of extrapyramidal fibers (COEPS) and the pyramidal system was outlined (Fig. 13-5), extensive overlap could be seen. The major cortical area where pyramidal fibers originate is area 4 on the precentral gyrus. The COEPS originated from premotor area 6 more than many other areas. However, many neurons of both systems originate from the same areas—the frontal and parietal lobes contribute to both systems. The origin of COEPS fibers is still more extensive. It is therefore not surprising that movement can be elicited by stimulating widespread areas on the cerebral cortex. This is especially true when the cortex retains its normal excitability and is not depressed by the drugs used to anesthetize the animal for study. Experiments on lightly anesthetized or paralyzed animals have shown that the primary motor area is more extensive than previously believed (Fig. 13-10). This is the area of major origin for pyramidal fibers and may include part of area 6 as well as area 4. The topographic organization of muscle groups in the monkey is the same as that described for man, except that the head is inverted instead of upright. Tail and hindlimb representation

begins deep in the longitudinal fissure. As the precentral gyrus is stimulated farther and farther down the side of the brain, movements occur more and more toward the "head end" of the animal. As mentioned before, stimulating cortical areas from the the central fissure forward causes a change in movements from the limbs to the body trunk. A "map" of the body is represented from tail to head in one direction and from extremities to the body axis in the other direction. As before, muscles of the lips and extremities have a larger cortical area devoted to them than do muscles of the body trunk. The contribution of the pyramidal system to movement is probably greatest for the extremities. The COEPS contribution is greater as stimulation moves forward across areas 4 and 6 toward the frontal part of the cortex, eliciting postural movements of the body trunk.

A **second motor area** has been discovered on the lateral surface of the precentral gyrus as it extends into the lateral fissure. The face is represented just above the lateral (sylvian) fissure, the right side of the brain controlling the right side of the body

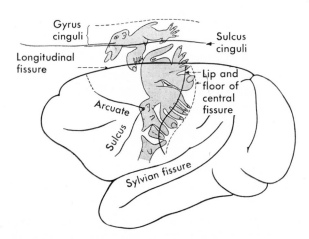

Fig. 13-10. Cortical representation of primary (classical), supplementary, and ipsilateral face motor areas in the monkey. Note that the primary area extends beyond area 4 into area 6. (From Woolsey, C. N., Erickson, T. C., Hampson, J. L., and Meyer, D. R.: Res. Publ. Ass. Nerv. Ment. Dis. **30:**238-264, 1951.)

and vice versa (ipsilateral face area). The topographical "map" of the movements obtained is opposite from that of the primary area in the head to tail direction. Body muscle representation is buried in the lateral fissure. This area may be phylogenetically older than the motor projection area, and it receives sensory input as well.

A **supplementary motor area** has also been discovered and "mapped." This area lies in the cortex of either hemisphere that is buried in the longitudinal fissure (Fig. 13-10). Stimulation of the facial part of this area often causes coordinated acts such as yawning, vocalization, or coordinated head and eye movements. Body responses involve assuming and holding a posture that outlasts the stimulation by many seconds. The representation is bilateral—a stimulus to one hemisphere can cause movements of both sides of the body. The supplementary motor area has connections to the primary and the second motor area. However, its control of movement is via the COEPS rather than pyramidal fibers.

Cerebellum

The cerebellum regulates the postural adjustments of the extrapyramidal system and governs certain interactions between extrapyramidal and pyramidal systems. The cerebellum brings kinesthetic and vestibular inputs to bear on both systems and plays an integral role in motor organization. It is treated separately in this chapter only for the sake of taking topics up one at a time; in the end pyramidal, extrapyramidal, and cerebellar influences are part of one motor organization system. The cerebellar contribution to motor organization includes all proprioceptive and cortical input to the cerebellum and all cerebellar output to cortical and subcortical centers involved in movement. The cerebellum aids in the regulation of balance and coordination.

Anatomy. The cerebellar pathways involve three sets of inputs to the cerebellum and three sets of outputs. All inputs and outputs interconnect via neurons that crisscross the cortex of the cerebellum in both directions; therefore all inputs to the cerebellum affect all outputs from the cerebellum. However, one input and output form a negative feedback loop from the premotor areas of the cerebral cortex to the cerebellum and back to the motor cortex. From the standpoint of evolution this feedback loop interconnects the newest part of the cerebrum with the newest part of the cerebellum (neocerebellum). A second input from the stretch receptors in the extensor muscles (muscle spindles) stimulates an older part of the cerebellum, the paleocerebellum. This part of the cerebellum regulates extensor tone by its output to the BSRF and other nuclei of the brainstem. The oldest part of the cerebellum (archicerebellum) receives input from the position and movement receptors of the inner ear. Its output also regulates extensor tone, but by way of the vestibular nuclei instead of the BSRF. The subdivisions of the cerebellum are given in Table 13-1 in terms of cerebellar anatomy and evolutionary age (phylogenetic divisions). Fig. 13-11 shows some of the parts of the cerebellum in relation to parts of the brainstem.

The **archicerebellum** is the oldest part of of the cerebellum and is found in very primitive vertebrates. It receives excitation from the inner ear, the semicircular canals signalling head movement, and the maculae signalling head position (Chapter 9). This input reaches the cerebellum via the eighth nerve, both directly and as relayed by the vestibular nuclei. The output of the archicerebellum feeds back to the vestibular nuclei. The archicerebellum regulates the excitatory output of the vestibular nuclei to extensor motoneurons (vestibulospinal tract). A pattern of background postural movement results, which depends on the position of the head. Postural adjustment to head position has been mentioned in studying righting reflexes. The archicerebellum helps to regulate these adjustments (of

Table 13-1. Organization of the cerebellum

Phylogenetic division	Anatomical division	Input	Output
Archicerebellum	Flocculonodular lobe	Vestibule, vestibular nuclei	Vestibular nuclei
Paleocerebellum	Vermal areas, anterior and posterior lobes	Vestibular nuclei, kinesthesis	BSRF, vestibular nuclei, midbrain thalamus
Neocerebellum	Cerebellar hemispheres	Premotor cortex, olive	Red nucleus (to area 4), thalamus, BSRF

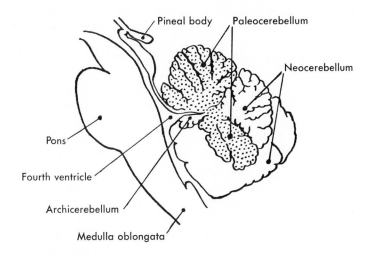

Fig. 13-11. Outline sketch of the major phylogenetic divisions of the cerebellum seen from the midline. For explanation, see text. (From Gardner, E. O.: Fundamentals of neurology, Philadelphia, 1963, W. B. Saunders Co.)

course the other two lobes of the cerebellum affect the vestibular nuclei via their interconnections with the archicerebellum). Anatomically, the archicerebellum consists of two small paired structures that overhang the brainstem beneath the main mass of the anterior cerebellum, the flocculi (sing., **flocculus**), and a medially placed structure that hangs down in the posterior part of the fourth ventricle, the **nodule.** The archicerebellum is identified with the **flocculonodular lobe.**

The **paleocerebellum** includes the medially placed **anterior** and **posterior lobes** of the **cerebellum** and the narrow central vermis that connects them. The paleocerebellum developed when animals left the sea to live on land. This subjected their muscles to the pull of gravity in the absence of the supporting effect of the water. Antigravity muscles, the extensors, developed receptors sensitive to stretch in their spindle fibers. Reflexes aroused by stretch resulted to extend the limbs against the pull of gravity. (The monosynaptic stretch reflex has already been discussed.) The annulospiral sense organs that respond to muscle stretch also connect with tracts of the spinal cord that ascend to the cerebellum. These tracts are the **spinocerebellar tracts** that carry excitation to the paleocerebellum. After integration with activity in other lobes of the cerebellum the paleocerebellum acts on the BSRF inhibitory areas with a pattern of suppression from the anterior and posterior lobes (Fig.

13-8, 3). As previously explained, the BSRF regulates the excitability of extensor stretch reflexes, and stretch reflexes are responsible for postural adjustment. The paleocerebellum responds to muscle stretch and other inputs by regulating stretch reflex excitability through the BSRF. The paleocerebellum suppresses inhibitory areas of the BSRF in a patterned fashion so that the extensor tone is regulated in an organized way. Changes in posture result. The whole "circuit" is a patterned mechanism of positive feedback; the excitation of extensor stretch reflexes also arouses centers in the paleocerebellum that act to sensitize stretch receptors. In developing a pattern of stretch reflex excitability, the paleocerebellum also receives input from the vestibular nuclei and other lobes of the cerebellum; it acts on them and on the midbrain and thalamus as well (Table 13-1).

The **neocerebellum** is the most recently developed part of the cerebellum in evolution. The development of the neocerebellum parallels the development of the motor areas of the cerebral cortex. As the great cerebral hemispheres began to cover most of the brain, the paired cerebellar hemispheres began to overlie the older areas of the cerebellum, forming the neocerebellum (Fig. 13-11). As the motor and premotor cortex assumed the task of integrating complex movements, interaction with the activity of the paleocerebellum and archicerebellum became necessary. The neocerebellum developed to provide this interaction, and two-way connections were established between cortical motor areas and the neocerebellum. The names of these tracts tell of their connections. The **corticopontocerebellar tract** runs from the premotor cortex (area 6) to the cerebellar hemispheres via nuclei in the pons. Fibers leaving area 6 descend in the cerebral peduncles to the pons, where they synapse in nuclei of that area. Neurons from these nuclei cross to the opposite side of the brainstem and ascend to the opposite cerebellar hemi-

sphere. The tract that returns from the neocerebellum to the motor cortex is also crossed so that the left cerebral hemisphere has two-way connections to the right cerebellar hemisphere and vice versa. The returning tract is called the **dentatorubrothalmic tract** for nuclei where it relays. It originates in the output nucleus of the cerebellar hemispheres, the **dentate nucleus.** The fibers cross, and the tract relays in the red nucleus and the thalamus before projecting to the motor area of the cortex (area 4). The two-way connections between cerebrum and cerebellum form a feedback loop that originates in the premotor cortex (area 6) and ends in the motor cortex (area 4). The premotor cortex is a major origin for the extrapyramidal system (COEPS), and the motor cortex is a major origin for the pyramidal system. The feedback loop takes "information" about the background movements initiated from area 6 of the COEPS, adds cerebellar inputs from kinesthetic and vestibular sources, and feeds back the result to area 4. By means of these pathways precise movements initiated by area 4 can be "programmed" by the cerebellum to agree with background movement from area 6 and with kinesthetic and vestibular input reaching the neocerebellum from other parts of the cerebellum. As Table 13-1 shows, the neocerebellum also receives inputs from the olive and sends outputs to the BSRF.

Symptoms of damage. Knowing the functions of the three major subdivisions of the cerebellum enables one to predict the consequences of damage to various parts of the cerebellum. The archicerebellum regulates postural extensor tone in response to the vestibular inputs that are governed by head position and movement. Damage to the flocculi or nodule, therefore, results in disturbances of balance. When the paleocerebellum is impaired by damage to the anterior or posterior cerebellar lobes, postural adjustments suffer with the lack of proprioceptive coordination, and a particular uncoordinated (ataxic) gait results, with exaggerated extensor muscle tone. Neo-cerebellar damage to the hemispheres causes **intention tremor** and over-or-under reaching when grasping for an object. Some coordination between background movements and precise voluntary movements has been lost. The patient's hand may be steady until he makes a voluntary motion. Tremor then results, and he is unable to coordinate the position of his body in space with the precise motion needed to reach and grasp an object and therefore overshoots or undershoots.

INTEGRATION OF THE MOTOR SYSTEMS

The simplest motor organization is the reflex, and even reflexes are subject to variability because of the influence of higher levels of motor organization. Postural stretch reflexes regulate the tone of the extensor muscles according to the load (stretch) imposed upon them by shifts in body position. Patterns of extensor tone are changed by extrapyramidal influences from the vestibular nuclei and BSRF. The vestibular nuclei send excitation directly to the extensor motoneurons; the BSRF regulates the sensitivity of stretch reflex receptors in the muscle spindles by contracting muscle spindles via the gamma efferents. The vestibular nuclei and BSRF are subject to sensory inputs and to influence by other brain centers. The vestibular nuclei are excited or inhibited in a patterned way by sensory input from the receptors that respond to head position and movement. The cerebellum, particularly the archicerebellum, influences the vestibular nuclei as well. The COEPS and subcortical extrapyramidal nuclei influence both the vestibular nuclei and BSRF in programming background movement. The BSRF has areas that facilitate and inhibit stretch reflexes; both areas are under extrapyramidal control. Finally, the BSRF receives collaterals from most of the general senses via tracts of the cord and

brainstem. Against all this regulation of posture via the stretch reflexes must be placed the precise "voluntary" movements initiated by the pyramidal system. Corticospinal neurons control both flexor and extensor muscles in a way that is topographically organized for precise movements. These movements are coordinated with posture and balance via two feedback circuits that link the pyramidal (area 4) and extrapyramidal (area 6) systems. One path feeds back via the basal ganglia and thalamus, where the patterns for many "automatic" movements seem to be organized. The other path feeds back via the neocerebellum for programming movement on the basis of vestibular and kinesthetic inputs. Motor organization of the CNS is a single integrated system and can be subdivided into pyramidal, extrapyramidal, and cerebellar contributions only at the cost of considerable oversimplification.

SUMMARY

Reflexes involve receptors, afferent neurons, interneurons, efferent neurons, and effectors. A reflex response, such as the flexion (withdrawal) reflex to pain, is under *stimulus control* because of the fixed nature of the connections between reflex elements, starting with the specialized receptors. Some response variability will occur, however, because of the influence of higher brain centers that coordinate the reaction with body posture. In opposed reflexes such as the flexion and extensor thrust reflexes, one will dominate because of the number of receptors activated, the influence of higher centers, or the built-in nociceptive dominance of the flexion reflex over the extensor thrust reflex. To reduce reflex variability for study of spinal reflex mechanisms the CNS is transected above the level of the input and output neurons for the reflex. The spinal preparation isolates spinal reflexes from higher CNS centers, but the resulting spinal shock reduces reflex sensitivity for several days, time enough for infection to set in. Chronic rather than acute preparations must be used since the reflex must recover from dependence on BSRF and vestibular facilitation. Vestibular facilitation of flexors and extensors is direct; BSRF facilitation is caused by excitation of the muscle spindles, which stimulates their stretch receptors to reflexly increase extensor tone. The decerebrate preparation involves a cut above the level of the vestibular nuclei and BSRF. This releases both of them from cortical and subcortical inhibition to cause a spastic condition of decerebrate rigidity of the extensors. The decorticate preparation is also spastic, but such an animal is useful for studying cranial nerve reflexes. Reflex mechanisms may be studied by comparing the reflex response of a muscle to a muscle twitch response of the same muscle. The muscle twitch is obtained by stimulating the motor nerve to the muscle. The reflex shows a longer latent period, contraction time, and relaxation time. The longer latent period is caused mostly by summation rather than conduction time or synaptic delay. The longer reflex contraction time results from recruitment of motoneurons into the active motoneuron pool a few at a time; all the motoneurons are fired at once in the muscle twitch. The longer reflex relaxation time is caused by afterdischarge of the motoneurons; reflex excitation outlasts the stimulus in parallel and loop circuits in the CNS. The motoneurons exciting the muscle response are the final common path to that response; they are subject to excitatory and inhibitory influences from many levels of the CNS. Facilitation of a response occurs when two stimuli to a reflex cause a larger response than the sum of the reactions to each stimulus. The two inputs summate to fire some motoneurons that neither input can control alone. Occlusion is smaller than expected reflex response to two inputs. It occurs because both inputs excite some of the same motoneurons.

Reflex inhibition can be measured by the reduction in reflex response caused by stimulating an opposed reflex. Inhibition shows all the phenomena cited for reflex excitation. Inhibition may be direct or indirect, but it is probably the former. Direct inhibition may be presynaptic and caused by axoaxonic synapses or postsynaptic and caused by axodendritic Renshaw cell synapses.

Reflexes are adaptive behavior. The stretch or myotatic reflex adjusts extensor muscle tone as weight is placed on a limb. The extensor thrust reflex stiffens a limb when plantar pressure receptors are stimulated or the toes are spread by body weight. The flexion reflex protects against injury by withdrawing a limb, whereas the crossed-extension reflex supports the animal and aids walking. The reflex figure involves the opposite reaction of the other pair of limbs and is a long spinal reflex. So is the scratch reflex. Higher-level reflexes are mediated by the brain. The vital reflexes of the medulla maintain breathing, heart rate, blood pressure, and oxygen and carbon dioxide balance. Reflex breathing is caused by reactions of the inspiratory center, expiratory center, and pneumotaxic center to blood CO_2 and to pressure receptors in the lungs. Circulatory reflexes that maintain heart rate and blood pressure involve cardioaccelerator, cardioinhibitory, vasodilator, and vasoconstrictor centers in the medulla. These centers react to blood CO_2 and to pressure receptors in the blood vessels. Higher-level postural reflexes involve the BSRF and vestibular nuclei that regulate stretch reflexes and therefore regulate extensor tone and postural adjustment. Postural reactions result from vestibular input with changes in head position. Righting reflexes are initiated by this input and by muscle proprioceptors that react to the twisted position of the body in righting. Placing and hopping reflexes are mediated by the cerebral cortex.

Motor organization involves feedback because sensory input causes behavior, and behavior changes sensory input. The proprioceptors are most intimately involved, but all receptors participate. The pyramidal system is most involved in precise movement. Pyramidal fibers originate prominently from the motor cortex (area 4) where they are topographically organized to control the opposite side of the body, but other cortical areas are involved as well. Precisely controlled muscles with small motor units occupy the largest cortical areas. The pyramidal tracts form the lateral and ventral corticospinal tracts that excite spinal motoneurons via interneurons and the corticobulbar tract that controls cranial motoneurons. Damage restricted to the motor cortex results in flaccid paralysis of the affected muscles. The extrapyramidal system controls background postural movements and originates prominently in the premotor cortex (area 6), although widespread cortical areas are involved in the cortically originating extrapyramidal system (COEPS); subcortical nuclei contribute to the extrapyramidal system as well. The pathways to the motoneurons involve synapses in many nuclei of the brainstem, with the output focusing on the BSRF and vestibular nuclei. The vestibular nuclei excite extensor motoneurons via the vestibulospinal tract. BSRF areas excite or inhibit gamma efferents to the extensor muscle spindles via the reticulospinal tract. Spindle receptors (annulospiral endings) react to spindle contraction, as they do to stretch, by increasing extensor muscle tone. Postural adjustments result from these two influences of the extrapyramidal system. Reciprocal innervation controls the opposite reaction of the flexors. The premotor cortex and caudate nucleus inhibit the BSRF excitatory areas; their removal therefore results in spasticity or decerebrate rigidity. The vestibulospinal tract carries excitation to the righting reflexes from the vestibular receptors. The extrapyramidal system also includes a negative feedback pathway from the premotor cortex via the basal ganglia and thalamus to the motor cortex. Besides spasticity and tremors at rest, extrapyramidal damage can cause Parkinson's disease, which is alleviated by destruction of the thalamic part of the feedback loop.

In addition to the classic motor area of the cortex (the primary motor area), stimulation studies show a topographically organized second area on the lateral precentral cortex and a supplemental motor area in the longitudinal fissure.

The cerebellum regulates the extrapyramidal system and its interactions with the pyramidal system. The archicerebellum regulates balance and posture with inputs from the vestibular nuclei and outputs via the vestibulospinal tract for extensor muscle excitation. It includes the flocculus and nodule. The paleocerebellum includes the anterior and posterior lobes and the vermis. It receives inputs from the extensor stretch receptors via the spinocerebellar tracts and regulates their reflex contraction via the BSRF. The cerebellar hemispheres form the neocerebellum. Neocerebellar input is from the premotor cortex via the corticopontocerebellar tract. Its output goes to the motor cortex via the dentatorubrothalamic tract. This feedback pathway integrates extrapyramidal and pyramidal system activities. All lobes of the cerebellum interconnect diffusely. However, symptoms of cerebellar damage depend on the locus of the injury. Archicerebellar damage causes disturbances of balance. Paleocerebellar damage results in ataxia, impairs postural adjustments, and increases extensor tone. Neocerebellar damage causes intention tremor and overshooting or undershooting when reaching for an object.

READINGS

Gardner, E.: Fundamentals of neurology, ed. 4, Philadelphia, 1963, W. B. Saunders Co.

Ochs, S.: Reflexes and reflex mechanism. In Selkurt, E. E., editor: Physiology, Boston, 1963, Little, Brown & Co.

Ochs, S.: Upper somatic and visceral control. In: Selkurt, E. E., editor: Physiology, Boston, 1963, Little, Brown & Co.

Sherrington, C.: The integrative action of the nervous system, New Haven, Conn., 1961, Yale University Press.

Chapter 14

Brain dynamics

OVERVIEW

In the second of the four parts of this book a reflex model of the CNS was presented. The model was based on comparing the association areas of the cortex and subcortical nuclei to the interneurons of a reflex. It was assumed that the association areas and subcortical nuclei related sensory input to motor output in a way similar to interneuron connections between sensory and motor nerves in a reflex. The major difference cited between a reflex and a complex response was that the complex response is variable, whereas the reflex is relatively fixed. Variable stimulus-response connections in the complex response allowed for trial-and-error behavior and for learning through new connections in the CNS. The reflex model was adequate for the discussion on sensation. This part of the book, however, deals with more complex phenomena of motivation, emotion, learning, and stress. To deal with these phenomena a more complex and complete understanding of brain function is required. The current chapter on brain dynamics presents a modern view of the organization of brain functions. The material is presented here rather than in the early chapter on the CNS (Chapter 6) so that it will be fresh in mind for the last four chapters on complex behavior (motivation, emotion, learning, and stress).

This chapter begins by restating the reflex model of CNS function and showing its origins. The reflex work of Sherrington, presented in Chapter 13, was the main root of the so-called reflex model. This led to an overemphasis on the cerebral cortex per se since animals with more cortex show more complex behavior. Animals without a cortex can learn and show some complex behavior, but it was assumed that these functions were transferred to the cortex in higher animals through encephalization. The more developed the cortex in a species, the more impairment to complex behavior from cortical damage, so that the idea of encephalization seemed valid. It was assumed that transcortical connections were made from one cortical area to another in variable and complex behavior.

This chapter then develops a new CNS model for complex behavior by showing the inadequacies of the old transcortical reflex model. Evidence from both anatomy and the behavioral effects of brain damage will be presented. The result is a *vertical organization* model of CNS function. The new model gives little importance to direct connections from one part of the cortex to another. Vertical organization means connections between *subcortical nuclei* made *by way of* the cortex. This makes the subcortical nuclei pivotal in complex behavior. Subcortical nuclei dominate the connections between sensory input to the cortex and elsewhere and motor output to behavior. This makes the neocortex only part of a vertically organized system.

The system is first presented from an evolutionary point of view. The allocortex, or paleocortex, was the first to appear in evolutionary development of olfaction (smell). Its parts and their location are described. Then transitional cortex is discussed in the same way, and finally the neocortex (the last to appear in evolution) is discussed. From here the chapter outlines the functional organization of the brain in terms of the neocortex, the reticular and projection systems, and the limbic system and hypothalamus. Functions of each of these parts of the brain in complex behavior follow. The chapter closes with a discussion on cerebral metabolism, which shows how the internal environment of the body acts on the CNS and vice versa. Maintaining consistency (homeostasis) in the internal environment is the basis for all behavior, complex or simple.

HISTORY OF THE
TRANSCORTICAL REFLEX MODEL

The fundamental work of Sir Charles Sherrington on the reflex provided psychologists with a model for more complex behavior. Sherrington showed that the reflex response varied somewhat with the posture of the animal even when the spinal cord was isolated from most of the higher nervous centers. As shown in Chapter 13 the variability in a reflex response depends on connections between interneurons. Pain stimulation always leads to a flexion (withdrawal) reflex, but the exact pattern of the movement depends on the posture of the animal. Interneurons bring the influence of posture sense organs (proprioceptors) to bear on the reflex response. The flexion is varied to maintain the animal's balance. The response varies with postural input because the interneuron pattern *varies* from one response to the next. The

interneuron "connections" between the pain stimulus and the withdrawal response therefore change from one occasion to the next. This concept of changing S-R connections seemed well-suited to explain more complex behavior. Complex behavior is more variable than a reflex because more interneurons are involved, and their connections are not fixed. Higher parts of the brain are more involved in a complex response than in a simple spinal reflex, and higher brain centers contain millions of "interneurons". The functional connections between these interneurons could change from one presentation of a stimulus to the next. As a result the response would vary from one stimulus presentation to the next. Complex and variable behavior would thereby occur. Repeated presentations of a stimulus would cause variable behavior in learning. The response could be followed by reward or punishment. The interneuron connections for responses that led to reward or avoided punishment would tend to become "fixed" like a reflex so that other responses to the stimulus would drop out. Learning would then have occurred.

Research on learning has been important to many fields of psychology, including physiological psychology. Psychologists and physiologists observed that development of the neocortex seemed to parallel the development of more complex and variable behavior. Phylogenetically more complex animals with a more developed cortex are able to learn more difficult patterns of behavior. The cortex, therefore, seemed to be the most important part of the brain for complex behavior, including learning. The cerebral cortex first developed as a sensory correlation center for smell. Some of the older ventral cortex still relates to smell, even in man. The more dorsal parts of the cortex have nothing to do with smell, however, and have been dubbed the neocortex, or "new cortex." It is the development of the neocortex that has been associated with more complex behavior and greater ability to learn in some species of animals, including man. Following the reflex model for learning, the concept of transcortical association was developed to explain the function of the neocortex in learning. Sensory input had been traced to the sensory projection areas of the neocortex. Pathways for response originate in the motor projection area. The connections between sensory input and motor output were assumed to be in "association areas" of the neocortex, which lay between sensory and motor areas. These transcortical, or "across-the-cortex" connections, should therefore "associate," or connect, input to sensory projection areas with motor output from the motor projection areas. Transcortical connections would therefore mediate stimulus-response associations of the highest level of the brain, the neocortex. Changes in transcortical connections should cause complex new responses to stimuli and therefore form a physical basis for learning.

Objections to transcortical association as a basis for most learning were soon pointed out. Animal species that do not have a neocortex can learn; from earthworms to alligators the more primitive species can be trained. The problems they can solve for reward or avoidance of punishment are simpler than the problems mammals can solve, but they learn without a cortex.

The objection was answered with the concept of **encephalization.** As each new species evolved with a neocortex, the cortex "took over" some of the functions of the lower brain centers. Learning was one of the most complex functions carried out by lower brain centers in species without a cortex. Learning would therefore be taken over by the neocortex as it was evolved, leaving simpler functions for lower brain centers. The more developed the neocortex in a species, the more it dominated the function of lower brain centers, and the less the lower brain centers could function without the neocortex. It was pointed out that

the visual responses of a frog are little disturbed by removing the cerebrum, but removing the visual cortex in man leaves him blind. The more developed the species, the more profound the effects of removing parts of the cortex. Removal of the motor cortex in man or monkey causes near-total paralysis of the extremities (Chapter 13); animals with a less developed neocortex are less paralyzed by motor area decortication. Finally, the more developed the cortex, the greater the effect of decortication on complex behavior. Decorticating a rat has far less effect on his ability to learn than decorticating a man.

However, it was decided that the transcortical connections involved in learning were widespread and variable. Lashley, in a series of pioneering studies, removed various cortical areas in rats. He studied the effect of this operation on the learning and retention of maze habits. No one cortical area seemed more important than another. The more cortex he removed, the greater the impairment of learning or memory. Yet the location of the area he removed seemed to make little difference. He concluded that the cortex acted "as a whole" in learning and memory (mass action, Chapter 17) and that one part was as useful as another for learning (equipotentiality).

INADEQUACIES OF THE TRANSCORTICAL MODEL
Transcortical vs. vertical connections

If the cortex acts as a whole in complex behavior such as learning and memory, destroying its connections should have as much effect as removing cortical areas. If the connections made in learning are transcortical from sensory to motor projection areas, cutting through the gray matter in both directions should destroy them. Lashley exposed the neocortex of rats and "sliced it up" with a fine brain knife in both directions. This left isolated squares of cortex only—isolated so far as transcortical connections are concerned. The operation had little effect on the learning or retention of maze habits. In a similar experiment Sperry even put thin sheets of mica (an insulator) in the slices to prevent transcortical nerve impulses from "jumping the gap." No significant changes in learning or retention were seen.

Finally, Doty performed an even more convincing experiment. By placing an electrode in the motor area of a cat's cortex, he could stimulate leg movement at will after the cat recovered from the operation. (A "socket" was left screwed to the skull so that the animal could be "plugged in" to a stimulator while freely moving about.) The electrical stimulation merely fired the neurons of the motor cortex that were connected to the final common path for limb movement. At the same time he placed another electrode in the visual cortex. Presumably when the cat was stimulated here, it would "see" a flash of light. Then he "conditioned" the animal. Stimulation of the motor cortex served as an unconditioned stimulus (US) because it always caused an unconditional response (UR) of leg movement. Stimulation of the visual cortex did not cause leg movement. Visual cortex stimulation served as a conditioned stimulus (CS) because Doty hoped to present visual cortex stimulation (CS) and motor cortex stimulation (US) together often enough so that visual cortex stimulation would cause leg movement (a conditioned response, or CR). In the usual conditioning experiment a UR such as leg flexion is forced by a US such as shock to the foot—a flexion reflex. Then a signal (CS) such as a light or bell is presented just before the US as a signal that shock is coming. If conditioning is successful, the animal lifts his leg to the CS signal before the response is forced by shock (US) or even when shock is omitted. A CR to the CS signal is established when this happens. Doty forced leg movement (UR), with motor cortex stimulation (US), after presenting a sig-

nal of visual cortex stimulation (CS). After doing this often enough, the cat moved the limb to the visual cortex stimulation as he had to motor cortex stimulation. New functional "connections" had been established between the visual cortex and the motor cortex.

The question is, were they transcortical or subcortical? That is, did the excitation go from visual cortex signal to motor cortex response by way of the gray matter of the cortex (transcortical association), or did the excitation go from visual cortex to motor cortex via subcortical centers? A second experiment was performed to answer this question. The cats were operated upon again, and two kinds of cuts were made in the visual cortex near the CS electrode. In some cats the electrode was isolated from transcortical connections by *circumscribing* the electrode site, or cutting through the gray matter in a circle around it. In other cats the electrode was isolated by *undercutting* it, isolating the visual area from *vertical* connections to subcortical nuclei, but leaving most transcortical connections intact. When the animals recovered, they were tested to see if they would still perform the CR to visual cortex stimulation. When the CS electrode had been isolated by cutting its transcortical connections, the cats responded to the CS with a CR of leg movement as they had before the operation. When the CS electrode was isolated by cutting its vertical connections, the cats failed to perform the leg movement CR to the brain CS. Evidently vertical connections rather than transcortical connections had been formed when the response to a visual cortex CS was learned. Cutting the vertical connections abolished the newly formed CR, but cutting transcortical connections did not disturb it. Of course the learned connections between cortical nuclei may have been made via **commissural** fibers that "loop" down from one cortical area into the white matter and ascend back to the cortex at another location. The answer to this possibility lies in destroying subcortical nuclei known to relay impulses from one part of the cortex to another. If such operations impair learning and other complex behavior more than does cortical damage, it is reasonable that subcortical "circuits" rather than commissural circuits are most important to the behavior.

Role of subcortical nuclei

Most of the early work of this type was done on the thalamus (Chapter 17). Lesions were made in the sensory and association nuclei of the thalamus. Association nuclei are those that could connect one part of the thalamus and cortex with another; they are not a part of the direct sensory pathways or motor pathways. The lesions were made with a **stereotaxic apparatus.** This apparatus fixes the animal's head in a known position by use of tapered bars in the ears (external auditory meatus) and a bar under the upper front teeth (incisors). A needle, insulated except at its tip, is held in a rack over the animal's head. The rack is devised so that the needle can be moved in all three dimensions. There is a scale for each dimension so that the tip of the needle can be accurately positioned in each dimension. The skull is exposed and the needle positioned over the bregma, a suture, or intersection of bones, in about the middle of the dorsal surface of the skull. This serves as a beginning landmark. Three-dimensional "maps" of the brain are available so that moving the needle a given amount in the two horizontal dimensions places its tip over the desired position. A small hole is bored in the skull here, and the needle is lowered a known distance into the brain. Its tip is then in the desired position. The insulated needle is small so that it causes little damage in passing through the cortex. A known d-c current is then passed through the needle for a fixed period. This causes bubbles at its tip (hydrolysis) and kills cells at that point. The extent of the damage is determined by the current intensity and duration. In this manner subcortical nuclei can be destroyed with little damage to the cortex. Of course the location and extent of the damage are confirmed by sectioning and staining the brain after the experiment is over and studying the tissue with a microscope.

By using the stereotaxic apparatus either sensory or association nuclei in the thalamus were destroyed. The effects on learning and memory for visual discrimination habits and maze habits were tested. The discrimination behavior was more affected than the maze behavior. Maze problems seemed to be affected more by the size of the lesion than by its location, at least in certain thalamic nuclei that connect to the cortex. Of course maze learning involves many sensory inputs, and one expects damage effects to be diffuse because many sensory pathways and association pathways are involved. The experiment does show, however, that both thalamus and cortex are involved in the learning. The organization of the pathways involved should be thought of as vertical, with excitation travelling up and down between the thalamus and the cortex. One sensory input was pivotal in the case of the discrimination problem; for example, the animal is dependent on vision when he must choose the brighter of two doors to enter to find food. In learning a maze it may depend on many sensory inputs, and one can substitute for another—a blinded rat is little impaired in maze learning. Damage to either visual or association nuclei impairs a visual discrimination habit more than damage to other projection areas in the cortex. The posterior thalamic nuclei, the lateral geniculate bodies, and the visual cortex seem to be involved in brightness discrimination. This again indicates a vertical organization, with both thalamus and cortex participating. Damage to the superior colliculus impairs pattern discrimination in rats. Some types of auditory discriminations are impaired by damage to the cortical projection area for hearing, but fine discriminations of pitch are made by the rat in the absence of auditory cortex.

Even "pure" sensory and motor functions show the pivotal role of subcortical nuclei. More profound paralysis and motor disturbances such as ataxia and tremor can be produced by damaging selected subcortical nuclei than can be produced by damaging an equivalent amount of cortex. Sensory impairment is more profound when the subcortical "relay" nuclei are destroyed than when the corresponding projection area is destroyed. It was pointed out earlier that removal of the visual cortex blinds a man, but decerebration little disturbs the visual responses of a frog. Despite the encephalization this indicates, destroying the lateral geniculate bodies in man not only blinds him, but also eliminates certain visual reflexes that remain after visual decortication.

The lateral geniculate bodies have functions other than simply relaying visual excitation to the cortex. Both motor and sensory pathways involve vertically organized *interaction* between subcortical and cortical nuclei.

Anatomical evidence

The cerebal cortex is a complex structure of three to six layers of a variety of cell types with complex synaptic structures. The structure of the cortex, however, seems designed for conduction in a vertical direction rather than a horizontal direction (Figs. 14-1 and 14-2). Horizontal cells are found only in the most superficial layer, occur only in more phylogenetically developed species, and then are found only in neocortex. Cortical structure seems more designed to concentrate incoming excitation from subcortical nuclei on a cortical focus,

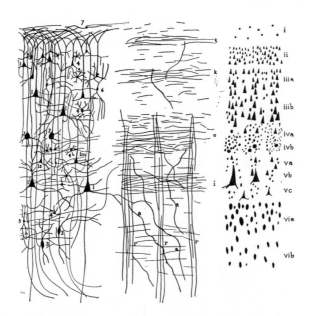

Fig. 14-1. Structure of the cerebral cortex, drawn from microscopic observation. Staining procedures (from left to right) brought out some whole cells, fibers, or cell bodies. Numbered cells are as follows: **1**, pyramid; **2**, star pyramid; **3**, fusiform; **4**, star (stellate); **5**, spider; **6**, double bush; **7**, horizontal. Six cortical layers are indicated on the right. (From von Bonin, G.: Essay on the cerebral cortex, Springfield, Ill., 1950, Charles C Thomas, Publisher.)

Cerebral cortex

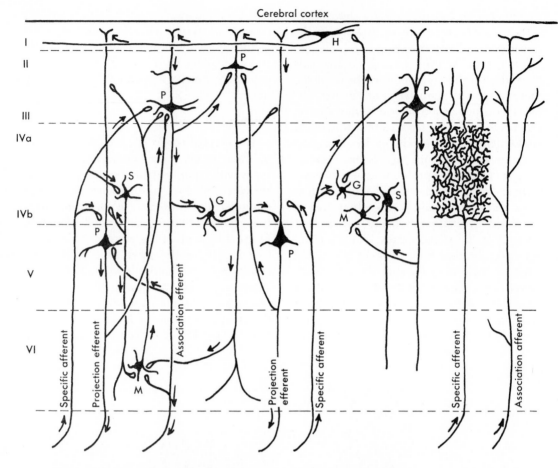

Fig. 14-2. "Circuits" in the cerebral cortex, showing the vertical nature of the conduction of incoming and outgoing excitation and the vertical conduction of impulses from one part of the cortex to another. The letters refer to different types of cortical cells. (From Truex, R. C.: Strong and Elwyn's human neuroanatomy, Baltimore, 1959, The Williams & Wilkins Co.)

spread it to nearby areas, amplify it, and redirect it to subcortical nuclei. The development of cortex would, then, not increase transcortical connections as much as increase the number of ways that subcortical nuclei could be interconnected and increase the number of subcortical nuclei that could be involved at once. The anatomical model suggested for the cortex is a collection of "loop" and "amplifier" circuits that interconnect subcortical nuclei. Damage to the cortex would destroy certain of these pathways, but alternate routes could be

found between subcortical nuclei. Damage to the subcortical nuclei, on the other hand, would destroy the centers to and from which excitation flows. This is why the subcortical nuclei have been called "pivotal" in brain function. Development of an increasingly elaborate cortex was the means of increasing the interconnections between subcortical nuclei, allowing more variable and complex behavior in response to more and more complex stimulus patterns perceived by the brain. In the vertical model of brain organization the cortex amplifies

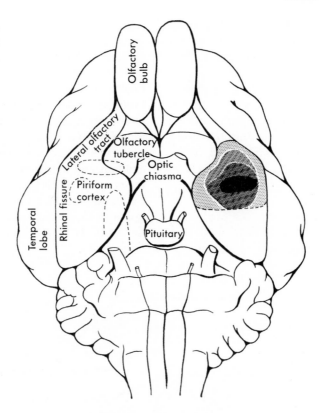

Fig. 14-3. Ventral view of the cat brain showing parts of the allocortex. Removal of the area marked on the right resulted in hypersexuality (Chapter 16). (From Green, J. D., Clemente, C. D., and deGroot, J.: J. Comp. Neurol. **108:**522, 1957.)

the interconnections that are possible between subcortical nuclei rather than replacing the connections that exist in simpler animals without a cortex.

Encephalization

All this means that encephalization is not the domination of lower centers by the neocortex, but the vertically organized connection of more subcortical nuclei *by* the cortex. The neocortex must be considered as part of a vertically organized system. The changes in interconnections in this system may lead to a change in response patterns to stimuli that is called learning. Whether the changes occur at synapses in the cortex or at synapses in subcortical centers or both, it is the organization of the system that has altered. Altering the orga-

nization of the system means altering the interconnections between subcortical nuclei. The more elaborate the cortex, the more elaborate the interconnection system, and the more complex and varied behavior can become.

PHYLOGENETIC ORGANIZATION OF THE CORTEX

Areas of the cortex can be divided into "old" cortex (**paleocortex,** or **allocortex**), **transitional cortex,** and **neocortex,** according to how recently they have developed in evolution. These three classifications of cortex differ in their anatomical structure and differ in the subcortical nuclei they interconnect; therefore the classification is a functional one. The allocortex may have as few as three recognizable layers of cells, whereas the neocortex has six layers of cells. The allocortex is related to subcortical nuclei once concerned with smell and is often lumped with these parts of the brain as **rhinencephalon** (rhine, smell; encephalon, brain) when certain parts of the transitional cortex are included. The neocortex is most closely related to the thalamus, geniculate bodies, and basal ganglia. Transitional cortex interrelates these two sets of centers.

Allocortex

The cerebrum originally developed as a correlation center for smell input, and the allocortex includes the parts originally devoted to smell. These parts of the brain can be seen in Figs. 14-3 and 14-4. Some parts of this cortex are still devoted to smell in higher mammals, including the **olfactory bulbs** and **tracts** and the **prepyriform area.** Other parts, such as the **pyriform lobe** and **hippocampus,** have developed into cortical centers involved in complex reactions of emotion and motivation. The pyriform cortex remains visible on the ventral surface of the brain, but the hippocampus gets "rolled up" into the interior of the cerebrum with the extensive development of the neocortex (Fig. 14-4).

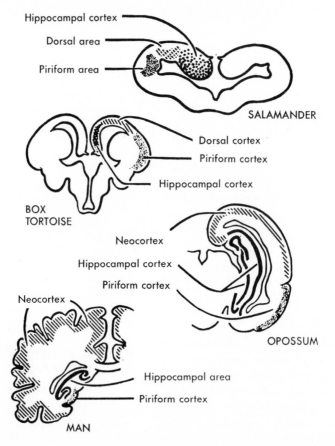

Fig. 14-4. Diagrammatic cross sections through the hemispheres of a phylogenetic series of vertebrates, showing how the hippocampal cortex has become buried in the hemisphere and the pyriform cortex has been displaced to the ventral surface. (Modified by McCleary, R. A.; from Herrick, C. J.: Proc. Nat. Acad. Sci. **19:**7-14, 1933. By permission of the publisher.)

Transitional cortex

The transitional cortex is intermediate in age and structure complexity. It is sometimes called **juxtallocortex.** Some parts of the transitional cortex are shown in Fig. 14-5. It includes the **cingulate gyrus,** which lies between the two hemispheres, deep in the longitudinal fissure and above the corpus callosum. The anterior part of this area is called the **septum.** The **presubiculum** lies in the fissure between the temporal lobes. Frontal and temporal lobe areas on the base of the brain are also included. Transitional cortex has connections with the pyriform lobe and hippocampus (allocortex areas) via subcortical tracts on the one hand and connections with the anterior thalamus (related to frontal neocortex) on the other. The transitional cortex connects therefore with that part of the allocortex that is no longer devoted to smell and connects with that part of the thalamus that supplies frontal neocortex.

Neocortex

The neocortex is the rest of the cerebral cortex and includes most of the frontal, parietal, temporal, and occipital lobes. The neocortex includes the classical sensory and motor projection areas and association areas. The sensory projection areas are in two-way connection with sensory nuclei of the thalamus and geniculate bodies. The motor projection area and premotor area has extensive two-way connections with the basal ganglia, as discussed in Chapter 13. Parietal, occipital, and temporal association areas are interrelated with certain posterior thalamic nuclei. These association areas seem to differ in function from the association areas of the frontal lobes, as will be seen later. The association areas of the frontal lobes interconnect with a cluster of nuclei in the anterior thalamus and, by way of these nuclei, relate to the rhinencephalon. The rhinencephalon has only been mentioned so far—it will be discussed later in the chapter.

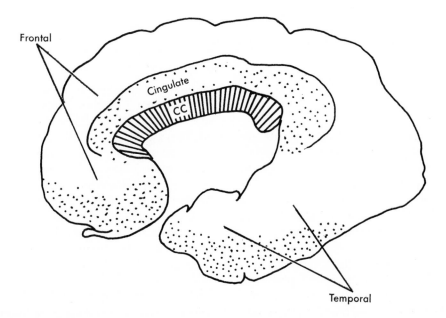

Fig. 14-5. Medial view of the brain showing transitional cortex. (**CC** is the corpus callosum connecting the hemispheres.) For details, see text.

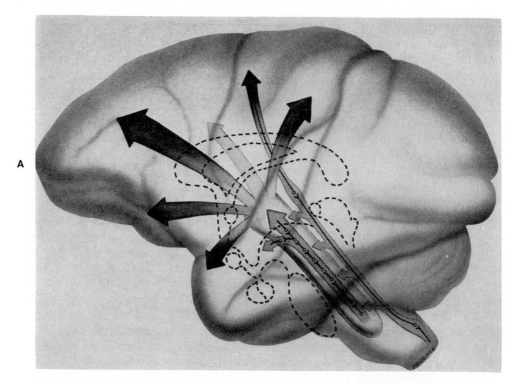

Fig. 14-6. A, Ascending reticular activating system (ARAS) schematically projected on a monkey brain (see text for details). **B,** Schematic diagram showing sensory projection to cortex via specific thalamic projection system (STPS), diffuse thalamic projection system (DTPS), and ascending reticular activating system (ARAS). (**A** from Lindsley, D. B.: Attention, consciousness, sleep, and wakefulness. In Field, John, editor: Handbook of physiology, vol. 3, Baltimore, 1960, The Williams & Wilkins Co.)

FUNCTIONAL ORGANIZATION OF THE BRAIN
Neocortex

The neocortex is the site of intricate and vertical organizations between subsystems of subcortical nuclei. The parietal, occipital, and temporal lobes (POT areas) receive sensory input and seem involved, along with subcortical centers, in learning and memory. The frontal lobes on the other hand include the origins of the motor projection systems. The more anterior parts of the frontal lobes, the so-called **prefrontal lobes,** seem to function in more complex ways. Animal experiments show that they affect ability to delay response to a stimulus and distractability. Human brain damage

in these areas results in subtle personality disturbances, including increased impulsiveness. The frontal lobes show the greatest increase in size of all cortical areas as one moves up the mammalian scale from rat to man. This has led some writers to speak of frontalization instead of encephalization. Not enough is known of the role of the frontal lobes in behavior to make such a distinction here. Further distinctions between frontal and POT functions in behavior will be given later.

Reticular and projection systems

The inputs to the cortex from lower brain centers involve states of arousal, attention, and sleep as well as the inputs governing

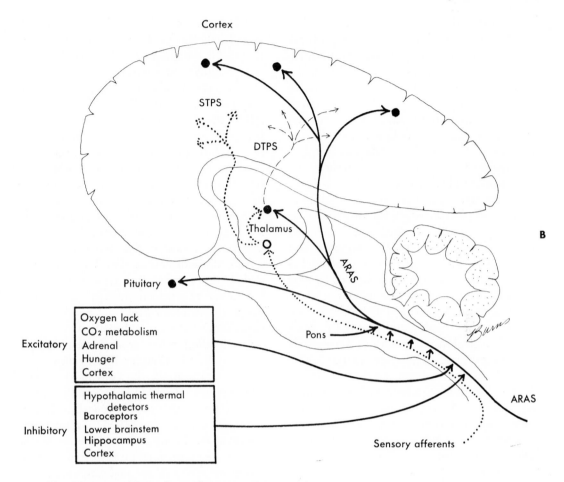

Fig. 14-6, cont'd. For legend see opposite page.

simple sensation. The brainstem reticular formation (BSRF) is involved as an ascending reticular activating system (ARAS).

Specific thalamic projection system. For vision, hearing, and somesthesis the classic sensory pathways form a **specific thalamic projection system (STPS)** that results in topographically organized sensory input for vision, hearing, and somesthesis. The pathways involved were fully discussed in the chapters on those topics. The somesthetic sensory pathways form the medial lemniscus and relay in the ventrolateral thalamus before ending in the postcentral gyrus of the cortex. The topographically organized projection area is Brodman areas 3, 1, and 2, sometimes called somesthetic

area I. The auditory pathway relays in the medial geniculate body and ends on the superior temporal gyrus in area 41, or auditory area I. The visual pathway relays in the lateral geniculate body and ends in the occipital lobe along the calacrine fissure of the striate cortex in area 17, or visual I. There are secondary sensory areas for all three senses, but these are not a part of the STPS.

Diffuse thalamic projection system. The secondary sensory areas for somesthesis, vision, and audition were described in the chapters on those topics. These secondary areas are supplied partly by the **diffuse thalamic projection system (DTPS)**—(Fig. 14-6). The DTPS has a more widespread distribution than the STPS and is less "modality specific." Its arousal by auditory stimulation, for example, may result in a change in nerve impulses reaching widespread areas of the brain. The reaction of the cortex to the DTPS is brief compared to its reaction to the ascending reticular arousal system (see below). The cortical responses observed have been called "recruiting responses" because the brain waves in areas supplied by the DTPS become more regular and synchronized and have a larger amplitude. Recruiting responses are probably caused by excitation reverberating back and forth between the thalamus and cortex. The sensory pathways involved begin with the STPS, which has collaterals to diffuse anterior and midline nuclei of the thalamus. These nuclei, in turn, send fibers to the basal ganglia and to widespread cortical areas, including the secondary sensory areas. The effect of the DTPS on the secondary sensory areas in particular may serve as a mechanism for *selective attention*. Certain cells in the secondary areas may be active only when the animal is attending to that specific sensory input. This would form a "modality-specific" mechanism for attention.

Ascending reticular activating system. The **ascending reticular activating system** (**ARAS**) serves the whole cerebral cortex. The ARAS originates in the central parts of the medulla, midbrain, and diencephalon as compared to the thalamic projection of the STPS and DTPS. The medulla, midbrain, and diencephalon are like the spinal cord in that the gray matter of nuclei and short interneurons lie in the central core, surrounded by the white matter of myelinated tracts. Much of this central gray matter is composed of short, many-branched, interconnecting cells, called the **brainstem reticular formation** (**BSRF**). Part of the BSRF forms the inhibitory and excitatory reticular activating systems discussed in Chapter 9. The role of this descending reticular activating system

(DRAS) in cortical arousal via reflexes will be further discussed later. Part of the BSRF makes up the ARAS (Fig. 14-6). The cells of the ARAS, like those of the DTPS, are fired by collaterals from the incoming sensory pathways to the STPS. The cells of the ARAS fire through many synapses, the relayed excitation being passed from cell to cell up through the central core of the brainstem to reach all areas of the cerebral cortex. The ARAS excites the cells of the cerebral cortex and lowers their threshold to incoming stimuli from other sources. The main function of the ARAS is to "keep the brain awake." The more active the ARAS, the more aroused and alert the animal. Quiescence of the ARAS results in a low level of cortical activity, a state of sleep, and a higher threshold for the cortex to incoming sensory stimulation.

Descending reticular activating system. As described in Chapter 13 on reflexes and motor organization, the cells of the BSRF can regulate muscle tone by exciting or inhibiting extensory stretch reflexes. To coin a term, this can be called a **descending reticular activating system** because of the role of *sensory feedback* in maintaining states of wakefulness and attention. Perhaps you have noted that your neck muscles ache or your leg muscles are tired after a period of alert concentrated study, although you have been sitting in a chair the entire time. When the BSRF is active and the cerebral cortex stimulated by the ARAS, the DRAS increases extensor muscle tone. The more the extensor muscles are contracted in maintaining this tone, the greater the stimulation of kinesthetic receptors, the receptors in muscles that are sensitive to muscle contraction. As discussed in Chapter 9, excitation from some of these receptors reaches the cerebral cortex and gives rise to sensations of muscle contraction. In states of alert attention, then, the BSRF activates the cortex via the ARAS and also increases muscle tone. Increased muscle tone fires kinesthetic receptors that feed back excitation to the cerebral cortex, further increasing cortical excitation. This is why the BSRF has both an ascending and a descending activating system.

Limbic system

Earlier it was pointed out that the cerebral cortex began in evolution as a correlating center for smell. The olfactory bulbs and tracts and prepyriform area are still closely related to smell, but the pyriform lobe and hippocampus are not (Fig. 14-3). Nevertheless, all the allocortex and its related subcortical centers are sometimes called the rhinencephalon ("smell brain"). Those parts of the rhinencephalon that are no longer directly involved in smell have formed close connections with some of the transitional cortex to form the **limbic system.** It was pointed out before that the

transitional cortex is in two-way connection with the allocortex on one hand and with the neocortex on the other. So, therefore, is the limbic system. The limbic system was so named by Papez because it forms a ring (limbus, perimeter) in the medial part of each cerebral hemisphere (Fig. 14-7). The limbic system includes the **septal area** (septum), the **cingulate gyrus,** the **hippocampus** and **entorhinal cortex,** most of the **amygdala** (amygdaloid nuclei), and the anterior thalamus. The limbic system receives input from (1) parts of the rhinencephalon still concerned with smell (olfactory bulb and lobe, prepyriform area), (2) sensory areas of the neocortex, (3) the BSRF, and (4) the hypothalamus. The limbic system sends excitation to (1) many areas of the neocortex, (2) the BSRF, and (3) the hypothalamus. In Fig. 14-7, the original circuit of Papez is shown by

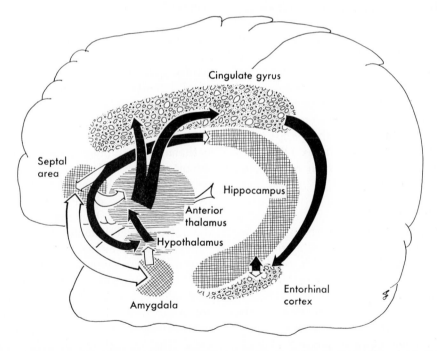

Fig. 14-7. Schematic diagram of the limbic system, projected on an outline of the brain. Black arrows represent the neural connections referred to by Papez as the limbic pathways. White arrows represent connections discovered since that time. Compare with Fig. 16-1. (Modified from McCleary, R. A., and Moore, R. Y.: Subcortical mechanisms of behavior, New York, 1965, Basic Books, Inc.)

the black arrows. The Papez circuit involves excitation in a closed reverberating loop from the hippocampus to the mammillary bodies of the hypothalamus, from there to the anterior thalamus, thence to the cingulate gyrus and entorhinal cortex, and finally back to the hypothalamus via the hippocampus. Papez suggested that this circuit provides a neural basis for emotional behavior and experience. The suggestion has been a fruitful one as Chapter 16 on emotion will demonstrate. The limbic system has recently been involved in learning research reported in Chapter 17. The hypothalamus governs the autonomic nervous system in emotional states, and two of the most important tracts connecting it with other parts of the brain are found in the limbic system. These are the **fornix,** which connects the hippocampus with the mammillary bodies, and the **medial forebrain bundle** between the BSRF, hypothalamus, and rhinencephalon.

The limbic system communicates with the frontal lobes of the neocortex via the anterior thalamus. The frontal lobes play an important role in human personality and damage to them often causes impulsivity and reduced affect (lack of emotionality). Limbic connections with the parietal, occipital, and temporal neocortex (POT "association areas") involve it in research on learning and memory.

Hypothalamus

The **hypothalamus** consists of a continuous group of nuclei occupying the walls and floor of the third ventricle of the diencephalon (Chapter 6). Research on the hypothalamus has shown that it plays a dominant role in (1) regulation of the motor activity of the autonomic nervous system, (2) homeostatic response to changes in the internal environment, either by sensitivity of its own cells to these changes or input from internal receptors, (3) regulation of endocrine output through connections to the pituitary gland, (4) drives,

or the arousal and maintenance of behavior, in states of hunger, thirst, sexual input, and so on, and (5) emotional responses in states of rage and fear. The hypothalamus seems to be the pivot point between somatic and visceral sensory input and somatic and visceral motor output in responses of the body to internal and external stress. The anterior hypothalamus has been called a **trophotropic** area by Hess because stimulation here causes parasympathetic responses—slowed heart rate, dilation of blood vessels in the stomach and intestines, and drowsiness, as if the animal were digesting a big meal. Responses of the parasympathetic nervous system were dominant. He called the posterior hypothalamus **ergotropic** because stimulation there raised the heart rate and blood pressure, made the animal alert and aroused, and often caused him to attack nearby objects or the experimenter. Responses of the sympathetic nervous system were dominant. It is evident that the anterior (and medial) hypothalamus is trophotropic because it stimulates parasympathetic responses. The posterior (and lateral) hypothalamus is ergotropic because it stimulates the sympathetic nervous system.

Understanding the connections of the hypothalamus with other areas of the brain is important to understanding the neural regulation of behavior. Anatomically, the hypothalamus is divided into two main areas, the **medial hypothalamic area** and the **lateral hypothalamic zones** (Fig. 14-8). The single medial hypothalamic area consists of densely packed cells that closely surround the walls and floor of the third ventricle. The paired lateral hypothalamic zones are found in the walls of the third ventricle, lateral to the medial hypothalamic area. The medial hypothalamic area receives inputs from the rhinencephalon and ARAS. The rhinencephalon input comes from the hippocampus and is a part of the Papez circuit (Fig. 14-7). The tract is an important one, the **fornix,** that leads from

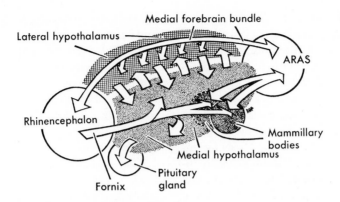

Fig. 14-8. Schematic diagram showing the major connections of the medial and lateral parts of the hypothalamus. For details, see text. (From McCleary, R. A., and Moore, R. Y.: Subcortical mechanisms of behavior, New York, 1965, Basic Books, Inc.)

the hippocampus in each hemisphere to the **mammillary bodies** and gives off collaterals to other areas of the medial hypothalamus. The medial hypothalamus also receives excitation from the ARAS via the mammillary bodies, which feed back fibers to the ARAS. Each mammillary body sends an important bundle of fibers to each anterior thalamus as shown in the Papez circuit of Fig. 14-7. The medial hypothalamus controls the pituitary gland via nerve fibers in its stalk and is in two-way communication with both lateral hypothalamic zones. The lateral hypothalamic zones have one main tract running through each of them, the **medial forebrain bundle (MFB).** The septal area and the hippocampus of the rhinencephalon send descending fibers through the lateral hypothalamic zones via the MFB; some of these fibers continue through to the ARAS, but most of them terminate in the lateral hypothalamus zone. Likewise, the MFB carries ascending fibers from the ARAS, most of which end in the lateral hypothalamic zone, but some reach the rhinencephalon.

BRAIN FUNCTIONS

This discussion will anticipate some of the material in Chapters 15 to 17. It will also review material already covered. In

this way functions of the brain circuits just discussed can be understood while the circuits themselves are fresh in mind. No one circuit of the brain can be completely explained without involving others. However, this section will be organized like Chapter 13 for simplicity's sake, taking up one part of the brain at a time. The cortex, reticular formation, limbic system, and hypothalamus will be discussed in that order.

Cortex

The cortex is the highest level of the vertically organized connections between subcortical systems. Through study of the cortex as much is learned about subcortical systems as about the way in which the cortex organizes them. On the sensory side the most direct input to the cortex arrives via the STPS. Even here the input for vision, audition, and somesthesis is integrated and topographically organized in the lateral and medial geniculate bodies and thalamus. The input from the DTPS initiates reverberatory activity back and forth between the cortex and thalamus, activity which seems important to attention for a specific sensory modality. Sensitivity to all inputs in states of wakefulness and alert attention is caused by the diffuse stimulation of the cortex by the ARAS. Once aroused the cortex can "stimulate itself" in a feedback manner, exciting the ARAS, which reexcites the cortex. Feedback also comes from cortical excitation of the DRAS, with heightened reflex tone and kinesthetic feedback from the muscles to keep the cortex awake. However, the brain cannot respond to all possible sensory inputs at once—some selective attention is necessary. The STPS seems involved in this selective attention. Also involved is **sensory gating,** a topic mentioned in Chapters 8, 11, and 12. In each of these sensory modalities efferent pathways have been found from the brain that reach either the receptors, first relay nuclei, or higher centers in the sensory pathways. Some of these efferent pathways are inhibitory. They *block* excitation from a sensory modality so that the brain can deal with other inputs more effectively.

On the motor side the cortex is stimulated to initiate movement and to control that movement via reverberation with subcortical centers. The motor area of the cortex initiates precise movement via the pyramidal system. At the same time the motor and premotor areas are interacting via subcortical nuclei and the extrapyramidal system to control position and "background movement." The two areas also interact via the cerebellum to control balance and coordination.

In association of sensory and motor areas the cortex is also part of a vertically organized system. The so-called association areas of the cortex are merely nuclei and fibers that are feedback loops between subcortical centers. The POT association areas are in two-way connection with the limbic system via the amygdala and hippocampus (Fig. 14-7). Reverberatory activity in the limbic system is set off by the ARAS. This activity seems to be integrated, as far as learning and memory is concerned, by the POT cortical areas. The limbic system is also connected to the prefrontal cortex via the anterior thalamic nuclei. The prefrontal cortex is involved in complex behaviors that are called personality, temperament, affect, and anticipation. These responses entail emotional reactions that include organized autonomic nervous system activity. The hypothalamus governs organized emotional behavior that involves both autonomic and somatic responses. The hypothalamus and prefrontal cortex are integrated via the limbic system.

The functioning of the prefrontal and POT cortex may be understood by contrasting what is known about each. In both cases most of the knowledge has come from ablation studies with animals and accidental damage or "psychosurgery" in humans, when the cortical damage was more or less restricted to either the prefrontal cortex or the POT areas. The prefrontal cortex undergoes more development than other areas of the cortex as the phylogenetic series of brains from rat to man are compared ("frontalization"). For this reason it was long thought to govern "thinking," consciousness, and most intellectual functioning. Examination of the evidence does not bear out this idea. The story begins in the mid-nineteenth century when Phineas P. Gage, a railroad construction foreman, had a crowbar (tamping iron) blown through the frontal lobes of his brain by an explosion. Surviving the accident, he changed from an "efficient and capable, sober and industrious" foreman into a "fitful, irreverent, profane, impatient, obstinate, and vascillating" fellow, according to his physician. The changes observed were more in temperament and personality than in "intellect" per se. Subsequent cases of prefrontal damage revealed flattened affect, indifference to pain, and reduced anxiety.

Some of these changes were seen as desirable in the case of certain psychotic patients for whom other remedies had failed, therefore operations called "psychosurgery" were developed. The operations involved either prefrontal lobectomy, topectomy, or lobotomy. **Prefrontal lobectomy** involves removing all dorsal cortex anterior to the premotor areas and has the most profound effects of the three procedures. **Prefrontal topectomy** is removal of selected areas of the prefrontal lobes. **Prefrontal lobotomy** is severing the fibers connecting the prefrontal lobes with the thalamus (and limbic circuit). Clinical reports following these operations indicate reduced anxiety, but this is accompanied by impulsiveness, flattened affect, lack of foresight, and increased distractability. Topectomy of area 11 has been used for the relief of intractable pain, particularly in terminal cancer areas. The patient reports that it "still hurts," but that it "doesn't bother" him any more. His threshold for pain is unchanged, but pain has lost its "insistant" quality; it "hurts just as much" if he pays attention to it, but he can "ignore it most of the time," which may relate to his distractability.

Before-and-after testing of intelligence is difficult with most psychosurgery patients because their psychosis affects test performance. The studies that have been done suggest that the operation has little effect on performance in intelligence tests for otherwise normal patients. Certain sorting tests that involve catagorizing objects in various ways show impairment because the subject persists in using an incorrect category after he has discovered that it is wrong.

Animal experiments involving the effect of prefrontal lobectomy on monkeys have been done. The task that seems most affected by the operation is called **delayed reaction**. The monkey is shown food being placed under one of two or more cups. He is restrained from going to the food for intervals of a few seconds to several minutes. The cups may or may not be out of sight during this interval. Then he is released to see if he selects the correct cup. The prefrontal monkey cannot correctly respond after as long an interval as a normal monkey and makes more mistakes at most of the intervals tested. His performance deficit has been attributed to his "distractability," or inability to keep his attention focused on the correct cup. Inability to "respond to an absent object" is another explanation. When the monkey cannot see the cups during the delay interval, he must respond to his "memory" of where the food is when he sees the cup again. The experiments show that both factors are probably involved.

Damage to POT cortical areas results in strikingly different symptoms in man when compared to prefrontal lesions. Association areas in these parts of the cerebral cortex seem most involved with the synthesis of input arriving via several different sensory modalities, with memory, and with language. Damage in some of these areas can cause **agnosia,** or inability to recognize objects presented, via one or another sensory modality. For example, a common object such as a hammer can be recognized visually but not by touch; the patient may report that it "feels rubbery" and he "doesn't know what it is," but he will recognize and correctly name it as soon as he sees it. Language difficulties are called **aphasias;** for example, the individual may recognize words by seeing them but not by hearing them or vice versa. **Amnesia,** or loss of memory, may be present. In this case memory for recent events (just before the brain damage occurred) suffers more than older memories do. Such **retroactive amnesia** (RA) is a common result of concussions, strokes, and other brain trauma. Memory formation in particular seems related to temporal lobe function. Penfield reports two cases of damage to both temporal lobes and underlying (amygdaloid) nuclei. In both instances the individuals had apparently normal memory for events that preceded the damage, although some RA occurred. They could also function well using "immediate memory," that is, recall over short periods, as one remembers a telephone number until after dialing it. However, the patients had difficulty learning anything new. If introduced to someone who then left the room and returned in 15 minutes or so, they would not recognize him or remember meeting him. Penfield also reports that stimulation of the temporal lobes in patients undergoing brain operations causes them to have a flight of images that recall past events in their life.

Language functions also seem to have more or less specific foci within the POT area. In the first place the disorders must be designated as *expressive* or *receptive*. Expressive disorders (aphraxias) involve inability to use the vocal cords, lips, etc. and have little to do with language ability as such. Expressive disorders involve frontal lobe damage, usually to motor or premotor projection areas. True receptive aphasias involve perceptual difficulties with language and are caused by POT damage. Localization is seen here, however, in the dominant hemisphere in man. Most precise acts are initiated by the pyramidal system and involve feedback from the kinesthetic receptors. Both systems are "crossed"; that is, the left hemisphere controls the right hand and receives the most kinesthetic feedback from it and vice versa. Therefore, if you are right-handed, the left hemisphere is the dominant hemisphere, controlling the better-trained hand and receiving more kinesthetic feedback from it. The converse may be true if you are left-handed. There is evidence that damage to the POT cortex of the left hemisphere causes more aphasia than right hemisphere damage in right-handed persons. The converse may be true for left-handed persons. The difference is a relative rather than an absolute one.

The brain, like the rest of the body, is in duplicate. Just as one has two arms, two legs, etc., one has two cerebral hemispheres, two thalami, pairs of brain tracts, and so on. This would suggest that the connections between the two hemispheres would be important, especially the corpus callosum, the great sickle-shaped band of nerve fibers running from one hemisphere to the other (Fig. 6-10). Sometimes brain surgeons are forced to cut the corpus callosum to re-

move tumors deep in the brain. They were puzzled by the lack of sensory, motor, or intellectual impairment in their patients after recovery. This led Lashley to remark that only the function of the corpus callosum seemed to be keeping the two hemispheres from falling apart! It was noted that epileptic seizures would not spread from one hemisphere to the other if the corpus callosum were cut. This led one prominent neurophysiologist to complain that the function of the corpus callosum was to spread seizures! The operation was sometimes performed to reduce the spread of seizures in the brain.

The right side of the brain controls the left side of the body and vice versa, as previously noted. Similarly, most sensory input from the left side of the body goes to the right side of the brain and vice versa. In the event of brain damage to one hemispere, however, the other hemisphere can take over these sensory and motor functions by using the corpus callosum and other crossing commissural fibers between the hemispheres to control the input and output of the damaged hemispheres. This caused Sperry to wonder what would happen if sensory input to a split-brain animal were confined to one hemisphere. He operated on cats and monkeys, cutting the corpus callosum and other fibers going from one hemisphere to the other (anterior and posterior commissures, etc.). He also cut through the optic chiasma so that input from the left eye went to the left hemispere only and input from the right eye was restricted to the right hemisphere (Fig. 14-9). He then blindfolded the left eye and taught monkeys a visual discrimination habit. Presumably only the right half of the brain learned because sensory input was restricted to the right eye and right hemisphere. To test this the monkey's right eye was blindfolded and the discrimination presented to the left eye (and left cerebral hemisphere). The monkey behaved as though he had "never seen" the discrimina-

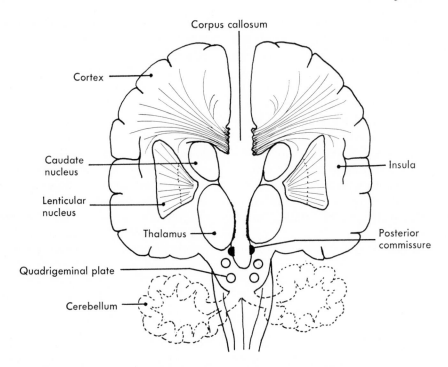

Fig. 14-9. Diagram of the split-brain operation. For details, see text.

tion problem before, and his left hemisphere had not, of course. The left hemispere could even be taught a discrimination that conflicted with the one "stored" in the right hemisphere. For example, a monkey could be taught to look with his right eye (and hemisphere) for food under a cube rather than a pyramid. With the right eye blindfolded the left hemisphere could then be taught that the food was under the pyramid rather than the cube! What happens when the two hemispheres have been taught conflicting correct choices, and the monkey sees the discrimination with both eyes open? The answer seems to be that one hemisphere dominates, usually the one controlling the arm that the monkey uses to indicate his response. Dominance may shift back and forth from one hemisphere to the other, and each hemisphere may take its turn at controlling the behavior, but there is no apparent conflict.

Man's hemispheres seem more specialized as far as language is concerned. As already

noted, most language functions seem to be controlled by the dominant hemisphere— the left hemisphere that controls the right hand in right-handed persons. One case in which the callosum was severed to prevent seizure spread has been tested. This patient had trouble reading with his left visual field (neurons from the right half of the retina go to the right half of the brain—Fig. 12-4). Writing anything meaningful with the left hand was impossible, as was carrying out verbal commands with the left arm or leg. The split-brain technique is an especially useful one for learning experiments. The results of some of these experiments will be described in Chapter 17.

Reticular formation

The reticular formation strongly influences the loop circuits interconnecting cortical and subcortical nuclei. The influence is most direct, lasting, and widespread when excitation reaches diffuse areas of the cortex via the ascending reticular arousal system (ARAS), which "keeps the brain awake." The influence is briefer and less widespread when excitation reaches the cortex via the diffuse thalamic nuclei (DTPS). In either case electrodes can be implanted in the BSRF or thalamus, respectively. In anesthetized subjects these areas can be stimulated, and the electrical response of the exposed cortex can be recorded from various sites. Records can be made of single cells with a microelectrode, or the summed responses of a number of cortical cells can be recorded with a larger electrode.

As in all nerve cells the cortical cell bodies do not reverse polarization or "fire" (Chapter 4), but their partly depolarized state results in firing of the axons they send to subcortical centers. Stimulation of the ARAS or DTPS causes a change in the polarized condition of the cortical cell bodies and therefore a change in the rate of firing of their axons that lead to subcortical centers. Stimulation of the ARAS results in widespread partial depolarization of cortical cell bodies and increased firing of their axons. A larger electrode on the surface of the cortex (**electrocorticogram**) records this state as a desynchronized negativity of widespread cortical

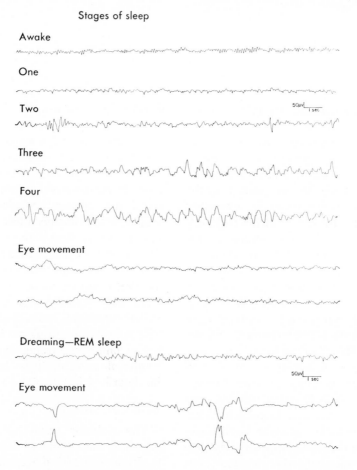

Fig. 14-10. EEG changes with sleep and dreaming in man and simultaneous recordings of rapid eye movements (REM sleep). For details, see text. (From Johnson, L. C.: U. S. Navy Report no. 66-9, San Diego, Calif., 1966, U. S. Navy Medical Neuropsychiatric Research Unit.)

areas. When ARAS stimulation ceases, regular fluctuations in cortical potential are recorded as brain waves. These brain waves can be recorded in humans or animals with electrodes glued to the surface of the scalp (the **electroencephalogram, or EEG**). An animal can have electrodes permanently implanted in the ARAS so that he can be "plugged in" for ARAS stimulation at any time, whether he is awake or asleep. The sleeping animal will show a large voltage fluctuation and regular series of EEG waves. Stimulation of the ARAS will wake the animal to a state of alert attention. At the same time the EEG will show desynchronized negativity, indicating negativity of cortical cell bodies and neuropil and rapid firing of cortical axons to lower centers. The EEG in man likewise indicates the state of activity of widespread cortical neurons. In the relaxed but awake state, the potential of the cortex fluctuates in a regular way so that alpha waves of about 10 cps are recorded, especially over the occipital lobes. If the subject is startled or is aroused by trying to actively solve problems in mental arithmetic, the alpha pattern disappears and desynchronized activity of the cortex is recorded. If the subject drops off to sleep, the reduced excitation of the cortex by the ARAS is shown in the EEG.

Various states of sleep can be distinguished (Fig. 14-10). Light sleep is called stage 1. Even the alpha rhythm is desynchronized, and low-voltage, 4 to 6 cps waves are seen with sporatic slower high-voltage delta (0 to 3 cps) waves present. Stage 2 includes spindles, or bursts, of fast waves (14 cps) against a background of delta waves with K complexes (10 cps fast waves). Stage 3 is still deeper sleep; the spindles disappear, delta is prominent, and some K complexes persist. In stage 4 high-voltage random delta waves dominate the record. Dreaming can be detected by a combination of stage 1 sleep and rapid eye movements (REM). The eye movements are measured by electrodes placed near the eye muscles. Relations between the EEG and sleep will be discussed more extensively in Chapter 18.

Limbic system

The limbic system, along with the hypothalamus, has been a fruitful area for study of the neural control of emotion. Parts of the limbic system have also been implicated in learning studies. Papez proposed that nerve impulses underlying emotional arousal originated in the hippocampus. From here they passed to the (hypothalamic) mammillary bodies via the fornix, and thence to the anterior thalamic nuclei and cingulate gyrus of the cortex (Fig. 14-7). Early experiments showed that removal of the parts of the neocortex, which stimulate this circuit, resulted in a placid and docile animal. Lesions of the amygdala and overlying pyriform cortex in monkeys and cats cause docility and hypersexuality. Dominance behavior in monkeys is abolished by removing the amygdala. On the other hand, destroying the septal cortex makes the rat very savage for a time. Destruction of the connections between anterior thalamic nuclei and the frontal cortex (prefrontal lobotomy) has already been cited as causing reduced anxiety and impulsiveness. Therefore limbic structures are definitely implicated in emotional behavior. The mechanisms involved will be discussed in Chapter 16.

Learning also involves activity in the limbic system. Kappa waves have been recorded from the hippocampus as a symptom of successful learning, for example. Evidence has already been cited to show that temporal lobe destruction (including the amygdaloid nuclei) in man impairs the ability to form lasting memory traces. It has also been shown that septal damage impairs the rat's ability to learn passive avoidance habits, whereas hippocampal lesions interfere with learning active avoidance habits. Passive avoidance habits require that the animal refrain from a normal response to avoid punishment. A passive avoidance task might require the animal to refrain from stepping off a low platform to avoid shock. Active avoidance means performing a response for a reward or to escape punishment. Experiments of this kind will be detailed in Chapter 17.

Hypothalamus

The hypothalamus has been described as closely related to the limbic system and as a focus of somatic and autonomic responses in emotion. The hypothalamus is also involved in *drives*—aroused and sustained external and internal responses to hunger, thirst, sex, and so on. Arousal in emotion or drive states seems to depend on the posterior and lateral hypothalamic areas that are **ergotropic** in function. These areas stimulate the sympathetic nervous system, which mobilizes visceral responses (such as heart rate, blood sugar, and so on) to meet a crisis (Chapter 6). Glandular response to stress results from connections of the hypothalamus to the pituitary gland—either direct nervous connections or the influence of secretions of hypothalamic neurons. Ergotropic areas seem to organize stereotyped emotional behavior. Rage responses to moderate stimulation occur when the ergotropic centers are released from cortical inhibition by removal of the neocortex. Stimulation of ergotropic centers via implanted electrodes causes rage and attack behavior. The ergotropic centers seem involved in drives and arouse and sustain behavior in hungry, thirsty, or sexually deprived animals. The **trophotropic** centers in the anterior and medial hypothalamus, on the other hand, seem to cause parasympathetic activity in animals. The responses resulting are those of emotional quiescence, digestion, satiation, and so on. Lesions in certain trophotropic nuclei can cause an animal to eat and drink to excess, whereas lesions to certain ergotropic nuclei can cause the animal to die of thirst or starvation. This seems to show that ergotropic centers arouse these drives, whereas trophotropic centers signal satiation. General theories of this kind will be outlined in Chapter 15 on motivation.

CEREBRAL METABOLISM

A review and extension of some of the material of Chapter 2 on cerebral metabolism is essential at this point. Many of the experiments to be reported in Chapters 15 to 18 involve the effect of drugs on the CNS. Others suggest the role of various neural transmitter substances in complex behavior. To understand these experiments one must know a few principles of general CNS metabolism, the blood-brain barrier, and neural transmitters.

General CNS metabolism

The metabolic rate of any tissue may be measured by its oxygen consumption (Chapter 2). Using this standard, the metabolic rate of the CNS is many times that of any other tissue in the body. The metabolic rate is higher in the gray matter than in the white matter and higher in the brain than in the spinal cord. The ratio of CO_2 given off by a tissue to the uptake of oxygen is the respiratory quotient (RQ) of that tissue. The RQ of the tissue differs, depending on whether fat, protein, or carbohydrate is being utilized as a source of food by the tissue. The RQ of CNS tissue is near unity, which shows that the CNS depends almost solely on blood glucose (blood sugar—a carbohydrate) as a source of food. Unlike other tissues the CNS is dependent on a constant supply of blood glucose and cannot depend on secondary sources of food energy. (This is not true of peripheral nerves the RQ of which is about 0.8). As a result of its high metabolic rate, O_2 and glucose are utilized in larger amounts by CNS tissue than by other tissues of the body. The high O_2 and glucose consumption of CNS tissue demands a more extensive blood supply than other tissues of the body need. The vascular (blood vessel) system of the brain and spinal cord is more extensive than that of any other organ in the body. In man the brain receives blood equal to its weight each minute. Although the brain constitutes only 2% of the total body weight, it receives one third of the total blood output of the heart to the body.

CNS circulation

The brain and spinal cord are covered by three layers of connective tissue (Chapter 6). The outermost layer is the tough fibrous dura mater. Just beneath that is the thicker and less dense arachnoid layer. A considerable space, the subarachnoid space, separates the arachnoid layer from the innermost layer, the pia mater. The pia mater is a thin and fragile layer that is closely applied to the brain and spinal cord. All the

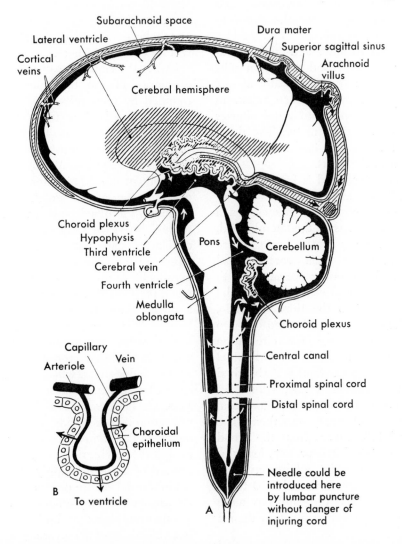

Fig. 14-11. A, Circulation of cerebrospinal fluid is shown (see arrows). Note opening in the fourth ventricle where fluid reaches the subarachnoid space. Note also one of the arachnoid villi that filters fluid out of the blood. **B,** Formation of cerebrospinal fluid from blood plasma in a choroid plexus is shown. For further details, see text. (From Gardner, E. O.: Fundamentals of neurology, ed. 4, Philadelphia, 1963, W. B. Saunders Co.)

space beneath the dura and all the ventricles and canals of the brain and spinal cord are filled with cerebrospinal fluid. Cerebrospinal fluid is a clear, plasmalike fluid that is secreted by the circulatory system. It seems to function mainly to cushion the brain and spinal cord, although some think it may serve a nutritive function as well. The cerebral arteries run in the subarachnoid space between arachnoid and pia layers until they enter the brain to branch and form capillaries (Fig. 14-11). Oxygen, carbon dioxide, and glucose exchange between the blood and brain cells takes place across the thin walls of the capillaries. The capillaries then rejoin to form veins that empty into **dural sinuses** formed within the dura mater. The dural sinuses, in turn, empty into major veins, which return to the heart.

The cerebrospinal fluid is formed in another way. There are dense networks of capillaries and supporting tissues, each called a **choroid plexus,** in the lateral, third, and fourth ventricles of the brain. These structures filter out clear cerebrospinal fluid from the brain under pressure (10 to 20 mm. Hg). The fluid circulates from the lateral ventricles into the third ventricle, thence to the fourth ventricle, and out into the subarachnoid space for circulation around the outside of the brain and spinal cord. The cerebrospinal fluid is reabsorbed by small tufts, or **villi** (sing., villus), of arachnoid tissue that project into dural venous sinuses and empty into them. The cerebrospinal fluid differs from the blood plasma in containing little protein, less glucose, and more chloride and by having a lower specific gravity. It is under 10 to 20 mm. Hg pressure and probably has more of a cushioning protective function than a nutritive role.

Blood-brain barrier

Fluid is filtered from whole blood in two places in the brain: (1) at the choroid plexus where cerebrospinal fluid is formed and (2) through the walls of the capillaries throughout the brain, where the extracellular fluid of the brain is formed. For this reason some authors speak of two barriers: (1) a blood-cerebrospinal fluid barrier formed by the capillary walls and epithelium of the choroid plexuses (Fig. 14-11) and (2) a blood-brain barrier formed by the capillary walls and glial cells that surround the capillaries throughout the brain. Since the cerebrospinal fluid probably plays a minor part in brain cell nutrition and metabolism, only the blood-brain barrier will be considered here.

Unlike the capillaries of other tissues the capillaries of the brain are closely surrounded by **glial cells,** types of cells that seem to have both a nutritive and a supporting function for the fragile nerve cells. The blood plasma must pass through the walls of the capillaries in all tissue to form intercellular fluid. This filters out red blood cells and the largest protein molecules. In the brain the blood plasma must also filter through the glial cells that adhere to the capillaries and pass through the thick masses of reticular fibers that surround the nerve cells. As a result large molecules never reach the fluid surrounding the nerve cells, a phenomenon known as the blood-brain barrier. The phenomenon is important in several ways; for example, the adenohypophysis (anterior pituitary) puts out more ACTH under stress, which causes the adrenal cortex to manufacture more corticosterone. Corticosterone reduces blood sugar utilization by other body tissues, but it cannot affect the brain because it does not pass the blood-brain barrier. The brain is thereby assured of a greater supply of blood sugar under stress because other cells are not using as much as they otherwise would. This is important because brain tissue cannot store blood sugar like liver and muscle cells can and must depend on a constant supply to function. Insulin is necessary to other cells of the body for using blood sugar. Insulin is too large a molecule to pass the blood-brain barrier; therefore brain cells obviously do not depend on insulin to utilize blood sugar. Glutamic acid will not pass the blood-brain barrier, yet it is one of the essential amino acids required by all the other cells of the body and manufactured by none of them. It may pass the barrier in another form and be reconstituted because it critically affects nerve cell excitability. Despite the amount of filtration involved, extracellular fluid, and therefore extracellular space, occupies about 25% of brain volume according to tests that depend on known differences in the concentration of certain ions in brain cells, extracellular fluid, and blood.

Neurosecretion

As seen in Chapter 6 nerve cells excite or inhibit one another at synapses by the release of chemical transmitters. Most of the nerve cells of the brain seem to excite one another by the release of acetylcholine (AChE) and are therefore called cholinergic cells. Others excite one another by the release of norepinephrine (noradrenaline) and are called adrenergic cells. The distinction is especially important in the hypothalamus where trophotropic cells seem to be cholinergic and ergotropic cells seem to be adrenergic. As pointed out before, anterior hypothalamic cells appear to be cholinergic and control parasympathetic functioning and satiation. Posterior ergotropic cells appear to govern sympathetic function and the arousal of drives. In some cases the difference seems more of cell chemistry than of location, as will be seen in the discussions on hunger and thirst. Finally, posterior adrenergic cells send fibers to the posterior pituitary gland to control its secretions. These cells also release their neurotransmitters into a portal system of blood vessels running from the posterior pituitary gland to the anterior pituitary gland. When the "neurohormone" secretions of nerve cells reaching the posterior hypothalamus flow to the anterior pituitary, they stimulate the anterior pituitary to release various hormones. The anterior pituitary secretions govern the output of several other endocrine glands. In this manner the function of the hypothalamus, autonomic nervous system, and endocrine glands are interrelated.

SUMMARY

This chapter was an attempt to present a model of brain function adequate to deal with the complex behavior described in Chapters 15 to 18. The model adds to the reflex model of CNS function given in Chapter 6. The reflex model was adequate for understanding the "simple" phenomena of sensation presented in Chapter 7 to 12 and for dealing with reflexes in Chapter 13. The history of the reflex model was given first. Sherrington's discovery that simple "spinal" reflexes varied somewhat with the posture of the animal showed that interneuron connections changed to modify the simplest behavior. The variability was caused by interneurons supplied by the proprioceptors—balance receptors of the inner ear and kinesthetic receptors of the joints and muscles. It was reasoned that the brain acted merely as a more complex and less fixed set of interneurons between stimulus and response.

The variable nature of these connections and the great number of interneurons would allow enough S-R connections to account for the most complex and variable behavior. Repeated presentations of a stimulus would lead to variable responses in learning because of the many possible interneuron connections. Those connections causing responses that led to reward or avoided punishment would become fixed like those of a reflex. The ability to learn and exhibit more complex behavior seemed to parallel the development of the cerebral cortex in animal species. Sensory input and motor output had been traced to the cortex. It was assumed that learning occurred by transcortical association of neurons running from sensory to motor projection areas. To meet the objection that animals without a cortex could learn, it was assumed that the cortex took over this and other complex functions from lower centers (encephalization). The concept seemed valid since the more developed the cortex in a species, the more profound the effect of decortication on sensory, motor, or associative functions. It was decided that the transcortical associative connections must be diffuse ones, however. The effect of cortical lesions on maze learning and retention seemed to depend on the amount of cortex removed rather than on the locus of the lesion.

Modern research has shown the transcortical association model to be inadequate. Destroying transcortical neurons by dicing the cortex does not impair learning in the rat. Vertical connections are important, however. If leg movement, induced by motor cortex stimulation, is conditioned to visual cortex stimulation, *undercutting* the visual cortex electrode abolishes the conditioned response. Furthermore, stereotaxic lesions of subcortical nuclei, chiefly in the thalamus, have more profound effects on sensory, motor, or association functions than destroying the cortical areas to which these subcortical nuclei connect. The correct model for brain function seems to be one of *vertically organized interaction* between cortical and subcortical centers. Anatomical study of the structure of the cerebral cortex bears this model out. The cortex appears to act as a complex set of amplifying interconnections between subcortical nuclei. Encephalization would merely mean an increase in the variety and complexity of this system.

Phylogenetically, the cortex is organized into the allocortex, the transitional cortex, and the neocortex. The allocortex is the oldest phylogenetically, being originally devoted to smell, and is the simplest anatomically. It includes the olfactory bulbs, pyriform areas, and hippocampus. The neocortex is the newest and most complex cortex and includes most of the frontal, parietal, occipital, and temporal lobes. The transitional cortex includes the cingulate gyrus, septum, and presubiculum; it inter-connects with the allocortex via subcortical nuclei and with the frontal lobes via the anterior thalamus.

Functionally, the neocortex is divided into the frontal lobes and POT areas. The prefrontal areas mediate complex personality functions and the POT areas are involved in learning and memory. The sensory inputs to projection areas for vision, audition, and somesthesis form the specific thalamus projection system (STPS). Collaterals of the STPS go to diffuse thalamic nuclei to form the diffuse thalamic projection system (DTPS) for more widespread cortical effects, including the secondary sensory projection areas. The DTPS may aid in attention to a specific modality. Collaterals of the STPS also supply the BSRF, parts of which diffusely connect with all cortical areas to form an ascending reticular activating system (ARAS). The ARAS activates the cortex in waking states of alertness and attention. BSRF cells also increase muscle tone, which feeds back excitatory sensations to the cortex in a descending reticular activating system (DRAS).

Some parts of the brain once devoted to smell (rhinencephalon) interconnect with the transitional cortex to form a loop circuit called the limbic system. The limbic system receives input from the rhinencephalon, neocortex, hypothalamus, and BSRF and feeds back into all but the smell areas. It includes the septal area, cingulate gyrus, hippocampus, entorhinal cortex, amygdala, and anterior thalamus. The limbic system is involved in emotion, learning, and memory; it connects with the frontal lobes via the anterior thalamus and POT areas via the septum, hippocampus, and amygdala.

The hypothalamus is involved in the limbic system via the fornix from the hippocampus and the medial forebrain bundle from the BSRF and rhinencephalon. It regulates the autonomic nervous system, emotional responses, homeostasis, drives, and endocrine reactions (via the pituitary gland). Anterior and medial parasympathetic activity in the hypothalamus is trophotropic, and responses are those of quiescence and satiation. Posterior and lateral sympathetic excitation is ergotropic, causing drive arousal and emotional responses. The medial hypothalamic area receives excitation from the rhinencephalon (via the fornix) and ARAS and connects to the pituitary and lateral hypothalamic zones. The lateral hypothalamic zones relate to the septum, rhinencephalon, and the ARAS via the medial forebrain bundle (MFB).

Operations called prefrontal lobectomy, lobotomy, or topectomy result in reduced anxiety, impulsiveness, and indifference to pain, suggesting a complex role for these areas. POT temporal lobe damage results in impaired ability to form lasting memory in man. Frontal lesions disturb delayed reaction in monkeys. POT damage also results in aphasia, agnosia, and retroactive amnesia (RA). Language functions seem restricted to the dominant hemisphere. Restricting sensory input to one hemisphere at a time in split-brain monkeys demonstrates that the hemispheres can learn conflicting habits in these preparations.

Reticular influence on the cortex can be seen in the electroencephalogram (EEG) in man or animals. ARAS stimulation in animals desynchronizes the EEG as does alert attention in man. Alpha waves are typical of the relaxed state, and four stages of sleep can be distinguished by brain wave patterns. Dreaming is indicated by rapid eye movements (REM).

The Papez circuit in the limbic system is implicated in emotion and learning. Amygdaloid lesions cause docility. Septal lesions interfere with passive avoidance and hippocampal lesions interfere with active avoidance.

The hypothalamus is involved in drives as well as in emotional behavior. Posterior ergotropic centers control drive arousal and rage, whereas anterior trophotropic centers stimulate satiation and quiescence.

Cerebral metabolism is important to complex behavior. The metabolic rate of the CNS is quite high and dependent on a constant glucose and oxygen supply. The cerebrospinal fluid is filtered from the blood in the choroid plexuses of the ventricles, is circulated through them, the subdural, and subarachnoid spaces, is absorbed by arachnoid villi, and is delivered to dural venous sinuses. The cerebrospinal fluid serves a cushioning protective function for the brain. The intercellular fluid of the brain is filtered through glial cells that surround the capillary walls as well as the capillary walls themselves. This filtration forms a blood-brain barrier so that the brain's extracellular fluid does not contain molecules as large as the extracellular fluid of other tissue. The blood-brain barrier keeps out corticosterone, which reduces blood sugar use by other cells; insulin, which other cells need to use glucose; and the essential amino acid, glutamic acid, which excites brain cells.

Nerve cells are cholinergic or adrenergic, depending on whether their neural transmitters are acetylcholine (ACh) or noradrenaline (norepinephrine). In the hypothalamus trophotropic cells are probably cholinergic and ergotropic cells are adrenergic. The hypothalamus stimulates the anterior pituitary via adrenergic neurosecretions.

READINGS

Chauchard, P.: The brain, New York, 1962, Grove Press, Inc.

Gardner, E.: Fundamentals of neurology, ed. 4, Philadelphia, 1963, W. B. Saunders Co.

McCleary, R. A., and Moore, R. Y.: Subcortical mechanisms in behavior, New York, 1965, Basic Books, Inc.

Milner, P., and Glickman, S., editors: Cognitive processes and the brain, New York, 1965, D. Van Norstrand Co., Inc.

Pfeiffer, J.: The human brain, New York, 1962, Pyramid Publications, Inc.

Sperry, R. W.: The great cerebral commissure, Sci. Amer., 210:42-52, Jan., 1964. (W. H. Freeman Co. Reprint No. 174).

Von Neumann, J.: The computer and the brain, New Haven, Conn., 1958, Yale University Press.

Walter, W. G.: The living brain, New York, 1963, W. W. Norton Co., Inc.

Chapter 15

Motivation

OVERVIEW

The first discussion in this chapter will be on neural mechanisms in sleep and arousal, which covers motivation in general because the animal must be aroused before it can satisfy a specific body need. On the other hand, the nervous system seems to need sleep for efficient functioning, and insufficient sleep can cause death. The concluding discussion covers more specific needs and motives such as thirst, hunger, and sex.

In treating sleep and arousal, this chapter begins with Kleitman's evolutionary theory of sleep. The theory distinguishes between the wakefulness of necessity seen in human children and lower animals when they are hungry, thirsty, or uncomfortable and the wakefulness of choice found in adult humans and some adult animals. Wakefulness of choice involves a single sleep and a single waking period during each day and is less dependent on the need state of the animal. Kleitman's ideas about the neural mechanisms underlying sleep and wakefulness are followed by modern theories and experiments on centers in the brain controlling sleep and wakefulness. Evidence obtained by the EEG (Chapter 14) on human sleep patterns follows. Four stages of depth of sleep are defined by the EEG patterns. The lightest sleep stage is often accompanied by

rapid eye movements (REM), which indicates dreaming. The depth and course of human sleep during the night is traced, and the evidence on learning during sleep is considered. The discussion closes with the topic of attention and vigilance. The role of the STPS, ARAS, and DTPS activity during vigilance as well as the topic of sensory gating are considered.

The section on specific motives begins with some definitions and a conceptual framework. The terms used in the study of motivation often have varied meanings for the reader, and a single meaning for each must be decided upon before going further. Terms are defined in a conceptual framework that distinguishes between what is going on in the animal and what is going on in the environment. The definitions distinguish changes in the environment that stimulate the animal and the behavior that follows from the altered body conditions in the internal environment that result. The distinctions assist in understanding the characteristics of drives and motives—hunger, thirst, and sex being used as examples. The role of more or less *"local states"* that accompany these motives are considered first—the dryness of the mouth in thirst or sensations of stomach contractions in hunger, for example. When these prove inadequate to explain motivated behavior, the *self-regulatory* characteristics of motives are added; for example, central factors that control eating and drinking behavior so that we eat and drink enough, but not too much, in maintaining the consistency of the internal environment. These behaviors are controlled by *multiple factors,* no one of which dominates the behavior. The role of the *hypothalamus* is central to motivated behavior, however. The specific mechanisms governing the thirst, hunger, and sex drives are then taken up in detail. Other drives such as pain, activity, and curiosity, are more briefly treated. Finally, some central neural mechanisms of reward and punishment are surveyed. Centers in the brain have been found whose stimulation is so "rewarding" that the animal (or human) will work to stimulate himself. Conversely, others have been found whose stimulation the animal will avoid even though it takes considerable work to do so.

MOTIVATION IN GENERAL: SLEEP AND ACTIVATION

It is evident that a motivated animal is not asleep. Further, the more motivated the animal is, the more *activated* it seems; the high level of CNS activity is accompanied by much restless behavior. In a sense, then, sleep can be treated as the lowest point on a scale of CNS activation that extends through quiet waking activity to extreme arousal. On the other hand, a certain amount of sleep is required for normal CNS functioning. Although sleep deprivation studies show that mental tasks such as arithmetic do not suffer from loss of sleep if the subject is well motivated, long-term alertness suffers, and bodily discomfort is felt. Animal studies have found that forced and long-continued wakefulness ends in death so that sleep is also a definite need for existence, like food or water. In this vein investigators sought for years to find out why we sleep. Kleitman, on the other hand, learned much about sleep by asking the opposite question: "Why do we stay awake?"

Kleitman's evolutionary theory of sleep and wakefulness

In primitive animals and children sleep seems to be a more "natural," or homeostatic, state than waking activity. Infants and many lower animals sleep unless they are aroused by bodily needs such as thirst, hunger, or discomfort. A human baby, for example, sleeps most of the day and night, waking at intervals when hunger or the discomfort of a wet diaper serves as a motivating stimulus to wakefulness. The wakefulness that results was called **wakefulness of necessity** by Kleitman since it was necessary for the infant to awaken to satisfy his hunger or to remove the source of the discomfort. Wakefulness of necessity is **polyphasic,** that is, it occurs in several phases or cycles during the course of a 24-hour day. The infant awakens because of the stimulus of a bodily need and returns to a contented state of natural sleep soon after his needs are satisfied. With growth and development, however, the child sleeps for longer periods without waking and stays awake for still longer periods. As even the afternoon nap is abandoned, the youngster sleeps for a continuous 8- to 10-hour period at night and remains awake for a continuous daylight period, during which most of his bodily needs are satisfied. Kleitman called such sleep cycle **monophasic** since it consists of a single sleep and waking cycle each day. The continuous waking period he called **wakefulness of choice,** since it did not depend on the stimulus of an immediate need. He suggested that wakefulness of necessity depended on a primitive center in the diencephalon (see below) stimulated directly by bodily needs. With evolution the cerebral cortex developed with an increase of learning ability from species to species. Need satisfaction became associated with daylight (except for nocturnal animals), and there were more stimuli to arouse the animal during daylight hours. The cortex began to control the center governing sleep. Cortical activity as well as body needs stimulated the primitive "sleep center" (really a waking center). The animal *learned* to remain awake during daylight hours, when the cortex was stimulated by environmental events. With reduced stimulation at night the cortex ceased to arouse the "sleep center" (or, rather, the waking center), and the center failed to drive the cortex and other parts of the brain to keep the animal awake.

Neural mechanisms

Kleitman suspected the existence of a sleep center because of the symptoms shown by victims of sleeping sickness (encephalitis lethargica), when the disease damaged the diencephalon. (In parts of Africa sleeping sickness is common; the spirochete is carried by the tsetse fly.) Victims of one variety of the disorder seemed to show only the primitive wakefulness of necessity, and Kleitman suggested that their "sleep center" (waking center) had been destroyed. The center was not aroused by cortical activity during daylight hours. As a result, the cortex instead of the sleep center "kept the brain awake," but only when it was directly stimulated by strong stimuli such as bodily discomfort, hunger, thirst, or other intense inputs. Dogs show a monophasic sleep pattern when adult. If decorticated, however, they revert to the polyphasic sleep cycle of puppyhood. Wakefulness of necessity in this case is maintained by the subcortical center instead of the cortex.

Nauta has reported both sleep and waking centers in a series of experiments on the rat. Lesions in the posterior hypothalamus of the diencephalon (near the mammillary bodies) produced rats that slept except when disturbed, like the victims of sleeping sickness. Other subcortical lesions produced no such effect. On the other hand, lesions in the anterior hypothalamus produced rats that never demonstrated normal sleep again. For the first 24 hours after the operation they appeared normal. Then symptoms of fatigue developed—a staggering gait and refusal of food and water. After about 3 days they fell into a coma and could not be aroused by the most intense stimuli. Death followed shortly. These results prompted Nauta to propose a waking center in the posterior hypothalamus (like the "sleep center" proposed by Kleitman) that stimulates the brain to activity and a sleep center in the anterior hypothalamus that must be present for normal sleep to occur. Experience with higher species have failed to confirm the existence of Nauta's sleep center, however, and the waking center is probably only a part of the BSRF mechanism that controls wakefulness and arousal.

Ranson was able to confirm the waking center in the posterior hypothalamus in the monkey. Lesions in this area produced somnambulant monkeys that slept except when aroused by intense stimulation. Unlike the rat, anterior hypothalamic lesions failed to produce wakeful monkeys. Brain damage in this area in humans also fails to change sleep patterns. One needs only to consider a waking center in the posterior hypothalamus, which is an important part of the activating system of the BSRF (ascending reticular activating system, or ARAS).

As described in Chapter 14 there are three major afferent channels from the sense organs to the brain. One is the specific thalamic projection system (STPS) that carries sensory information to the primary cortical projection areas for vision, audition, and somesthesis. The diffuse thalamic projection system (DTPS), on the other hand, is supplied by collateral fibers from the STPS to nonspecific or diffuse thalamic nuclei. These nuclei send fibers to the secondary sensory projection areas, which also receive relayed excitation from the primary areas. The secondary sensory projection areas for vision, audition, and somesthesis seems to receive a pathway "parallel" to the STPS from the sense organs. This pathway may be involved in attention to the input arriving via the STPS, or it may have some other important function that is unknown as yet. Finally, collaterals from the STPS reach the BSRF. Part of the BSRF acts as an ascending reticular activating system (ARAS), activating the whole cerebral cortex as well as many subcortical centers. The pathways involve many synapses among the short and many-branched neurons of the BSRF. Thus visual input via the ARAS, for example, could arouse the whole brain to increased activity, and a state of alertness and attention would result.

The importance of the ARAS to states of alertness and attention can be seen in several ways. For instance, electrodes can be permanently implanted in the ARAS of a cat and used to stimulate the ARAS electrically. Such a stimulus will rouse a sleeping cat to a state of alert attention immediately. A similar stimulus delivered to areas located elsewhere in the brain has no such effect. When the ARAS is stimulated, the EEG of the sleeping cat is transformed immediately, from the high-voltage slow waves characteristic of sleep into the desynchronized low-voltage activity typical of alert attention. The ARAS seems much more important to attention and wakefulness than the STPS. The pathways of the STPS are carried in the laterally placed white matter of the brainstem, whereas the ARAS occupies the central core of the brainstem. Cutting the lateral sensory (somesthetic and auditory) pathways in the midbrain of a cat has no obvious effect on behavior, surprisingly enough. The sleeping cat is aroused as readily as before by a sound stimulus, although the STPS is not carrying the sensory information to the cortex. Perhaps the ARAS serves in its stead. In any case the cat remains as alert as before, and the EEG shows the normal wakeful pattern. If the central core of the midbrain is severed, however, a different result follows, even when the lateral STPS pathways are left intact. The operation abolishes normal

waking behavior and the desynchronized EEG pattern that accompanies it. The cat shows the slow-wave EEG pattern typical of sleep, and the most intense stimuli fail to wake it. Evidently the ARAS is necessary to wakefulness, although the part of the ARAS that is located in the posterior hypothalamus (waking center) may play a vital role in waking behavior and brain activity.

The ARAS (and associated DTPS) shows an inherent or "spontaneous" 3 to 5 per second rhythm of electrical activity, which seems important to its function in arousing the brain. Implanted electrodes show that this rhythm is intensified in alert states of arousal and suppressed during sleep. The spontaneous 3 to 5 per second waves seem subject to both excitatory and inhibitory influences from other brain centers (including the cortex) and from sensory input. A schema of the many influences on the inherent wakefulness rhythm of the BSRF can be seen in Fig. 15-1. Metabolic influences on the inherent BSRF waking rhythm can be excitatory or inhibitory. The excitatory influences come into play when the metabolism of the internal environment is upset by bodily needs of one kind or another. For example, an excess of carbon dioxide stimulates nerve cells in the medulla, which, in turn, stimulate the BSRF. A stress-induced increase in norepinephrine can directly stimulate the BSRF. In either case the BSRF increases its 3 to 5 per second inherent rhythm. Parts of the BSRF act as an ARAS in stimulating the cortex and other parts of the brain to arouse the animal to a state of vigilance and attention. This represents wakefulness of necessity in Kleitman's terms. The BSRF, especially the hypothalamic reticular cells, arouse the animal because of bodily need or discomfort. In the same manner excitatory inputs from the sense organs can stimulate the ARAS via collateral afferents to cause wakefulness of necessity via the "waking centers" of the ARAS. Inhibitory influences from visceral

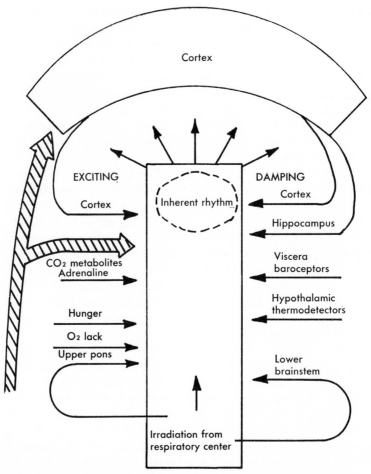

Fig. 15-1. Factors affecting brainstem reticular formation ARAS to influence sleep or wakefulness (see text). The large arrow on the left represents sensory input. (From Oswald, I.: Sleeping and waking, Amsterdam, 1962, Elsevier Publishing Co.)

and other internal receptors can reduce the activity of the BSRF when the animal's needs have been satisfied, terminating wakefulness of necessity by direct inhibition as well as reduced excitation.

Wakefulness of choice is represented by the interactions of the cerebral cortex and the wakefulness centers of the BSRF. The cortex can excite or inhibit the inherent rhythms of the BSRF to arouse or not arouse the brain (Fig. 15-1). Action of the cortex on the BSRF depends partly on the sensory input to the cortex, which tends to be greater during the day than the night for

most animals that develop a monophasic sleep pattern through conditioning.

The role of that part of the BSRF that extends into the hypothalamus is emphasized by some experts such as Hess and Gellhorn. Gellhorn believes that wakefulness is caused by proprioceptive and nociceptive input ("reflex excitation") to the posterior hypothalamus. The posterior hypothalamus, in turn, arouses both the cortex and the sympathetic nervous system. Cortical arousal makes the animal more receptive to incoming sensory input. Sympathetic arousal produces the other symptoms of vigilance such as increased heart rate and breathing—the sympathetically governed mobilization of the body for action (Chapter 6). So far Gellhorn's ideas differ from the ARAS concept only in how much the hypothalamic part of the BSRF is emphasized as a waking center (he calls it an ergotropic area—Chapter 14).

Gellhorn also stresses the role of the anterior hypothalamus in controlling states of quiescence as well as digestive activities. He calls these trophotropic centers. They control reflex reactions in digestion via the parasympathetic nervous system. The trophotropic centers are more active than the ergotropic centers resting state or during sleep. The parasympathetic reflex dominance over sympathetic reflexes leads to low heart rate and blood pressure, increased digestion, and the other symptoms of parasympathetic dominance that occur during sleep and/or quiescence.

EEG during sleep and wakefulness

The **electroencephalogram (EEG)** is measured by cementing small electrodes to the scalp and by picking up gross electrical changes in potential from the surface of the cortex through the skull (Chapter 14). At the surface of the cortex (**electrocorticograph, or ECG**) these potential changes amount to about 1 millivolt (1/1000 volt). As measured at the surface of the skull, the electrical changes are as small as 1 microvolt (1/1,000,000 volt). The changes in potential are amplified and used to drive an ink-writing oscillograph. These changes wax and wane in a rhythmic fashion and appear to represent the moment-to-moment state of partial depolarization of nerve cell bodies in the more superficial layers of the cortex. The more depolarized the cell bodies, the more rapidly their axons are firing and, roughly speaking, the more "active" is the cortex. In states of extreme arousal the EEG is desynchronized; many of the cells are partly depolarized (negative) and fire their axons at a rapid rate.

As the cortex becomes less excited, the cells appear to wax and wane in potential in a synchronous fashion, producing regular brain waves of voltage change. Generally speaking, the less excited the cortex, the lower the frequency of the brain waves and the greater their amplitude. In other words, a less excited cortex features brain cells whose potential changes at a slower and rhythmic rate with greater changes in amplitude. These and other predictable changes occur in the EEG pattern with reduced excitation of the cortex, from aroused excitation through a state of resting wakefulness, dozing, and deeper sleep. The changes in sleep can be compared to how much stimulation is required to wake the subject, and a scale of EEG changes with depth of sleep has been constructed. The most widely used scale of this kind was published by Dement and Kleitman.

In the Dement and Kleitman scale four stages of sleep are added to the patterns that distinguish the aroused state from the resting but alert state. In the aroused state, as indicated above, the cortex is desynchronized so that few regular rhythmic brain waves are seen. The **alpha rhythm** is dominant in the resting state of wakefulness of most human subjects. The alpha rhythm is a 10- to 14-cycle per second (cps) pattern of low and slightly irregular amplitude (Fig. 14-10). This pattern shows its greatest amplitude from electrodes in the occipital region. Some subjects show a slightly faster low-amplitude beta rhythm. As the subject goes to sleep, differences in the EEG pattern occur. Four stages of sleep can be distinguished in the EEG pattern, which represent increasing depths of sleep as measured by waking time to a standard stimulus. Stage 1 occurs when the subject is dozing and is easily aroused. The stage 1 EEG pattern includes desynchronized (broken up or intermittently absent) alpha waves, with low-voltage, 4 to 6 cps waves, and occasional **delta waves** of 3 to 5 cps and larger voltage change. Stage 2, a light sleep stage, is characterized by 1 to 6 cps waves, spindle-shaped rhythms of 14 cps that wax and wane in amplitude to form a spindle-shaped train, and some K complexes, or bursts of high-frequency waves. All the foregoing are mixed with low-voltage delta waves. In deeper sleep, stage 3, the spindle waves disappear and higher-voltage delta waves are seen as well as a few K complexes. Stage 4, the deepest sleep, is dominated by high-voltage, random delta waves.

The course of sleep during the night varies for different subjects. Some persons never demonstrate stage 4, for example. However, all subjects show *phasic* shifts in stages of sleep during the night, shifting back and forth from stage 3 or 4 to stage 1 or 2. Light and deep sleep stages alternate in cycles of 30 to 90 minutes in length. When averaged out over the course of a night's sleep, the typical subject spends more time in deep sleep during the second, third, and perhaps fourth hours of sleep than he does earlier or later in a 7- or 8-hour sleep period. From about the fourth hour until morning, an increasing amount of time is spent in the lighter sleep stages. However, if deep sleep is prevented by waking the subject each time he shows a stage 3 or 4 sleep pattern for a night or two, he will spend a greater part of his sleep period in deep sleep on the subsequent night.

Dreaming can be detected by a combination of EEG changes and eye movements. If electrodes are placed on the temples, muscle action potentials will be picked up when the muscles moving the eyeballs are active. In deep sleep the eyes are relatively motionless in the eye sockets, and the extrinsic eye muscles are not very active. As the subject begins to dream, the eye muscles become active and move the eyeballs rapidly. The recording of rapid eye movements (REM) is accompanied by a change in the EEG from deeper stages to stage 1. The change from deeper stages to stage 1 is often called

an E-1, or emergent stage 1. There is some controversy about all of this, but if a subject is awakened while he is showing the E-1 and REM patterns, he usually reports that he has been dreaming and can usually recall at least part of the dream. If he is not awakened during this period, he may or may not remember the dream.

If REM and E-1 are taken as signs of dreaming, there is evidence that dreams can last as long as half an hour. Further, nearly all subjects have three or four dreams during the night, whether they remember the dreams or not. Subjects have been prevented from dreaming by waking them every time they showed the E-1 and REM pattern for three or four nights. Compared to subjects wakened equally often during deeper (dreamless) sleep, the dream-deprived subjects are reported to be more irritable and anxious during their waking hours. If dream-deprived subjects are permitted uninterrupted sleep on subsequent nights, they will dream more (by REM and E-1 criteria) for a night or two. These observations have led some to speculate that dreaming is a symptom of some metabolic activity of the brain that is necessary for its proper recovery during sleep. Infants spend more time in REM sleep than do adults (up to one half of sleep periods); as the polyphasic sleep cycle gives way progressively to the monophasic cycle, less time is spent in REM sleep. Observers have speculated that longer periods of REM are necessary in the infant, who sleeps more than the adult and whose brain would not otherwise be active enough of the time for proper development.

Paradoxically, it is harder to wake an animal from REM sleep than from deeper stages of sleep. Cats showing REM sleep are harder to wake, even by ARAS stimulation. (This is not true of humans—see above.) The brain seems more under the control of a center in the pons than subject to outside stimulation. In the BSRF of the rostral pons there is a nucleus (nucleus pontis caudalis) whose destruction abolishes REM sleep in cats. These cats subsequently show the other normal stages of sleep, but this progresses to insomnia and finally death. On the other hand, a decorticate cat shows nothing but REM sleep, so that the cortex is perhaps necessary for dreamless sleep.

Recent studies by Jouvet on cats have pointed to chemical differences in the brain between light (dreamless?) sleep and E-1 sleep and have helped identify nerve centers that may be responsible for each state. In cats, during paradoxical sleep (REM sleep), the neck muscles are completely relaxed and the cat is hard to waken; yet the EEG shows E-1 stage activity and the cat shows movements (dreaming?). In light sleep in the cat REM is not evident, yet the neck muscles show some tension and the cat is easily awakened. It has been found that certain midline nuclei in the brainstem (raphe nuclei) produce serotonin, a hormonelike substance found throughout the brain. If most of these nuclei are destroyed, the cat becomes sleepless (less than 10% of the time spent in sleep compared to 66% in the normal cat). On the other hand, certain nuclei of the pons (locus ceruleus—but see nucleus pontis caudalis, above) produce epinephrine. When these nuclei are destroyed, paradoxical E-1 (REM) sleep is abolished. In the cat, then, serotonin produced by the raphe nuclei may stimulate light sleep, whereas epinephrine produced by nuclei of the pons may result in REM sleep. It is interesting to note, however, that the deeper stages of sleep in man (who sleeps much less) are not reported for the cat.

Objective measures of "dreaming" and "depth" of sleep have revived scientific interest in the possibility of learning while asleep. The history of attempts to demonstrate learning during sleep goes back at least to World War I, when attempts were made to teach army telegraph operators the Morse code while they slept. The attempt was not very successful and was abandoned. Interest in sleep-learning continued, however; many were attracted by the possibility of effortless memorization of boring material such as the vocabulary of a foreign language. Others were excited by the idea that personality defects (such as lack of self-confidence) could be relieved by repeated suggestions made during sleep. It was argued that the subject would be more receptive to suggestion (easily persuaded) during the sleeping state.

Many untrained persons entered the field, and sleep-learning schools and personality-improvement courses have become widespread since the advent of automatically controlled tape recorders. In a typical program the tape recorder may be set to present the material to be learned during the first 15 minutes as the individual goes to sleep, again for 15 minutes in the middle of the night, and for 15 minutes just before waking up in the morning. From what has already been said about the depth of sleep, or EEG stages of sleep, the fallacy of this program is evident. During the first 15 minutes of sleep and just before waking the subject is usually dozing, or half-awake, as indicated by the presence of alpha waves in his EEG record. Therefore, in two out of three of the learning periods the individual is at least partly awake and can learn, although not very efficiently.

Studies have been made to see if simple verbal material can be learned during deeper sleep, as indicated by the absence of alpha waves. These studies produced no evidence for learning during "true" sleep. Other studies have tried to condition specific brain waves that occur during sleep (K complexes, for example) to a tone. Some success has been reported.

Attention and vigilance

The distinction between the STPS, the DTPS, and the ARAS has already been made in this chapter and in Chapter 14. To summarize again, the STPS seems to carry sensory information to the visual, auditory, and somesthetic projection areas of the cerebral cortex via the classical sensory pathways. Collaterals from the STPS go to diffuse thalamic nuclei to form a "parallel" pathway to secondary sensory areas (visual, auditory, and somesthetic). The ARAS receives collaterals from most sensory inputs and acts to arouse the whole brain in a nonspecific fashion.

Role of the DTPS. Both the ARAS and the DTPS are involved in states of arousal and attention. However, the DTPS and the secondary (areas II and III) sensory projection areas may be more modality-specific than the ARAS. Area I is served by area II as well as the STPS, and area II receives fibers from the DTPS. One investigator (Galambos) has found area I cortical cells in the cat that are active only when the animal is "paying attention" to that modality. The cats were prepared with implanted electrodes in single cells of the auditory projection area. These cells seem to be fired by the DTPS rather than the STPS; for example, if the animal was not orienting toward an auditory stimulus, the auditory "attention cells" in the auditory projection system would be silent. When a novel sound stimulus such as a squeaking toy mouse was introduced, the cat would orient toward the stimulus, and the "attention units" in the auditory cortex would fire. With repeated sound stimuli the cat would adapt to the sound and quit paying attention. At the same time the auditory attention units would stop firing.

Vigilance. The ARAS and DTPS seem to be involved in the attention required for an animal to make a rapid discrimination. If the animal is awake but inattentive, alpha rhythms are seen in the EEG. If he is aroused, the ARAS is activating the cortex and a desynchronized EEG pattern is seen. This pattern, along with behavioral arousal, can be produced by stimulating the ARAS

with electrodes implanted in an otherwise normal cat. Two flashes of light, presented 50 msec. apart, produce only one potential in the visual cortex if the cat is inattentive, and the EEG shows mostly alpha rhythms. If a sound stimulus warns the cat that the light flashes are to follow, the EEG desynchronizes. The two light flashes then produce separate evoked potentials in the visual cortex. The more the alpha waves are blocked by a desynchronized EEG in man, the faster his reaction time to a visual stimulus. Finally, both the reaction time and discrimination rate in monkeys can be improved by BSRF stimulation. If electrodes are implanted in the BSRF of an otherwise normal monkey, the ARAS can be stimulated before he is forced to choose between two objects for a food reward. Stimulating the ARAS reduces the time that it must see the objects before it can discriminate between them. It also improves its reaction time to the stimuli—how fast it reaches for the correct object.

Sensory gating, habituation, and attention. It is evident that attention to one sensory modality often requires inattention to another. When a student is reading and attending to a complex visual input, he may have to be called several times before the auditory input shifts his attention. It is as if the auditory input were turned off, and some of the evidence from animal experiments supports this interpretation. On the other hand, a repeated, monotonous auditory stimulus such as a dripping faucet may arouse attention at first, as a novel sound, and then no longer be "heard" if one is attending to other things.

In one demonstration (Hernandez-Peon) electrodes were permanently implanted in the cochlear nucleus of an otherwise normal cat. The cochlear nucleus is the first relay nucleus for nerve cells from the auditory receptors. Regularly spaced click sounds caused potentials at the nucleus that arrived at the same regular intervals. When the clicks first appeared, the evoked potentials were large, but with continued regular stimulation the evoked potentials became smaller—**habituation** had occurred, and the animal was no longer paying attention to the monotonous stimuli. Then two mice in a jar were presented to the cat; the cat oriented to them visually and sniffed at the jar. Although the click stimulus continued, evoked potentials stopped arriving at the cochlear nucleus at all! **Sensory gating** had occurred; response of the sensory pathway had been blocked, in this case at the receptor.

Efferent pathways to the cochlea have been discovered that can inhibit sensory input (the olivocochlear tract of Rasmussen—Chapter 11). Similar efferent inhibitory pathways have been found for vision and somesthesis. (In the case of somesthesis, input is blocked at the gracile and cuneate nuclei; visual input is altered at the retina.) Efferent pathways to sensory input are not all inhibitory—the "gate" may be opened wider instead of closed. There are both excitatory and inhibitory efferent pathways to the thalamus and geniculate bodies to affect the STPS and the DTPS. Efferent pathways from higher levels can more diffusely excite, sensitize, or inhibit the ARAS, as has already been seen. The general principle of *efferent control of afferent impulses* is important to general arousal and specific attention as well as to habituation. By blocking or sensitizing specific sensory inputs in the STPS and DTPS, the CNS can pay attention to one or two sensory modalities while minimizing the input of others. At the same time the general arousal of the CNS may be increased by excitation of the ARAS from higher centers, creating a state of **vigilance.** Not only do higher centers *select* the sensory input attended to, they also excite themselves by stimulating increased input from the ARAS. Repetitive stimuli, on the other hand, result in at least partial inhibition of their sensory channel and may reduce activity in the ARAS as well.

SPECIFIC MOTIVES

The neural mechanisms of specific motives will be discussed next—thirst, hunger, and sex motivation serving as the primary examples. Before taking up these topics, one must agree on the terms to be used in describing stimulus events preceding motivated behavior, the resulting events in the internal environment of the animal, and the consequent observed behavior. Much of the difficulty experienced in early studies of motivation came from confused terminology. In using the term "need," for example, some would be referring to a lack, or absence, in the external environment, whereas others would be referring to a change in the animal's (internal) *condition.* The statement that "the dog needs water" could refer to an empty water dish or be an inference about the animal's internal condition when it was panting in hot weather and probably dehydrated. In other instances an attempt would be made to explain behavior by merely naming it. "The dog inherits a 'water need' (internal state)." How does one know? "He drinks water every day (external behavior)." Similar difficulties led to the controversy over instincts, or complex motivation, which was presumed to be inherited. Women were assumed to inherit a "maternal instinct" defined as behavior involving child care. "Women inherit a love for children." How does one know this? "They love children." All these statements ignore the complex of internal conditions, external stimuli, and the rewarding or punishing effects of the resulting behavior.

Terminology

In the definitions and the schema to be used here, an attempt will be made to *predict* behavior as a *consequence* of predetermined external stimulus events and known internal conditions of the organism. Stimulus events interact with preexisting conditions in the internal environment of the organism; stimulus events also result in further changes in the internal environment. From this interaction of external and internal events, behavior results. The behavior changes the external stimulus conditions and the internal state of the animal to result in further behavior.

Both external and internal stimuli result in behavior, whether or not the stimuli are "known" to the organism and whether or not the stimuli can be seen by an outside observer. The organism may respond to an external stimulus that is not evident to another observer, as when a dog barks in response to a high-pitched whistle that is outside the frequency limits audible to a human observer. (The observer, of course, may use instruments to detect the sound and eventually discover that it is usually followed by a barking response.) The animal may react to some change in his internal environment that results from lack of water, an aspect that affects some center or centers in the CNS. Only tedious and ingenious research can detect (1) what changes in the internal environment result from lack of water, (2) which of these changes affect the CNS, (3) how and

where do they affect the CNS, and (4) what kind of CNS activity leads to the behavior that usually follows lack of water.

Table 15-1 summarizes the order of events in motivated behavior and the terms to be used in the remainder of the chapter. A **need condition** is any state of affairs in the external environment that disturbs equilibrium, or homeostasis, in the internal environment. The need condition is *inherent* if it is required for individual or species survival; otherwise it is *acquired,* or learned. Thus a condition of adequate water would be required for the individual to survive, or presence of the opposite sex would be needed for the species to survive. Higher animals, especially man, acquire the need for many conditions not originally related to survival—approval by others, status symbols, etc.—and his internal equilibrium is upset in the absence of these conditions. Whether inherent or acquired, a need condition leads to a **need state,** the complex of *inherent* or *acquired* changes in internal equilibrium that results. A **sensitizing stimulus** is that aspect of a need state that sets off a drive mechanism in the CNS. A **drive**

Table 15-1. Schema for motivated behavior

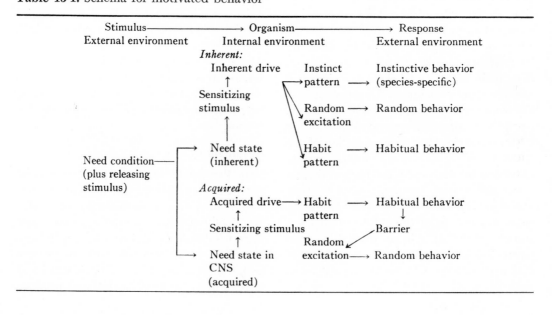

is a CNS mechanism for arousing and sustaining behavior when the need state exists. The lack of water (need condition), for example, causes many changes in the tissues (need state). The CNS is sensitive to some of these changes (sensitizing stimulus), and parts of the CNS (drive) arouse and sustain behavior. Of course there are acquired drives as well—behavior can be aroused and sustained for many learned reasons from pay to patriotism—and all acquired drives must have sensitizing stimuli whether or not one is aware of his upset condition. Not all inherent need states have sensitizing stimuli, however. Vitamin B_1 is required for survival, and a lack of this vitamin severely disturbs internal equilibrium. Yet aroused behavior does *not* result directly from vitamin B_1 deficiency (although an animal can *learn* to choose B_1-rich foods because of the rewarding effects on his internal condition).

A drive arouses and sustains behavior; it does not direct or channel behavior. Behavior appropriate to the drive occurs only in the presence of a **releasing stimulus** that is somehow related to the **incentive.** The incentive is the external stimulus that changes the need condition and therefore the need state, drive, and sensitizing stimulus. Water, for example, would be the incentive for the thirst drive. It is also a releasing stimulus for thirst since it releases behavior appropriate to the drive, that is, drinking. Other stimuli that serve as *cues* to the presence of water are also releasing stimuli for behavior appropriate to thirst. For a thirsty man a water fountain leads to complex behavior that is appropriate to thirst; the water fountain is a releasing stimulus but not the incentive, per se, because a water fountain cannot relieve thirst. The water fountain leads to thirst-related behavior only as a result of learning.

Inherent need states and inherent drives arouse behavior. In the case of some lower animals, behavior appropriate to the drive is "built in" the nervous system, and this

behavior is the same for all members of the species (species-specific). In this case one speaks of an **instinct,** consisting of an inherent drive and inherited CNS systems for complex behavior. The behavior may or may not require releasing stimuli. For example, nest-building is an instinct in many species. For certain wasps the only need condition required is absence of a nest; the wasp produces its own nest-building material and will usually build a nest whenever a nest is lacking. The rat, however, builds a nest only in the presence of nest-building materials (releasing stimuli) *and* certain internal conditions (sensitizing stimuli) such as cold or the hormone changes of pregnancy.

The primates, including man, do not seem to inherit CNS patterns for complex organized behavior in response to inherent drives. Primates appear to lack instincts. Drive arousal results in random behavior until the incentive is reached. Behavior becomes less random and variable with learning, and the animal develops a **habit**—behavior patterns appropriate to the drive under the conditions in which he lives. The existence of a drive *and* a habit is referred to as a **motive.** Organized and learned behavior follows an aroused hunger drive in adult man so that the adult has a hunger motive. An infant responds to the hunger drive with random behavior since he has no hunger motive prior to learning how to obtain food. If hunger-motivated behavior does not lead to food, however, it will become more variable and random until new and successful habits have been learned. Finally, there are certain habits that lead to changes in the internal environment to cause **addiction.** The habitual use of certain drugs can change the internal equilibrium of the body so that the CNS no longer functions well in the absence of the drug. Strong need states and sensitizing stimuli result from withdrawal of the drug, and the CNS reacts as it does to an inherent drive.

It should be stressed at this point that

no explanation of motivated behavior has been given so far. Definitions of terms have been made explicit to avoid confusion later on. The schema in Table 15-1 is not explanatory because it is essentially "circular"—a need condition leading to a need state, drive, motive or instinct, behavior related to an incentive, and removal of the need condition. The explanation of drives and motives will require proof of what conditions terminate motivated behavior as well as what conditions initiate it. Nearly all references to thirst, hunger, and sexual behavior will refer to inherent needs and drives because the neural mechanisms underlying acquired drives are complex and largely unknown. The terms "need" and "drive'" will refer to inherent needs and drives unless otherwise specified. However, the role of learning in developing motivated behavior must be recognized as one goes along so that terms relevant to learning are necessary.

Characteristics of drives and motives: local states

Early approaches to the thirst, hunger, and sex drives assumed that man was *aware* of their sensitizing stimuli. In this view, need states in the body resulted in consciously perceived stimuli that were restricted to local sensory areas of the body; hence the term "local states." In thirst one is aware of dryness of the mouth and throat. When extremely hungry, powerful stomach contractions may be perceived as "hunger pangs." In the male it was assumed that accumulation of seminal fluid in the vesicles made the penis more sensitive to stimulation, arousing the sex drive. All these stimulus sites are "peripheral" to most of the internal environment, although the stimulation *results* from changes in the internal environment. Local-state drive theories have been called "peripheral theories" for that reason, in contrast to theories about the direct effect of internal changes on the brain. To prove that "local states" are the

sensitizing stimuli for drives, they must be shown to be both *necessary* and *sufficient* to the arousal of appropriate motivated behavior.

Thirst. When the body is dehydrated, or low on water, salivation is reduced as one way of reducing loss of water in the tissues. This results in the dry mouth sensations one experiences when thirsty. A famous physiologist (Dr. Walter B. Cannon) suggested that dryness of the mouth and throat aroused and sustained thirst-drive behavior when an animal is thirsty. This means that mouth and throat dryness is the sensitizing stimulus for the thirst drive. Is mouth and throat dryness a necessary and sufficient condition to arouse and sustain the thirst drive? The evidence suggests that it is not. In the first place, the first swallow of water when one is thirsty abolishes these senations, yet drinking behavior continues for some time before one is satiated. Dryness of the mouth and throat could therefore arouse the first swallow, but what sustains subsequent drinking behavior? Experimenters have tied off the ducts of salivary glands in animals to make them permanently "dry mouthed." Such animals drink more frequently, but they do not consume more water in the course of the day than do normal animals. The same has been found true of humans born without functional salivary glands. It is evident that mouth and/or throat dryness has something to do with the *initiation* of drinking behavior, but it has little to do with the *regulation* of how long drinking behavior is sustained or the amount of water drunk. It does not show that mouth and throat dryness is *necessary* to the initiation of drinking behavior, although the sensation may contribute to initiation of drinking. (Other experiments have induced mouth dryness by blocking salivation with atropine, with much the same results. These experiments must be cautiously interpreted, however, because atropine has widespread effects on the nervous system.)

Hunger. Another local stimulus that could arouse a drive comes from stomach contractions that may accompany hunger and are sensed by the subject as hunger pangs. Sensations of stomach distention usually accompany satiation and could terminate eating behavior. A low blood sugar level induced by insulin injections can cause stomach contractions, but whether blood sugar gets that low during ordinary hunger is not clear. Dr. Cannon suggested that hunger was caused by stomach contractions after an experiment in which a subject swallowed a balloon, connected by a tube to a pressure-measuring device. When the stomach contracted, it squeezed the balloon, and increased pressure was indicated. Without seeing the pressure measurements, the subject signalled when he sensed a hunger pang. The sensations corresponded with stomach contractions. Subsequent studies have cast some doubt on this famous experiment. It has been shown that the presence of the balloon in the stomach stimulates stomach contractions, for example. However, powerful stomach contractions and hunger pangs do occur during starvation, although they are reported to last for only 3 to 5 days. None of this tells us whether stomach contractions, as a sensitizing stimulus, are necessary and sufficient to arouse and sustain the hunger drive. Other evidence suggests that stomach contractions are unnecessary to the hunger drive, although they may contribute to the aroused and sustained behavior for a time. (Certainly the starving man is still hungry for days after the contractions cease!)

Some of the evidence comes from operations performed on people with stomach ulcers. In some cases nerves leading to the stomach were cut to block parasympathetic facilitation of automatic stomach contractions and stop the stimulation of acid secretion by the stomach. Denervating the stomach also cuts sensory nerves and eliminates sensations caused by stomach contractions. It does not alter the arousal or regulations of eating behavior in these patients. In other ulcer operations all or part of the stomach is removed without interfering with eating behavior, except that less can be eaten at one time (until the small intestine enlarges to store food as the stomach once did). Although these patients eat less, they eat more frequently so that food intake is regulated as before. (Nausea is a chronic condition in some patients, but others adjust well). Removing the stomachs of animals produces the same general effects. Animals without stomachs show aroused and sustained behavior when deprived of food, and they will learn complex habits to obtain a food reward. Therefore, stomach contractions as a sensitizing stimulus are neither necessary nor sufficient to arouse or sustain the hunger drive—nor are they important to regulating normal food intake.

Sex. In the mature male, semen is stored in the seminal vesicle after its production by the gonads and associated glandular tissue. If the accumulation is not drawn off by intercourse, nocturnal emissions occur at fairly regular intervals. In the absence of regular copulation and ejaculation, the accumulation of unspent semen in the vesicles might act as a sensitizing stimulus that arouses the sex drive in males. No similar mechanism was proposed for females. Research on the function of the endocrine glands has now shown that both sex drives and the production of germ plasm are under the control of the endocrine glands in most vertebrate species (Chapter 3). In man the sex drive becomes dominated by learning, and sensitizing stimuli are more a function of past experience than hormone levels. As a result, the female sex drive becomes largely independent of the regular monthly changes in hormone level caused by the estrus cycle, and sexual behavior continues after germ plasm and sex hormone production cease in both sexes with aging. This is not to say that the strength of the sex drive or the frequency of intercourse is independent of sex hormone level in the human. However, sex hormones are neither necessary nor sufficient to arouse and sustain sexual behavior, at least in the human adult with past sexual experience.

Characteristics of drives and motives: self-regulation

In general, motivated behavior is organized to maintain the consistency of the internal environment. Evidence will be presented to show that animals, including man, can estimate their need for food or water very closely after a given amount of deprivation. Experiments show that animals drink or eat the amount necessary to replace a loss from deprivation, and very little more or less. The time required to replace the lost food or water is not enough to enable the body to restore internal equilibrium. An animal will drink enough to restore body water level (within 0.5% of body weight) within a few minutes and *stop*, even though the body has not had time to distribute the water to most of the tissues. This means that there must be shut-off stimuli to signal satiation as well as a sensitizing stimuli to signal need. Furthermore, behavior that satisfies one need of the body can create others. For example, perspiring to keep the body temperature down in hot weather results in dehydration and consequent thirst. Continuous adjustment is necessary to keep the body's needs in balance. There are, however, inherent drives or "appetites" that seem independent of the body's needs. They are externally controlled by releasing stimuli instead of internal changes (for example, in animals and children, the taste for nonnutritive sweet substances such as saccharin). On the other hand, there are need states threatening survival that appear to have no sensitizing stimuli because they do not arouse and sustain behavior. Certain vitamin deficiencies are examples. Finally, the self-regulation of drives and motives extend beyond

the energy requirements (caloric needs) of the body for food, to its requirements for specific amounts of fats, proteins, etc.—specific as well as general hungers.

Hierarchy of need states. The need states of the body are not independent of one another. They compete or cooperate for behavior priority when their drives are aroused by need conditions in the environment and need states in the body. In general, the priority of a need state that arouses a drive depends on how long that internal imbalance can be tolerated by the body. For example, needs for breathing, heat regulation, thirst, and hunger coexist in that order of priority in the body. Breathing must be regulated from moment to moment as the body stores little oxygen. Yet breathing may be interrupted momentarily to permit swallowing water when thirsty. Heat regulation has more "inertia" of gain or loss—errors may be corrected over periods of many minutes without an undue change in body temperature. Body heat is continuously lost in breathing, whatever the body temperature. A change in body temperature has more immediate effects than water loss; therefore, water may be sacrificed for cooling (as in a perspiring man or panting dog) since a water deficit can be tolerated for 2 or 3 days. Food intake and energy output can be out of balance for even longer, and a thirsty animal eats little because water is required for digestion and waste elimination. The behavior that results from drives and regulates drives depends on other drives and the effect of the behavior on the internal environment.

Satiation. Experiments have shown over and over again that deprived animals are able to estimate their food and water deficiencies quite accurately. A dog will begin to drink when it has lost only 0.5% of its body weight in water. If deprived of water for a period of time, the amount of water it drinks will accurately estimate the deficit it has undergone. Furthermore, it will drink this amount within 5 minutes. Five minutes is almost surely too short a time for water to be absorbed from the stomach and change the dehydrated state of the other tissues of the internal environment. Whatever state of the tissues initiated the thirst drive has not changed—the sensitizing stimulus is still there. Therefore, one must look for satiation, or stop stimuli that halt drinking behavior when enough has been ingested to eventually restore internal balance (even though the balance has not yet been restored).

Hunger seems to act in much the same way. Animals seem to estimate their caloric needs and respond accordingly. Animals, including man (not always!) maintain their weight at a constant level by varying their intake according to the caloric value of a changing diet—less will be eaten of high calorie than low calorie foods to maintain body weight within narrow limits. An animal will stop eating when it has "had enough," even though the food it has eaten is not utilized until after digestion has taken place. Since animals eat at intervals, some state of the body arouses eating behavior and serves as a sensitizing stimulus. But animals stop eating before digestion has taken place; therefore, satiating stimuli must be found that tell the organism when enough calories have been ingested. If the customary diet of a dog or a rat is "diluted" with a nonnutritive bland substance, the animal will increase its intake accordingly, up to the limit of stomach capacity. If offered diluted alcohol, rats (like some people!) will prefer a certain amount of alcohol to pure water. They will, however, reduce their caloric intake of food enough to compensate for the calories gained from the alcohol. Most convincing of all is the fact that rats will restore their normal body weight by reduced caloric intake after having been artificially fattened.

Insulin is required in certain amounts to utilize the blood sugar obtained from food. If too much insulin is present, the animal must eat more or suffer insulin shock—fainting and possible death because the blood sugar has been used up by other tissues and does not reach the brain, where a constant supply is necessary for brain function. Injections of insulin will cause an animal to eat more to keep up blood sugar supplies to the brain. The extra calories form fat deposits, and the animal gains weight and becomes obese. As soon as the injections are stopped, however, the rat will reduce his caloric intake for 20 days or so, losing weight until his normal body weight is reached. When the rat is overweight, either the sensitizing stimulus loses potency, or (more probably) satiation stimuli are more readily aroused.

Through all the arousal and satiation mechanisms for hunger and thirst, it must be recognized that hunger and thirst interact. A hungry animal drinks less because less water is required for digestion, and for waste elimination by the kidneys. For the same reason a thirsty animal eats less. Both sensitizing and satiation stimuli seem involved because drinking or eating behavior are aroused less often and do not last as long in both instances.

Drives controlled by releasing stimuli: "appetites," and palatability. Either the initiation or the cessation of eating or drinking behavior is influenced by the palatability of the substances ingested, although not beyond the bounds of keeping water and food intake in balance with each other and with the need states of the body. If water or food is made bitter with quinine, it is avoided by the animal when other sources of water or food are available. If not, the animal will eat or drink just enough of most quinine concentrations to maintain itself. On the other hand, it will prefer water sweetened with saccharin to natural water, even though saccharin has no nutritive value. Here is a case of an "appetite"—a drive controlled by the releasing stimulus in the absence of an internal sensitizing stimulus. Rats prefer the taste of saccharin to many nutritive solutions, even when deprived of food, and will choose saccharin-flavored water over pure water when satiated for food.

Inherent need states without sensitizing stimuli or drive mechanisms. In some instances need states in the body that imperil survival have no apparent way of arousing and sustaining behavior. The body requires minimum amounts of vitamins A and D for survival, but the complete absence of either or both will not arouse and sustain behavior. Breathing is almost completely regulated by the CO_2 level of the blood. In a closed room a lack of oxygen is accompanied by increased CO_2 level. But a lack of O_2 not accompanied by increased CO_2 (as at high altitudes) causes no aroused and sustained behavior and no symptoms of suffocation (though some intoxication may result). Other need states of the body without effective sensitizing stimuli to the CNS could be cited.

Multiple-factor control of motivated behavior. Both external (releasing) and internal (sensitizing) stimuli control the arousal of motivated behavior in a complex fashion. There may be several releasing stimuli for thirst, hunger, or sexual behavior because the cues vary from one situation to another. As a result, even instinctive behavior such as sexual behavior in the rat is complex and variable rather than stereotyped and falls under the control of a variety of releasing stimuli. Smell, taste, touch, visual, and other stimuli combine to release sexual behavior in the rat. Experiments that eliminate these sensory inputs, singly or in combination, show that several sensory channels must be lost before the sexual response of the male rat to the female is eliminated. Furthermore, the number of sensory inputs that must be eliminated to abolish sexual behavior depends on the internal level of sex hormones. The higher the hormone level, the more sensory inputs must be eliminated to abolish male sexual behavior. Since the sex hormones act

as sensitizing stimuli for sexual behavior in the male, it is evident that the effectiveness of releasing stimuli depends on the level of sensitizing stimuli. (Sexual behavior in the female is harder to eliminate by depriving her of sensory input, but the responses required of the female are less complex and less subject to varied stimulus control. All she has to do is "relax and enjoy it," aside from reflex responses. This point will be more fully discussed later.) Thirst and hunger behavior are also jointly under the control of sensitizing and releasing stimuli. The effectiveness of cues (releasing stimuli) in a learning situation to a food or water reward depend on how deprived the animal is. Up to a point, the greater the deprivation, the stronger the sensitizing stimulation, the higher the drive level, the more effective the releasing stimuli, and the more rapid the learning.

Hypothalamic centers

The hypothalamus contains important centers regulating drives. The hypothalamus receives nervous input from higher centers to regulate its activity, but it is also aroused by, and forms a part of, the ARAS. The discussion of sleep emphasized the role of the posterior hypothalamus in mobilizing the brain's activity in states of alertness and attention, states important to drive-aroused and sustained behavior. On the motor side the hypothalamus governs the activity of the sympathetic and parasympathetic nervous systems. Sympathetic activity is increased when the animal mobilizes to meet the threat of deprivation. The parasympathetic is more active in states of quiescence and satiation. Finally, cell groups in the hypothalamus are *directly sensitive* to conditions in the internal environment (extracellular tissue fluid). The internal changes that accompany thirst, hunger, sexual deprivation, and possibly loss of sleep affect different centers in the hypothalamus. As a result, behavior is aroused and sustained. In some cases (for example, thirst) it is known which tissue fluid changes affect what centers in the hypothalamus. In other cases it is only known that the centers exist because removing them abolishes the drive in question and/or stimulating them initiates specific motivated behavior. Therefore, these are termed "excitatory" hunger, thirst, or sexual centers. In some drives (for example, hunger and possibly sleep) *inhibitory* centers have been found. Stimulating these centers *abolishes* the motivated behavior. Ablating the inhibitory area, for hunger as an example, causes overeating in rats. The inhibitory area may respond to sensory input from the nervous system or to changes in the internal environment to

tell the animal when it has "had enough." Therefore, the inhibitory area for a given drive may act as a satiation or stop center. The excitatory area would respond to sensitizing stimuli as the "start" center for motivated behavior.

One author (Stellar) has proposed that there is an inhibitory and an excitatory center for each drive in the hypothalamus. He further suggested that the inhibitory center acts only in regulating the excitatory center. It is doubtful that all drives act in this way. However, the notion illustrates the variety of influences affecting the hypothalamus in its pivotal role in regulating some kinds of behavior (Fig. 15-2).

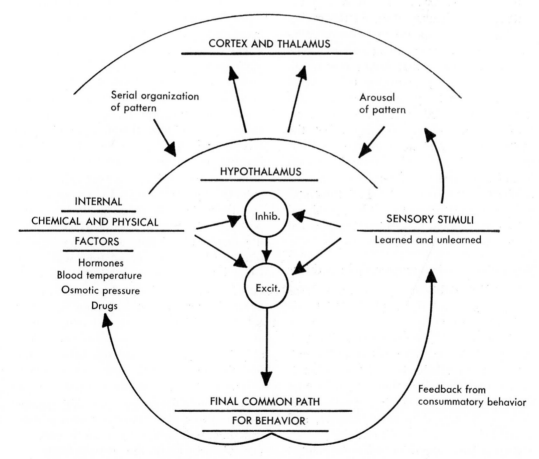

Fig. 15-2. Schematic diagram of physiological factors controlling motivated behavior. For details, see text. (Redrawn from Stellar, E.: Psychol. Rev. **45**:96, 1952.)

Either the excitatory or the inhibitory center can be stimulated by the animal's internal state, providing for both sensitizing and satiation effects. Releasing stimuli, both learned and unlearned, can affect the excitatory center to trigger motivated behavior, either by themselves, or when sensitizing stimuli add their effect on the excitatory center. Other sensory stimuli can act on the inhibitory center to terminate motivated behavior when the animal has had enough or when the food, water, or sex incentive is aversive. The behavior that results is patterned by the cortex and thalamus. If the pattern is inherited, one speaks of an instinct; if learned, a motive is involved. After learning has occurred, the pattern of behavior may be aroused by the cortex and thalamus acting on the excitatory centers in response to releasing stimuli, or even in their absence (memory). The motivated behavior that results may terminate the drive by changing the internal balance of the body (removing the need state). Consummatory behavior (for example, eating, drinking) may effect the excitatory and inhibitory centers to "tell" the animal when it has had enough—enough laps of water or swallows of food. Satiation results in either case. Fig. 15-2 illustrates many of the factors that must be considered before it is known how thirst, hunger, and sexual drives are regulated.

Regulation of thirst, hunger, and sex drives

In studying the thirst, hunger, and sex drives, one needs to know (1) what internal sensitizing stimuli are necessary to arouse the behavior, (2) how these stimuli act on the hypothalamus, (3) what stimuli terminate motivated behavior, that is, what is satiation, and (4) how these stimuli act on the brain. Evidence concerning these questions in the regard to thirst, hunger, and sexual behavior will be discussed.

Regulation of the thirst drive. As pointed out before, the body is continually losing water through (1) respiration, (2) perspiration, and (3) formation of urine. The body has little control over water loss from breathing or sweating, both processes that cannot be interrupted long enough to prevent significant water loss. However, the kidney can reabsorb about one third of the water it uses to flush wastes from the blood. The kidney acts to reabsorb water when it is stimulated to do so by the antidiuretic hormone (ADH) of the posterior pituitary gland (Chapter 3). The posterior pituitary releases ADH in response to excitation from nerve fibers that originate in the anterior hypothalamus (supraoptic nucleus). The fibers release **neurosecretions** in the posterior pituitary. Perhaps these are transmitter substances that stimulate gland cells to release ADH. What stimulates the anterior hypothalamus to begin this chain of events when the water supply of the body is low? Apparently it is the change in osmotic pressure of the blood that normally occurs when the fluid level of the body falls. Most of the solid particles in the blood and tissue fluids (except for wastes) are retained by the kidney; therefore, as the water level is reduced, the blood and tissue fluids become more concentrated. This draws fluid from the cells, including cells in the anterior hypothalamus. In response the hypothalamic cells seem to stimulate the posterior pituitary to release ADH. A minute amount of salt deposited in the anterior pituitary by an implanted tube will cause water-satiated goats to drink. (Not enough salt is used to affect other areas of the brain.) Therefore, dehydration of these cells can initiate drinking behavior as well as kidney regulation; the behavior is probably initiated by connections between the hypothalamus and other parts of the brain.

It seems to be the amount of water inside rather than outside the cells that counts. Evidence for this statement comes from experiments in which the osmotic pressure (or viscosity) of the tissue fluid was changed in different ways. Injection, or drinking of salt water (or sorbital), draws water from the cells to dilute the body fluids. The sodium ion (or sorbital molecules) cannot pass the cell membrane to make the fluid inside the cell more concentrated, and therefore water is drawn from the cells. Drinking behavior results from saltwater injections in water-satiated animals. The body fluids may also be "thickened" (made osmotically hypertonic) with urea. But urea molecules pass the cell membrane, both the fluid inside and outside the cell membrane become more viscous, and no drinking results in the same animals.

Cellular dehydration is the sensitizing stimulus for the thirst drive, and the cells involved appear to be located in the anterior hypothalamus. The same area contains cells that seem to regulate the hunger drive. Although these cells cannot be "labelled" anatomically, they can be distinguished chemically. The injection of minute amounts of norepinephrine (noradrenaline) in the anterior hypothalamus stimulates drinking behavior, whereas injection of equally small amounts of acetylcholine in the same area initiates eating behavior. It seems that the cells involved in the thirst and hunger drives differ in the transmitter substance that other nerve cells release to excite them. The thirst cells receive adrenergic and the hunger cells cholinergic stimuli.

Satiation stimuli. All this says something about the sensitizing stimuli for thirst, but nothing about satiation stimuli. How does the CNS know when the animal has "had enough" water? In the first place, water intake is dependent on food intake, as water is required to digest food. A second factor appears to be the act of drinking itself—consummatory behavior. In dogs the esophagus can be cut and the upper and lower ends brought to the surface. When the animal drinks, the water passes through the throat and out the upper end of the esophagus, never reaching the stomach—"sham drinking." A thirsty dog, prepared in this way, will drink enough water to replace the deficit in about 5 minutes and stop,

almost as if it had a water meter in its throat or was counting the swallows. If the water balance is not restored, however, the dog will go back and drink again in a few minutes, so that consummatory behavior is not the only factor regulating the thirst drive. If water is placed in the lower end of the esophagus, the thirsty dog can be "preloaded" with water and released to see if it will drink. If released immediately it will "sham drink" as before. If 15 minutes elapse after "preloading," it will not drink at all. This is probably enough time for water to reach the tissues via the intestinal walls and reduce the osmotic pressure stimulation to cells, presumably in the hypothalamus. Regulation of intake by water reaching the stomach may be more precise than this, however. Rats can be prepared with tubes inserted into the stomach so that all water intake bypasses the mouth and throat and enters the stomach directly. Rats prepared in this fashion can be trained to press a level to receive a squirt of water directly into the stomach. After initial training they can regulate their water intake solely by this means over a long period of time—and they do it about as well as normal animals do.

Finally, the osmotic pressure of the fluid consumed may be a factor in regulating the amount that a thirsty animal will drink. It takes more slightly salty water than pure water to reduce the osmotic pressure of the cells because the sodium ion remains outside the cells. A thirsty animal will drink more slightly salty water than "pure" water (up to salt water of the same concentration as the body fluid). In Chapter 10 on taste, fibers in the nerves originating in the tongue that fire in response to salt solutions were described. They have a resting rate of firing, probably in response to the salt content of the saliva (about the same as other body fluids). Pure water reduces this rate of firing. Therefore, the rate of firing in some taste nerves depends on the salt content of the water that is ingested. The "salt fibers" may excite more drinking via impulses reaching the hypothalamus so that enough salt water is ingested to balance the body fluids. Even when sham drinking is used in rats, and the fluid never reaches the stomach, animals will drink more salt water than pure water (up to the point at which the water has the same salt content as the body fluids). A reduced rate of firing from salt fibers in drinking pure water may reduce the excitation of the hypothalamic drinking centers.

Regulation of the hunger drive. As in the case of the thirst drive, food intake depends on water intake. It will be seen that regulation of hunger as well as thirst is determined by osmotic pressure in some ways and that the hypothalamic centers controlling both drives overlap. However, regulation of the hunger drive is more complex, and more factors are involved. In thirst, arousal of the drive had little to do with oral factors such as dryness of the mouth and throat—dehydration of hypothalamic cells governed arousal. In hunger, sensitizing stimuli probably act on the hypothalamus to arouse activity, but the oral releasing stimuli of taste (and smell) are more important to whether the animal will eat or not—water is water, but there are many tastes to food. Oral factors also determine *what* foods are eaten according to the animal's dietary needs, but that is a subject for a later section. Here the interest is in whether the animal eats or not and how much. Thirst satiation can be regulated by oral factors in sham drinking, but an animal can also learn to control the amount of water directly delivered to his stomach, so that both oral and gastric cues *can* be used. (Of course, animals without stomachs can control both food and water intake.) In hunger, many factors can influence satiation, although they seem to act through an osmotic mechanism that "counts calories" and affects the hypothalamus. Earlier it was seen that animals could regulate their intake according to the caloric value of the diet available and their caloric needs—forced exercise such as swimming to exhaustion will cause rats to increase their caloric intake to meet the demand.

Sham feeding. One way of determining the importance of oral factors in arousal and satiation is sham feeding. A dog with the esophagus severed and stitched to the surface will eat, but the food never reaches the stomach. Experimenters agree that a hungry animal prepared in this way will work to obtain food that only passes through the mouth so that oral taste (and smell) stimuli serve as effective releasing stimuli. There is disagreement about whether oral factors—taste and the act of eating and swallowing—have anything to do with satiation. It has been reported that a hungry animal will sham feed to exhaustion so that oral stimuli are not a major factor in satiation. However, milk taken by mouth (that reaches the stomach) reduces intake more than direct gastric (stomach) injection does, indicating that oral factors may have an influence in satiation. Gastric factors seem more important, however. Just as in thirst, rats can be prepared with tubes leading directly to the stomach and can learn to feed themselves through these tubes by pressing a lever that controls injections of liquid food directly to the stomach. The animals can maintain their normal weight for a long time in this apparatus. Furthermore, they will regulate the amount they feed themselves according to how much the diet is diluted with tap water. Quinine added to the diet in concentrations that cause normal animals to reduce their intake had no effect on intragastric feeding because oral factors of taste are not involved. All this control of the diet by intragastric factors is puzzling in view of the fact that animals (and humans) *without* stomachs can regulate their food intake. However, since food absorption takes place in the intestine, perhaps the control site lies there; liquid food reaches the intestine quite rapidly.

Osmotic pressure. Whether gastric or intestinal, the *osmotic pressure* of ingested food seems important to satiation. In one experiment two kinds of sugar solutions (glucose and sucrose) were presented to rats in pairs to determine their preference. (Presumably, the animals would select the sugar that tasted sweeter.) At concentrations in which glucose and sucrose were matched in preference (drunk in equal amounts), the glucose was more concentrated than the sucrose. This meant that the glucose had a higher osmotic pressure. The rate of drinking was tested for the two sugar solutions. The rate was equal at first, but the animals slowed down their rate of glucose intake before they slowed down on sucrose intake. The animals showed satiation effects sooner on the sugar with the higher osmotic pressure. Therefore, osmotic pressure of the contents of the stomach (or intestine?) is a factor in satiation. This could be because the fluid drawn into the stomach distends it and "fills it up." On the other hand, osmotic changes could directly signal the hypothalamus by hormones or other means.

Satiation factors. Many factors are involved in satiation; however, it is not known what they have in common or how they signal the hypothalamus. The intake of food causes a variety of changes in the internal environment (Fig. 15-3). Gastric distention occurs. Water is lost to the gas-

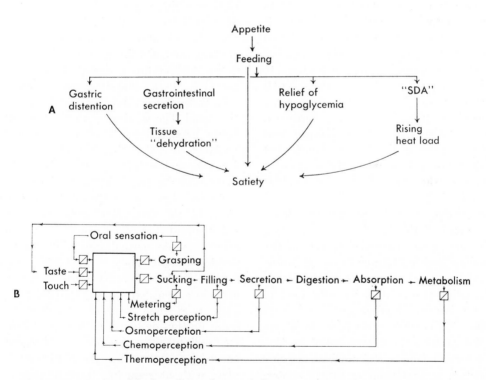

Fig. 15-3. A, Simplified outline of a multifactor concept of satiation (see text). **B,** Schema of sensory feedback relationships involved in regulation of feeding. (**A** from Brobeck, J. R.: Regulation of feeding and drinking. In Field, John, editor: Handbook of physiology, vol. 2, Baltimore, 1960, The Williams & Wilkins Co.; **B** from Brobeck, J. R.: Review and synthesis. In Brazier, M. A. B., editor: Brain and behavior, vol. 2, Washington, D. C., 1962, American Institute of Biological Sciences.)

trointestinal (GI) tract, where it is attracted by the high osmotic pressure of the food, causing dehydration of other tissues. Any existing hypoglycemia (low blood sugar) is relieved. The metabolic activity involved in digestion increases the "heat load" on the body. Other changes could be cited, but these serve to show how many factors *could* affect satiation. It is not known which are the most important normally, much less which ones are *necessary* to signal the hypothalamus that enough has been eaten. Finally, it is not known what tissue changes affect hypothalamic hunger and satiation centers, although there is knowledge of their location.

Glucostatic theory. One theory, the **glucostatic theory,** proposed that the level of blood sugar affects hypothalmic cells to arouse eating when the blood sugar level is low. This view has been largely abandoned for a number of reasons, chiefly a lack of relationship between normal fluctuations in blood sugar and the hunger drive. This leaves us with the suspicion that some change or changes in the tissue fluids, osmotic or otherwise, affects hunger and satiation centers in the hypothalamus, but this does not tell us what these changes are or how they are affected by food or lack of food.

Hypothalamus and the hunger drive. Many parts of the brain are involved in the hunger drive, particularly parts of the brain described in Chapter 14 as the limbic system. However, certain focal centers in the hypothalamus seem to have the most to do with hunger drive arousal and with satiation. Two centers seem to be involved. The first center is the **ventromedial nucleus** of the hypothalamus. This nucleus appears to function as a **satiation,** or **satiety center;** it probably reacts to changes in the tissue fluid that signal when the body has had enough food. Activity in this center may initiate the widespread CNS changes that accompany satiation. The second center is made of a pair of nuclei, located in the lateral hypothalamus on either side and overlapping with centers controlling thirst behavior. These nuclei are more scattered than the ventromedial nucleus, but their location is well known. The **lateral hypothalamic nuclei** appear to react to sensitizing stimuli—changes in the tissue fluid that occur when the animal's food reserves are low. For this reason they have often been called the **feeding center.** Their activity seems to set off the widespread CNS and behavior changes of the aroused hunger drive.

Hypothalamic hyperphagia. Lesions in various parts of the limbic system will cause rats to overeat and become quite obese (fat). Lesions of the ventromedial hypothalamus (satiety center) seem most effective in this regard. After the nucleus is destroyed, the animals double or triple their normal food intake within a few days and continue eating at this rate until their weight is two or three times normal. Then their intake drops to the amount necessary to maintain their obese condition and remains at that level. The syndrome is called **hypothalamic hyperphagia.** The most reasonable explanation is that the shut-off mechanism for hunger has been partly destroyed by destroying the ventromedial nucleus.

Several lines of evidence support this view. In the first place, hyperphagic rats fed a liquid diet of low bulk eat no more often than do normal rats while they are gaining weight. They just eat for a longer period of time. Second, hyperphagic rats are more sensitive to the palatability of their food than normal rats—they seem more finicky about what they eat. Normal rats will tolerate considerable "bitterness" caused by adulterating the food with quinine, without reducing their food intake; small amounts of quinine will reduce the hyperphagic rats' intake drastically. Third, normal rats will eat more when the caloric value of their food is reduced by mixing it with nonnutritive kaolin (clay) or cellulose; hyperphagic rats will not. Since hyperphagic rats are more finicky about their food than are normal rats, their overeating cannot be caused by increased avidity. They just stop eating less readily. If required to press a bar to obtain food, they will not work as hard or as long as normal rats; if required to cross a shocking grid to obtain food, they will not tolerate as much shock as a normal animal. Because their metabolism is otherwise normal, it is reasoned that they are less sensitive to tissue fluid changes that result from overeating; an essential part of the stop mechanism has been removed with the ventromedial nucleus so that they have a *higher threshold* of satiation.

Hyperphagics regulate their weight just as normal animals by reducing their food intake *after* they have become obese; they just maintain that weight at a higher level, being less sensitive to the internal changes that accompany obesity and excess fat storage. It seems to make no difference whether the animal is made obese before or after the operation—he will still level off at the same weight. As previously noted, normal rats can be made obese by injecting them with insulin since they must eat more to keep the brain supplied with blood sugar. Normal rats fattened in this manner become almost as obese as hyperphagic rats. If they are operated upon *after* being fattened in this way, they will increase their food intake only enough to reach the same weight as that of the control animals that are already hyperphagic. The hyperphagic rat, then, just has a higher threshold to the tissue fluid changes that accompany overeating or obesity. Whatever these changes in the tissue fluid, they seem to be present in the hyperphagic as much as in the normal rat, and they are carried in the bloodstream like a hormone.

Experiments on **parabiotic** rats provide the evidence for this statement. Parabiotic rats are pairs of rats that are operated upon to connect their circulatory systems so that they have a common blood supply. Whatever is in the bloodstream of one animal is therefore found in the other. If the ventromedial nucleus of one of two animals is removed, it becomes hyperphagic, but its "Siamese twin" does not. As a matter of fact, the control rat becomes quite thin. This suggests that fat deposits cause a biochemical change in the blood that stimulates the ventromedial nucleus to make an animal stop eating or stop eating sooner. The operated rat was less sensitive to this change than normal and became hyperphagic; its parabiotic twin was *normally* sensitive and stimulated by blood from *excess* fat deposits in his twin and therefore ate *less* than normal. At least this is the best explanation of the results so far.

Stimulation. If the ventromedial nucleus is a satiation center, one would expect a feeding animal to stop eating when it is stimulated, and this is just what happens. Furthermore, there is a rebound effect, and the animal resumes eating more rapidly after the stimulus ceases, or if the animal was not eating before the stimulus, it often begins to eat. Animals that have learned a response to obtain food will not perform the response during stimulation; they will not cross a shocking grid to obtain food during stimulation, but will do so either before or afterward. Of course, electrical stimulation of the hypothalamus may be aversive or may inhibit all behavior. But if cannulas (tubes) are implanted in the ventromedial nucleus, the same results can be obtained with chemical stimuli, which are less likely to be widespread in their effects. Anesthetics injected in the same area act like ventromedial lesions by causing overeating until the anesthetic wears off.

Lateral hypothalamic syndrome. If the ventromedial nucleus acts as a satiety center, any hunger arousal center should be found at a different location in the hypothalamus. A hunger arousal center should respond to changes in the internal environment (sensitizing stimuli) caused by lack of food intake by arousing hunger drive behavior. If the hunger arousal center(s) are destroyed, the animal should be insensitive to body changes in hunger, and **aphagia** (lack of appetite) should result. These centers have been found in the *lateral hypothalamus* in the rat on either side; their destruction results in sudden and continued refusal to eat, and the animal starves to death. As previously described, certain centers in the anterior hypothalamus that stimulate eating and drinking behavior overlap and can only be distinguished by their transmitter substances (acetylcholine and norepinephrine, respectively). The lateral hypothalamic centers that seem to arouse eating behavior also overlap with centers regulating drinking. Ablating these centers therefore results in **adipsia** (refusal to drink) as well as aphagia.

Certain methods of reintroducing food and water can result in recovery from the effects of lateral hypothalamic lesions. There are four definite steps in the recovery process, which are described as the **lateral hypothalamic syndrome.** In the first stage the animals refuse food or water and must be tube-fed; they are aphagic and adipsic. After several days of this the animals will eat moist and palatable food, but will continue to refuse water. In the second stage they still will not eat enough to maintain body weight, and supplemental tube feedings are required. In the third stage the animals regulate their own food intake normally (even on dry foods) if fluid intake is artificially maintained; they will not drink "pure" water, however, and if they become dehydrated, their food intake drops below maintenance level. They will drink water only if it is sweetened by sugar or saccharin. The fourth stage constitutes recovery—the animals maintain themselves on dry food and "pure" water. They are still finicky about their food, however. Like hyperphagic rats, they will not tolerate as much "bitter" quinine in their food as normal rats do.

Recovery by stages suggests relief from the effects of the lesions that is due to recovery of a few undamaged cells. The symptoms also suggest that the hunger and thirst mechanisms overlap anatomically. As expected, satiated animals can be made to eat by stimulating the lateral hypothalamus electrically or with local injections of epinephrine. It is interesting to note that the lateral hypothalamic feeding centers are among the ones whose stimulation is rewarding to the rat—at least the animal will work hard to obtain electrical stimulation in the lateral hypothalamus. (The reward areas will be discussed later.)

Specific hungers

The body requires *qualitative* regulation of food intake as well as adequate calories to meet its energy requirements. Minimum intakes of fats (for fatty acids), proteins (for amino acids), essential fatty and amino acids (that the body does not manufacture), and trace amounts of vitamins and minerals are required (Chapter 2). The neural mechanisms underlying **specific hungers** are not well understood, but naive children and laboratory rats seem to be able to maintain a *balanced* diet that includes all these essentials when offered their choice of a selection of natural foods. With their intake averaged over a period of time, young children maintain themselves on a balanced diet and grow normally when they select from a variety of natural foods, each containing some of the essentials of a balanced diet. As they grow older, dietary habits seem to interfere with this ability, and older children frequently will not eat foods that are "good for them." Different strains of laboratory rats vary in their ability to self-select an adequate diet, and maturational level, as indexed by age, seems important to this ability. As with humans, they can develop maladaptive eating habits under artificial laboratory conditions. Specific changes in food preferences with changes in body needs can be seen in pregnancy and lactation (nursing)—pregnant and nursing rats usually prefer foods rich in sodium, phosphorus, calcium, fats, and proteins. Removal of the parathyroid glands causes rats to increase their calcium intake, removal of the adrenals causes great avidity for salt, and removal of the pancreases reduces the rats' sugar intake. All these reactions are adaptive (Chapter 3).

Regulation of the sex drive

To make a long story short, sexual behavior seems to be under joint hormone and nervous control, and the major site of interaction of these factors is the hypothalamus and its connections with the pituitary gland. Hormonal factors (Chapter 3) will be briefly reviewed first. Then neural factors will be considered. A review of the effect of sensory input on the system will conclude this section.

Hormonal factors. In adolescence the increased output of gonadal hormones causes the appearance of secondary sexual characteristics (Chapter 3). The sex hormone level also governs the sex drive in lower animals. The constant level of androgen output by the testes in most adult male species (except seasonal mating species) maintains the sex drive in males. The fluctuating estrogen level of the monthly cycle in females causes them to come into heat during ovulation, when the female egg or ovum is produced to be fertilized by copulation with the male. In lower species removal of the gonads, either before or after puberty, often abolishes sexual behavior as soon as the hormone level drops enough. Normal sexual behavior in adult castrates of either sex can be restored by injections of sex hormones. Early puberty can be induced in man or lower animals of either sex by injection of sex hormones before the gonads have begun to produce them. In lower animals the effects of senility on the sex drive (when the gonads cease producing hormones) can be overcome by injections of sex hormones. As the nervous system develops in higher species, it be-

comes as important as the hormones to the sex drive in primates and more important than the hormones in man. The increased influence of the CNS on the sex drive is caused by the enormous effect of learning on sexual behavior. In subhuman primates castration before puberty prevents the appearance of most normal sexual behavior in either male or female (though fragments of sexual responses may survive). Castration before puberty may prevent adult sexual behavior in man. After puberty and sexual experience, sexual behavior takes some time to disappear in lower species— longer than hormone levels would predict. The effect of castration, however, is more severe in the female than in the male. In higher primates, such as chimpanzees, sexual behavior may survive castration in the adult and may be unaffected in the male. In man, adult castration has little effect on the male and a variable effect on the female. Both sexes seem to show little reduction in sexual behavior after sexual senility has abolished hormone effects. The general picture is one of decreased importance of the hormones and increased importance of learning as the brain develops through evolution.

Important as they are, the gonadal hormones are governed by pituitary hormones controlled, in turn, by the hypothalamus. As explained in Chapter 3, the anterior pituitary controls the output of germ tissue (ova or sperm) by the gonads via its production of FSH; it governs the output of sex hormones (and thus the onset of puberty) by its output of LH. The fluctuating sexual cycle and sex drive of females and the maintained sex drive of males of most species are governed by the output of anterior pituitary LH. LH production, in turn, is under the influence of the hypothalamus. Ablation of the pituitary may abolish sexual behavior just as castration does (the production of sex hormones falls off because of loss of LH), but hormone injections restore the sex drive.

Neural factors. At the lowest levels of nervous organization, erection and ejaculation are spinal reflexes and can be elicited by genital stimulation, even in spinal man. Erection is largely governed by the parasympathetic nervous system and ejaculation by the sympathetic nervous system. As such, these reflexes come under the control of the hypothalamus, which largely controls the autonomic nervous system. It is probable that the hypothalamus also governs the output of LH and FSH. The output of these hormones from the anterior pituitary seems controlled via nerve fibers from the hypothalamus to the posterior pituitary. These fibers release **neurohumors** that are carried by a portal system of blood vessels from the posterior pituitary to the anterior pituitary, to affect hormone output there. At least this is what the neuroendocrinologists are beginning to believe.

The hypothalamus is also sensitive to the level of sex hormones in the internal environment and regulates the sex drive accordingly. Studies show that estrogen crystals implanted in the hypothalamus of female rats do not dissolve for up to 2 months, and during all that time the female remains in heat. The sensitivity of the hypothalamus to hormone level may be destroyed when lesions are made in ventral and anterior areas of the hypothalamus. The gonads do not atrophy, yet sexual behavior is abolished and not restored by hormone injections. The normal condition of the gonads suggests that they still receive normal LH and FSH stimulation by the pituitary and produce a normal supply of gonadal hormones. The damaged hypothalamus is just not sensitive to the hormones. On the other hand, destruction of the mammillary bodies of the hypothalamus probably abolishes its ability to stimulate the output of pituitary FSH and LH. As a result, the gonads atrophy, and sexual behavior is impaired—the gonads are not being stimulated to produce sex hormones. Injection of sex hormones reverses the con-

dition and restores normal sexual behavior. Therefore, a feedback relationship seems to exist between the hypothalamus and gonads. The hypothalamus stimulates sex hormone output by the gonads via pituitary LH, and the sex hormone level arouses the sex drive by stimulating the hypothalamus. More extensive neural structures are involved, of course, but the hypothalamus appears to play a pivotal role.

Other drives

The list of need states of the body that arouse and sustain behavior is a very lengthy one, and the neural mechanisms involved vary from simple reflexes such as breathing to complex behaviors such as nest-building and migration. Hunger, thirst, and the sex drive have been used as examples in this chapter because more research has been done on these than on other drives and because they are more complex than homeostatic reflexes. Other drive-related phenomena such as pain, activity level, "curiosity" behavior, and the homeostatic reflexes and drives deserve mention, however.

Pain stimulation acts like a drive in that it arouses and sustains behavior—the sensations act as releasing stimuli that control the drive mechanism.

Another drive with a more complex basis is the activity drive. Food taken in by the organism is stored as fat and glycogen or released as energy for metabolic activities, including behavior. The activity level of an animal is thus related to its food intake in a complex fashion that aids in energy storage and expenditure. The neural regulation of activity level is quite complex and little is known about how activity is regulated by the metabolic requirements of the body.

Curiosity behavior in monkeys and higher primates is a kind of behavior controlled by the releasing stimulus about which little is known. A monkey in a small featureless room will perform work to open a window, the only reward being the opportunity to see another monkey, a moving toy, or some other complex visual stimulus. It will take apart simple latch puzzles for hours, each time the experimenter puts them back together.

At the other end of the continuum of behavior complexity, there are relatively simple homeostatic drives that arouse and sustain reflexes and behavior to maintain the consistency of the internal environment. The hypothalamus or medulla seems to be sensitive to many changes in the internal environment that act as sensitizing stimuli for these homeostatic drives. Changes in body temperature, acid-base balance, CO_2 content, etc., reflexly cause changes in respiration, heart rate, blood distribution, etc. These changes also arouse behavior from shivering or muscle tension or sweating to complex behaviors from general activity level to specific learned adjustments to bodily discomfort.

NEURAL MECHANISMS OF REWARD OR PUNISHMENT
Reward centers

Sites in the brain of the rat have been discovered where electrical stimulation via implanted electrodes has the effect of reward. A physiological psychologist (Olds) was investigating the effect of stimulating the brainstem reticular arousal system (ARAS) in healthy and active rats with permanently implanted electrodes. One of the electrodes was misplaced, and he made the serendipitous discovery that the rat seemed to "like" being stimulated there—at least the animal would return often to that part of the table where he received the brain stimulation. It was then discovered that the rat would learn a T maze for a reward of brain stimulation or press a lever in a Skinner box when the lever was wired to the stimulator so that the rat could stimulate himself.

Systematic studies were made, and a variety of reward centers were discovered,

some more effective than others. For brain stimulation in the most effective centers, rats would cross a shocking grid at currents they would not endure for food when hungry, water when thirsty, or copulation with another rat when stimulated by sex hormones. Reward areas have been found in the septal areas, cingulate gyrus, dorsal thalamus, tectum, anterior hypothalamus, and medial forebrain bundle (Chapter 14 and Figs. 14-4, 14-5, 14-7, and 14-8). Some of these centers are related to other drives. For example, the lateral hypothalmic "feeding center" (see lateral hypothalamic syndrome, above) presumably arouses the hunger drive. It is an effective reward center, but more effective when the animal is hungry than when he is satiated by food, or by stimulating the ventromedial satiety centers. Psychiatrists have tried implanting electrodes in reward centers in the brains of psychotic patients in an attempt to improve their condition by effectively rewarding more normal behavior. The reports of these patients on their sensations when stimulated are open to some question because of their disorganized condition, but more rational epileptics have been tested in a similar way. Some sites of stimulation resulted in vague sensations of "well-being" or "pleasure." Others gave rise to sexual fantasies. Obviously the reward centers are complex systems that are intimately related to specific drives, but little is known of these complex relationships.

"Punishment" centers

The work of other investigators (Delgado, Miller, and others) has led to locating punishment centers in the brain of the cat. Stimulation of these brain centers will serve as a negative reinforcement, just as painful electric shock does, in the learning of escape or avoidance habits. Cats will learn to turn a wheel to end or avoid stimulation in these areas of the brain, or they will learn to escape a compartment where they had been stimulated previously.

Some of these areas lie in the medial lemniscus and posteroventral nuclei of the thalamus and are part of the pain sensation pathways from pain receptors to the brain. Stimulation in these areas should affect the cat in the same way as stimulating pain receptors. However, other areas of the posterior parts of the brain have elicited reactions in animals that look more like "fear" responses, and these negative reinforcement centers are also effective in teaching cats avoidance or escape habits. Implanted electrodes in human psychotics and epileptics have produced aversive sensations as well as pleasurable ones. Reports indicate fright, feeling sick, or apprehension. A more extensive and intricate system than mere pain stimulation seems indicated.

SUMMARY

Motivation has been treated as general arousal, from a state of sleep to a state of aroused vigilance, and as specific bodily needs in terms of water, food, and sex as well as the need for sleep. Although sleep-deprived subjects can perform mental tasks normally if motivated enough, insufficient sleep causes death. To Kleitman, sleep seemed a more homeostatically normal state than wakefulness, and therefore his theory attempted to explain wakefulness. In Kleitman's theory wakefulness of necessity in lower animals and children results from bodily needs or other discomforts and causes a polyphasic sleep cycle. As need satisfaction becomes conditioned to daylight, wakefulness of choice and a monophasic sleep cycle ensues. He postulated that a sleep center (really a waking center) in the diencephalon aroused the whole brain to wakefulness on stimulation because of the somnambulance and wakefulness of necessity shown by some encephalitis victims with brain damage in that area. The sleep center in normal adults could be stimulated by the cortex during daylight hours to cause wakefulness of choice.

Both sleep and waking centers have been found in ablation studies of the rat hypothalamus, but only the posterior waking center was found in studies on the monkey. The waking center is probably only a focal part of the ARAS of the brainstem. The ARAS is aroused by collaterals from the classic sensory pathways (STPS) to the primary sensory projection areas. A DTPS supplies secondary cortical projection areas, which also receive input from the primary areas. Stimulation of the ARAS by implanted electrodes in the cat arouses the sleeping animal to alert attention and changes the EEG from a sleeping to a waking pattern. Transecting the STPS pathways in the brainstem has no gross effect on the animal, but cutting the ARAS pathways makes it somnambulant. The inherent 3 to 5 per second EEG of the BSRF is intensified during arousal and suppressed during sleep. Many influences, sensory and metabolic, act to excite or suppress this wakefulness rhythm, and higher brain centers can excite it during "voluntary" wakefulness.

The role of the hypothalamic part of the ARAS is emphasized by some writers as an ergotropic center that arouses the sympathetic nervous system as well as higher centers, whereas anterior trophotropic centers stimulate parasympathetic activity during quiescence and sleep. Changes in the EEG parallel states of arousal from deep sleep to vigilance. EEG waves are believed to be synchronous changes in the partial depolarization of cortical cell bodies that reflect the rate of firing in their fibers. During arousal they are largely depolarized and firing rapidly, producing a desynchronized EEG. With increasing quiescence and sleep, brain waves become generally synchronized and of lower frequency.

Using waking time to a standard stimulus as a measure, four stages of sleep can be distinguished, each with its characteristic EEG pattern, while the alpha rhythm is often characteristic of the relaxed waking state. Sleeping subjects show phasic shifts between the sleep stages every 30 to 90 minutes during the night, but generally spend more time in deeper stages 3 and/or 4 during the second through the third or fourth hours. If deprived of deeper stages by being awakened from them during one night, the subject will compensate with longer deep sleep periods the next night. Dreaming can be detected by emergence of the EEG to stage 1 (E-1) and rapid eye movements (REM). When deprived of E-1 and REM by being awakened, subjects become irritable and anxious and spend more time showing these patterns on the subsequent night. Infants and other polyphasic animals spend more time in REM sleep than do adults. It is harder to wake animal (but not human) subjects from REM than from deeper sleep stages. REM sleep seems to be controlled by a center in the pons; its destruction abolishes REM and causes insomnia and death. When the EEG is used as a measure of "true" sleep (absence of alpha rhythms), no evidence is found that learning during sleep is possible in man.

During the waking state "attention" cells have been found in the visual and auditory projection areas of the cat cortex, which fire only when the animal is "paying attention" to those modalities. Vigilance, as indicated by a desynchronized EEG from ARAS stimulation, "separates" the cortical evoked potentials produced by two light flashes 50 msec. apart. The same stimulation in a monkey reduces the time it must see two objects to discriminate between them as well as reducing its reaction time. Efferent inhibitory output to nuclei of the STPS from higher centers reduces or blocks sensory input in habituation. Efferent excitatory output sensitizes these channels; both are known as sensory gating and provide efferent control of afferent input in states of attention. The ARAS and DTPS are under similar control.

Precisely defined terminology is needed to distinguish between events in the environment and events in the organism before specific motives can be discussed. A need condition in the environment sets up a need state in the organism, some aspect of which may serve as a sensitizing stimulus to arouse a drive in the CNS. The drives discussed are inherent, but there are acquired need conditions, states, and drives. If the behavior that results from an inherent drive is caused by "built-in" nervous patterns, the whole is an instinct; a drive and learned behavior that lead to the incentive is a motive.

The incentive or cues to its presence are releasing stimuli for motivated (goal-directed) behavior. Addiction results when drugs alter the CNS so that their absence causes a need state. Thirst, hunger, and sex deprivation cause local states such as mouth dryness, stomach contractions, and full seminal vesicles (in the male). These states are neither necessary nor sufficient to arouse drives. In the case of hunger and thirst, local states are abolished immediately by eating and drinking and cannot tell the animal when it has "had enough." In adult man the sex drive is more a function of learning than either local states or hormone levels. Furthermore, need states affect one another, one need state being increased to satisfy another. In general, a hierarchy is established, and the need state or internal imbalance that can be tolerated for the shortest time is given priority. Mechanisms for signalling satiation to the CNS must also be sought for each drive—an animal stops eating or drinking before the need state of its tissues has time to change, and an animal regulates its food and water intake accurately.

Some drives, however, are controlled by their releasing stimuli; these are called appetites, or aversions. There are need states, such as those for certain vitamins, that do not arouse drives (have no sensitizing stimuli). Most motivated behavior is controlled by many factors that serve as releasing stimuli once the drive is aroused, and their effectiveness depends on the degree of drive arousal by sensitizing stimuli. Sensitizing stimuli to drives usually act on the hypothalamus, which is sensitive to internal need states, is a part of the ARAS, and controls the autonomic nervous system. Stimulation and ablation studies have shown excitatory and inhibitory centers for several drives in the hypothalamus, responsive to sensitizing and satiation stimuli, respectively.

In thirst, the body conserves water by release of ADH from the posterior pituitary gland that is excited by the neurosecretions from the hypothalamus. Intercellular dehydration appears to stimulate this process as well as arouse the thirst drive. The thirst and hunger drive cells in the anterior hypothalamus differ chemically, the former being adrenergic and the latter cholinergic. Experiments in sham drinking show that consummatory behavior alone serves as a temporary satiation stimulus—the animal stops drinking for a few minutes after it has "replaced" the lost water, even though none of it reaches the stomach. "Salt fibers" in taste may act to control drinking because rats drink more salt water than pure water, as required for cellular hydration. A rat can, however, learn to control its water balance by lever-pressing for intragastric injections of water.

Food intake depends on water intake since water is required for digestion. Animals accurately regulate their caloric intake, but this depends more on gastrointestinal factors than on oral factors since a hungry sham-fed animal eats to exhaustion. Animals that press a lever for intragastric squirts of food can regulate their intake according to their needs and the caloric value of the food. Foods of higher osmotic pressure cause quicker satiation. Water loss, relief of hypoglycemia, increased metabolic heat load, and other factors can affect satiation. The glucostatic theory proposes that blood sugar level controls the hypothalamically regulated hunger drive, but re-

liable relationships have not been found. The ventromedial nucleus seems to be the hypothalmic satiation center since its ablation causes hypothalamic hyperphagia, and chemical or electrical stimulation of this center stops eating behavior. Several lines of evidence show that hyperphagic rats are more finicky about their food than are normal rats, and therefore the hunger arousal centers are not involved; the satiation threshold is just higher. Whatever stimulates the satiation center is carried in the bloodstream since the normal parabiotic partner of a hyperphagic rat becomes thin, perhaps because of some factor carried in the blood from excess fat deposits in the hyperphagic. The lateral hypothalamus seems to contain the hunger centers since ablating these centers makes a rat aphagic. The animal shows adipsia as well, and four separate stages are found in recovery, called the lateral hypothalmic syndrome. Recovery is probably caused by the restored function of injured cells in the lesion area. Electrical or epinephrine stimuli to the lateral hypothalamus cause eating behavior. However, hunger is specific as well as general, and animals and small children can maintain a balanced diet when allowed free access to an array of *natural* foods. Maladaptive feeding habits or "tastes" can develop with later learning. Dietary changes in pregnancy and lactation or after adrenalectomy reflect changed bodily needs.

The sex drive, on the other hand, seems to be under both nervous and hormonal control. Male androgen and female estrogen output by the gonads is stimulated by anterior pituitary LH and FSH at puberty, and the anterior pituitary is stimulated by neurosecretions from hypothalamic fibers reaching the posterior pituitary. The maintained hormone level and sex drive of the male as well as the estral flunctuations of both in the female are under anterior pituitary control via FSH and LH. In higher animals the sex drive is controlled by learning, and the drive survives castration or senility in adults (more effectively in the male than in the female). In lower animals, ablation of the pituitary, like castration, abolishes most sexual behavior, but hormone injections restore it. Estrogen crystals in the hypothalamus of females maintain estrus and heat. Ventral and anterior hypothalamic lesions can abolish sex behavior without change in hormone levels so that these may be drive arousal areas. Mammillary body destruction probably destroys anterior pituitary output since the gonads atrophy.

Other drives vary from homeostatic reflexes to those that arouse very complex behavior patterns. Pain acts like a drive in arousing and sustaining behavior, a drive controlled by the releasing stimulus. The activity level of animals is regulated to meet their metabolic conditions. Primates show curiosity behavior controlled by novel stimuli, the basis of which is unknown.

Reward centers have been found in the rat brain—stimulation of these centers serves as reinforcement for maze learning and a rat will rapidly learn to stimulate itself with a Skinner box lever. Some of these centers seem related to those for hunger and sex. Punishment centers have been found in more posterior brain areas, some in the pain pathways, but some in areas that appear unrelated to pain. In both instances a complex and interrelated neural system is probably involved.

READINGS

Anderson, B.: The effect of hypertonic NaCl solutions into different parts of the hypothalamus of goats, Acta. Physiol. Scand. **28**:188-201, 1953. (Bobbs-Merrill Reprint No. P-9.)

Beach, F. A.: Evolutionary changes in the physiological control of mating behavior in mammals, Psychol. Rev. **54**:297-315, 1947. (Bobbs-Merrill Reprint No. P-27.)

Butler, R. A.: Curiosity in monkeys, Sci. Amer. **190**:70-75, Feb., 1954. (W. H. Freeman Co. Reprint No. 426.)

Cannon, W. B.: The wisdom of the body, New York, 1963, W. W. Norton & Co.

Carlton, P. L.: Cholinergic mechanisms in the control of behavior by the brain, Psychol. Rev. **70**:19-39, 1963. (Bobbs-Merrill Reprint No. P-416.)

Cicala, G. A.: Animal drives, Princeton, N. J., 1965, D. Van Nostrand Co., Inc.

Dement, W., and Kleitman, N.: The relation of eye movements during sleep to dream activity: an objective method for the study of dreaming, J. Exp. Psychol. **53**:339-346, 1957. (Bobbs-Merrill Reprint No. P-87.)

Deutsch, J. A., and Howarth, C. I.: Some tests of a theory of intracranial self-stimulation, Psychol. Rev. **70**:444-460, 1963. (Bobbs-Merrill Reprint No. P-427.)

Fischer, A. E.: Maternal and sexual behavior induced by intracranial self-stimulation, Science **124**:228-229, 1956. (Bobbs-Merrill Reprint No. P-113.)

Fischer, A. E.: Chemical stimulation of the brain. Sci. Amer. **210**:60-68, June, 1964. (W. H. Freeman Co. Reprint No. 485.)

Fuller, J. L.: Motivation: a biological prespective, New York, 1964, Random House, Inc.

Hebb, D. O.: Drives and the CNS (conceptual nervous system), Psychol. Rev. **62**:243-254, 1955. (Bobbs-Merrill Reprint No. P-151.)

Kleitman, N.: Patterns of dreaming, Sci. Amer. **203**:82-88, Nov., 1960. (W. H. Freeman Co. Reprint No. 460.)

Kleitman, N.: Sleep, Sci. Amer. **187**:34-38, Nov., 1952. (W. H. Freeman Co. Reprint No. 431.)

Levine, S.: Sex differences in the brain, Sci. Amer. **214**:84-90, April, 1966. (W. H. Freeman Co. Reprint No. 498.)

Malmo, R. S.: Activation: a neuropsychological dimension, Psychol. Rev. **66**:367-386, 1959. (Bobbs-Merrill Reprint No. P-507.)

Margules, D. L., and Olds, J.: Identical feeding and rewarding systems in the hypothalamus of rats, Science **135**:374-377, 1962. (Bobbs-Merrill Reprint No. P-508.)

Olds, J.: Pleasure centers in the brain, Sci. Amer. **195**:105-116, Oct., 1956. (W. H. Freeman Co. Reprint No. 30.)

Olds, J.: Self-stimulation of the brain, Science **127**:315-324, 1958. (Bobbs-Merrill Reprint No. P-264.)

Sharpless, S., and Jasper, H.: Habituation of the arousal reaction, Brain **79**:655-680, 1956. (Bobbs-Merrill Reprint No. P-558.)

Stellar, E.: The physiology of motivation, Psychol. Rev. **61**:5-22, 1954. (Bobbs-Merrill Reprint No. P-334.)

Teevan, R. C., and Smith, B. D.: Motivation, New York, 1967, McGraw-Hill Book Co.

Chapter 16

Emotion

OVERVIEW

At first glance this chapter may seem to be written in reverse. Although it begins with definitional problems, it continues with theories of emotion, examining the evidence only after the theories have been discussed. There is a reason for this approach. In the first place, definitions of emotion vary so widely that one must understand an investigator's theoretical approach before one can understand why he designed his experiment and what his results contribute to the understanding of emotion. In the second place, studies on the role of parts of the nervous system in emotion produce such variable and conflicting results that they can be understood only in terms of a widespread nervous circuit that governs emotional behavior—proposing such a circuit involves theory. Thus the chapter begins with definitional problems in distinguishing emotion from other kinds of motivated behavior and experience. Then the criteria for useful theory in emotion are established. The phenomena to be explained are set forth—conscious states, behavior, and physiological events. The phenomena explained determine the position the theorist adopts and whether he thinks that emotion organizes or disorganizes behavior. Theories of emotion, each contributing to the understanding of emotional phenomena, are taken up in historical

order so that they increase gradually in complexity and generality. When the known factors contributing to emotion are understood, the evidence can be studied in a meaningful context. Neural mechanisms in emotion constitute therefore the last major topic in the chapter. The topic begins with the effect of somatic and visceral feedback on emotion, proceeds to the role of the autonomic nervous system, then to the hypothalamus, and, finally, the limbic system. The chapter concludes with some remarks on the expression of emotion.

APPROACHES TO EMOTION

The first problem encountered in the study of emotion is definitional—what is being studied? Older writers on the topic were attempting to explain emotion *experience*, the conscious events accompanying the highly motivated states of anger, fear, joy, etc. Others, both long ago and recently, have attempted to explain emotional *behavior*—why one snarls, runs, or laughs. Still other students of emotion have tried to understand the *physiological events* accompanying emotion from the responses of the autonomic nervous system to activity in various centers of the brain. The nature of any investigation of emotion will depend on which of these phenomena the investigator is trying to "explain," and his theory, or explanation, will concern mostly these limited phenomena. To assert a theory of emotion is to state what emotion *is* or what emotions are—conscious states, behavior, or physiological events. A theory should state the conditions that are both *necessary* and *sufficient* for that emotional state.

Definitions

What is an emotion? Although no two authorities seem to agree completely, an emotion may be characterized as a highly motivated state, usually accompanied by heightened awareness (in man), often recognizable approach or withdrawal behavior, much autonomic activity, and widespread activation in the central nervous system. Consider the classic emotional states of fear, anger, or joy. All involve a high degree of motivation. Changes in conscious content are evident. Fear involves withdrawal behavior, whereas anger or joy implies approach, aggressive or peaceful. In all three states increases in heart rate, rapid breathing, and "butterflies in the stomach" signal heightened autonomic activity. Finally, none of these conditions can be maintained without widespread increases in CNS activity.

Conscious states. Literature, many philosophers, and early psychologists tried to classify emotion as a "conscious state." Different kinds of awareness resulting from the perception of external events "caused" different conscious states. These conscious states *were* emotions, each, in turn, causing a different kind of emotional behavior. This position asserts that conscious events are *necessary* to emotional behavior and *sufficient* to cause emotional behavior. Because so much behavior (emotional or otherwise) is not accompanied by awareness, such assumptions seem unfounded. Much emotional behavior is "unconscious," that is, the "cause" of the behavior cannot be verbalized. It is a common occurrence to encounter hostile behavior from persons who insist they are not angry, timidity and anxiety

from persons with (objectively) nothing to fear and exhilarant behavior for "no good reason," perceived or experienced. A given conscious state seems neither necessary nor sufficient for a given kind of emotional behavior. However, conscious states can serve as *clues* to the presence of emotion *if* one recognizes that these clues are not always reliable.

Behavior. Other writers have asserted that emotion *is* behavior of one kind or another. Anger *is* aggressive behavior, fear *is* flight or withdrawal, joy *is* laughter, and so on. This approach ignores many instances when the defined overt behavior does *not* accompany conscious states and physiological events that strongly indicate the presence of emotion. A well-controlled individual can avoid emotional behavior, from a "poker face" to calm and unhurried normal movements, when he is angry, frightened, or happily excited. The internal physiological responses may be present, the pounding heart etc., but an external observer can sense no change in his demeanor. This may be true only of man, however. Some forms of emotional behavior, such as the rage-attack pattern in animals, seem to be controlled by the same CNS centers that govern autonomic arousal in emotion.

Physiological events. Emotional behavior and emotional awareness are accompanied by physiological events, many of them mediated by the autonomic nervous system. In aroused emotion the heart beats faster, blood pressure may rise, blood may drain from the stomach, causing "butterflies," "goosepimples" form from erecting the body hair, and so on. Both these events and somatic responses, such as striking out or running, are caused by physiological events in the central nervous system. The necessary and sufficient conditions for emotion may therefore be certain kinds of autonomic activity or events in certain brain centers that control *both* autonomic activity and behavior. Those who assert that autonomic arousal is the necessary and sufficient condition for emotion must explain different emotions by different patterns of autonomic arousal. Some differences in autonomic activity have been found between rage and fear and between either of these and "positive" emotions such as joy or sexual arousal. As far as is known, however, there are not enough differences in the patterns of autonomic arousal to account for the variety of emotions experienced and acted out by man. Furthermore, simple exercise causes autonomic arousal. Most theorists would not call the bodily changes in exercise an "emotional state." On the other hand, centers or systems can be sought in the central nervous system that control *both* the patterns of autonomic response *and* the overt behavior in emotion. "Centers" have been found for rage, fear and "pleasure," but they exist in bewildering variety. More subtle emotions, moreover, seem to depend on learning and involve widespread CNS activity. A *system* interrelating emotional "centers" seems necessary if emotion is to be understood in terms of CNS activity. Such a system should include all brain centers whose stimulation or removal directly alters emotional behavior and (in humans) emotional experience. The interrelationships among these centers are far from understood, but some attempts have been made to systematize them as a "limbic system," to be discussed later.

Centralist vs. peripheralist positions

A theorist's position on emotion depends on whether he defines externally measureable events, such as behavior or ANS responses, *as* emotion or whether he defines central events as necessary and sufficient for emotion when these events (conscious states or brain center activity) *result* in emotional behavior or autonomic changes. The former approach can be called a "peripheralist" position and the latter approach a "centralist" position. This chapter is written from a centralist position, which assumes that activity in certain interrelated brain centers is the most necessary and sufficient condition for emotion. Conscious changes, autonomic activity, and behavior are taken as the usual symptoms of activity in such centers, symptoms whose reliability depends on the experimental situation. This approach seems the most effective way to organize and present in a general way what is known about emotion from a physiological point of view. As a theory, the reader may wish to take issue with the point of view after studying the evidence to be presented later.

Behavior organization and disorganization in emotion

Much of the early interest of psychologists in emotion came from the apparent effect of emotion on learning behavior in both humans and laboratory animals. The "goal-seeking" activity of a highly motivated rat in a maze became disorganized when the animal encountered a barrier in its accustomed path. Error behavior increased, and emotion was seen as a "disorganized" state that resulted from interference with highly motivated behavior. The behavior of a highly motivated student often becomes similarly disorganized when he encounters a question he cannot answer on an examination, and he misses subsequent questions that he would otherwise have answered correctly. P. T. Young and others have proposed, therefore, that emotion is the disorganization that results from blocking highly motivated goal-oriented behavior. Later theorists (Duffy, Leeper, and others) have taken issue with this point of view. They point out that autonomic emotional responses and the overt behavior patterns of rage, fear, and so on would not have developed in the course of evolution if such internal and external responses did not have survival value for the organism. It is further evident that autonomic responses in rage and fear are highly organized and support highly organized overt behavior. Cannon's emergency theory (Chapter 6) states that the sympathetic nervous system responses in rage and fear prepare an animal for "fight" or "flight," and in a general way this seems to be the case. Fight or flight are both highly motivated and very organized responses, and sympathetic arousal helps prepare an animal for the exertion required in either case. Neither type of behavior, however, is appropriate for a rat learning a maze or a student taking an examination. But neither maze-runing nor exam-taking was important to survival in the primitive world in which emotional behavior evolved; fighting and fleeing *were* important survival mechanisms. The conclusion follows that emotional responses, autonomic and somatic, are highly organized and serve as a primitive mechanism for *motivation,* arousing and sustaining behavior appropriate to a primitive "emergency." The fact that such behavior is not appropriate to highly artificial situations such as maze-running for the rat or exam-taking for the student seems beside the point.

THEORIES OF EMOTION

As suggested earlier, attempts to explain emotion often differed widely because theorists were trying to explain different phenomena, each considered to *be* emotion. Attempts to explain the conscious events accompanying emotion will be quite different from attempts to explain observed emotional behavior, autonomic responses in emotion, or brain function in emotion. From this point of view, none of the theories to be considered is "right" or "wrong," and each contributes something to the understanding of emotional phenomena. On the other hand, one can better examine which of these phenomena—conscious, behavioral, autonomic, or CNS activity—is a necessary and sufficient condition for emotion after one sees how each could theoretically control emotional "states."

James and Lange theories

For William James emotion was a *conscious state* that caused emotional behavior. He sought the causes of this conscious state in the reactions of the body to stimuli that called forth anger, fear, or joy. His famous dictum that we do not run because we are afraid, we are afraid because we run, summarizes his position. To James, a perceived stimulus became a consciously emotional stimulus *after* reaction to the stimulus began. When a threatening stimulus resulted in flight, it also resulted in sensations of running and sensations from the visceral reactions of the autonomic nervous system. The somatic sensations of running and the sympathetically aroused sensations of rapid heartbeat, panting, "gooseflesh," and so on were added to the "simple" perception of the threatening stimulus. Adding the somatic sensations of running to the visceral sensations from the autonomic reactions resulted in a perception of fear. The stimulus was therefore feared after the reaction to it began. A simple example might be your own reaction to an emergency while driving an automobile at high speed. Another car pulls out in front of you, you react quickly to avoid it, and only after the incident is over do you begin to tremble, sweat, and feel frightened. Anger, as another emotion, would include some of the same sensations of autonomic arousal, but it would also include somatic sensations of overt or suppressed attack behavior. Joy would involve more parasympathetic arousal, perhaps, and sensations of approach reactions; sexual arousal would involve a different autonomic sensation pattern, feedback from copulation responses, and so on. Lange proposed the same kind of theory, except to restrict the sensations to those coming from the blood vessels.

Behavioristic theory of emotion

Several decades ago the famous behaviorist John B. Watson rejected consciousness as a cause of behavior. Stimuli caused behavior as a direct result of their action on the sense organs and nervous system, and consciousness did not belong in this sequence of events.

For Watson rage *was* attack, fear *was* flight, and lust *was* sexual behavior. He sought to determine which of these and other emotional responses were "inherited," in what form they began, and what stimuli controlled them. His experiments with 6-month old children convinced him that there were three inherited patterns of emotional behavior controlled by four stimuli. Pattern X, tentatively identified as "fear," consisted of withdrawal responses and wailing cries in response to either a loud noise or sudden loss of support when being held (falling). Pattern Y, assumed to be "rage," was aroused by restraining an infant's movements, which resulted in strident crying, and a flushed face. Pattern Z, called "lust," was inhibition of more active behavior accompanied by gurgling, smiling, and sometimes erection of the penis. The stimulus was stroking of the skin, especially near the genitals. To Watson, the more complex emotional behavior of adults to more varied stimuli resulted from conditioning. If the child was frightened by a loud noise while he was petting a rabbit, he would "attach" the fear response to the rabbit. Furthermore, he would show the fear response to objects resembling the rabbit in any important way; he would *generalize* his fear, and any furry object would result in the fear response. With learning, the fear response would also become more varied, and the withdrawal response would include running and other means of avoiding the feared stimulus. Although these notions may seem oversimplified today, physiologists have found centers in the brain that seem to control both visceral and somatic reactions of flight and attack. Other centers have been found controlling sexual behavior. Certain responses such as smiling seem to have inherited neural mechanisms. In this sense,

perhaps Watson was correct in his assumptions about the inheritance of mechanisms for emotional behavior.

Autonomic response theories of emotion

Many writers have identified autonomic nervous system responses with emotion. Most of them state that parasympathetic nervous system reactions, or PNS dominance, are necessary (at least at first) to positive or pleasurable emotions. Sympathetic nervous system reactions are necessary to rage or fear, with a different SNS pattern of response for rage as compared to fear. Some assert a different autonomic pattern acquired through learning for each of the more subtle emotions. Others have said that different autonomic patterns are inherited as a few beginning emotional reactions— PNS dominance for elation or joy, and SNS patterns for rage, fear, and perhaps a few others such as "disgust" or "apathy." In some cases it is suggested that the autonomic reaction *is* the emotion and is always necessary to it. Other writers believed it was necessary only at first—after learning has occurred, only activity in the brain centers that normally control the ANS is necessary. Some have suggested inherited autonomic patterns that *are* simple emotional reactions such as lust, rage, and fear; the more subtle and varied emotions are one or more of these patterns plus varied somatic responses. Jealousy, for example, could be a mixture of rage and fear of a given degree along with both approach and avoidance reactions. In any case all assert that the ANS reactions *are* emotion, at least at first.

Cannon-Bard theory of emotion

The Cannon-Bard theory originated as an attempt to explain the behavior of decorticate cats. After removal of the cerebral cortex the animals do not respond except in a reflex fashion to vision, audition, or smell. However, they are capable of reflex standing, and their response to somesthetic input from the skin is attack. Stimuli such as pinching the skin or pulling the tail merely cause moving away in normal cats. In decorticates an immediate and integrated rage-attack behavior pattern results. The response was called **sham rage** because the animal lacked the sensory and nervous equipment to direct and maintain the attack behavior. The animal attacked in whatever direction it happened to be "pointed" at the moment, without attacking the source of the stimulation. Furthermore, the attack behavior stopped as soon as the stimulus was removed—rage behavior did not continue for a time as in the normal animal. However, the rage response was integrated; both organized overt behavior, *and* a generalized autonomic nervous system reaction were present. In further experiments more and more of the higher nervous system centers were removed. As long as the posterior third of the hypothalamus was intact, the sham rage pattern was present. When these centers were removed, the sham rage behavior disintegrated into isolated "part responses" of somatic and visceral reactions. Snarling might occur, or some autonomic change, but the organized rage reaction had disappeared. The experimenters suggested, therefore, that centers in the posterior part of the hypothalamus organized *both* the ANS responses in rage *and* the behavior pattern in rage. Extending this idea, others assumed that the hypothalamus contained centers that are responsible for both behavior and autonomic reactions in each of the major emotional "states." They also proposed that activity in the same centers stimulated the cerebral cortex to give rise to the "conscious state" appropriate to the emotion. Overt behavior, autonomic responses, and conscious states in emotion were assumed to be aroused by stimuli from the sense organs that reached appropriate centers in the hypothalamus. Other emotions could, of course, be added by learning—conditioning the hypothalamic

centers to new stimuli and elaborating the response patterns initiated there.

Subsequent experiments on sham rage have shown that decortication, which spares the cingulate gyrus and ventral paleocortex (Chapter 14), makes cats *placid,* raising their rage threshold rather than lowering it. Yet either cingulate lesions or lesions in the ventral complex (amygdala, pyriform cortex, and hippocampus) make these placid animals ferocious! It is evident that a more widespread neural "circuit" than the hypothalamus is involved in the control of rage and perhaps other emotions as well. There is little doubt that rage-attack behavior and autonomic responses are *organized* at a subcortical level. Posterior thalamic lesions produce somnambulent animals (Chapter 14) that are unemotional, and medial and ventromedial lesions of the hypothalamus make cats ferocious. With the rest of their nervous system intact, however, the ferocity of the lesioned cats is well directed and outlasts the stimulus—they are difficult and dangerous to handle. However well the hypothalamus organizes the rage-attack pattern and perhaps other emotional responses, more widespread areas of the nervous system are involved in its *control.* For example, selective lesions in the pyriform areas, amygdala, or hippocampus make animals ferocious, beginning several weeks *after* the operation. Other investigators report placidity following lesions in some of these same areas. Stimulation of one part of the amygdala causes rage responses, stimulation of another part, fearlike responses; stimulation of the latter site can suppress rage behavior from hypothalamic stimulation. Lesions of the septal area lower the rage threshold, but removal of the amygdala reverses this effect, and so on. Even changing stimulus parameters such as voltage or frequency can elicit fright behavior or rage behavior from the same stimulus site. Obviously, widespread centers *control* the expression of emotional responses, even if they are organized in the hypothalamus. Even stimulation of still *lower* centers in the midbrain can suppress rage behavior caused by hypothalamic stimulation; these sites are often more effective in suppressing rage behavior than are higher centers.

Finally, the role of sensitivity to stimulation must be considered. Cannon and Bard assumed that intact animals did not show a low threshold to rage because the cerebral cortex normally inhibits the rage centers in the hypothalamus. An alternate hypothesis has been suggested. Perhaps the decorticate animals were made hyperalgesic (abnormally sensitive to pain) by the operation. Since the stimuli to sham rage were tactile (pinching, hair pulling, tail twisting), these stimuli could arouse pain centers in the decorticate cat, pain centers whose activity was suppressed by the cortex in the normal cat.

Papez-McLean theory

The Papez-McLean theory is a gradually evolving set of notions about a system of nervous centers that perhaps *control,* rather than organize, emotional behavior

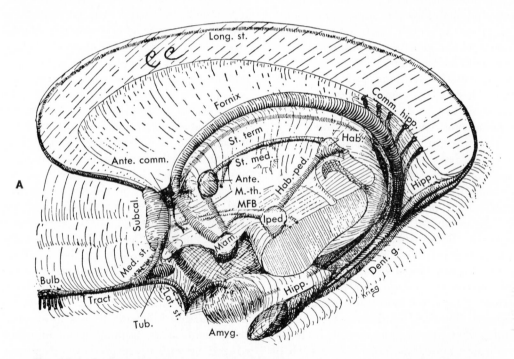

Fig. 16-1. A, Reconstruction of a medial view of the human rhinencephalon. **B,** Reconstruction of the rhinencephalon as seen from above. **Amyg.,** amygdala; **Ante. comm., A.C.,** anterior commissure; **Ante.,** anterior nucleus of thalamus; **Bulb,** olfactory bulb; **Comm. hipp.,** hippocampal commissure; **Dent. G.,** dentate gyrus; **Diag. bd.,** diagonal band; **Hab.,** habenula; **Hab-ped.,** habenulopeduncular tract; **Hipp.,** hippocampus; **Iped.,** interpeduncular nucleus; **Lat. st.,** lateral olfactory stria; **Long. st.,** Longitudinal stria; **Mam.,** mammillary body; **Med. st.,** medial olfactory stria; **MFB.,** medial forebrain bundle; **M.-th.,** mammillothalamic tract; **St. med.,** stria medullaris; **St. term.,** stria terminalis; **Subcal.,** subcallosal gyrus; **Tract,** olfactory tract; **Tub.,** olfactory tubercle. Compare both **A** and **B** with Fig. 14-7. (From Krieg, W. J. S.: Functional neuroanatomy, Evanston, Ill., Brain Books, Inc.)

(and perhaps emotional experience). The centers and pathways involved were described in Chapter 14 as the limbic system (Figs. 14-7 and 16-1). The septal area of the cortex, the cortical cingulate and entorhinal areas, the hippocampus, and most of the amygdaloid nuclei are involved. Papez suggested a circuit from the entorhinal cortex to the hippocampus, thence to the hypothalamus via the fornix, from here to the anterior thalamus, and, finally, to the cingulate gyrus. Most of these structures had been associated with smell input, but Papez suggested that they were involved in emotional experience. McLean elaborated on Papez's ideas, and the additional circuits shown in Fig. 14-7 have been traced by

subsequent work. Since then, the work of many scientists have shown the involvement of many of these structures in emotional *behavior*, whereas stimulation and surgery on human epileptics and psychotic patients have shown some of them to be involved in emotional *experience*. The "circuits" of Fig. 14-7 are supposed to integrate perception by higher centers with emotional behavior that is organized by the diencephalon (chiefly the hypothalamus) and perhaps midbrain structures.

Lindsley activation theory

The ARAS and DTPS were described in some detail in Chapter 14. The ARAS extends through the scattered gray matter

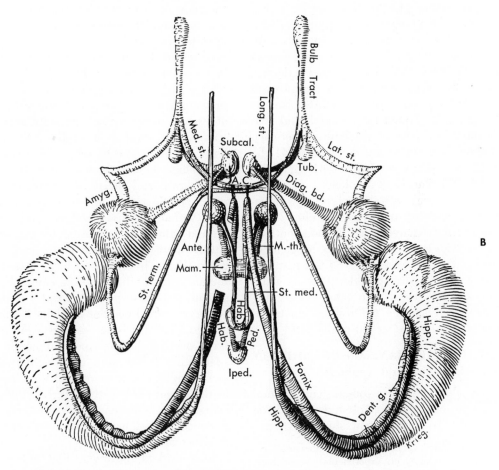

Fig. 16-1, cont'd. For legend see opposite page.

cells of the medulla, pons, midbrain, and diencephalon, including much of the hypothalamus. The ARAS receives collateral input from many sensory pathways, and its intrinsic rhythm, in turn, keeps the brain "awake" by stimulating higher centers. The extensive invasion of the hypothalamus by the ARAS assures that activation will reach any emotional "centers" in the hypothalamus. These connections and the thalamic interconnections of the DTPS both involve the limbic system. The role of the ARAS and DTPS in motivation has been surveyed in Chapter 15, and emotion is certainly a highly motivated state. Lindsley points out that (1) the EEG in emotion has an "activation pattern," including depressed alpha rhythms and much low-voltage fast activity; (2) the same EEG pattern can be reproduced by electrical stimulation of the BSRF (ARAS), which extends into the basal diencephalon (including the hypothalamus) and via these paths reaches the thalamus; (3) if the basal diencephalon is destroyed (the anterior parts of the ARAS), an activated EEG cannot be obtained, and synchronized rhythmic discharges between thalamus and cortex are dominant; (4) the behavior resulting from (3) includes apathy, lethargy, somnolence, catalepsy (rigid posture), hypokenesis (little movement), and so on; and therefore, (5) the BSRF mechanism that includes outflow to behavior termed emotion, "is either identical with or overlaps, the EEG activating mechanism, described under point 2, which arouses the cortex."[*] In other words, the neural mechanisms controlling emotional behavior are to be sought in the BSRF.

NEURAL MECHANISMS IN EMOTION
Somatic and visceral feedback

To what extent are somatic and visceral reactions essential to emotion as it has been defined? To what extent do visceral re-

[*]From Lindsley, D. B.: Emotion. In Stevens, S. S., editor: Handbook of experimental psychology, New York, 1951, John Wiley & Sons, Inc.

actions vary for different emotions and are they essential for emotional experience? Rage and fear involve the diffuse reactions of the sympathetic nervous system as well as fight or flight behavior. In one early experiment Cannon removed the sympathetic chain ganglia and collateral ganglia from cats, which abolished most sympathetic responses. After recovery these cats appeared normal, except that their tolerance for cold and stress was reduced. Their reaction to a dog showed normal "emotionality," including the baring of teeth and claws, arched back, spitting, and hissing.

It could be argued that the brain centers controlling sympathetic response had already been conditioned to "emotional" stimuli, and that these were intact and were sufficient for the emotional behavior now that learning had taken place. Yet it is evident that major sympathetic *reactions* are unnecessary to emotional behavior, at least in the adult animal. In man emotional *experience* does not seem to depend very much on sensations from autonomic or somatic reactions. **Paraplegic** patients, with the spinal cord severed as high as the neck level, have become a common casualty of war. These patients are paralyzed from the neck down, and facial expression is their only somatic expression of emotion aside from verbal responses. Diffuse sympathetic arousal cannot be organized by the brain. Furthermore, sensations from the body cannot reach the brain so that any isolated autonomic reflexes that *do* occur cause no sensations. Yet these patients display and experience normal emotions. Again, it can be argued that the brain *centers* controlling both overt behavior and autonomic response are intact, and their activity had been conditioned to emotional stimuli prior to the spinal cord section. Activity in such centers may be necessary for emotional experience, and a later discussion will provide evidence on this point.

It is evident, however, that autonomic *reactions* are not *necessary to* either emotional experience or emotional behavior. There is little doubt, on the other hand, that autonomic and somatic reactions *contribute to* emotional experience and behavior. An injection of epinephrine, which mimics the effect of mass sympathetic response, will cause the subject to experience a "cold emotion"—sensations such as a pounding heart, empty stomach, and so on. Unless the subject *perceives* these inputs as resulting from emotional upset, no emotional behavior will result. In one experiment (Schacter) subjects were injected with epinephrine and either informed, not informed, or misinformed as to the effects of the drug. While supposedly waiting to be subjects in a vision experiment, they were joined by a confederate of the experimenter who began behaving in an exhilarant fashion, sailing paper airplanes about the room and tossing wads of paper at the wastebasket. Subjects who had been informed of the effects of the drug they had just taken "knew" why they were experiencing a rapid heartbeat and other internal upsets, and they reacted like subjects not given epinephrine at all—they regarded the exhilarant behavior as inappropriate and took no part in it. However, misinformed or not informed subjects, experiencing the effects of adrenaline without knowing their cause, joined in the exhilarant behavior and experienced elation as well. In another experiment injections of a tranquilizer that reduces autonomic activity also reduced the laughter and reported amusement to a slapstick movie, whereas epinephrine had the opposite effect when the subjects were not informed of the effects of the drugs. Although autonomic reactions seem *unnecessary to* emotional experience and behavior, they *can* initiate both.

ANS and emotion

According to Cannon's emergency theory diffuse sympathetic discharge prepares an animal for fight or flight, both highly emotional responses. Both responses are highly organized and motivated, as already pointed out. Are different emotional behavior patterns, such as rage, fear, and others, accompanied by different autonomic nervous system reactions? Do the different autonomic nervous system reactions influence typical emotional "experience" in man? It appears that there *are* different autonomic response patterns for rage, fear, sexual arousal, and perhaps others, such as apathy. Studies of psychotic patients suggest that their predominant autonomic pattern strongly influences their reported "mood" as well as their behavior. So far as the more "pleasant" emotions are concerned, many of them appear to be accompanied by widespread but discrete parasympathetic responses, which are cholinergic and governed from the anterior and medial hypothalamus. Such parasympathetic reactions include those of sexual excitement and dilation of blood vessels supplying the viscera and the skin. Rage and fear, on the other hand, are accompanied by diffuse sympathetic discharge, reinforced by hormones from the adrenal medulla.

The adrenal gland produces two hormones, epinephrine and norepinephrine. Epinephrine is sympatheticomimetic (has the same effect as SNS discharge), while norepinephrine is not. Epinephrine raises the blood pressure by cardioacceleration (increasing the rate of beating of the heart). Norepinephrine raises the blood pressure by constricting blood vessels leading to the skin and viscera. It appears that more epinephrine is released in fear reactions, and greater norepinephrine release accompanies anger. Parasympathetic stimulation would therefore lower the blood pressure more in fear than in anger because it slows the heart and combats the effect of epinephrine more directly. This can be tested by injecting a drug (methacholine [Mecholyl]), which mimics parasympathetic stimulation. The drug rapidly lowers the blood pressure of depressed psychotics or normal people experiencing fright because it slows their rapid heartbeat. A smaller effect on blood pressure is typical of a high norepinephrine response in rage because the drug has no effect on constricted blood vessels that raise the blood pressure. This response is found in paranoid psychotics and normal subjects experiencing anger. The tests show that predatory animals such as lions have a higher norepinephrine level in the blood, whereas animals that survive by flight such as the rabbit, produce more epinephrine. Funkenstein suggests that sympathetically active animals exhibit only rage and fear, but man experiences self-directed anger, which leads to depression. Depression, like anxiety or fear, is accompanied by a high epinephrine output. Since the visceral blood flow is not reduced in fear, the stomach is flushed, making a large hydrochloric acid output possible, which can cause ulcers. If physiological development parallels psychological development, one would expect the young child to demonstrate more anger than fear and produce more norepinephrine than epinephrine. With training—"development of a conscience"—more self-directed anger and anxiety should be accompanied by a higher epinephrine output. So far as the adrenal output is concerned, the ratio of norepinephrine to epinephrine *is* higher in infants than in older children.

Endocrine glands and emotion

Under the stress of emotion sympathetic stimulation often increases epinephrine output by the adrenal medulla, which, in turn, elicits ACTH output by the anterior pituitary. ACTH increases corticoid output by the adrenal cortex to improve carbohydrate metabolism and nervous excitability (Chapter 3). Output of the thyroid glands is also increased to raise the metabolic rate. If the emotional stress is frequent or of a long duration, these glands hypertrophy (increase in size) to keep up with the demand for their secretions (Chapter 18). This chain of endocrine events can be interrupted by removal of the adrenal medulla.

Conditioning of endocrine and sympathetic responses may be important to emotion (Mowrer). If this is the case, animals without an adrenal medulla should have more difficulty learning to avoid a painful stimulus because of inadequate endocrine responses. The experiment has been tried by several investigators; unfortunately, the results are conflicting. Others (Solomon and Wynn) have suggested that neuroendocrine responses in emotion are terminated when the animal avoids a painful stimulus and that termination of neuroendocrine responses is rewarding to the animal. As a result, the animal continues to avoid the painful stimulus and does not need to be "reminded" by failing to avoid punishment now and then. If an animal learns to avoid shock by jumping from one compartment to another at a signal, the response *is* very resistant to extinction. The adrenal cortex is enlarged after such training and, with increased hormone output, should support any neuroendocrine changes that prevent extinction by serving as a reward. To test this idea ACTH injections to increase adrenal output, blocking ACTH output, and adrenalectomies have all been tried to see if avoidance learning is affected. No significant change in avoidance learning resulted from these procedures.

Hypothalamus and emotion

Removal of the brain anterior to the posterior third of the hypothalamus leaves a cat able to display sham rage—integrated attack behavior, however brief, accompanied by the autonomic responses of typical rage. Subsequent removal of this area reduces the rage behavior to fragments of the original response. Posterior hypothalamic lesions of the rage area in an otherwise intact animal results in placidity and somnambulance. These observations led many to conclude that the hypothalamus was the seat of integration of the somatric and visceral responses in rage and perhaps other emotions as well. Subsequent studies with implanted electrodes seemed to confirm these conclusions, although the locations differ, since stimulation of the anterior hypothalamus and related areas (basal septal nuclei, preoptic area, lateral hypothalamus, basal medial thalamus) all produce organized and lasting rage behavior. Furthermore, stimulation of the posterior hypothalamus produced fear-escape responses (Hess), and self-stimulation "reward" areas (Chapter 15) lie in the anterior median hypothalamus. It appears that there are centers in the hypothalamus that are important to rage, fear, and "pleasure" whose stimulation produces both the autonomic and somatic reactions of these emotions. The questions are, how dependent are these centers on input from other centers at higher and lower levels, and to what extent do these centers dominate the activity of other parts of the brain at higher and lower levels? Stimulation of a hypothalamic center may be merely exciting a pathway to another part or parts of the brain where the somatic and visceral responses are actually integrated. And ablation of a center in the hypothalamus may be merely interrupting a major pathway going to a more important integrating center elsewhere in the brain. Small stereotaxic lesions in the ventromedial hypothalamus produce chronic savage behavior in cats that survives frontal or temporal cortex ablation and destruction of the mammillothalamic tracts, fornix, and mammillary bodies; therefore centers above the hypothalamic area do not seem to organize rage. On the other hand, lower centers may be important. Most of the reactions of sham rage can be produced in an animal with no brain above the pons, but the behavior, in addition to being brief, is not coordinated. Stimulation of certain midbrain areas is more effective in abolishing the rage behavior that results from hypothalamic stimulation than is stimulation elsewhere in the brain. Important as the hypothalamus is to integrating the somatic and visceral responses of emotion, it appears to be part of a larger system involving higher and lower centers that organizes emotional response and perhaps emotional experience as well.

Limbic system and emotion

In more primitive animals the cerebral cortex began as a set of centers for correlating smell input As a result, many of the older cortical structures such as the hippocampus and prepyriform areas (Fig. 16-1) were classified along with the olfactory bulbs as **rhinencephalon,** or smell brain. Papez, in a theory elaborated by McLean, proposed that some of these cortical centers and certain subcortical structures serve to integrate preception by higher centers with emotional expression that originates in the diencephalon (primarily the hypothalamus). As previously explained, he proposed a "circuit" (Fig. 14-7) from the hippocampus and amygdala to the hypothamus via the fornix and thence to the anterior thalamus and gyrus cinguli. Subsequent studies have added other pathways to the system as indicated in Fig. 14-7.

Pribram and Kruger, taking a phylogenetic approach to the development of cortical and associated subcortical structures, have traced the evolutionary development of cortical and subcortical centers from their origin in smell. They classify as "smell brain" the olfactory bulb connections with the prepyriform areas on the base of the brain and parts of the amygdaloid nuclei. Connections exist from these areas, but not the olfactory bulb, to areas beneath the corpus callosum (subcallosal), the presubiculum, and the frontotemporal areas. Connections from here go to the third system of hippocampus and cingulate gyrus. In terms of evolutionary age of the cortical parts of this system, the hippocampus, pyriform lobe, and olfactory bulb are the oldest or **paleocortex.** The cingulate gyrus, presubiculum, and frontotemporal areas are intermediate, or **transitional, cor-**

tex. The **neocortex,** or "new cortex," is the rest of the cerebral cortex.

Papez's original speculations were fruitful ones, leading to experiments on what has been called the **Klüver-Bucy syndrome,** after its discoverers. They found that bilateral (both sides) temporal lobe ablations made rhesus monkeys docile, oral (mouthing things), indiscriminative (put anything in their mouths), and hypersexed. The changes in emotional behavior were profound and obvious. The ablations involved included, along with the temporal lobes, the frontotemporal cortex, pyriform lobe, amygdala, presubiculum, and hippocampus. These areas are involved in Papez's circuit and the second and third systems that Pribram and Kruger believe to have evolved from the olfactory brain.

Subsequent experiments have shown that various parts of the areas destroyed in the Klüver-Bucy surgery are important to different aspects of the syndrome. Hypersexuality, for example, can be produced by pyriform lesions alone. It is abolished by castration and returns with hormone therapy. Lesions of the amygdala alone seem related to the taming effects of the Klüver-Bucy syndrome. If a boss monkey in a cage group suffers amygdaloid lesions, he falls to the bottom position in the "social heirarchy" more frequently than not. Even the wild agouti and the lynx of the cat family can be tamed by removing the amygdala and pyriform cortex. None of these effects seems directly related to the olfactory origin of the limbic system since the Klüver-Bucy syndrome appears even if the olfactory tracts are severed prior to the Klüver-Bucy type of surgery. Finally, if only one temporal lobe is removed, only the taming effect is obtained.

Passive and active avoidance

Most of the research on brain mechanisms in emotion discussed up to now has involved rather obvious changes in the emotional behavior of animals. Ablation or stimulation of parts of the brain has been shown to result in rage behavior, flight, or extreme docility. More subtle changes in emotional behavior may be seen in studies of learning a response to an emotional stimulus, usually electric shock. The response that the animal learns usually allows him to avoid the electric shock, and so the technique is called avoidance learning. In some cases an animal learns to jump a barrier from one side of a shuttlebox to another in response to a signal such as a buzzer or light, thus avoiding shock that would otherwise follow the signal at a fixed interval. Such a response is called **active avoidance** because the animal avoids the shock by an active response, or a **conditioned avoidance response (CAR).** In other cases the animal must only stop what it is doing to avoid the shock. After being shocked on approach to a plate of food, a cat may learn not to approach the food, a **passive avoidance response.** Finally, "fear-induced" behavior such as "freezing" and crouching at a signal that precedes an *unavoidable* shock may be studied. Because this behavior shows that the animal "knows what is coming," is called a **conditioned emotional response (CER).** It has been reliably found (McCleary) that animals with bilateral cingulate lesions are slow to learn an active avoidance response, and animals with bilateral septal lesions are slow to learn a passive avoidance response. The converse is not the case, that is, the cingulate animals learn passive avoidance readily, and the septal animals are normal or superior at learning active avoidance.

Stimulation of the cingulate gyrus *facilitates* autonomic arousal and behavioral activity. It should therefore be expected that removal of this area would make an animal "less aroused" in response to punishment, that is, "less frightened" and therefore slow to learn active avoidance. When the warning signal is repeatedly presented without punishment, the cingulate-damaged animals extinguish faster than normal animals—that is, they fail to respond to the signal with active avoidance sooner. This also supports the idea that cingulate-damaged animals are less easily frightened. However, they respond normally on a CER, freezing and suppressing food- or water-motivated behavior when a signal heralds the onset of shock.

Septally lesioned animals, on the other hand, seem unable to suppress their behavior. The septal area is a potent *inhibitory* area for autonomic and behavioral arousal. Its bilateral removal may therefore leave an animal unable to suppress his ongoing behavior. Inability to suppress ongoing behavior may be seen in the septal animal's reactions in the CER and passive avoidance situations. They fail to develop the normal "freezing" and crouching responses to a signal followed by unavoidable shock—their ongoing behavior is not changed by the signal. Septal animals also seem unable to repress approaching food or water even after they have been shocked repeatedly for doing so. It must be realized, however, that septal animals are feral—savage and easily aroused to rage behavior. Some kind of imbalance between rage and fear behavior may have been created by the operation.

The impaired active avoidance created by cingulate lesions and the impaired passive avoidance created by septal lesions may be understood in terms of the Papez-McLean theory of the role of the limbic circuit in emotion. Both the cingulate gyrus and the septal nuclei are part of the limbic system (Fig. 14-7). Cutting the pathways between the hypothalamus and that part of the thalamus that sends fibers to the cingulate gyrus (that is, the mammillothalamic tract—Fig. 16-1) interferes with active avoidance just as cingulate damage does. Areas in the amygdaloid nuclei that facilitate active behavior can be removed and active avoidance is impaired. Stimulation of either the cingulate gyrus or amygdala arouses flight behavior, which is similar to active avoidance.

On the other hand, ablation studies that involve learning can be interpreted in other ways. Septal lesions increase hunger and thirst; perhaps this is the reason why septal animals are less able to show passive avoidance of food or water or do not freeze or crouch (CER) when eating or drinking in response to a shock signal. Either cingulate or septal lesions may interfere with the animal's *ability to learn* active or passive avoidance, respectively, rather than their ability to respond or suppress response. The hippocampus is part of the same limbic circuit and hippocampal lesions impair passive avoidance and facilitate active avoidance. Yet the hippocampus has no known facilitation or inhibition effects on autonomic arousal and ongoing behavior. Finally, the effect of the lesion on the animal's emotionality may interfere with or aid learning, depending on the response that is called for. Cingulate animals are somewhat placid and may be poor at active avoidance for this reason. Septal animals are fierce and easily aroused and may find it difficult to suppress ongoing behavior because of their temperament.

All in all the limbic system is known to be involved in the interrelated behaviors that are arbitrarily classified as "motivation," "emotion," and "learning." Until the role of each part of the limbic system is known and how it interacts and affects other parts of the brain, few conclusions are possible. The remaining task is to see what parts of the limbic system and what other parts of the brain have the most to do with the behavior, experience, and autonomic arousal classified as emotion.

PARTS OF THE BRAIN: THEIR ROLE
Medulla

As explained in Chapter 6, the medulla contains many reflex centers that regulate autonomic response to events in the viscera and elsewhere under the influence of higher centers, particularly those of the hypothalamus. The medulla mediates regulation of heart rate, blood pressure, pupillary response, vomiting and intestinal motility, and many other autonomic reactions that are also involved in emotion. Such reflex regulation aids homeostasis, the control of internal conditions, to keep the internal environment relatively constant. Under the stress of emotional arousal visceral changes are reflexly made by the medulla, which is influenced by higher centers as well as stress-induced changes in the internal environment.

Midbrain

From the midbrain through higher centers to the cortex, localized stimulation and ablation changes emotional behavior. In most instances, however, it is not known whether the behavior is organized at the level where the stimulation or ablation occurred. Stimulation at a given focus in the midbrain may merely excite a pathway to higher centers where the behavior is organized. Ablation, on the other hand, may merely interrupt input to higher centers where the behavior is organized. In some instances stimuli in the midbrain excite sensory pathways for pain that, of course, arouse emotional behavior governed by widespread brain centers. Human patients have reported pain from stimulation of the classical spinothalmic sensory pathways, from areas ventral to this tegmental (floor) location, and from the tectum (roof) of the midbrain as well. Stimulation of other areas in the midbrain besides these can lead to emotional behavior in animals, however. Rage behavior, fear behavior, and flight have been elicited by stimulating the central gray matter of the midbrain in various locations. In the case of rage behavior an interaction with the hypothalamus seems indicated. Certain midbrain foci of stimulation are more effective than other brain stimulus locations in suppressing the rage behavior that follows hypothalamic stimulation. Lesion studies also suggest that the midbrain organizes certain emotional reactions, particularly defensive ones. Stimuli to the affective field of the midbrain results in

defensive behavior in the cat. Ablation of this region produces placidity and abolishes some defensive responses that otherwise could be obtained by stimulating the amygdala.

Hypothalamus

Ablations of the defense-reaction areas in the hypothalamus also prevents stimulation of the amygdala from eliciting such reactions. The midbrain seems most important for these reactions, with the hypothalamus more important than the amygdala. It has already been reported that bilateral lesions in the posterior hypothalamus produce placid animals, and ventromedial lesions result in chronic savagery. Rage behavior follows stimulation to the anterior hypothalamus. Flight results from stimulation of various sites in the anterior, lateral, and posterior hypothalamus. Finally, it will be recalled that reward sites for self-stimulation are found in the anterior hypothalamus and that aversive sites can be found in the posterior and lateral hypothalamus (Chapter 15). If the midbrain is most important to defensive reactions, the hypothalamus seems most important to integrating rage-defense, fear, and reward with activity in the limbic sytsem.

Hippocampus

Another important part of the limbic system is the hippocampus. The hippocampus is the buried cortical focus for excitation to the hypothalamus via the fornix in the Papez circuit (Fig. 14-7). Studies on the effect of lesions and stimulation in the hippocampus indicate that it is involved in learning and memory as well as affective reactions. As already noted, hippocampal lesions impair passive avoidance learning and facilitate active avoidance learning. Fear and rage behavior may be elicited from stimulating different sites in the hippocampus, but amygdaloid stimulation is more effective in this regard. Human patients have reported unpleasant sensations from hippocampal stimulation. Yet Olds has reported some areas in the hippocampus as effective for reward-type stimulation in the rat. The hippocampus seems to have a role in both emotion and learning.

Amygdala

The amygdaloid nuclei are located inside the temporal lobes of the cerebrum. Each is a collection of nuclei with different roles. Some of these nuclei form part of the Papez circuit, and, as already seen, amygdaloid lesions seem responsible for the taming aspect of the Klüver-Bucy syndrome in monkeys and for placidity in cats. Fear and rage behavior can be elicited in cats by stimulating different sites in the amygdala; the rage sites are less effective than either the midbrain or hypothalamus, but more effective than the hippocampus. There seems to be an interaction between the amygdala on one hand and the ventromedial hypothalamus and septal area on the other. Lesions in either of the latter two areas result in ferocity. Sometimes these effects can be reversed by the amygdaloid lesions that normally make an animal placid. Both temporal lobes (including the underlying amygdala) have been removed in humans to treat severe epilepsy or else assaultive psychoses with quite variable results. A decrease in aggressiveness is frequently reported. Psychotic patients stimulated in various sites in the amygdala act as though they were having unpleasant hallucinations. Considering all this evidence and the placement of the amygdala in the limbic system, it seems probable that nuclei in the amygdala serve as "relay stations" for excitation of emotional behavior and experience excitation that is organized in other parts of the limbic system.

Cortex and thalamus

The role of pyriform cortex ablation in the hypersexuality of the Klüver-Bucy syndrome has already been noted. The temporal cortex seems to play a role in learning (Chapter 17), but it also has extensive connections with the amygdala. Epileptics that are undergoing brain operations report sensations of fear when the temporal lobe is stimulated. The most important cortical area for emotion, however, seems to be the frontal lobes and their connections with the limbic system via the thalamus. Incidental to animal experiments on the role of the frontal lobes in complex learning situations in monkeys (Chapter 17), changes in emotional behavior were noted. Accidental brain-damage cases in humans were followed by emotional change when the frontal lobes were involved. Removal of the anterior frontal lobes was tried on humans for the relief of psychotic anxiety or for relief from intractable pain (prefrontal lobectomy, Chapter 14). It was found that the same emotional effects could be achieved with less brain damage by severing the fibers connecting the frontal lobes with the thalamus—prefrontal lobectomy. In many cases anxiety was relieved by the operation, but the patients often became impulsive, irresponsible, and less concerned with the consequences of their actions. "Flattened" affect was also noted. Patients operated upon for the relief of pain reported that they still sensed the pain, but it "didn't bother them" unless they "paid attention to it." In the case of severe anxiety it has since been found that ablations in the anterior cingulate and posterior orbital areas (topoctomy) are followed by anxiety relief, with fewer unfortunate personality changes and other side effects. Anterior cingulate ablations in monkeys can cause decreased fear and increased aggressiveness, but the aggressive effect has not been reported in humans. Aside from the thalamic (dorsomedial and anterior) nuclei supplying the frontal lobes and cingulate gyrus, few emotional centers have been found in the thalamus. Fear behavior can be elicited by stimulating certain lateral thalamic nuclei, however.

FACIAL EXPRESSION AND EMOTION

Almost a century ago Sir Charles Darwin published a book on the expression of emotion in man and animals. The book pointed out the biological usefulness to survival of the facial expressions, vocalizations, and body postures of animals expressing emotion—baring of the canine teeth (for biting), erection of the hair (to increase apparent size), stiff posture, and growls in anger. Joy is expressed in reactions that are the *opposite* of anger—tail wagging in dogs or purring in cats. Freezing (to avoid being seen) or flight are both survival mechanisms and have associated facial expressions. Darwin believed that man's facial expressions and gestures were the inherited rudiments of the facial expressions and body postures of animals undergoing emotion. If this is the case, neural mechanisms controlling facial expressions should be found among those controlling the other automatic reactions of emotion. As already stated, *patterns* of emotional expression can be obtained by stimulating various points in the hypothalamus and limbic system. Neurological human patients (pseudobulbar palsy) show involuntary laughing or crying without experiencing emotion. Victims of Parkinson's disease (damage to the basal ganglia) may display a masklike face, experiencing emotion while impassive and expressionless. These facts suggest that certain human emotional expressions are inherited and form part of the automatic reactions that occur during emotion. In modern man, however, many facial expressions and gestures that express more subtle emotions than primitive anger, fear, or joy are undoubtedly learned. These would vary from culture to culture, for example, the Chinese expression of surprise by sticking out the tongue. Laughing, crying, growling, and expressions of this kind, however, and probably part of man's inherited emotional response equipment.

Emotional development

Most writers on emotion agree that the emotional responses an organism displays at birth are not all the emotional responses inherited. Some of these responses require the *maturation* of necessary structures before they can appear. After maturation responses must often be *used* or their underlying functional and structural relationships will die away. It is therefore difficult and perhaps meaningless to evaluate the influence of heredity apart from the influence of learning. It is possible, however, to trace the normal *development* of emotional expression in the human. Most writers agree that infants first display only greater or less excitement or arousal, with crying the only specific response seen. The excited state then differentiates into "delight" and "distress," distress then becoming recognizable as "rage" or "fear." More subtle emotions appear to emerge from these beginnings.

SUMMARY

Students of emotion have been variously concerned with emotional experience (conscious events), overt emotional behavior, or the internal physiological events accompanying emotion. Individual differences in emphasis determine the way emotion is defined and theoretically explained.

The most useful definition includes all three aspects of emotion and how they are organized by the CNS. Theories emphasizing conscious states fail because awareness is neither necessary nor sufficient for emotional behavior. Theories emphasizing emotional behavior ignore instances of physiological and conscious signs of emotion without evidence of overt emotional responses. Theories emphasizing autonomic response fail because ANS response does not differ for each emotion; emotion occurs when the ANS response is blocked by drugs or surgery, and simple exercise causes ANS response changes without emotion. A centralist position that emphasizes the role of the CNS in organizing emotional experience, overt behavior, and ANS response seems the most fruitful approach. Because emotion disrupts complex learning behavior, it was once defined as a disorganized response; the evolutionary development of emotion suggests that it is a highly organized, primitive CNS mechanism for motivation in an emergency. James thought that conscious emotional events were sensations aroused by visceral and somatic emotional responses. For Watson, emotion *was* overt behavior, inherited fear, rage, and lust responses to specific stimuli; the responses were made more variable and the stimuli eliciting them increased through conditioning and generalization. ANS response has been identified with emotion by other writers who believe the ANS responses are necessary to emotion, at least until some learning has occurred.

The Cannon-Bard theory of emotion originated as an attempt to explain the sham rage behavior of decorticate cats by assuming that centers in the hypothalamus organized overt and autonomic emotional responses on the one hand and caused the perception of emotions by higher centers on the other. However, more widespread centers in the CNS that control emotion have been discovered since the Cannon-Bard work. The Papez-McLean theory proposed that these centers formed a circuit in the rhinencephalon that included the entorhinal cortex, hippocampus, hypothalamus, anterior thalamus, and cingulate gyrus. Subsequent work has shown some of these centers to be involved in both emotional behavior and experience. Lindsley's activation theory of emotion, however, identifies emotion with states of activation in the ARAS.

Somatic and visceral feedback contributes to emotion, but this feedback seems unessential to emotion in the adult because sympathectomized cats show emotional behavior and paraplegic humans report emotional awareness. However, ANS responses can cause emotion. If human subjects are aware that the internal ANS responses they perceive are caused by a drug, they do not become emotional; if they are unaware of the cause of the internal upset, they often think they are emotional and behave accordingly. Although ANS responses are not varied enough to account for all emotions, pleasure seems to be accompanied by parasympathetic responses, whereas rage and fear involve widespread sympathetic responses.

In fear the adrenal medulla produces mostly epinephrine, which raises the blood pressure by increasing the heart rate. In rage it produces more norepinephrine, which raises blood pressure by constricting the arteries supplying the viscera and skin. Man is capable of learning self-directed anger and depression that leads to epinephrine output like fear responses do. Epinephrine causes increased ACTH output that stimulates corticoid production by the adrenal medulla. Stress therefore hypertrophies the pituitary and adrenal glands. Experiments on avoidance conditioning after adrenalectomy are conflicting, however, and so are studies involving injection of the various hormones.

It seems that there are centers in the hypothalamus that are important to the autonomic reactions of rage, fear, and pleasure, whose stimulation produces both the autonomic and somatic reactions of these emotions. These centers seem dependent on lower midbrain centers for rage behavior and dependent on rhinencephalic centers of the Papez-MacLean variety for all three emotional responses. For example, bitemporal lobectomies, including the amygdala and hippocampus, make monkeys docile, hypersexed, indiscriminative, and oral in their behavior (the Klüver-Bucy syndrome). The hypersexual symptom seems caused by pyriform cortex lesions and the docilty to loss of the amygdala. Lesions of facilicatory areas in the cingulate gyrus impair active avoidance learning in the rat, whereas septal (inhibitory area) lesions impair passive avoidance behavior. Septals also fail to show a CER and are unable to suppress ongoing behavior such as eating or drinking when punished. Alternate interpretations are possible since septals show more hunger and thirst and since hippocampal lesions in areas that do not facilitate or inhibit behavior and ANS arousal impair passive avoidance and facilitate active avoidance. Interpretations based on emotionality changes are also possible.

The role of centers of the brain in emotion depends on their relation to other parts of the brain. The medulla organizes ANS responses in emotion in response to internal changes and in the influence of higher brain centers. The midbrain seems involved in overt responses to pain input and conscious pain sensations as well as in defensive reactions to emotional stimuli. The hypothalamus plays a less important role in this respect, but it integrates autonomic and behavioral reactions in rage and fear with activity in the rest of the limbic system. The hippocampus is involved in learning and memory as well as in affective reactions. Nuclei in the amygdala are important to rage and fear behavior, although less so than the midbrain and hypothalamus. The temporal cortex plays a role in learning and sensations of fear and has extensive connections with the amygdala. The anterior thalamic nuclei or prefrontal cortex can be ablated (lobectomy) or their connections severed (lobotomy) to cause relief of pain, flattened affect, relieved anxiety, and irresponsibility in man. Cingulate and posterior orbital topectomies relieve anxiety with less personality change. Subcortical nuclei seem involved in facial expressions developed in lower animals and man through evolution. Most writers on emotion believe that emotional responses develop from simple delight and distress in the newborn to the variety of emotions displayed by the adult as a result of both maturation and learning.

READINGS

Andrew, R. J.: The origins of facial expressions, Sci. Amer. **213**:88-99, 1965. (W. H. Freeman Co. Reprint No. 627.)

Ax, A. F.: The physiological differentiation between anger and fear in humans, Psychosom. Med. **15**:433-442, 1953. (Bobbs-Merrill Reprint No. P-16.)

Brady, J. V., and Nauta, W. J. H.: Subcortical mechanisms in emotional behavior: affective changes following septal forebrain lesions in the albino rat, J. comp. physiol. Psychol. **46**:339-346, 1953. (Bobbs-Merrill Reprint No. P-46.)

Candland, D. K., editor: Emotion: bodily change, New York, 1962, D. Van Norstrand Co., Inc., 1962.

Cannon, W. B.: Bodily changes in pain, hunger, fear and rage, New York, 1963, Harper & Row, Publishers.

Darwin, C.: The expression of the emotions in man and animal, Chicago, 1965, The University of Chicago Press.

Funkenstein, D. H.: The physiology of fear and anger, Sci. Amer. **192**:74-80, 1955. (W. H. Freeman Co. Reprint No. 428.)

Hunt, H. F., and Brady, J. V.: Some effects of electro-convulsive shock on a conditioned emotional response ("anxiety"), J. Comp. Physiol. Psychol., **44**:88-98, 1951. (Bobbs-Merrill Reprint No. P-170.)

Kluver, H., and Bucy, P. C.: Preliminary analysis of functions of the temporal lobes in monkeys. In Isaacson, R. L., editor: Basic readings in neuropsychology, New York, 1964, Harper & Row, Publishers.

McCleary, R. A., and Moore, R. Y.: Subcortical mechanism in behavior, New York, 1965, Basic Books, Inc.

Rosvold, H. E., Mirsky, A. F., and Pribram, K.: Influence of amygdaloidectomy on social behavior in monkeys, J. Comp. Physiol. Psychol. **47**:173-178, 1954. (Bobbs-Merrill Reprint No. P-296.)

Schacter, S., and Singer, J. E.: Cognitive, social and physiological determinants of emotional state, Psychol. Rev. **69**:379-399, 1962. (Bobbs-Merrill Reprint No. P-553.)

Watson, J. B., and Rayner, R.: Conditioned emotional reactions, J. Exp. Psychol. **3**:1-13, 1920. (Bobbs-Merrill Reprint No. P-360.)

Chapter 17

Learning

OVERVIEW

This chapter is divided into four main sections. The first discussion concerns the anatomical location of changes in the brain that could occur with learning because this is the oldest problem in the physiological psychology of learning. Its consideration gives perspective for what is to follow. The second section questions the time course of changes in the brain with learning. This does not seem to mean very much until it is seen that most of the internal changes called learning take place *after* practice is over! Then in the third section some theoretical systems to explain brain function in learning are compared. The systems are sketchy, but the way they deal with theoretical issues shows the magnitude of the problem. Finally, after showing that learning changes probably occur at synapses between nerve cells, the last section deals with the nature of change at the synapse with learning. More gross biochemical and anatomical changes in the brain are surveyed first in a "molar" approach. The chapter closes with a "molecular" approach that concerns what happens in each single nerve cell involved in the learning process.

To begin with, in attempting to explain learning, the first question that physiological psychologists asked was where in the brain does it happen? They tried to find out by taking out parts of the brain to see how the loss of each part affected learning and memory. The ambiguities and failures of this approach define much of the problem. The effect of brain damage depends on the many sensory inputs required to solve problems such as complex maze learning. Even when the conditioned response is used to restrict learning to a signal and a response, the neural "trace" of learning, or engram, is hard to locate. Many diffusely located parts of the brain seem involved in learning in a poorly understood way. Surgical and drug methods can be used to restrict input, and therefore learning, to one hemisphere of the brain at a time. The results clear up the problem somewhat, but they do not restrict the engram to a known location. Techniques of brain stimulation and recording *during* learning help identify the parts of the brain involved in the process, however. The parts of the brain necessary to relating sensory input and motor output in learning are considered and their connections "tested." Electrodes are used to monitor electrical changes in various parts of the brain during learning. The role of "reward" and "punishment" centers in the brain receives attention. The effect of brain stimulation *during* learning and the way brain stimulation gives rise to memories in patients during brain surgery add to our information. Yet the problem remains a complex one.

Another attack on the problem of learning concerns the time course of forming a "permanent memory." Apparently, immediate memory, such as remembering a telephone number until one can dial it, depends on continuous brain activity (perseveration). If the brain activity continues for long enough, a permanent memory is formed (consolidation) so that one can remember the number later. The evidence on this two-phase theory of learning and memory is considered in some detail.

With the evidence surveyed thus far some theoretical systems of brain function in learning and memory are sketched. Beginning with what is known of the parts of the brain and their possible role in learning and memory, ideas relating brain function in learning and reward and punishment are reviewed. The review, again, shows the complexity of the problem.

Finally, a new question is asked. If it can be shown that learning changes occur at synapses between nerve cells (*whatever* parts of the brain are involved), what is the nature of the synaptic changes? "Molar" changes are discussed first. What gross anatomical or biochemical changes occur at synapses when one learns? Then a molecular approach is considered. What happens to a single nerve cell when it is involved in learning? Although the answers to these questions are far from complete, important findings emerge, with implications ranging from child rearing to education. Part answers to the physiological psychology of learning are not really satisfying, but even these are important and useful.

LOCUS OF THE MEMORY TRACE
Historical background:
search for the engram

Two principles seemed to guide early investigators who studied the physiological basis of learning and memory. The first principle was the "reflex model" of the nervous system, which was presented in Chapter 6 as a first approximation to how the brain mediates responses to stimuli. In this model simple connections are made at synapses among incoming sensory neurons, association neurons, and outgoing motor neurons. Such connections in the brain are variable so that responses to stimuli vary. An act would follow a sensory stimulus by chance, and the act would be rewarded. The rewarded response would be repeated more often when the stimulus appeared, and the synaptic connections between this stimulus and response would be improved by *use* until the stimulus-response relation became automatic like a reflex. The model does not say, however, how reward affects synaptic connections in the first place. This problem will be encountered in a more sophisticated form later.

The second principle that seemed obvious to early researchers was **encephalization.** As newer parts of the brain developed through evolution, they came to dominate the activity of older parts of the brain. In mammals such as man the newest part of the brain is the cerebral cortex. The most distinctive feature of complex animals such as man is their superior ability to learn complex behavior. It was therefore assumed that the cerebral cortex had taken over the newest kind of complex brain function—the formation of new connections between stimulus and response at synapses. If these synaptic connections were to be found in the cerebral cortex, they would be found in the association areas rather than in the sensory projection areas for incoming stimuli or the motor projection areas for outgoing responses; the synaptic connections of the association areas would link the sensory and motor projection areas.

Of course, it is known now that there are two or three sensory projection areas for some senses as well as two or three motor projection areas, and many cortical connections are made via lower brain centers rather than directly with other cortical areas. However, the simple model of the early investigators explains why they sought the **engram**—the physical synaptic changes of learning—in the cerebral cortex. They used the method of **ablation,** taking out parts of the cortex and observing the effect on learning and memory. If removing a given part of the cortex impaired learning and memory, it would be assumed that the stimulus-response connections for the habit being studied were ordinarily made in the part of the cortex that had been removed.

Cortical ablation effects on maze learning and retention. Karl Lashley studied the effects of ablating cortical tissue in rats. He studied their ability to learn and remember mazes of three levels of difficulty (number of blind alleys) by operating upon them either before or after they had learned. The results of his pioneering experiments can be summarized, in an oversimplified way, by three conclusions. (1) Cortical ablation had more effect on retention of a given maze habit than on ability to learn mazes; that is, if the rat were operated upon before he learned, his ability to learn was impaired in comparison with control rats. However, if he learned a maze, was operated upon, and then tested on the same maze, his retention was affected more than his ability to learn new mazes. (2) The more difficult the maze (that is, the more blind alleys), the greater the effect of removing a given amount of cortex on *either* learning or retention. Removing 10% of the cortex would affect learning or memory for complex mazes more than simple ones. (3) It did not seem to matter which areas of the cortex were damaged, but the *amount* of cortex removed was critical. Removing 10% of the frontal area had about the same effect as removing 10% of the parietal area, but removing 50% of any area would have a greater effect on learning and memory. From these results Lashley evolved the principles of **mass action** and **equipotentiality,** each a corollary of the other. Mass action states that the cortex acts *as a whole* in learning—that all areas of the cortex are involved at once. Equipotentiality therefore means that one cortical area is as good as another for learning the maze habit; if a rat has 75% of the cortex left, it does not matter where the 75% is located so far as the rat's ability to learn or retain the maze habit is concerned.

Projection area damage. Rat brains are small, and Lashley's cortical ablations destroyed sensory and motor projection areas as well as association areas. Semiparalyzed rats learned well so that the damage to motor projection areas did not seem to be vital. The sensory projection areas were a different matter. Critics were quick to point out that the cortical lesions impaired the sensory inputs for vision, hearing, touch, and so on and that the rat uses all this sensory information in learning mazes. Damage to the striate area might blind the rat, for example, and a blind rat does not learn mazes as well as a rat with sight. With vision as an example, it was finally established that rats without eyes learn better than rats without a visual cortex. There was some disagreement about the size of lesions involved (Lashley, Ades), but the visual cortex plays a role in learning beyond that of a simple receiving station for sensory information. It functions in learning as well as in sensory input.

Cortical connections. It was originally assumed that learning consisted of establishing synaptic connections between (incoming) sensory projection areas and (outgoing) motor areas via the neurons of the association areas of the cortex. Perhaps these connections could be cut to affect learning and retention, even if they differed from one rat to another. However, thin cuts in the cortex in both directions that isolated small squares of cortex had no effect on learning or retention (Lashley). Even electrically insulating these squares from one another by placing small strips of mica in the cuts is without effect (Sperry). Cortical cells seems to conduct vertically rather than horizontally. On the other hand, cuts of this kind do not sever fibers that "loop" down through the interior white matter to connect one cortical area with another, and they do not sever the crossing or **commissural fibers** that connect corresponding areas of the two hemispheres.

More will be explained later about the effects of cutting the fibers that connect the two hemispheres.

Subcortical centers. The cortex is "vertically organized"; that is, most cells connect with others above or below them, and one part of the cortex connects with another mostly via subcortical routes, including the thalamus. Accordingly, thalamic areas were damaged in rats (Gheselli and Brown) with minimum cortical damage by using the stereotaxic instrument (Chapter 14). The effects on learning and retention resembled mass action. With the exception of the anterior thalamic nuclei, the location of damage to the thalamus was unimportant to learning or retention, but the *extent* of the damage was critical. The role of anterior thalamic nuclei in learning will be discussed later; these nuclei are important because of their connections with the limbic system on the one hand and with the frontal lobes on the other.

CONDITIONED RESPONSE: FURTHER LOCALIZING THE ENGRAM
Rationale

Some investigators attributed Lashley's "mass action" results to the complex nature of the maze habit. The rat used many sensory inputs and made many complex responses in learning a maze so that ablation of any part of the cortex was likely to affect a part involved in the habit. The neural connections might be more precisely located if an animal learned to make a simple response (**conditioned response,** or CR) to a simple signal. For example, if a bell was followed by a shock to the leg of a dog often enough, the normal leg flexion response to shock would begin to occur whenever the bell rang. The shock is an **unconditioned stimulus** (US) that forces leg flexion, the **unconditioned response** (UR); the US-UR relationship exists before training begins. When the bell precedes the shock for several conditioning trials, the bell serves as a signal to the dog that shock is coming. The bell has become the **conditioned stimulus** (CS) to a **conditioned response** (CR) of leg flexion that anticipates the shock. A CS could also be a signal for reward. An animal could learn a CR of salivating in response to a bell CS as it does in response to food (US) when the bell serves as a signal that food will follow.

Controls

The initial response to a CS changes after several presentations of the CS alone because of **habituation.** When first presented, the CS is a novel stimulus, and the animal pricks up its ears, sniffs the air, and so on—a group of responses that the European writers have called the **orienting reflex,** or "what-is-it?," response. After several presentations of a bell CS without shock (US) **reinforcement,** habituation to the bell occurs and training can then begin from a stable level of minimum response to the CS. Changes in response to the US can also occur to cause **pseudoconditioning**—a reaction to the CS that is caused by **stimulus sensitization** rather than conditioning. Repeated presentations of the shock US could sensitize the dog so that it would withdraw its leg to any stimulus. The animal might respond to any signal with a flexion UR that could be mistaken for the similar CR. Response to the shock US must be stabilized by repeatedly presenting the US alone until the subject adapts to shock and sensitization is no longer evident. Then training can begin. Controls for habituation and sensitization are mentioned here because some of the conditioning experiments in the remainder of this chapter failed to take these factors into account. Such experiments must be interpreted accordingly.

Spinal conditioning

One way to isolate the stimulus-response connections in learning is to confine them to a simple level of the nervous system. If the CR is a simple one, it could be learned at any level of the nervous system, perhaps even the spinal cord. One investigator (Shurrager) transected the spinal cord of young dogs in the lumbar region, isolating the lower cord from higher levels of the nervous system. He used stimuli and responses mediated by the lower cord to see if learning could occur at this level of the nervous system. The animals were **acute preparations,** and all testing was done under anesthesia within 48 hours or so of the operation. Reflex responses were nearly absent because of spinal shock (Chapter 13). By exposing a hindlimb flexor muscle Shurrager could, however, see a small flexion response (UR) to shock of that hind paw (US). He found he could condition this response to a tap on the tail in about half of his subjects. He could **extinguish** the response by repeated CS presentations without shock reinforcement, recondition and reextinguish in successively fewer trials, and so on—all the usual phenomena of conditioning. He even suggested that conditioning of the first motor unit to respond to the CS represented the learning of single synapses at the final common path—the motor neuron for the motor unit. However, the CR to a tap on the tail was sometimes present in one hindlimb (only) prior to conditioning, when it required the usual conditioning procedure to switch it to the other limb. Another investigator (Bromiley) showed evidence of stimulus sensitization in the phenomenon—US presentations increasing CR probability. Still another investigator (Kellogg) was unable to condition *chronic* spinal dogs who had recovered from spinal shock and were not anesthetized. Kellogg used a CS of shock to the contralateral paw, however, and the crossed extension reflex may have opposed a flexion response in the limb being tested.

Decorticate conditioning

An early experimenter (Bechterev) was unable to condition decorticate dogs, which led Pavlov and other Russian originators of the conditioning technique to believe that conditioning was impossible without the cortex. In more recent years and with more sophisticated techniques, conditioning has been obtained in decorticate animals. The techniques involved have led to a **two-stage hypothesis** to explain some CR's. A common early technique was bell-shock conditioning. A dog learned to lift its leg in response to a bell because shock from a plate under its paw followed the bell. The learning appeared to proceed in two stages. In early trials the dog would begin to struggle in its harness when the bell was sounded, showing **type I CR** of struggling to the bell just as it did in response to the shock. In later trials the dog learned to lift its paw calmly from the plate when the bell sounded, thus *avoiding* shock. This is a **type II CR,** in which the response is *instrumental* in avoiding punishment or obtaining a reward. Type II conditioning is often called **instrumental conditioning** for this reason.

In type I conditioning the US follows the CS whether or not the CR occurs. Thus food (US) will follow a bell CS whether or not the animal salivates (CR) before the food arrives. In the early type I stage of bell-shock conditioning, the animal learned to struggle (CR) in response to the bell (CS), but this response did not avoid a subsequent shock (US). Later the dog would lift its leg (CR) in response to the bell CS, and this new CR was instrumental in avoiding punishment, a new and rewarding US (reinforcement). This is type II conditioning because the US follows the CR and depends on it; the dog must lift its paw (CR) to avoid shock (US), or the rat must press a lever (CR) to obtain a food pellet (US). In bell-shock conditioning, then, the type I CR of struggling was followed by a type II CR of avoiding shock. Yet early experiments with decorticate animals seemed to show that they were capable of type I but not type II CR's, at least in the bell-shock situation. The decorticate subject would learn to struggle to the bell CS as it did to the shock US, but it would not learn to avoid shock by lifting its leg (CR) before the shock arrived. However, a decorticate animal is hypersensitive to all stimuli and will show a sham rage response to shock (Chapter 16) that includes struggling. By presenting the bell CS only when the animal was not struggling, later investigators avoided conditioning the sham rage responses to the bell CS and obtained a type II CR of shock avoidance. Using this technique, they were able to investigate the role of the cortex in visual and auditory conditioning.

It has been shown that decorticate animals can learn simple CR's to either a brightness CS or a simple tone CS. However, decorticates are incapable of discriminating *patterns* of either light or tone stimuli from other patterns without the visual or auditory cortical projection areas, respectively. A type of temporary decortication can result from the injection of certain drugs (for example, curare). Visual (brightness) CR's, learned in the normal state, are unaffected by these drugs or by decortication; apparently brightness CR's are mediated by subcortical centers. However, auditory (bell-shock) CR's in normal animals are abolished by decortication or by drugging the cortex and must be relearned by subcortical centers. It has been found that prestriate (visual II) lesions do not affect visual pattern or form discrimination, but parietal lesions impair such learning. Somatic I and II and posterior parietal lesions impair somesthetic discriminations, but relearning is possible unless all three areas are destroyed.

Finally, prefrontal lobectomy impairs instrumental delayed responses in monkeys (Jacobsen); the animal is shown food being placed under one of two cans and is forced to delay response, usually in darkness, before being allowed to make a choice. Although removal of certain dorsolateral frontal areas may be important to the delayed reaction, major factors are distractability, hyperactivity, and lack of attention that are shown by monkeys with frontal lobe lesions.

Role of the response in conditioning

One way to localize the changes in the brain in conditioning is to ask whether the UR and CR must actually take place for type I conditioning to occur. Will the animal learn to lift its leg to the bell that is followed by shock if it is prevented from doing so during training? If it does not, the changes in the nervous system may require feedback sensations of making the response for learning to occur. If the animal learns without the opportunity to respond, the nervous system changes must be sought farther "upstream" in the sequence of CNS events, perhaps in neural interactions between the CS and the US toward the sensory rather than the response side of events. Several experiments have shown that the response is *not* necessary to type I conditioning. If response to the shock US, and therefore to the bell CS, is prevented during bell-shock training, the animal will demonstrate the CR on a later test if it is able to do so. In bell-shock conditioning the flexion response may be prevented by crushing the motor roots of the cord or by administering drugs that prevent conduction between motor nerves and muscles at the myoneural junction (erthrodine, tubocurarine), and the CR to a test CS will appear after the animal recovers. A conditioned salivary response can be prevented during training by injections of atropine, yet appear in response to the CS when the drug is removed. Finally, as more fully explained in a later section of this chapter, electical responses of the brain that involve no overt behavior can also be conditioned.

Second signalling system

There are few differences between species, from those with complex brains to those with simple brains, in the time required to learn a simple CR. This fact suggests that simple CR's are formed in simple neural mechanisms shared by all species. Man, however, acquires simple CR's at a more rapid rate by the use of language and other symbols and is also capable of other kinds of complex learning that depend on language. Russian investigators have advanced the idea that language is a **second signalling system** of conditioned stimuli that cannot be acquired by other animals since it is dependent on a complex cerebral cortex that is unique to man. The finding of special speech areas (for example, Broca's area—Chapter 18) in the cerebral cortex of man lends some support to this view.

SPLIT-BRAIN AND SPREADING DEPRESSION APPROACHES
Split-brain techniques

The two hemispheres of the brain, and therefore the cortex of those hemispheres, are connected by **commissural fibers,** particularly the **corpus callosum** (Fig. 6-10 and Chapter 6), although the anterior and posterior commissures participate as well. Neurosurgeons were puzzled for years by the absence of any gross behavioral or perceptual abnormalities in human patients after the corpus callosum was severed. In some instances the operation was necessary to remove brain tumors in the third ventricle. When no apparent consequences were seen, one prominent investigator factitiously remarked that the only apparent function of the corpus callosum was mechanical—to keep the hemispheres from sagging apart! Another reason for the operation was to keep epileptic seizures from spreading from one hemisphere to the other—which prompted the remark that the function of the corpus callosum was to spread seizures! However, subsequent careful investigation has developed a technique for confining visual and somesthetic input to one hemisphere of the brain and for separating one hemisphere of the brain from the other

(Sperry). The initial experiments using the technique asked the following questions: (1) if sensory input is restricted to one hemisphere of the brain in training, will the other hemisphere learn too (with the two hemispheres still connected), and (2) if the sensory input requires the cerebral cortex for discrimination and the connections between the two hemispheres are cut, can the training be restricted to one hemisphere.

Pattern discrimination requires the cerebral cortex, as discussed previously in this chapter. Each eye supplies both hemispheres, the left visual field field (right half of both retinas) stimulating the right visual cortex and the right visual field (left half of both retinas) stimulating the left visual cortex (Fig. 12-5). Thus it is not surprising that a cat that has been taught a visual discrimination with the left eye blindfolded can perform the discrimination with the right eye blindfolded; both sides of the cortex receive information from either eye and both sides learn the habit at once. If the crossing fibers of the optic chiasma are cut, however, only fibers from the temporal halves of the retina will survive (Fig. 12-5). The cat will have "tunnel" vision, and the right eye will supply only the visual cortex of the right hemisphere, whereas the left eye supplies only the left visual cortex. If such a cat is trained in a visual discrimination with the right eye only (left eye blindfolded), then tested with the left eye only, he will perform perfectly. Obviously, the trace laid down in the right visual cortex has been transferred to the left visual cortex via the parts of the corpus callosum that connect them.

What happens if the corpus callosum and other commissural fibers are severed prior to training under the above conditions? If the corpus callosum and other commissural fibers are severed, the two hemispheres are no longer in communication. The operation severs the anterior and posterior commissures, thalamic connections, and midbrain tectum so that no crossing fibers exist above the hindbrain. If such cats are trained in a pattern discrimination with one eye only and then tested with the other eye only, they show no evidence of learning. The memory trace has been confined to the cortex of one hemisphere. For food, split-brain cats can be taught to go to the door with the cross on it with one eye blindfolded and to go to the adjoining door with a circle on it with the other eye blindfolded. The two hemispheres have learned contradictory habits. Furthermore, contradictory training can occur on alternate trials, by blindfolding one eye and then the other. Finally, polarized glasses can be fitted to these cats so that the left door has a cross and the right door a circle as seen by one eye, while the left has a cross and the right a circle as seen by the other eye. As training proceeds, one hemisphere learns to go to the cross and the other hemisphere learns to go to the circle on the same trials. The effect is not confined to vision. Roughness discrimination requires the somesthetic cortex, and the sensory input from one paw goes to somesthetic sensory projection areas in the opposite hemisphere (the fibers cross in the hindbrain, below the split-brain section—Figs. 8-6 and 8-7). Split-brain cats and monkeys cannot perform a roughness discrimination with the left paw if trained with the right, and vice versa; the memory trace has been confined to one hemisphere.

Spreading depression

According to Leao and Bures animals without cortical convolutions (fissures, gyri, and sulci), such as the rat, are useful in a technique that depresses the activity of one hemisphere at a time. Potassium chloride (KC1) solution can be administered to the cortex of one hemisphere thorugh a small hole in the skull. This causes a depression of electrical activity in the cortex that spreads over the entire hemisphere, "anesthetizing" it, so to speak. The spreading

depression will not cross the fissure dividing the two hemispheres; thus the effect is confined to one hemisphere of the brain. Furthermore, the cortex recovers after a period of time so that the technique allows a reversible decortication of one hemisphere at a time. If a rat is trained in a visual pattern discrimination with one hemisphere depressed, allowed to recover, and then tested with the other hemisphere depressed, it shows no results from the training. Only one hemisphere learned when the other was inactive, and the inactive hemisphere could not "copy" the trace. However, only a few trials are needed with both hemispheres active for the untrained hemisphere to copy the trace, and depressing the originally trained hemisphere will not impair performance thereafter.

Locating the trace in the cortex

In a cat or monkey learning a visual discrimination with the chiasma sectioned, the input from one eye goes to one hemisphere; the information is available to the other hemisphere only via the corpus callosum. The same thing is true for an unoperated cat or monkey taught a somesthetic discrimination with one paw. When tested with the other eye or paw, the animal performs perfectly. But did an "untrained" hemisphere use information taken from the "trained" hemisphere via the corpus callosum at the time the animal was tested, or did the hemisphere without sensory input copy the input of the "informed" hemisphere during the training trials? Apparently the trace is laid down in both hemispheres at the same time during training, the hemisphere without sensory input copying the trace in the hemisphere with sensory input *during* training. A chiasma-sectioned cat is taught a pattern discrimination with one eye before the split-brain operation is performed. *After* a split-brain operation the animal is tested with the other eye and performs well—the information had been stored during training in the hemisphere that lacked sensory input.

Can the trace be more precisely localized in a specific area of the cortex? Both split-brain and spreading depression experiments indicate that it can. Split-brain cats can be taught a tactile discrimination with their left paw, confining the input to the right hemisphere. Removal of all the cortex of the right hemisphere but the sensory-motor and frontal areas does not affect the habit. Neither does removing the sensory motor and frontal lobes of the left (untrained) hemisphere. The inference is that the trace was formed in the right sensory motor cortex. In the same vein the right hemisphere of rats can be depressed with potassium chloride and the left hemisphere trained in a somesthetic habit. After recovery, the sensory motor cortex of the trained left hemisphere can be protected from depression with magnesium chloride solution and the rest of the trained left hemisphere depressed, leaving the naive right hemisphere normal. The animals performed well, localizing the habit to the protected left sensory-motor cortex.

All these experiments suggest that rats, cats, and monkeys can learn as well with the cortex of the right hemisphere as with the cortex of the left hemisphere. Is the same true of man? The left side of the brain controls the right hand and vice versa in humans, and humans exhibit right- or left-handedness far more frequently than do animals, especially where language skills such as writing are concerned. In humans language habits seem localized in the left hemisphere (right-handed subjects) whereas less complex traces are laid down in the right hemisphere or in both. Split-brain surgical patients have difficulty responding to verbal commands with their left hand. Since the right hemisphere controls the left hand, it does not have access via the callosum to verbal information stored in the left hemisphere. These patients also have difficulty responding to written material in their left visual field (input to the right

hemisphere does not have access to the verbal information stored in the left cortex). So some "division of labor" between the cortex of the right and left hemispheres seems indicated for man as far as the traces of language habits are concerned.

BRAIN STIMULATION AND RECORDING

Another way of finding out what parts of the brain are involved in learning consists of permanently implanting electrodes in various parts of the brain. The electrodes can then be used to stimulate various parts of the brain or record from them *during learning.*

Conditioning via implanted electrodes

As one example of this technique, brain stimulation can be used as a CS in a simple conditioning habit. This bypasses all the receptor input and shows that receptor activity is not essential for the brain changes involved in learning. Stimulation of a variety of cortical centers and even the cerebellum can serve as an effective CS in bell-shock conditioning experiments with cats and dogs. Furthermore (Chapter 14), in a leg-flexion CR stimulation of the motor projection area to cause leg flexion can act as an effective US (Doty). Pain input need not cause the leg flexion before it can be conditioned to a CS. This suggests that a simple connection between a CS center in the brain and activity in the motor projection area can be made. The change in brain activity with learning need not be made farther "upstream" as a relation between two sensory inputs rather than a sensory input and a motor output, even though the senory-sensory arrangement may normally be the case. As pointed out in Chapter 14, the connections are "vertical" ones, however, and probably involve subcortical nuclei. Cuts in the cortex that circumscribe or surround the location of the CS electrode do not disturb later performance of the habit. However, *undercutting* the CS electrode abolishes response to stimulation at that point on later tests.

Conditioned responses of the brain

The brain changes involved in learning can be confined to the brain itself, no overt response being required. It was previously shown that an overt response was not necessary for conditioning. Now it will seem that the rhythmic electrical activity of the brain itself can be conditioned. During rest (especially with the eyes closed) human subjects often demonstrate a 10 cps pattern of brain waves called the alpha rhythm (Chapter 14 and Fig. 14-10). The pattern is most clearly seen in electroencephalograph (EEG) recordings made with the electrodes placed on the occipital area of the scalp above the visual projection area. A flash of light in the subject's eyes will desynchronize the alpha rhythm into low-voltage fast activity, an event called the **alpha block.** A tone can be used just before the light flash to signal the onset of the flash. When this is done often enough (about fifty trials), the alpha block will occur in response to the tone before the onset of the light or in the absence of the light. This is a case of **alpha block conditioning.** The light flash and resulting alpha block have been used as US and UR, respectively. The tone has served as a CS for type I conditioning of the alpha block. An electrical response of the brain to one sensory input has been conditioned to another sensory input. The records indicate a spread of the CR from parietal (auditory projection area) to occipital (visual projection area) regions as conditioning trials with the tone and light flash proceed.

A more complex conditioning of the alpha waves is **alpha wave driving.** A light of lower intensity is used, a light that does not block the alpha waves. If this light is flashed on and off at a rate of 12 per second, for example, a 10 per second alpha rhythm will "follow" the flashing light by increasing its frequency to 12 per second.

A tone can be used as a signal that the flashing light is going to be turned on. After repeating this sequence of events a number of times, the alpha rhythm will increase from 10 to 12 per second in response to the tone.

Alpha block and other brain wave responses also accompany bell-shock conditioning, and alpha block accompanies any aroused state (Chapter 14). Beta and kappa waves accompany the alpha block. Implanted electrodes in the BSRF (ARAS) show 5 per second waves that appear along with the alpha block at the onset of the CS, and last up to 1 minute, a typical arousal response in this area. During the interval between the CS and the US, when the trained animal responds, 3 to 5 per second waves are recorded from the hippocampus and responses of the caudate and amygdaloid nuclei appear, responses that were not present prior to conditioning. This means the involvement of the limbic system (Chapter 14 and Fig. 14-7). It appears that many parts of the brain, including the ARAS and limbic system, are involved in even the simplest conditioning. The ARAS potentials are essential to the waking state and are increased in alert attention (Chapters 14 and 15). When a tone previously conditioned to shock is sounded, the potentials appear in the BSRF and the sleeping animal awakens. Other tones, different in pitch, do not have this effect. Perhaps a similar thing occurs when a well-conditioned mother sleeps through many other sounds but awakens when her baby cries. As will be explained later, the limbic system is as involved in "learning" phenomena as it was in "motivation" and "emotion"; the separation of these topics is more apparent than real.

The widespread response changes of the brain in learning, however, can be restricted to the brain alone and be made independent of the sense organs or overt responses. In an anesthetized animal a motor cortex UR will occur to a pain-shock US, even thought the animal cannot move. The motor cortex response can be conditioned to stimulation of the occipital (visual) cortex, showing conditioning of the brain that bypasses all sensory inputs and motor outputs.

Reinforcement centers of the brain

As pointed out in Chapters 14 and 15, brain centers for reward and punishment have been found, centers that must be included in any account of the physiological psychology of learning. Experiments were cited showing that a rat would work to stimulate itself via electrodes implanted in limbic, anterior midbrain, and anterior (parasympathetic) hypothalamic areas. Within these areas hunger reward centers have been discovered that work only when the rat is hungry. Sexual reward centers have been found that will not work with castrate rats, but only with normal males or castrates injected with male sex hormones. Human patients have reported erotic sensations and daydreams from stimulation in some of these areas and more generalized pleasure from stimulation in others. Rats will learn complex tasks if rewarded with such brain stimulation. On the other hand, centers have been found in the thalamus, midbrain, and limbic areas that are punishment centers. Some of these centers are involved in the pain pathways, but others are not; human patients report feelings of anxiety and panic from stimulation in certain of the sites included in the punishment group. Stimulation of these sites in animals leads to all the responses typical of fear. Cats will learn a wheel-turning avoidance CR (type II conditioning), when a light or tone signals the onset of brain simulation unless the cat turns the wheel within a few seconds. This CR is very resistant to extinction.

Brain stimulation and learning

Small stimulating cortical shocks, delivered during the course of each trial, improve maze and discrimination learning in rats. However, subcortical stimulation to the thalamus impairs a bar-pressing response in cats, and caudate stimulation abolishes an avoidance response in dogs. Small stimuli seem more disruptive at certain subcortical centers than at cortical locations. This may suggest an important role for selected subcortical centers in learning.

Brain stimulation and memory

Operations for brain tumors are often carried out under local anesthetics so that the patient is conscious, but experiencing no pain. Under these conditions the surgeon can stimulate the brain electrically, and the patient can report the sensations he experiences as a result. (The procedure is followed so that the surgeon can "map" the brain to avoid damaging sensory projection areas in removing a tumor, for example.) If the patient has a tumor in the temporal lobe, the temporal lobe will have a low threshold to brain stimulation and will give a large electrical response to stimulation. Vivid reinacted memories are reported by such patients during temporal lobe stimulation. They will "see" a friend walking across the room toward them or "hear" a familiar piece of music. This is of interest to the physiological psychology of learning because of the close connections of the temporal lobes with the limbic system via the amygdaloid nucleus.

TIME COURSE OF BRAIN ACTIVITY IN LEARNING: PERSEVERATION AND CONSOLIDATION

Two-phase hypothesis

Another approach to events in the brain with learning concerns the time course of these events, irrespective of their location. It should be evident by now that activity in many brain centers, both cortical and subcortical, accompanies learning and memory. Experiments have shown that the brain activity accompanying learning lasts for a longer time than was previously suspected. It may outlast the practice experience by as much as a half hour. A **two-phase hypothesis** of learning and memory has gained wide acceptance, a hypothesis that further distinguishes between immediate memory and long-term memory. During the brain activity that immediately follows practice, the subject remembers perfectly; thus one may dial a telephone number without error just after reading it. However, unless the brain activity continues for a time without interruption, no "permanent" trace in the brain (memory) will be formed. Brain activity that follows practice is called **perseveration,** and the consequent formation of a learning trace is called **consolidation.** Perseveration is believed to be the basis for immediate memory and is perhaps necessary for consolidation of the memory trace. Whether ordinary environmental events can interrupt perseveration and thereby prevent consolidation is a moot question to be taken up later.

Development of the hypothesis. The two-stage, or perseveration-consolidation, hypothesis was invented to explain **retroactive inhibition** (Müller and Pilzecker). It was found that subjects could not remember a list of nonsense syllables well if they had learned a subsequent list. It was proposed that learning the second list interrupted perseveration of the first list before consolidation of a permanent trace of the first list was complete. Later experiments showed, however, that most of the forgetting was caused by confusion between the syllables of the two similar lists. In the same way one might have difficulty remembering two telephone numbers that were very much alike—digits from one phone number might appear in one's attempt to recall the other. Besides this, the second list was learned more than an hour after the first, and it was doubtful that perseveration of the first list would last that long. Much more recently, another writer (Hebb) was speculating about perceptual learning. He proposed that the stimuli of learning initiated activity in reverbrating circuits of the associative cortex, self reexciting "circles" of

nerve cells (Chapter 13). This activity constituted the basis for immediate memory and could last for up to an hour. The activity spread to **cell assemblies,** whose synapses were changed by their activity; therefore they were more likely to excite each other the next time. When a series of cell assemblies are excited in order in a perception, such as successively viewing the corners of a triangle, a **phase sequence** was built up, with the cells that unite the cell assemblies being the basis for the permanent memory of the perception.

Interruption of consolidation

At about the same time the above hypothesis was proposed, another investigator (Duncan) was studying the effects of **electroconvulsive shock (ECS)** on learning and memory in rats. ECS is a strong electrical current stimulus to the brain, usually delivered by electrodes attached to the head. The massive brain stimulation that results causes a convulsion that resembles an epileptic "fit," or the seizures that result from insulin shock or overdoses of stimulating drugs. All three methods of inducing seizures were in use for the treatment of mental patients. Side effects on memory were noted that were the same as those following other trauma or damage to the brain—retroactive amnesia, or RA (Chapter 14). Memory for events that occurred immediately before the treatment was impaired more than older memories.

In investigating RA at short time intervals, the RA effect in rats for just-practiced habit was profound, even though a simple habit was used. (RA for complex habits such as a maze can occur, even when treatments follow practice by several hours.) In Duncan's pioneering study, rats were trained to jump a barrier to avoid electric shock. If they jumped from the black side of a box to the white side of the box within 10 seconds after being placed in the apparatus, they avoided shock to the feet. If ECS followed each trial by 20 seconds, 40 seconds, 4 minutes, or 15 minutes, they learned more slowly than did rats given no ECS. ECS given 2 to 14 hours after each trial did not affect learning of this simple response; therefore brain trauma could not have been the reason for the impairment (as may be the case for ECS effects on more complex habits, such as mazes). Brain trauma would not depend on the interval between practice and ECS, yet the shorter this time interval, the more poorly the animals performed. The rats could have hesitated to jump the barrier if the ECS treatment that followed was painful. The effect of punishment on learning the response was checked with control groups. It was found that punishment (foot-shock with the ECS apparatus) had to be given within 2 minutes after each trial to impair performance, whereas ECS was effective at much longer intervals. Duncan reasoned that the massive brain stimulation of ECS caused a convulsive "storm" of neural activity in the brain. This interrupted the perseveration of the habit in the brain after each trial if ECS was given while perseveration was still going on. The longer perseveration was allowed to go on after each trial before interrupting it with ECS, the greater the consolidation of the memory trace, and the better the performance on subsequent trials.

Since this pioneering study, it has been found that less traumatic treatments can be used to interrupt perseveration and thereby impair consolidation. For example, anesthetizing rats (sodium Pentothal) within 5 minutes after each trial in a maze slows learning. Furthermore, both anesthesia and convulsions impair one-trial learning of a CAR if given within a few minutes of the trial. The animal was shocked while bar-pressing in a Skinner box for water and then given a convulsive or drug treatment to interrupt subsequent consolidation of the experience. If it did not learn, it would continue to bar-press for water the next day. This proved to be the case for many of the treated animals. If the treatment had been punishing, the animals would

have avoided bar-pressing because they anticipated shock for doing so as well as a painful treatment afterward. Other agents have proved useful in interrupting the consolidation process—anoxia in rats by simulated altitude or carbon dioxide, or heat narcosis in goldfish, for example. Finally, human patients undergoing deep surgical anesthesia often report RA for the events just preceding onset of the anesthesia.

Stimulating consolidation

Another group of experiments (McGaugh, and others) have shown that brain stimulants (such as strychnine), administered within a few minutes *after* each practice trial has ended, can improve the rate of maze acquisition in rats. Presumably, the neural processes underlying consolidation are more effective when the brain is more active. A variety of stimulants have been used (Metrazol, caffeine, picrotoxin, 1757 I.S., etc.) so that the effect is not specific to any one drug. The treatment is more effective for rats bred to be poor maze learners (maze-dull) than for maze-bright rats. Other experiments seem to show that the maze-bright rats consolidate faster after each trial than do the maze-dull rats. Consolidation can be interrupted, or at least learning is impaired, when ECS is administered at a longer interval after each trial for the maze-dull rats than for the maze-bright rats. The "bright" rats appear to finish consolidation within 45 minutes, but the "dull" rats do not. These experiments are exciting because of their elimination of any punishment hypothesis (rats would not learn *faster* if the treatment following practice were punishing) and because of their implications for improving the learning rate in subnormal people.

Alternate explanations

No alternative explanations have been offered for improved learning following drug stimulants *after* practice. Other explanations have been proposed, however, for impaired learning resulting from ECS treatment after practice. Some investigators (Coons and Miller) have shown that repeated trials, each followed by ECS in an avoidance box or in a runway-to-food situation, can impair the animal's performance in a way that suggests fear of the treatment. Other experimenters (Hudspeth and others) have used a passive avoidance task to analyze this fear conditioning. If a rat is placed on an elevated platform, it will naturally step down onto a grid floor. If the animal is shocked through the grid floor for doing so, it will avoid stepping down on subsequent trials. If ECS immediately after each trial prevents it from learning its lesson, the animal will step down on each following trial. If it "remembers" and is afraid of the ECS, foot-shock followed by ECS will be even more effective than foot-shock alone in keeping it on the platform. The results show that the rat begins to avoid stepping down when the daily trial is followed by ECS, but only after 4 to 8 days, when 1 or 2 days is enough to train a control rat. Repeated ECS does cause avoidance. However, a single ECS treatment can impair a habit ordinarily learned in *one* trial, as has already been seen.

Others (Lewis and Adams) have offered a conditioning explanation of ECS effects. They suggest that convulsive responses to ECS become conditioned to the stimuli of the learning task and that these responses are incompatable with correct performance in the learning task. This does not explain, however, how non-ECS treatments such as depressing or stimulating drugs can impair learning or improve it when administered after practice. Finally, a moot point remains. Even if drugs or ECS can affect consolidation to impair or improve learning, these are extreme conditions. Is there any evidence that the stimuli of everyday life can interfere with consolidation of a just-practiced habit? One writer (Walker) thinks not. Walker believes that a consolidating neural trace system is protected from interference by subsequent stimuli. He points to the fact that animals tend to vary their behavior, alternating sides when they are fed in either arm of a T maze, for example. This effect is increased when the trials come one after another,—each trial occurring when perseveration from the previous trial is supposed to be going on. Still others have proposed a three-stage memory system. Immediate memory depends on perseveration, memory over minutes or hours on consolidation, and the usefulness of the permanent trace on the ability of the nervous system to retrive the stored information. Retrieval is impaired by ECS and other brain trauma as well, but memory improves as the animal recovers. In any case there is no clear evidence that everyday experiences interfere with consolidation.

The superior recall that occurs when sleep rather than waking activity follows learning or when practice trials follow each other by hours rather than by minutes has been cited as an example of improved learning caused by less stimulus interference with consolidation. Interference explanations that depend on confusion at the time of recall caused by stimulus similarity are also offered. Similar events can become confused because they occurred one after the other rather than because one event interfered with consolidation of a previous one. There is much to learn in this area, but it has already taught us much about when, if not how, the brain learns.

Learning in the octopus

If perseveration does occur in the brain, where does the perseveration occur? Where is the permanent trace laid down? Although the octopus has a much different brain than man, experiments with this animal (Boycott and Young) suggest that one part of the brain may be responsible for keeping neural activity going after practice (perseveration), whereas the permanent trace (consolidation) is laid down in another part of the brain. Two important parts of the brain of the octopus are the vertical lobe and the optic lobe. The optic lobe is closely related to vision and seems to control attack responses to prey. The vertical lobe has connections with various parts of the octopus brain and seems to have less specific functions. It is therefore not surprising that removal of the vertical lobe does not impair attack responses to prey so long as the optic lobe is intact. Removal of the vertical lobe does, however, abolish the ability to learn or to delay response. The octopus is then unable to reverse normal attack responses, even after repeated punishment. It is unable to continue to pursue prey after the prey has vanished from sight behind an obstacle (response to an absent object). The vertical lobe seems essential for the perseveration needed for "immediate memory," and the vertical lobe seems to be needed to lay down a trace for more permanent learning (consolidation).

Subsequent work suggests that the permanent trace is laid down in the optic lobe, but the process requires continuing stimulation (perseveration) of the optic lobe by reverberating circuits in the vertical lobe. The learning process requires comparison of the attack stimulus and later signals that indicate the results of attack—taste or pain. This is only possible when the "attack excitation" continues until the "result excitation" occurs. Evidence already considered suggests that many memory traces are laid down in the cerebral cortex in man, as they are in the optic lobe of the octopus. Evidence now to be cited suggests that the hippocampus is involved in perseverating excitation that lays down these traces in a manner similar to the role of the vertical lobe in the octopus.

Short- and long-term memory and the hippocampus

It has already been reported that stimulation of the temporal lobes causes vivid reenacted memories in patients being operated upon for brain tumors. The same investigator (Penfield) has reported two cases of penetrating brain injury that damaged the temporal lobes and underlying parts of the hippocampus in both hemispheres. These patients seemed unable to form new memories, even though their recall for events prior to their accidents seemed normal for brain-damaged individuals. Yet they were not able to recall anything new over an interval longer than 10 minutes. Perhaps some of the connections between the hippocampus and temporal cortex destroyed in these patients are essential to the process of forming permanent memories, the process called consolidation. As an overstatement, the patients seemed able to operate on perseverating neural traces only, but the perseveration left no permanent traces, or "memory." Upon meeting someone new, for example, they could converse with him and use his name. If the person left for an hour and returned, they would be unable to recall ever having met him.

Old and new memories

Although many variables control how well one remembers things, an old memory is frequently recalled with more clarity than a recent event. When an event becomes a part of the array of memories that can be recalled on demand, an older memory can often be recalled more readily than a newer one. Some suggest that this is because it has been recalled more often. In line with such an idea, one writer (Russell) has suggested that the underlying trace of a memory in the nervous system is a pattern of excitation that is more readily aroused by random activity than is a new pattern. If this is the case, it would have been stimulated more often by random brain activity the longer the pattern has existed—a series of many perseverations and consolidations. Perhaps this is why old memories are less susceptible than newer memories to the brain trauma of ECS, strokes, concussions, etc.—their neural traces have been activated more often, have become more numerous and fixed, and thus are less susceptible to severe disruption.

SYSTEMS TO EXPLAIN LEARNING
Brain systems and their possible role in learning (Fig. 17-1)

Only general and tentative statements may be made in this section. Enough evidence has accumulated, however, to ask the following questions: (1) how does the brain select the relevant stimuli for learning from those bombarding it at all times from many sensory channels, that is, how does selective attention occur; (2) what centers are involved in the perseverating neural activity that seems necessary for learning; and (3) how does reward and punishment interact with perseveration to determine what is learned. The problem of selective attention involves sensory gating in the specific thalamic projection system (STPS), input to sensory projection areas via the diffuse thalamic projection system (DTPS), and arousal of the brain to any and all inputs by the ascending reticular activating system (ARAS). All these inputs were discussed in Chapter 14 and are schematically represented in Fig. 17-1.

As far as the classic sensory pathways of the STPS to the cortex are concerned, a sensory efferent system exists to selectively block or sensitize input for vision, hearing, or somesthesis. This could enable the animal to block some sensory inputs while "paying attention" to others. Efferent pathways in the STPS exist that may inhibit excitation at the retina for vision, at the organ of Corti for hearing, and at the gracile and cuneate nuclei for somesthesis (Chapters 12, 11, and 8, respectively). Efferent pathways may selectively inhibit or excite the sensory inputs at other levels of their afferent pathways as well. Proprioceptive feedback from the muscles is also subject to control from many levels of brain via the gamma efferent system to the muscle spindle fibers, as discussed in Chapter 9. By varying the threshold of stretch reflexes, the amount of muscle tone may be varied in a selective way, changing the pattern of sensations of muscle tension. Such control may be important in selective attention, the incipient movements that accompany vicarious participation in a motor act and the more generalized muscle tension that supplies widespread excitation to the brain in states of aroused attention. The DTPS, on the other hand, supplies less "modality-specific" inputs to the brain by way of the more diffuse nuclei of the thalmus and contributes to the so-called "secondary" sensory projection areas for vision, hearing, and somesthesis. It is not known whether this system is critical to attention or is an alternate sensory pathway, perhaps older in evolutionary history. In any case the DTPS is probably involved in selective sensory excitation of the brain.

Finally, parts of the brainstem reticular formation (BSRF) are activated by sensory inputs to act as an ascending reticular activating system (ARAS) to arouse cortical and subcortical centers that are not directly linked to specific sensory inputs. This arousal specifically includes the limbic-midbrain circuit indicated in Fig. 17-1 as including the hippocampus, amygdala, and hypothalamus. The entire limbic system, as discussed in Chapter 16, is probably involved. Continuing excitation in the limbic "loop" and the hypothalamus may be the basis for the perseveration discussed in a previous section, the long-continued activity following sensory input, activity that seems necessary for learning. As related in Chapter 14, the parietal, occipital, and temporal association areas of the cortex (POT areas) seem more important to learning, whereas the frontal cortex appears involved in the more subtle patterns of personality, distractability, and the ability to delay response.

No discussion of the role of parts of the brain in learning is complete, however, without including brain mechanisms for re-

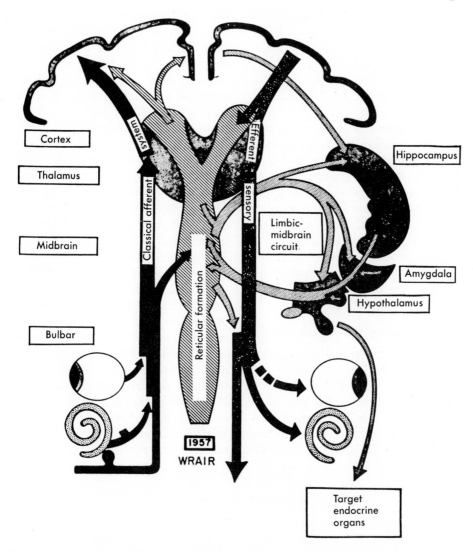

Fig. 17-1. Simplified anatomical plan of the neural systems involved in learning. For details, see text. (From Galambos, R., and Morgan, C. T.: The neural basis of learning. In Field, J., editor: Handbook of physiology, vol. 3, Baltimore, 1960, The Williams & Wilkins Co.)

inforcement—for reward and punishment. As explained in Chapter 15, brain centers have been found in animals whose stimulation is rewarding or punishing. Animals will stimulate themselves in reward centers for hours and will suffer severe punishment or learn difficult task to gain the opportunity to stimulate these brain centers. Human patients report generalized feelings of well-being from stimulation in some reward areas and sensations from other reward areas that are related to satisfaction of specific needs such as sex or hunger. Punishment or fear centers have been discovered in other areas of the brain. Animals will learn avoidance habits to prevent stimulation of fear centers, and human patients report sensations of anxiety and fear from stimulation of these areas of the brain. Both reward and punishment areas, cortical and subcortical, are closely related to the hypothalamus on one hand or the limbic circuit on the other.

If the limbic circuit is involved in perseveration, the hypothalamus is involved in monitoring changes in the internal environment that constitute need states, such as hunger, thirst, or sexual arousal. The hypothalamus contains centers sensitive to need states and to satiation of these need states (Chapter 15). Activity in hypothalamic drive centers could stimulate perseveration in the limbic circuit, selectively affect sensory input (attention) via the DTPS, and arouse the whole brain via the ARAS.

TOTE-system analogy for learning

If perseverative nervous activity is necessary for learning, the "reflex plan" of the nervous system (introduced in Chapter 6 as a temporary expedient) is inadequate to explain brain activity in learning. A simple model of sensory pathways, association pathways, and motor pathways does not al-

low for comparing sensory input to the brain with memory traces already in the brain so that behavior can vary until sensory input matches trace content in the act of recognition. One writer (Pribram) has proposed a model for just this sequence of events (Fig. 17-2). In the model sensory input is "tested" against trace content, and when incongruity is found, the brain "operates" to shift attention until another test shows congruity of sensory input and trace content. This event leads to response, the "exit" of the system when recognition occurs. The letters **TOTE** stand for "test, operate, test, exit," the sequence of events leading to recognition.

Pribram believes that the TOTE negative feedback system controls the *directional* components of behavior, whereas **homeostats** in the hypothalamus control the *equilibratory* or motivational components of behavior. Homeostats are the drive arousal and satiation centers in the hypothalamus that are sensitive to need states in the internal environment, such as hunger or thirst. He believes that the homeostats *selectively* arouse specific parts of the brain according to the need states of the body

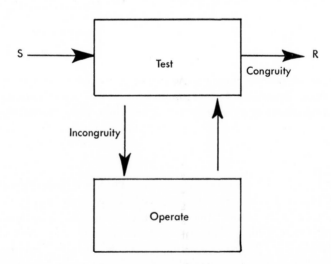

Fig. 17-2. TOTE analogy for learning. For details, see text. (Modified slightly from Miller, G. A., Galanter, E., and Pribram, K. H.: Plans and the structure of behavior, New York, 1960, Holt, Rinehart, & Winston, Inc.)

rather than diffusely arousing the cortex, as the activation theory would propose. He suggests that limbic system function concerns memory *rather than* emotion. As evidence, he cites the two patients mentioned earlier who had temporal lobe and hippocampal (limbic) injuries and who seemed unable to form new memories. Animal experiments with such lesions are cited, showing disturbances of feeding, fighting, fleeing, or sex, all sequential activities.

Limbic lesions are held to destroy sequential behavior because sequential behavior requires access to memory for the ordering of acts. Such access and ordering involve making comparisons between immediate memory (perseverating neural activity) and long-term traces contained in the parietal, occipital, and temporal cortex—the POT areas. The comparison requires perseveration, which is held to be a function of the limbic system. In making comparisons the limbic system utilizes the traces and current input of the POT intrinsic cortex (excluding sensory projection areas) for corrective matching by the TOTE sequence explained above. The limbic system utilizes the frontal intrinsic cortex (excluding the motor projection area) for matching corrective motivational inputs (feeding or drinking for example) with the need state of the internal environment. This role for the frontal intrinsic cortex is suggested because damage to these areas in man by lobotomy or lobectomy results in defects in attentional, motivational, and emotional behavior (Chapters 14 and 15).

Theory of need and reinforcement pathways

Some comparisons between instrumental lever pressing for a food reward and lever pressing for brain stimulation in the reward areas have been instructive for one writer (Deutsch). He notes that acquisition of the response is gradual in both cases. However, extinction differs in the two situations. When lever pressing no

longer results in a food reward, the response rate slows gradually to a halt. If brain stimulation is turned off, lever pressing ceases abruptly. If reward is again available, response rate for food increases slowly during a "warm-up" period. But when brain stimulation is provided again, response rate becomes maximum quite suddenly without a gradual warm-up. From these and other results, Deutsch suggests that there are two pathways between groups of cells in the hypothalamus that are sensitive to bodily needs and groups of cells elsewhere in the CNS that govern behavior. One pathway is a motivational pathway, which leads to action when a need exists. The other pathway is a reinforcement pathway, active when the animal is rewarded. The reinforcement pathway must be excited before the motivational pathway can function. So far, this seems just a complicated way of saying that a motivated animal will not perform unless it is rewarded. But Deutsch suggests that rewarding brain stimulation excites *both* pathways, which explains why the animal stops responding abruptly when the stimulation stops and begins again abruptly when stimulation is restored. The animal's lever-pressing for food, however, has its motivational pathway excited by internal conditions. The motivation pathway causes action only when a reinforcement pathway is activated by eating—two events that are separated in time. Activity in both pathways is gradually synchronized by learning and gradually desynchronized by extinction. The changes are more abrupt when brain stimulation starts or stops acting on both paths at once.

CHANGES AT THE SYNAPSE IN LEARNING
Molar biochemical changes

Learning involves a change in response to stimuli. Many writers believe that memory is caused by some physical change, or "memory trace," in the nervous system that results from learning. Whatever parts of the brain are involved in learning, any physical changes should logically occur at synapses, the anatomical sites where one neuron excites another neuron. Synapses appear to be the only places in the central nervous system where pathways between stimulus and response can be changed, however complex the pathways. This section concerns the nature of the change at synapses during learning without regard to where the synapses are located.

Older ideas. Several suggestions have been made for gross changes at the synapse to enable one cell to excite another more easily as a result of use during learning. The physical movement of nerve cells (neurobiotaxis) observed during development in the embryo is one possibility. Another is increase in the number of axon terminals "contacting" cell bodies and dendrites. Swelling of the end feet endings of axon terminals could also increase their effectiveness. Improved connections between stellate (star) cells and pyramidal cells in the cortex has been suggested. Glial cell movement to interpose between synaptic contacts to block excitation could occur, whereas growth of neuropil would have the opposite effect. None of these changes has been reliably observed after learning, however, and they remain speculations.

Biochemical and anatomical changes in the rat brain. Synapses in which one neuron stimulates another by the release of **acetylcholine** (**ACh**) have been demonstrated in autonomic ganglia, the spinal cord, and in some centers of the brain. The ACh acts only briefly because it is hydrolized (chemically removed), a reaction speeded by the enzyme **acetylcholine esterase** (**AChE**) that is present at all cholinergic synapses. Such cholinergic synapses may be involved in learning. Repeated synaptic "use" during learning could increase the efficiency of synapses by leading to the release of more ACh. The difference between fast and slow learners could be caused by a biochemical difference in the ACh/AChE ratio rather than by anatomical differences in their brains. Either high ACh or low AChE could make synapses more excitable.

Such speculations have led to a fascinating series of experiments under the direction of Krech, Rosensweig, and Bennett. The earlier studies in the series demonstrated chemical differences in the brains of rats, selectively bred to be maze-bright or maze-dull, according to their ability to learn a complex maze. The maze-bright rats had a greater brain AChE content than the maze-dull rats. Later studies showed that this difference was largely confined to the cortex and that in different strains of rats it was the ACh/AChE *ratio* that seemed most closely related to learning ability. ACh and AChE content appeared to be independently determined, genetically. Breeding for AChE content in the brain, for example, can lead to high-AChE, maze-dull animals and low-AChE, maze-bright animals, provided the ACh content varies only randomly.

Having established that hereditary differences in brain chemistry could affect learning ability, this Berkeley group asked whether or not environmental stimulation could affect brain chemistry and, perhaps, the anatomy of the brain as well. In these experiments one group of rats were raised in solitary confinement (isolated controls, or IC rats). Their littermates were raised in groups and given training in several tasks as well as frequently changed toys in their cages (ladders, wheels, etc.) for stimulation (environmental complexity and training, or ECT). Animals given ECT for 30 days after weaning were compared with those suffering IC for a similar period. In over seven strains that were tested, the ECT animals had less cortical and more subcortical AChE in their brains than did the IC rats when sacrificed. In other experiments they were found to have thicker and heavier cortical tissue, better blood supply to the brain, and biochemical changes (in proteins, hexokinase, and serotonin) expected of a more active brain.

The effects do not seem restricted to early growth and development; similar results have been obtained when the difference in treatment began at 105 days of age (young adult rats). With the attention being given today to human mental deficiency and with "head start" preschool programs for environmentally deprived children, the Berkeley experiments may have far-reaching implications. Biochemical and anatomical differences in the brain may be effected in man in the same general way as in the rat, by differences in environmental stimulation.

Calcium model (Overton). The nerve impulse involves ACh that is found inside the nerve cell. One by-product of ACh changes during nervous activity is acetic acid. The calcium hypothesis proposes the following events. If the cell is stimulated frequently, acetic acid accumulates and converts calcium and calcium compounds into soluble forms that dissipate. Reduced calcium increases the excitability of neurons at synapses. Therefore the more active a neuron, the lower the calcium level around it, and the more excitable it becomes. Frequent stimulation could thereby increase the excitability of the synapses involved in learning. The synapses involved in learning probably include the reverberating, or self-reexciting circuits, supposed to be involved in perseveration. The evidence for the model includes similar graphs for calcium consumption in children and for the amount of forgetting, both as functions of age. In the early years of rapid bone growth, calcium intake is high in children (milk, etc.), and children remember few events that occurred during those years. Experiments also show that rats on a low-calcium diet learn mazes more rapidly than rats on a high-calcium diet. The theory does not clearly explain permanent changes in calcium metabolism that could be the basis of "permanent" memory traces, however.

Molecular biochemical changes

As explained in Chapter 3, the cell reproduces itself and repairs its parts according to patterns contained in the DNA molecules of the chromosomes in its nucleus. In cell reproduction by cell division each DNA molecule is reproduced in the nucleus of each of the two daughter cells. In repairing parts of the cell sections of the DNA molecules assemble simpler RNA molecules, the form of the DNA section serving as a pattern. The messenger RNA, so assembled, migrates from the nucleus to the cytoplasm of the cell. There it assembles transfer RNA by a similar process. The transfer RNA, in turn, assembles enzymes to speed the needed chemical reactions of cell repair. Some theorists believe that changes in the DNA molecules, the RNA molecules, or the enzymes they form produce changes in nerve cell excitability that accompany learning. DNA, RNA, or enzymes could change the structure of a nerve cell. Changes in the structure of the nerve cell membrane could make the cell more excitable. It is pointed out that nerve cells in mammals do not reproduce themselves. Perhaps part of the DNA-RNA mechanism involved in cell repair and cell reproduction is used for learning instead. (Such changes would not be passed on to the animal's progeny—inheritance of acquired characteristics—because the reproductive cells in the gonads would not be affected. Only the nerve cells would change, and these would die when the animal did.)

Most of the evidence for this view comes from experiments with flatworms, small primitive invertebrates with a "nerve net" nervous system, a primitive ganglion-type "brain" in the head end, and visual receptors in the head. Unlike vertebrates, they reproduce asexually as well as sexually and can reproduce missing parts after amputation, *including nervous tissue,* to the extent that two complete **planaria** are regenerated if one is cut in two. The head end grows a new tail and the tail end grows a new head. McConnell and his colleagues wondered if changes in the nerve cells caused by learning would be passed on to new nerve cells as the new nerve cells were formed to regenerate amputated parts of the worm. The DNA-RNA-enzyme mechanism is involved in cell reproduction. Any change in nerve cells caused by learning might involve the same mechanism. If this is true, the change resulting from learning would be reproduced when new nerve cells were "copied" from old ones in cell division. To test these notions, flatworms were trained, cut in two, and tested after regeneration. Flatworms respond to electric shock by curling into an **S** shape. The response was conditioned to a flash of light. The worms were then cut in two, and the head ends grew new tails while the tails grew new heads. The regenerated worms were cut in two again, and again the missing parts developed. A group of worms consisting entirely of regenerated tissue (one fourth the total) could be isolated. Upon testing, these worms acquired the original CR faster than "naive" worms, even though none of their nerve cells had existed at the time of original training. Their nerve cells had been reproduced, however, from "trained" nerve cells.

The next question concerned the role of the nerve ganglion in the head that serves as a flatworm's "brain." If the head is split so that the ganglion is cut in half longitudinally, each half of the head creates a matching half, and a two-headed worm results. The two-headed worm learns the CR faster than a normal worm. Two heads seem better than one, at least for this purpose, and the head ganglion seems to dominate the nervous system of the flatworm. A further test of the head dominance hypothesis was made in the following way. An enzyme, RNase, interferes with the regeneration process and would presumably interfere with learning patterns being passed on to regenerating tissue. After learning the CR the worms were cut in two, and their missing parts were regenerated in RNase solution. The trained heads were thus prevented, at least partly, from passing on the learning change and developed "naive" tails; the trained tails developed "naive" heads. If the head dominates, the worms with experienced heads should show the results of training, whereas those with "naive" heads should not. In a general way this is what happened.

Another line of evidence for the DNA-RNA-enzyme-protein synthesis idea comes from the effects of the drug puromycin. Puromycin inhibits protein synthesis in the cell. It must be injected directly into the brain to affect learning because it does not pass the blood-brain barrier (Chapter 6). Strangely enough, the injection must follow learning (a Y-maze) in the rat by 3 to 6 days to be effective. Under these conditions it blots out the habit, leaving responses learned before or after this period intact.

In applying the DNA-RNA hypothesis to humans it has been found that administering RNA (but not DNA) to elderly individuals, improves their memory. However, the improvement does not outlast the treatment and may have merely overcome a nutritional deficiency. Still, it *has* been found that the supply of nerve cell RNA increases in humans from ages 3 to 40, is constant to 60, and decreases rapidly thereafter. This roughly parallels changes in the ability to learn new material (intelligence).

Other approaches. It has been suggested (Smith, 1962) that nerve cells active in learning increase their output of transmitter substance as a result of an increase in the cell enzymes necessary to produce the transmitter. Rimland advances the idea that some nerve cells are "frequency-specific," that is, they fire only at certain frequencies (entelechy). This specificity, he argues, could be "learned" and prove to be the basis for the memory trace. He suggests the BSRF as the site of such cells since they could excite selected areas over the entire brain via the diffuse connections of the BSRF. Although many cells would be involved, a single cell at a crucial point in the chain could provide the basis for learning.

SUMMARY

Using a reflex model and assuming encephalization, early investigators sought to locate the "trace" left in the brain by learning, removing parts of the cortex of rats and observing the effect on learning and memory for mazes of different difficulty. The lesions had more effect on memory than on new learning, impaired performance in difficult mazes the most, and the effects depended on the size rather than on the locus of the lesion. The latter finding led to the mass action and equipotentiality principles. The findings did not result from damage to sensory projection areas alone since blind rats learned better than did rats without a visual cortex. Cortical connections made in learning seem vertically organized via subcortical centers because thin cuts isolating sections of rat cortex from one another impair neither learning nor memory. Damage to the thalamus affects learning, but again the size rather than the locus of the lesion determines the effect.

Attempts to simplify the memory trace to make it easier to locate were no more successful. The conditioned response was used to this end. Controls for habituation to the CS and sensitization to the US (pseudoconditioning) were necessary. Experiments showed conditioning in acute spinal animals, but this appeared to be pseudoconditioning; spinal conditioning in chronic preparations was not found. Decorticate conditioning appears possible. If bell-shock conditioning is used with these animals, care must be taken to avoid conditioning sham rage responses (struggling).

Otherwise, only type I classical CR's of anticipatory struggling to the bell CS will appear. With this precaution the type II instrumental response of lifting the leg to avoid the shock can be obtained as the second stage of conditioning. Decorticate animals can learn simple auditory or brightness CR's, but they cannot learn to differentiate visual or auditory patterns. Parietal lesions impair pattern and form discrimination; all three somesthetic "sensory" areas must be destroyed to abolish somesthetic discrimination. Prefrontal lobectomy impairs delayed reactions in monkeys, but their distractability is an important variable. Several experiments have shown that ability to respond is not essential for conditioning; presentation of the CS and US is enough. A second signalling system of cortical language CR's may explain why man learns simple CR's more rapidly than the various other species that lack language and differ little in their rate of simple conditioning.

If the commissural fibers connecting the two cerebral hemispheres are cut, little difference is seen in the behavior of man. Animal experiments show, however, that visual input from one eye can be restricted to the hemisphere of the same side if the crossing fibers of the optic chiasma are cut in split-brain cats and monkeys. Somesthetic input and motor control is restricted to the opposite hemisphere in split-brain animals. The traces of visual or somesthetic learning can be restricted to the one hemisphere by the split-brain technique, and contradictory habits can be taught the two hemispheres. "Temporary decortication" of one hemisphere in rats can be caused by a spreading depression of neural activity that follows application of potassium chloride to that hemisphere. Discrimination learning in rats can be confined to one hemisphere in this manner. Only a few trials are necessary after recovery for the untrained hemisphere to "copy" the trace in the trained hemisphere. Split-brain and spreading depression experiments can be used to locate the trace of a visual discrimination more precisely in the sensory-motor cortex of a split-brain cat and the sensory-motor cortex of a rat (when the latter area is protected with magnesium chloride). In humans, however, language habits seem restricted to the dominant hemisphere (the left hemisphere in right-handed people).

In anesthetized animals the response to brain stimulation in a motor area of the cortex can be conditioned to stimulation in a sensory projection area. The alpha block to a bright light can be conditioned to a tone in humans as can "driving" of the alpha rhythm with a flashing light. Alpha block to the CS appears in bell-shock conditioning, along with changed activity in the BSRF, amygdala, and hippocampus. ARAS potentials wake a sleeping animal in responding to a tone conditioned to shock. Reward centers in the brain seem important to learning; some are generalized but others are closely related to hunger or sexual behavior in animals and human patients. Fear or punishment centers are found in both humans and animals in sites that have no known relation to the pain pathways. Small stimulating electrical shocks, delivered during learning, impair acquisition at subcortical sites more than cortical sites. Stimulation of the temporal lobes in patients undergoing brain surgery leads them to report vivid memories.

It appears that neural activity that outlasts practice (perseveration) is necessary to forming a "permanent" memory trace (consolidation). Perseverative activity may link cell assemblies into a "phase sequence," in a perceptual task such as successively viewing the corners of a triangle. This two-phase hypothesis of learning and memory is supported by experiments showing that the longer posttrial perseveration is permitted to go on before interruption by ECS the faster an avoidance habit is learned by the rat. Drugs can also be used to interrupt perseveration with similar effects on

maze learning or a one-trial CAR. Stimulating drugs seem to potentiate perseveration and consolidation to improve learning when administered *after* practice in a maze. The effect is greater for maze-dull than for maze-bright animals. The latter appear to consolidate faster because ECS 45 minutes after practice does not impair their learning, but it does affect the maze-dull rats. Punishment hypotheses and conditioning hypothesis have been offered as alternate explanations to account for ECS effects on learning; these hypotheses do not explain the drug experiments. It is still not known whether everyday stimuli can interrupt the consolidation process. It is contended that they do not because an animal usually shows variable rather than perseverative behavior.

Experiments with the octopus seem to show that perseveration in the vertical lobe drives consolidation in the optic lobe. Learned and unlearned visual responses are unimpaired by vertical lobe removal, but new visual responses to prey are not learned without the vertical lobe. In a similar way human patients with bilateral damage to the temporal lobes, amygdala, and hippocampus have normal memories but seem unable to learn anything new. Over longer periods of time older memories seem less susceptible to trauma than newer memories, perhaps because they have been recalled more often, thereby becoming more fixed and less subject to impairment.

Selective attention in learning can be explained by sensory gating (efferent control of afferent input) and activation of the DTPS as well as the STPS for the sensory modalities involved. The whole brain is activated by the ARAS, and gamma efferent control of muscle tone provides for proprioceptive arousal and incipient movement. The limbic system may mediate perseveration, with traces consolidated in the POT cortical areas, the frontal cortex controlling motivational-emotional aspects of the task. The reinforcing reward and punishment centers previously noted should be involved, whereas the hypothalamus monitors the need states of the internal environment.

In the TOTE-system analogy for learning sensory input is tested against trace content for congruity, and attention is shifted until congruity is found before the learned response occurs. This controls the directional aspect of behavior, whereas the hypothalamus controls motivational aspects via selective excitation of higher brain centers. In this system memory and sequential acts are controlled by perseverating limbic stimulation of POT areas, whereas the frontal lobes match corrective motivational changes with need states in the hypothalamus. Another theory distinguishes reinforcement from motivational pathways between the hypothalamus and higher centers and asserts that both must be active for learning to occur.

Wherever learning occurs, changes in the excitability of nerve cells at synapses may be involved. Such changes may involve the chemical transmitter, ACh, or the enzyme that speeds its removal, AChE. Rats selectively bred to be maze-bright have a higher ACh/AChE ratio in their cortex than rats bred to be maze-dull; ACh and AChE are under separate genetic control in different strains of rats. Rats isolated for 30 days after weaning (IC group) were compared with their littermates raised in groups with maximum "play" and learning opportunities (ECT group). The ECT rats had less cortical and more subcortical AChE, thicker cortical tissues, and superior cortical circulation and biochemical activity. The results are the same if the experiment is done with young adult rats. Another theory assumes that ACh release at active synapses reduces the surrounding calcium level, which, in turn, increases synaptic activity. Such a change may not be permanent enough to account for learning, however.

The nerve cell changes in learning may be more molecular, involving the DNA-RNA-protein enzyme mechanism, for cell repair and alteration. DNA and RNA are involved in cell reproduction (including nerve cells) in flatworms that have the ability to regenerate missing parts. A simple flexion response to a shock is conditioned to a light stimulus in these animals. After learning the CR, flatworms were cut in two and regenerated twice to produce a group of worms that were composed entirely of regenerated tissue. These subjects "relearned" the CR faster than did "naive" worms. The head ganglion dominates the CR for two reasons: (1) two-headed flatworms (produced by regeneration) learn the CR faster than normal planaria and (2) trained flatworms, cut in two and regenerated in RNase (that interferes with DNA-RNA processes in cell reproduction) retain the habit only if the tail end (not the head) was the regenerated part. Puromycin, which interferes with protein synthesis, may be injected into the brain to affect retention of a Y maze in rats. The effect appears only if the habit is 3 to 6 days old. In man the supply of nerve cell RNA increases from 3 to 40 years, is constant to 60, and then declines. This curve parallels that for the ability to learn new material (intelligence).

Other approaches to the trace problem include suggestions of increased output of cell enzymes and frequency-specific cells in the BSRF

READINGS

Bennett, E. L., Diamon, M. C., Krech, D., and Rosenweig, M. R.: Chemical and anatomical plasticity of brain, Science, **146**:610-619, 1964. (Bobbs-Merrill Reprint No. P-400.)

Best, J. G.: Protopsychology, Sci. Amer. **208**:54-62, Feb., 1963. (W. H. Freeman Co. Reprint No. 149).

Bitterman, M. E.: The evolution of intelligence, Sci. Amer. **212**:92-100, Jan., 1965. (W. H. Freeman Co. Reprint No. 490.)

Boycott, B. B.: Learning in the octopus, Sci. Amer. **212**:42-50, March, 1965. (W. H. Freeman Co. Reprint No. 1006.)

Breen, R. A., and McGaugh, J. L.: Facilitation of maze learning with post-trial injections of picrotoxin, J. Comp. Physiol. Psychol. **54**:498-501, 1961. (Bobbs-Merrill Reprint No. P-591.)

Brogden, W. J.: Sensory pre-conditioning, J. Exp. Psychol. **25**:323-332, 1939. (Bobbs-Merrill Reprint No. P-51.)

Bures, J., and Buresova: The use of Leao's spreading depression in the study of interhemispheric transfer of memory traces, J. Comp. Physiol. **53**:558-563, 1961. (Bobbs-Merrill Reprint No. P-412.)

Chauchard, P.: The Brain, New York, 1963, Grove Press, Inc.

Gerard, R. W.: What is memory? Sci. Amer. **189**:118-126, Sept., 1953. (W. H. Freeman Co. Reprint No. 11.)

Glickman, S. E.: Perservative neural processes and consolidation of the memory trace, *Phychol. Bull.* **58**:218-233, 1961. (Bobbs-Merrill Reprint No. P-459.)

Hudspeth, W. J., McGaugh, J. L., and Thompson, C. W.: Aversive and amnesic effects of electroconvulsive shock, J. Comp. Physiol. Psychol., **57**:61-64, 1964. (Bobbs-Merrill Reprint No. P-591.)

Hyden, H.: Sattelite cells in the nervous system, Sci. Amer. **205**:62-70, Dec., 1961. (W. H. Freeman Co. Reprint No. 134.)

Landauer, T. K.: Two hypotheses concerning the biochemical basis of memory, Psychol. Rev., **71**:167-179, 1964. (Bobbs-Merrill Reprint No. P-499.)

Lashley, K. S.: Brain mechanisms and intelligence, New York, 1963, Dover Publications, Inc.

Louttit, R. T., editor: Advancing psychological science, vol. 4., Belmont, Calif., 1965, Wadsworth Publishing Co., Inc.

McConnell, J. W., Jacobson, A. L., and Kimble, D. P.: The effects of regeneration upon retention of a conditioned response in the planarian, J. Comp. Physiol. Psychol. **52**:1-5, 1959. (Bobbs-Merrill Reprint No. P-222.)

Overton, R. K.: Thought and action, New York, Random House, Inc., 1959.

Peterson, L. R.: Short-term memory, Sci. Amer. **215**:90-95, July, 1966. (W. H. Freeman Co. Reprint No. 499.)

Pfeiffer, J.: The human brain, New York, 1965, Pyramid Publications, Inc.

Skinner, B. F.: How to teach animals, Sci. Amer., **185**:26-29, Dec., 1951. (W. H. Freeman Co. Reprint No. 423.)

Sperry, R. W.: The great cerebral commissure, Sci. Amer. **210**:42-52, Jan., 1964. (W. H. Freeman Co. Reprint No. 174.)

Warden, C.: Animal intelligence, Sci. Amer. **84**:64-68, June, 1951. (W. H. Freeman Co. Reprint No. 424.)

Chapter 18

Stress and psychosomatic relationships

OVERVIEW

This chapter is concerned with the effects of stress on the human organism. The stresses discussed range from those common to everyone and easily tolerated to those that result in metabolic disorders, disease, abnormalities of personality, drug addiction, neuroses, psychoses and feeblemindedness. Much of the evidence comes from clinical studies of individual cases; therefore the information is not as reliable as information from well-controlled experiments. A book on physiological psychology should not end, however, without an attempt to survey the effects of stress on man.

The chapter opens by considering the relations among stress, conscious states such as anxiety, and physical symptoms. Individual differences in tolerance for stress and the syndrome (set of symptoms) that follows stress beyond tolerance limits are considered next. The balance of the chapter comes in four parts: (1) normal stressors and metabolic activity, (2) abnormal stressors and functional disorders, (3) brain injury, and (4) mental deficiency. These categories overlap, but they seem as effective a way as any to organize the material.

The "normal" stress conditions that are met every day include variations in diet,

hormones, exercise, anoxia, and sleep. Adjustment to small variations in these conditions are considered, and the effects of extreme stresses of this kind on behavior are outlined. Then "abnormal" stressors are discussed—those that often result in functional disorders of brain activity and behavior. Isolation, drugs, and epilepsy as well as neurosis and psychosis are included. Some physical therapies for psychosis and behavior therapy for neurosis are discussed. Brain injury effects are next. The results of traumatic injury, diseases, and senility on brain activity and behavior organization are included. Finally, the causes and consequences of mental deficiency are briefly discussed. The chapter concludes with some general observations on how man may avoid the kind of stress that causes lasting impairment.

STRESS AND THE MIND-BODY PROBLEM

According to many philosophers of science, conscious events are not legitimate scientific data because conscious events are *directly* observed by only one person. The content of his conscious experience can be reported by that individual, but the accuracy of his report cannot be verified by the *direct* observation of others; others cannot "look into his head," so to speak. However, the presence or absence of conscious activity and its "intensity" *can* be verified by publicly observed means. The presence of conscious activity in man is accompanied by activity in certain parts of the brain, notably the brainstem reticular formation (ARAS areas) and cerebral cortex. Activity in the cerebral cortex that accompanies various levels of conscious awareness—from sleep to aroused vigilance —can be publicly monitored with the electroencephalograph (EEG). Experts observing the EEG can agree whether a subject is asleep or awake, whether his sleep is light or deep, whether he is "daydreaming" or in a state of aroused vigilance, and so on. From one point of view conscious events can be considered as a *symptom* or "by-product" of certain levels of cortical activity that are measureable. From this point of view consciousness is not a cause of behavior, but a symptom of activity in the cerebral cortex, activity that is necessary to some kinds of complex behavior. Other varieties of compex behavior may not be accompanied by conscious events or corresponding EEG changes at all.

Psychosomatic disorders

The term **psychosomatic** originates with the notion that certain mental or psychic states can cause somatic or bodily disorders, as in the case of continuous anxiety that results in stomach ulcers. The term is too well embedded in the literature to discard, although the premise implied seems to be a false one. Environmental stress that results in a physical symptom is not always accompanied by conscious (that is, reportable) anxiety. The individual may not be aware of being under stress and may not feel anxious, whatever physical symptoms he shows—irritability, muscle tension, and so on. It *can* be shown that enough environmental stress will reliably produce physical disorders—psychosomatic disorders,

if you will. It *cannot* be reliably shown that psychic states such as sensed anxiety always produce physical disorders. It is therefore well to look for the conditions underlying psychosomatic disorders among environmental stresses and use reports of psychic states such as anxiety only as clues to the possible existence of stress.

Stress

Stress can be defined as any stimulus, internal or external, that disturbs the dynamic equilibrium (changing balance) of the systems of the body (homeostasis, Chapter 2). In these terms any stimulus is a **stressor**, but it is considered to cause stress only to the degree and for the time that homeostasis is disturbed. The body is continually encountering stressful stimuli, or stressors, as a condition of life and adjustment to a variety of environmental changes—heat or cold, the consequences of exercise, food deprivation, and so on. Stressors also include impedences to, or frustrations of, highly motivated behavior of very complex varieties in man. Frustration in attempts to perform well in an executive position can disturb the body's equilibrium as much as exposure to severe cold. Stress is more or less severe, depending on how successful the body is in restoring homeostasis, or the internal equilibrium necessary to sustain life over a long period. Restoration of equilibrium will depend on the severity of the stress, on the stress tolerance or the adaptability of the individual, and on how long the stress is continued.

Stress tolerance

Individuals differ in their ability to resist or adjust to many varieties of stress— temperature change, disease organisms, strenuous physical exercise, or the work and social demands of a complex society. An individual may have a high **stress tolerance** for one variety of stress and a low stress tolerance for another variety, depending on age, physical conditioning, learned behavior adjustments, and many other factors. The tolerance for some kinds of stress can be increased by physical conditioning or the learning of more effective modes of behavior. These statements may seem self-evident, but must be kept in mind in evaluating the complex consequences of stress.

Stress syndrome

If the severity of a stressor is well within an individual's stress tolerance, the stress can be adjusted to over a long period of time. The more a stress exceeds an individual's stress tolerance, the shorter the period before the resources of the body are exhaused and physical deterioration sets in. The sequence of events is a predictable one (Selye). A **period of adjustment** and apparent tolerance of the stress will be followed by a period of disorganization, physical disorders, a **stage of exhaustion,** and, finally, death (Fig. 18-1). The adjustments to stress and their eventual failure

can be seen in rats kept in freezing temperatures. Their metabolism will increase to produce body heat with the aid of enlarged pituitary, thyroid, and adrenal glands during the period of adjustment. As the resources of the body are exhausted, however, physical deficiencies such as loss of weight, decreased activity, and stomach ulcers will result. Finally, the loss of homeostasis will exceed the limits that support life, and death will ensue. This sequence of events is remarkably similar when rats are intolerably stressed by means varying from daily swimming to exhaustion to continued exposure to unpredictable electric shocks. Presumably, the same things happen to humans who are exposed to intense stress of many varieties.

NORMAL STRESSORS AND METABOLIC ACTIVITY

Normal stressors are those that fall within the range of conditions to which the body adjusts easily—those conditions encountered

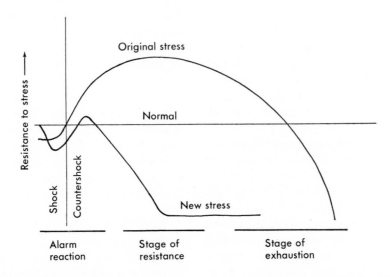

Fig. 18-1. General adaptation syndrome. Under prolonged stress, initial shock and countershock reactions may be followed by a stage of resistance and then a stage of exhaustion that culminates in death. Adding a new stress to the original stress will accelerate the process. (From Selye, H.: The physiology and pathology of exposure to stress, Montreal, 1950, Acta, Inc.)

in everyday life. Changes in diet, exercise, anoxia, and sleep are included as examples. The effects of these changes are most easily understood in terms of the "metabolic equation" of Chapter 2, the balance between the intake of food and oxygen on one hand and the output of work, carbon dioxide, and waste on the other. The effect of extreme deficiencies or excesses in any factor is considered only to illustrate the more normal variations. Those effects on the CNS that influence behavior will be emphasized.

Diet

The body requires carbohydrates, fats, and proteins, although the first can be manufactured from the other two. In addition, certain vitamins, traces of certain minerals, and several essential fatty acids and amino acids that the body cannot reconstruct from fats and proteins, respectively, are required. The diet, or food intake, may therefore be deficient or excessive in either a quantitative or a qualitative fashion. An individual on a balanced diet—one containing all the essentials just mentioned—may eat too much or too little. The diet would then contain too many or too few calories of food intake for that individual's work output. On the other hand, the diet may contain adequate calories, but an oversupply or an undersupply of one of the essentials previously listed. Quantitatively, excess intake of calories results in excess fat deposits in the body, but fat acts as a stressor only because of the excess load put on the heart and circulatory system in supplying the excess tissue. The efficiency of the nervous system seems unimpaired, and a fat man is as intelligent as a thin man—even if getting fat seems a stupid thing to do. Qualitative excesses also have little effect; the body rids itself of excess vitamins, amino acids, or minerals. (One experiment suggests that feeding excess calcium lowers nerve excitability and impairs maze learning in rats—Chapter 17.) Starvation, however, puts

greater stress on the nervous system, whether the starvation is selective or general.

General starvation. Insufficient caloric intake may or may not be accompanied by vitamin or mineral deficiencies or by not enough protein or fat. In most areas of the world where malnutrition is common, general starvation is accompanied by selective starvation, particularly for vitamins and protein. So far as general starvation is concerned, however, there is no clear evidence that postnatal (after birth) malnutrition affects the nervous system, although it may have severe and lasting effects on other systems of the body. Metabolism seems organized to supply the CNS at the expense of the other tissues of the body when there are not enough dietary essentials to go around. Prolonged infant or adult malnutrition does not appear to affect intelligence, provided that certain amino acids and vitamins do not drop below critical levels (see below). Motivational effects are profound, however, and many may impair test performance. Starving individuals are motivated by little but food, show extreme lassitude, and sleep much of the time to conserve energy.

Selective starvation. Severe deprivation of vitamin B^1 in infancy or lack of certain amino acids (lysine, cystine) at any age impairs learning ability. Diets deficient in iodine lower the metabolic rate, and those deficient in calcium or magnesium may cause CNS irritability and seizures. If any of these elements are available, however, the nervous system seems to be supplied at the expense of other tissues.

Endocrine factors

Hormones are necessary to control the metabolic processes of the body and to integrate activity in differently specialized tissues. Deficiencies or excesses in the hormone output of the various endocrine glands can cause profound changes in the body, with important consequences for behavior (Chapter 3). Vigor and sexual behavior, for example, are influenced by the output of the anterior pituitary, adrenal cortex, thyroids, and gonads. Growth and body development depend on the anterior pituitary and thyroid. Major effects on the CNS seems to result only from thyroid insufficiency, and then the effects are most severe during growth (cretinism). Insufficiency of the other hormones appears to affect the CNS only if long-continued and severe. However, the effects on personality of dwarfism, giantism, abnormal or absent secondary sexual characteristics, and so on cannot be ignored. Physical abnormalities profoundly affect human behavior, even when the nervous system is untouched, because of the way that other persons react to abnormal physical appearance.

Exercise

Physical exercise increases the metabolic rate and consumes blood sugar stored in the liver and muscles as glycogen. These stores are replaced by increased food intake or by converting stored fat into glucose for consumption by the cells. In reacting to the stress of vigorous regular exercise, the heart and circulatory system become more efficient, the contractile efficiency of muscle tissue is improved, the lung capacity is increased, and the body becomes able to tolerate increased exercise for longer periods. On the other hand, continous or repeated exercise to exhaustion may permanently impair these systems.

Fatigue

Physiological fatigue results from an insufficient oxygen supply to the muscles, when they consume oxygen faster than the lungs, heart, and circulatory system can provide it. An **oxygen debt** of the amount of oxygen needed to restore equilibrium accumulates. At the same time the waste products of muscle metabolism—CO_2 and lactic acid—accumulate faster than the circulatory system can remove them. Accumulated lactic acid can result in cramps, or

contractures of the muscles (contractions without nerve cell excitation), and nerve endings for pain are stimulated. **Impairment** of the muscles' ability to do work results, and a **work decrement** follows. The CNS, however, seems immune to oxygen debt under most conditions. Work decrement resulting from long periods of mental work can usually be ascribed to boredom or conflict of motives. An office worker, for example, would show no physical impairment at the end of a long day, despite reports of fatigue. Factory workers seldom show impairment either. Studies of their output often show an end spurt of increased output near the end of each work period, before a coffee break, lunch, or the end of the day. Their output increases at the end of a work period, at a time when one would expect more fatigue and a work decrement. Such end spurts probably reflect increased motivation at the prospect of stopping a monotonous task. Their increased level of performance "spills over" into increased work output.

Anoxia

Anoxia is a condition in which the tissues are not receiving enough oxygen from the lungs via the circulatory system to sustain their metabolic activity. The tissues therefore accumulate an oxygen debt. Sensations of suffocation and hard breathing result only if carbon dioxide accumulates in the tissues at the same time; the nervous system is sensitive to increases in carbon dioxide, but does not respond in many ways to decreases in oxygen. As already explained, anoxia can result from physiological fatigue. It can also result from impairment of the lungs or circulatory system, as in cases of emphysema (a lung disorder) or reduced cardiac output (heart failure). **Anemia**, or lack of enough red blood corpuscles to carry oxygen from the lungs to the tissues, can cause anoxia. In all these cases capacity for physical work is reduced (impairment), an oxygen debt is acquired with less work, and sensations of suffocation and fatigue result. Anoxia can result from reduced air pressure at high altitudes. In diving, increased air pressure has opposite effects, which raise their own problems for the body.

Altitude effects. Air consists of a mixture of about 20% oxygen and 80% nitrogen. Air pressure is the amount of these gases per cubic foot of air. With increases in altitude there is less air per cubic foot, and, whereas the *proportion* of oxygen in the air remains constant, its *partial pressure* (20% of the total pressure) decreases along with the total air pressure. Oxygen diffuses into the blood from the lungs because the partial pressure of oxygen in the air of the lungs is greater than the partial pressure of oxygen in the blood returned by the heart from the tissues. As the partial pressure of oxygen falls, there is less difference between the concentration of lung oxygen and the concentration of blood oxygen. As a result, less oxygen diffuses from the lungs into the blood for distribution to the tissues. The outside pressure can be so low that one can breathe pure oxygen at that pressure and still not absorb enough oxygen for the tissues. Aircraft or manned satellites at high altitudes must be pressurized at about 5 pounds per square inch of oxygen pressure to provide for enough absorption of oxygen by the blood (sea level air pressure is about 15 pounds per square inch). Alternatively, a pressure suit and helmet may be worn. When the lungs are exposed to a vacuum, the blood "boils" as all its absorbed gases come out of solution, and immediate and total anoxia results, accompanied by widespread tissue damage (explosive decompression). When the blood oxygen drops sufficiently at high altitudes, the cerebral cortex ceases functioning, and sleepiness, followed by unconsciousness, results. Continued oxygen lack results in brain damage, coma, and death. No sensations of suffocation result because carbon dioxide is readily diffused and does not accumulate to stimulate the CNS.

Diving effects. In deep sea diving, air must be delivered to the lungs at a pressure equal to the outside water pressure or the diver is unable to expand his chest to inflate his lungs. In a diving bell or diving suit, air is delivered to the diver from the surface via a hose until enough air has accumulated to equal the outside water pressure. In scuba diving (self-contained underwater breathing apparatus), a valve from tanks attached to the diver's back senses the water pressure and delivers air at the same pressure to a mouthpiece in the diver's mouth. In either case water weighs much more than air, the pressure on the diver's chest increases as he descends, and air must be delivered to him at increasing pressures. More and more air (oxygen and nitrogen gases) is forced into solution in the blood. Much more nitrogen (80%) than oxygen (20%) goes into solution in the blood. At great depths enough dissolved nitrogen accumulates to cause nitrogen narcosis, sometimes romantically called the "rapture of the deep." Disorientation, euphoria, disturbances in judgment, bizarre behavior, coma, and death may result. In returning to the surface—decompression—another difficulty is encountered. The deeper a diver has been, and the longer he has been down, the more nitrogen gas is dissolved in his body tissues and blood. If he returns toward the surface too rapidly, water pressure and the competing air pressure are reduced too fast. The lungs cannot rid the body of dissolved nitrogen fast enough, and bubbles of nitrogen gas come out of solution in the bloodstream. These cause intense pain when they accumulate at body joints (the bends). They burst capillaries in the brain, causing permanent brain damage. The only cure is rapid return to high air pressures (recompression) in a tank or beneath the water. The only prevention seems to be slow decompression if normal air is breathed, giving the lungs time to rid the body of accumulated nitrogen. Strangely enough, helium gas, as inert as nitrogen, does not cause narcosis and comes out of solution in the body much more readily than nitrogen. Experts have been experimenting with mixtures of oxygen and helium to avoid nitrogen narcosis and reduce decompression time.

Sleep

The topic of sleep was covered in some detail in Chapters 14 and 15. Most attention was paid to the role of sleep as absence of arousal, the function of the ARAS in sleep and waking, and the evolutionary theory of sleep (Kleitman). At the same time it was pointed out that sleep was a bodily need like hunger and thirst since brain operations or continuous stimulation that keep an animal awake result in death after several days. The role of sleep is an unknown one in the metabolic equation of food and air intake, energy, carbon dioxide, and waste disposal. The usual diet contains enough calories to sustain 24-hour waking activity. Yet sleep is a known requirement that seems especially essential to the CNS. In man those functions most related to higher CNS activity—alertness, problem-solving, etc.—demonstrate most clearly the effects of loss of sleep. Yet experiments on the effect of prolonged wakefulness in man show no evident tissue damage effects, and complex mental tasks *can* be performed normally if the subject is sufficiently motivated and aroused.

It has been suggested that the high level of CNS activity in the waking state results in the accumulation of some waste product of nervous metabolism, a **hypnotoxin.** If the hypnotoxin accumulates faster than it can be eliminated during waking periods of CNS activity, it drugs the CNS, and sleep results. During sleep the production of hypnotoxin is reduced, and it is gradually disposed of by the circulation until waking levels of CNS metabolism can again be sustained. Such a hypnotoxin has neither been isolated nor its effects clearly demonstrated. However, the neural mechanisms underlying the waking state have been found in the reticular activating system. The ARAS is profoundly depressed by some drugs and could be affected in a similar way by a hypnotoxin. It has been suggested that dreaming is a symptom of metabolic activity in the CNS that accompanies disposal of hypnotoxins. If dreaming (detected by rapid eye movements during sleep, or REM sleep) is prevented by waking the subject, he will dream more on subsequent nights. This may suggest accumulation of hypnotoxin caused by preventing its removal, since the subject is awakened when he dreams. On the other hand, depriving the subject of the EEG-detected deeper stages of sleep will cause more deep sleep on subsequent nights. The role of sleep in metabolism, and how lack of sleep acts as a stress, is an important and unsolved problem.

ABNORMAL STRESSORS AND FUNCTIONAL DISORDERS

Stresses that are imposed on the nervous system by a variety of factors such as isolation or persistent conflict can cause disorders of the *functioning* of the CNS—**functional disorders.** Long-continued functional disorders of the CNS can damage the *structure* of various organs of the body whose activities are controlled by the CNS. Damage to body organs caused by functional disorders of the nervous system *are* the psychosomatic symptoms already discussed. Many psychosomatic symptoms can result from functional disorders as well as from disease or allergies—asthma, hives, stomach ulcers, colitis (irritation of the colon), and piles (hemorrhoids) are a few examples. More specific agents such as drugs and toxic agents can likewise disturb the functioning of the CNS; these can also damage nerve tissue, which cannot be replaced in man.

Isolation

The brain seems to require a minimum level of sensory input to maintain normal functioning. Human subjects, deprived of sensory stimulation, develop bizarre hallucinations ("seeing things" or "hearing things") after a period of time. The length of time required for the effects depends on the extent of the **sensory deprivation.** In extreme cases the subject may be blind-folded (visual deprivation), ears plugged (auditory deprivation), and lowered into a bath of tepid water (deprivation of temperature sensations and kinesthetic input from the muscles stretched by gravity). An initial period of sleep ensues, followed by disembodied feelings; then bizarre hallu-cinations develop within 24 to 48 hours. Some have speculated that sensory input is so necessary to organization of the brain's activities that the brain hallucinates sensa-tions when they are not provided by the sense organs. Some of the symptoms resem-ble those of psychosis (see below), and psychiatrists have subjected themselves to sensory deprivation in an attempt to under-stand the experiences of psychotics.

Drug effects

As would be expected from its high rate of metabolism, the CNS is more sensitive to drugs than are other cells of the body. The specific effects of various drugs on the CNS vary widely, however, and neither the site of their action nor how they affect nerve cells is known in many cases. Some drugs may *stimulate* activity in the CNS, prevent-ing sleep when they affect the cortex either directly or via the ARAS. Other drugs may *depress* the cortex or ARAS, resulting in drowsiness, unconsciousness, or coma. Still other drugs are *selective* in their effects for largely unknown reasons, interfering with the perception of pain or with sympathetic nervous system arousal, for example. Some drugs *disorganize* CNS activity, causing dis-torted perceptions or hallucinations. Finally, some drugs may alter the functioning of the CNS if taken habitually over a period of time so that the CNS cannot function normally in their absence—this is **addic-tion.** Table 18-1 gives a classification of some of the major drugs and their proper-ties and indicates which drugs appear to be addicting. A drug may be found in more than one category, when it seems to have more than one kind of effect. For example, lysergic acid diethylamide (LSD) is a stimulant, but also a psychotogenic drug (one that produces delusions and hallucina-tions, like a psychosis). Only drugs that are likely to be of greatest interest to the student will be discussed. The psychothera-peutic drugs will be saved for a later section on physical treatments for psychosis.

Stimulants. Stimulants increase the meta-bolic rate of cells of the CNS and increase their excitability. Some stimulants affect the whole CNS, whereas others have their greatest effect at selected sites in the brain. Some act directly on the ARAS or cortex; others excite sympathetic nervous system arousal via their influence on the hypo-thalamus. A few stimulants reset the "ther-mostats" regulating the level of SNS arousal, presumably in the hypothalamus or ARAS. The latter drugs are adapted to so that their removal results in a lower-than-normal level of CNS activity. A crav-ing or addiction for these drugs results be-cause the CNS is no longer able to func-tion normally without them.

Caffeine is an example of a mildly ad-dicting cortical stimulant present in coffee, tea, cocoa, and some soft drinks. The effect on the user depends on the *tolerance* he may or may not have for the drug. Toler-ance is increased by habitual usage. Small doses of caffeine seem to improve per-formance in psychomotor tasks such as typing. However, doses that exceed individ-ual tolerance levels can result in indiges-tion, nervousness, and inability to sleep.

Nicotine is not the only drug in tobacco, and the action of all the various drugs taken by smoking is not understood. To-bacco smoking acts as a selective stimulant, leading to increased SNS activity. This re-sults in increased heart rate, peripheral vasoconstriction, release of blood sugar from the liver and muscles, and so on. The extent and intensity of these effects depend on how much tolerance the individual has developed through habitual smoking and how much he inhales. (Inhaling enables the drugs in tobacco smoke to reach the bloodstream rapidly via the lungs.) In addition to drugs such as nicotine and pyridine that cause the above effects, tobacco smoke contains **carcinogens,** agents such as "tars" that irritate tissue and seem thereby to predispose the tissue to **cancer.** Cigarette smokers are probably predisposed to cancer of the lungs and pipe smokers to cancer of the mouth. For reasons not clearly understood, cigarette smokers seem to be predisposed to circulatory disorders, including heart disease. Habitual tobacco smoking is addicting for most persons, altering their physiological equilibrium so that abnormal sensations and irritability follow withdrawal. One to three weeks of abstinence are required for most of these people before the physiological withdrawal symptoms disappear. Some studies suggest that adjustment to exercise is impaired for about a half hour after smoking; other studies detect no effect.

Benzedrine is the common term for **amphetamine,** a kind of drug that mimics some of the SNS arousal effects such as peripheral vasoconstriction. For this reason it was introduced in nasal inhalers as a decongestant, it shrinks the mucous tissue by constricting its blood vessels to increase the size of the nasal passages for freer breathing when they are clogged by a head cold. It is also a cerebral stimulant that combats sensations of drowsiness and fatigue and may lead to feelings of euphoria in larger doses. It has been widely used by the military, night truckdrivers, and students cramming for examinations, but toxic side effects have lead to deafness and nervous disorders and have restricted its use. It raises the metabolic rate and diminishes appetite for food; therefore it is employed as an aid to losing weight—reducing food intake while "burning up" stored fat deposits at a more rapid rate. As a stimulant, benzedrine and its derivatives have been used to combat psychotic depression (see below) or the low metabolic rate caused by thyroid insufficiency. In an attempt to reduce undesirable side effects, drugs derived from or similar to benzedrine, such as Dexedrine, Dexamyl, etc., have been developed. Amphetamines probably are addicting, and "bennies" are often taken among potential drug addicts for "kicks" (euphoria from large doses).

Depressing drugs. Drugs that depress the activity of the CNS may act in several ways. The sedatives and hypnotics produce a general lowering of CNS activity for general depression or sleep, respectively. The general anesthetics such as ether reach the brain almost directly via the bloodstream as they are inhaled. A coma results that leaves the individual insensitive to pain so that surgery can be performed. Local anesthetics work only at their site of application for local surgery. Analgesic drugs relieve more general pain without causing unconsciousness. Little is known of their mode of selective action on pain. Analgesics range from aspirin (acetylsalicylic acid) to the opium derivatives such as heroin and morphine and include any depressing drug in a dosage that relieves pain without causing unconsciousness. Unfortunately, many of them are addicting. (Aspirin is not.) Paralytic drugs do not act on the CNS at all; they merely block neuromuscular transmission, producing complete relaxation of all the muscles of the body. Some of the depressing drugs are of interest because they are used socially (alcohol), as sleeping pills (barbiturates), as anesthetics (ether), or as addicting drugs (opium). An initial sensation of euphoria may be experienced after taking these drugs as the CNS combats their effects with overexcitation, but the result of increased dosage in every case is unconsciousness. Intake of enough of any depressing drug disorganizes coordination and abstract thinking because

Table 18-1. Classification of some major drugs*

Drug class	Group	Example	Trade or common name	Natural or synthetic	Usage	How taken	First used	Evidence of addiction
Psychotherapeutics These drugs typical of many used in treatment of psychological and psychiatric disorders								
Antipsychotic drugs used primarily to treat major psychoses such as schizophrenia and manic-depressive and senile psychoses	Antipsychotic Rauwolfia alkaloids	Reserpine	Serpasil	Nat.	Greatly diminished	Injected Ingested	1949	No
	Phenothiazines	Chlorpromazine	Thorazine	Syn.	Widespread	Injected Ingested	1950	No
Antianxiety drugs used to combat insomnia, induce muscle relaxation, treat neurotic conditions, and reduce psychological stress	Antianxiety Propanediols	Meprobamate	Miltown	Syn.	Widespread	Ingested	1954	Yes
	Benzodiazepines	Chlordiazepoxide	Librium	Syn.	Widespread	Ingested	1933	Yes
	Barbiturates	Phenobarbital	See *Sedatives*, below					
Antidepressant drugs effective in treatment of psychiatric depression and phobic-anxiety states	Antidepressant MAO inhibitors	Tranylcypromine	Parnate	Syn.	Diminished	Ingested	1958	No
	Dibenzazepines	Imipramine	Tofranil	Syn.	Widespread	Ingested Injected	1948	No
Stimulants (see *Stimulants*, below)	Stimulant	Amphetamine	See *Stimulants*, below					
Psychotogenics These drugs produce changes in mood, thinking, and behavior; resultant drug state may resemble a psychotic state with delusions, hallucinations, and distorted perceptions; little therapeutic value	Ergot derivative	Lysergic acid diethylamide	LSD, Lysergide	Syn.	Widespread?	Ingested	1943	No
	Cannabis sativa	Marijuana	Hemp, hashish	Nat.	Widespread	Smoked	?	No
	Lophophora williamsii	Mescaline	Peyote button	Nat.	Localized	Ingested	?	No
	Psilocybe mexicana	Psilocybin		Nat.	Rare	Ingested	?	No
Stimulants These drugs elevate mood, increase confidence and alertness, and prevent fatigue; analeptics stimulate central nervous system and can reverse depressant effects of an anesthetic drug	Sympathomimetics	Amphetamine	Benzedrine	Syn.	Widespread	Ingested Injected	1935	Yes
	Analeptics	Pentylenetetrazol	Metrazol	Syn.	Rare	Ingested Injected	1935	No
	Psychotogenics	Lysergic acid diethylamide	See *Psychotogenics*, above					

Class	Description	Agent	Common name	Source	Distribution	Administration	Year	Addicting
Nicotinics	Caffeine and nicotine, found in beverages and tobacco, are mild stimulants	Nicotine		Nat.	Widespread	Smoked	?	Yes
Xanthines		Caffeine		Nat.	Widespread	Ingested	?	Yes
Bromides	*Sedatives and hypnotics* — Most of these drugs produce general depression (sedation) in low doses and sleep (hypnosis) in larger doses; used to treat mental stress, insomnia, and anxiety	Potassium bromide		Syn.	Widespread	Ingested	1857	No
Barbiturates		Phenobarbital	Luminal	Syn.	Widespread	Ingested / Injected	1912	Yes
Chloral derivatives		Choral hydrate		Syn.	Rare	Ingested	1875	Yes
General		Alcohol		Nat.	Widespread	Ingested	?	Yes
General anesthetics	*Anesthetics, analgesics, and paralytics* — These drugs are widely used in field of medicine. General anesthetics act centrally to cause a loss in consciousness	Nitrous oxide	"Laughing gas"	Syn.	Rare	Inhaled	1799	No
		Diethyl ether		Syn.	Greatly diminished	Inhaled	1846	No
Local anesthetics	Local anesthetics act only at or near site of application	Chloroform		Syn.	Rare	Inhaled	1831	No
		Cocaine	Coca	Nat.	Widespread	Applied / Ingested	?	Yes
		Procaine	Novocain	Syn.	Widespread	Injected	1905	No
Analgesics	*Analgesic* drugs, many of them addicting, typically produce euphoria and stupor; effective pain relievers	Opium derivatives	Morphine, heroin	Nat.	Widespread	Injected / Smoked	?	Yes
Paralytics	*Paralytic* drugs act primarily at neuromuscular junction to produce motor (muscular) paralysis; commonly used by anesthesiologists	d-Tubocurarine	Curare	Nat.	Widespread	Injected	?	No
Cholinergic	*Neurohumors (neurotransmitters)* — Adrenergic and cholinergic compounds known to be synaptic transmitters in nervous system; other natural compounds (e.g., 5-HT, -aminobutyric acid, substance P) may also be neurotransmitters	Acetylcholine		Nat. / Syn.	Laboratory	Injected	1926	No
Adrenergic		Norepinephrine		Nat. / Syn.	Laboratory	Injected	1946	No
Others (?)		5-Hydroxytryptamine	5-HT, serotonin	Nat. / Syn.	Laboratory	Injected	1948	No

*From Jarvik, M. E.: The psychopharmacological revolution, Psychology Today **1**:51-59, 1967.

depressing drugs usually affect the highest centers of the brain first.

Ethyl **alcohol** is contained in beer, wine, and whiskey. It is usually produced by the effects of living organisms in yeast on the sugars contained in grapes or grain (fermentation). The alcohol content of beer and wine is measured in percent of total volume, being 3 to 6% in most beer and up to 12% in naturally fermented wine. Some wines are fortified by the addition of ethyl alcohol obtained by distillation, principally ports and sherrys that may contain up to 20% alcohol. Whiskeys, by contrast, are all distilled. After natural fermentation their alcohol content is increased by boiling; the alcohol boils first and is condensed, with water being left behind. The alcohol content of whiskey is measured in *proof,* with 200 proof being pure ethyl alcohol. A 100 proof burbon is therefore half alcohol, and an 86 proof scotch is 43% alcohol.

The effects of alcohol on the CNS depend on the concentration of alcohol in the blood and tissue fluid. As little as 0.1 to 0.2% alcohol impairs reaction time and complex behavior such as driving an automobile as well as impairing most accurate tests of judgment and depth perception. About 0.5% results in coma. Blood alcohol content depends, in turn, on (1) rate of intake, (2) rate of elimination, and (3) size of the individual (since the human body is 96% fluid, larger individuals must ingest more alcohol to reach a given fluid percentage of alcohol). Rate of intake depends on the percent alcohol content of drinks, their rate of consumption, and, at first, stomach contents (alcohol is absorbed through the stomach wall like water, and the presence of food, especially greasy food, retards this process until the food leaves the stomach). The rate of elimination depends largely on metabolic rate, especially as it is increased by exercise, since alcohol is converted into blood sugar, which is used up in metabolism. Coffee and most other common stimulants do not "sober" a drunk very much

because they do not increase the metabolic rate enough. Stimulants do more toward combating the depressing effects of alcohol on the CNS so that the drunk is a wide-awake drunk rather than a sleepy drunk!

Aside from body size and its effects on the percent alcohol content, some persons appear to "hold their liquor" better than others. In large measure this is because of learned reactions such as habits of speech, walk, and self-arousal to compensate superficially for the effects of alcohol on their behavior. Alcohol does not seem to be addicting, as addiction has been defined, unless it is used consistently over a period of years. Some studies report that alcoholics seem less able to tolerate anxiety than nonalcoholics can and depend on the relief from anxiety that alcohol gives them. In addition, alcohol taken for the symptoms of a hangover can result in continuous drinking, whose cumulative effects on the CNS can eventually result in hallucinations known as delirium tremens, or the "d.t.'s". Alcoholism often results in dietary deficiencies (especially vitamin B_1) since it reduces appetite by providing immediately available blood sugar without providing needed fats, proteins, and vitamins. Alcohol affects the highest levels of the CNS first, impairing cortical functions while the vital functions of the medulla (breathing, heart rate, etc.) remain unimpaired, even after the individual has "passed out." Continuous overindulgence in alcohol for many years can cause cortical damage that leads to psychotic symptoms (Korsakoff's syndrome).

Opium (heroin is a close relative), extract of the opium poppy, is one of a class of alkaloids whose active ingredient is **morphine.** The action of the drug is narcotic, whether smoked as opium or injected as heroin or morphine. With daily usage addiction results within 3 weeks, secondary to the development of increasing tolerance for the drug. Its use as an analgesic is therefore limited. Withdrawal symptoms for the addict are severe, including vomiting, incessant yawning, sweating, and sometimes collapse and death.

Cocaine is a drug obtained from the leaves of the coca tree of South America. Peruvian Indians chew coca leaves to alleviate symptoms of hunger and fatigue from hard work at high altitudes (where some anoxia is inevitable). Cocaine is used medically as a local anesthetic for mucous tissue. Addicts take cocaine through the mucous tissue of the nose by sniffing it, as tobacco was commonly taken as snuff long ago. Cocaine is a powerful CNS stimulant that causes "mood swings" from euphoria to depression, epinephrine-like effects on the CNS, insomnia, weight loss, and sensory hallucinations of "bugs" crawling on the skin. There is conflicting evidence on whether or not cocaine is addicting.

Psychotogenic drugs are also called hallucinogens because they distort perception and cause hallucinations. Overdoses of several drugs (bromides, cocaine, etc.) can have this effect. The major hallucinogens, however, cause hallucinations at any effective dosage and are called **psychotomimetic** or psychogenic drugs because they mimic the effect of psychosis in producing hallucinations. They are also called **psychodelic** (Gr., mind-destroying) drugs. Marijuana, LSD-25 (lysergic acid diethylamide), mescaline, and peyote are examples. Peyote has been used in some American Indians religious ceremonies.

LSD is a synthesized drug that is effective in minute doses. It produces bizarre perceptions, hallucinations, and a state that often resembles catatonic schizophrenia, a psychosis. For this reason it has been used experimentally to study psychotic disorders. Research is under way on its effects on alcoholism and drug addiction. More recently, its use has become a fad among the "hip" segment of American culture. There are indications that some forms of LSD may cause brain damage. Its effects also seems to depend on the personality of the user, with reports of individuals becoming actively psychotic after taking LSD and not recovering. There are also reports of delayed effects, symptoms of taking the drug returning after weeks or months.

Marijuana on the other hand, barely qualifies as a psychotogenic drug because its chief effects are mild distortions of perception, particularly time perception. It comes from the leaves of a plant that grows wild over most of the country. The leaves are dried, crumpled, and made into cigarettes by users in the same way that tobacco leaves are made into cigarettes. Inhaling the smoke from one or two marijuana cigarettes is enough to make the user "high." The initial sensations are usually those of euphoria and feelings of "floating," while events seem to occur very slowly. Feelings of depression frequently follow. Marijuana is not known to be addicting, but those who use it are sometimes prone to experiment with addicting drugs as well.

Neurohumors are drugs that act as neurochemical transmitters at synapses or are suspected to act in this fashion. Their chief use is in research on the way the nervous system functions; other applications are rare except for the use of epinephrine as a stimulant.

Epilepsy

Epilepsy is considered here because it is a disorder in the functioning of the brain and therefore an abnormal stress caused by a functional disorder. It may have an organic cause in a brain tumor, or it may be caused by an unknown and widespread overexcitability of the brain cells with no structural abnormality that can be seen. Epilepsy does not usually result in brain damage, nor does it cause psychotic symptoms. Epileptic symptoms are the result of abnormally increased brain excitability, detected by a peculiar spike and slow wave pattern in the EEG of the victim. Epileptic seizures vary from momentary loss of awareness (petit mal) to a convulsive seizure of the whole body (grand mal). Grand mal is caused by massive excitation of most of the brain cells, which causes a rigid extension of the body (tonic phase), followed by convulsive movements (clonic phase), and then coma. The seizures are similar to those caused by electroconvulsive shock (ECS), Metrazol injections, or the extremely low blood sugar caused by insulin injections—all treatments that massively stimulate brain cells. Seizures induced by the latter methods are used in treating mental patients (see below), and they cause greater tissue damage and disturbances of memory than epilepsy because the induced seizures are usually given daily or every other day—epileptics seldom have more than one seizure a month. Epilepsy that is caused by a brain tumor can often be cured by surgical removal of the tumor. Epilepsy of all varieties can usually be controlled by small doses of drugs that reduce brain activity (anticonvulsive drugs) to prevent the seizures.

Neurosis

The term **neurosis** has become a catchall category for persistent maladaptive behavior, accompanied by reports of anxiety and physical symptoms of muscle tension, digestive disorders, "fatigue" and lassitude, as well as other psychosomatic symptoms. **Hysteria** is a variety of neurosis in which the individual becomes functionally blind, lacks skin sensations in a limb, or is functionally paralyzed in a limb. Sensory and motor disturbances of this kind have no known cause in disease or damage, often disappear under hypnosis, and are often susceptible to psychotherapy of one kind or another. The usual report is that they result from self-punishment to relieve guilt feelings. The origins of the maladjustive behavior of the neurotic seem to lie in stress beyond the individual's tolerance, and early and highly developed learning of inadequate behavioral adjustments to stressful

situations. No physical damage can be found in the nervous system, but the persistent autonomic arousal that accompanies constant anxiety leads to stomach ulcers, colitis (irritation of the lower intestine), hemorrhoids (piles), allergies, and many other physical disorders. The physical disorders are no less debilitating because they have functional rather than organic (disease or brain damage) causes. In general, neuroses and some psychoses are termed "functional" for two reasons: (1) they have no known organic causes and (2) they are relieved by psychotherapy or improve without treatment (spontaneous remission).

Psychoses

A **psychotic** individual is one who suffers from unrealistic and illogical **delusions** (false beliefs) and bizarre hallucinations and whose behavior is so disorganized that he is unable to care for himself in society, although there are many borderline cases who manage, especially in low-stress occupations. These disorders seem to differ in a qualitative way from neuroses since organic causal factors seem involved in even functional psychoses and since the psychotic shows symptoms that the neurotic does not have—delusions, hallucinations, and frequent lack of response to the "outside world." The psychotic in a low-stress situation may be free of these symptoms much of the time, but they often recur in an unpredictable way. "Organic" psychosis can result from brain damage (see below), but many psychotics are termed "functional" because even an autopsy reveals no abnormalities in the brain.

If a hereditary predisposition to a specific psychosis moves the disorder from the functional to the organic category, schizophrenia and manic-depressive psychoses might be termed "organic." A higher proportion of these psychoses appears among offspring and siblings of those with the same disorder than appears in the normal population. Schizophrenics appear to beget schrizophrenics, and manic-depressives pass their susceptibility to the disorder on to their offspring. Furthermore, protein metabolism in schizophrenics appears to differ from the normal population; the output of adrenal steroids in response to stress is subnormal, and the autonomic balance is abnormal. Which among these factors underlie the disorder and which *result* from it, is difficult to say. However, metabolic factors may underlie both schizophrenia and manic-depressive psychosis, and the most promising research leads may be found in brain metabolism. Schizophrenia and manic-depressive psychosis do differ clearly from one another and seem to offer the most promising categories for research of this kind. Varied symptoms accompany schizophrenia, but the most prominent are delusions, hallucinations, withdrawal, and apparent lack of affect (feeling tone). By contrast, manic-depressive psychosis involves, besides delusions and hallucinations, alternating periods of extreme euphoria and depression that may last days, weeks, or months. There are other kinds of psychosis and many other symptom patterns, but no one has come up with a classification system that the majority of psychologists and psychiatrists can agree upon. Some experts believe that all psychosis has an organic basis, probably in disorders of brain metabolism. Other experts suggest that rejection and traumatic childhood experiences can result in functional psychoses—the so-called psychogenic theory of psychosis. As is usual in the area of behavior disorders, the specialists disagree.

Therapies

Various forms of psychotherapy are the most common treatment for neuroses. Most psychologists and psychiatrists agree that neurotic behavior disorders are *learned,* and some kind of learning experience—psychotherapy—is therefore required to rid the patient of his anxiety and other symptoms.

Disagreement is found on the nature of the most effective kind of psychotherapy, dividing the experts into two general schools of thought, as will be seen later. Psychoses, on the other hand, are usually treated with physical therapies of one kind or another, although psychotherapy may be used as well. Physical therapies seem to be the treatment of choice for psychoses because many believe they have an organic basis and because physical therapies can alter the withdrawn or violent behavior of the psychotic to make him accessible to psychotherapy. Physical therapies include drug treatments, brain operations, induced seizures, and so on. Evaluating the effectiveness of the various therapies is difficult because an unknown number of patients recover without treatment (spontaneous remission). Untreated groups are often not compared with treated groups, and a before and after comparison does not allow for spontaneous remission. In addition, treatment effects are seldom systemically compared by disorders.

Psychotherapy. Psychotherapists can be very roughly classified into two theoretical groups: (1) neofreudian and (2) behavior therapists. Freudian theory holds that neurosis begins in early childhood, when some experience results in more fear and anxiety than the child can bear. The experience is therefore *repressed* and becomes inaccessible to recall. Later, however, some stimulus associated with the repressed experience rearouses the original anxiety, causing otherwise unexplained emotional behavior. A man may show an irrational fear of trains—a phobia—because of the repressed memory of his parents having abandoned him in a railroad station. A woman may become a lesbian (female homosexual) because she is terrified of men, due to a repressed childhood sexual experience. Freudian therapists believe that such neuroses can be cured only by many sessions of painstakingly probing the patient's memory for the original traumatic experience and revealing its relationship to the patient's present plight. Unless this is done, they feel the patient will develop new symptoms as fast as the therapist counsels him regarding the old ones, as new stimuli arouse the original emotion. Behavior therapists, on the other hand, hold that the symptoms *are* the disorder, and the disorder can be cured by simple conditioning techniques such as those described in Chapter 17.

One investigator (Wolpe) has been attempting to cure neurotic fears, or phobias, by conditioning. One technique is called *desensitization*. The patient is trained first in a procedure called "progressive relaxation" (Jacobsen), a method of relaxing the muscles of the body a few at a time, extending the relaxation from one part of the body to another. The patient is asked to visualize or imagine some aspect of the feared stimulus, an aspect previously reported as arousing only mild anxiety. Then he is told to relax progressively. The anxiety is reported to disappear after the patient has thoroughly relaxed; the imagined stimulus has become *conditioned* to relaxation, a response incompatible with anxiety. Imagining the stimulus now gives rise to relaxation rather than to anxiety. Next, more anxiety-arousing stimuli are conditioned to relaxation, proceeding until the patient can imagine every aspect of the feared object without anxiety. The man with the fear of trains, for example, might begin by relaxing while imagining a toy train, then a real train at a distance, then a train coming toward him, and so on.

Aversion therapy is another behavior therapy technique. The female homosexual described previously might be given painful electric shocks (aversive stimuli) while looking at pictures of naked females, the shock being terminated (pleasant stimulus) when the picture of a naked male appears. Type II, or *instrumental conditioning,* is also used, where the patient's behavior is instrumental in obtaining a re-

ward or avoiding punishment. In one case a woman with paranoid delusions (delusions of persecution) was treated in this manner. She continually voiced the idea that communists were following her in an attempt to kill her. The therapist fitted her with earphones and pressed a button delivering an unpleasant noise through the earphones every time she mentioned her paranoid ideas. She gradually dropped the topic, not only in the therapist's presence, but in her hospital ward as well.

Which approach is more effective; traditional freudian psychotherapy or behavior therapy? The evidence is only beginning to accumulate, but much of it favors behavior therapy for neurosis. Some studies show that the spontaneous remission rate (relief of symptoms without treatment) approaches 90% over a period of 5 years or so. The behavior therapist would predict this state of affairs, and the freudian therapist would not. The freudian therapist would predict that the neurotic would develop new symptoms unless he understood the relation between his original traumatic experience and his present anxieties. The behavior therapist would predict that feared objects and situations would be encountered in the absence of traumatic consequences more and more often as the years went by. In the absence of painful consequences, or negative *reinforcement,* the anxiety response to feared stimuli would gradually be extinguished like any other conditioned response. Some studies that plot the relief of symptoms during the course of freudian psychotherapy parallel the rate of spontaneous remission! Other studies favor the freudian treatment in rate of symptom relief, showing that learning is going on. Some experiments use objective measures of emotion such as heart rate and palmar sweating (GSR, Chapter 16) in the presence of a feared object as well as subjective symptom appraisal. A number of these experiments compare behavior therapy with conventional psychotherapy or no treatment at all. The majority of the results report that only behavior therapy was effective. Behavior therapy is usually briefer (nine sessions over 18 weeks versus twenty-one sessions of conventional therapy over 31 weeks in one study) and seems as effective treating several patients at once compared to one at a time in some studies, and the simple, monotonous training procedures are sometimes as effective when presented by programmed tape recorder as when presented by a bored psychotherapist. These points are important—there are so many more neurotics than therapists that there appear not to be enough of the latter to treat the former! The comparative evaluation of freudian psychotherapy and behavior therapy has just begun, however, and any sweeping conclusions are far in the future.

Drug therapies. Tranquilizers are used to calm neurotics and psychotics who show extreme anxiety, and "energizers" (stimulants) are used to arouse patients who evince depression and withdrawal. The tranquilizers appear to relieve anxiety and to make psychotic patients easier to manage, although wide individual differences in reaction occur. Drug therapies are reported to be most successful when combined with psychotherapy, but, again, systematic and well-controlled studies are few. Some of the psychotherapeutic drugs are shown in Table 18-1. Reserpine and chlorpromazine seem to calm neurotic anxiety reactions and psychotic agitation. Both are therefore classed as tranquilizers and have replaced the restraints and strait jackets used to keep agitated mental patients from injuring themselves or others in many mental hospitals. A large proportion of these patients can get along at home if they keep using tranquilizing drugs. The action of either drug on the CNS is far from understood, but both drugs seem to reduce the level of sympathetic arousal without depressing the CNS in general as much as sedatives and hypnotics do. The antianxiety

drugs (Table 18-1) are more often used as tranquilizers for neurotic patients and others undergoing temporary stresses such as bereavement or illness. Antidepressant drugs are better understood than are the tranquilizers. One theory holds that feelings of well-being depend on adrenergic stimulation of brain receptors by catecholamines such as norepinephrine or dopamine. A compound called monoamineoxidase (MAO) destroys catecholamines. Therefore anything that inhibits MAO (MAO-inhibitors) increases the supply of norepinephrine and produces feelings of well-being. Anything that depletes the supply of brain catecholamines would induce a state of depression. Reserpine, one of the antipsychotic tranquilizers, is believed to have this effect, and its use has been limited as a result. The theory has not been thoroughly tested, but it seems to be holding up well, so far.

Prefrontal lobotomy. Prefrontal lobotomy has been mentioned before (Chapters 14, 16, and 17). In extreme cases, especially psychotics with debilitating anxiety, the fibers connecting the anterior part of the frontal lobes with lower brain centers may be cut surgically. Individual reaction to the operation differs widely, but reduced anxiety is common. Personality changes also occur, however, including irresponsibility, indifference to consequences, disturbances in attention, and possible impairment of abstract intelligence. More restricted topectomy (ablation) of selected cortical areas in the frontal lobes seems to relieve anxiety with fewer side effects in personality changes, but the effects of such operations need further evaluation.

Shock therapies. Various treatments massively stimulate the brain to cause a convulsive seizure that resembles an epileptic convulsion. A stimulant drug such as Metrazol may be used (Metrazol shock), the blood sugar may be reduced with insulin (insulin shock), or an electrical current may be passed briefly through the brain from electrodes on the temples (electroconvulsive shock, or ECS). A series of twenty-five treatments or more may be given daily or on alternate days. Disturbances of memory follow, the retroactive amnesia (RA) being greatest for recent events. Theorists have proposed that the amnesia (forgetting) of stressful events precipitating the disorder may account for any beneficial effects of the treatment. Hypertrophy of the pituitary and adrenal glands occurs, in the pattern previously described as part of the stress syndrome. Some claim that this mobilization of the body in response to the stress of the treatment is useful to the patient in combatting psychological stress or recovering from apathy and depression. As usual, the shock therapies have had widespread use with little really systematic evaluation.

Carbon dioxide therapy. More recently, breathing a mixture of 30% carbon dioxide and 70% oxygen to unconsciousness has been held to be beneficial to neurotics and psychotics because it causes hyperexcitability of the hypothalamic-cortical nervous system. This treatment has had even less evaluation than the others.

BRAIN INJURY

Brain injury can result in derangement of any or all the brain function described in Chapter 14, plus more complex disorders from impairment to the interaction of parts of the brain with different functions. Damage to the motor projection areas or the premotor areas of the cortex or to subcortical motor centers results in paralyses, spasticity, tremors, and incoordination. Damage to the sensory projection areas or the subcortical thalamic and related nuclei that project to them produces sensory impairment. Damage to parietal, occipital, and temporal cortex impairs memory and learning ability and causes language disorders (aphasia, agnosia, and aphraxia). Damage to the frontal lobes results in widespread personality changes and impaired

abstract behavior. Finally, damage to paleocortical areas or the hypothalamus can cause irritability or rage behavior, whereas temporal lobe damage can result in docility as well as memory disorders. Any or all of these symptoms can be seen singly or in combination, depending on the location and extent of the brain damage. Reeducation for motor and some sensory impairment is possible, healthy cortical areas substituting for the damaged ones. Focal lesions are often more easily compensated for than are widespread and diffuse ones. If the damage is widespread enough, the whole functional organization of the brain is upset, and psychosis may result.

Traumatic brain injury

Damage to the brain can result from tumors, blows to the head, anoxia, and long-standing alcoholism. The symptoms that result depend on how widespread the brain damage is or on its location if it is focal. Tumors, for example, cause focal lesions. Subcortically, therefore, they may cause sensory or motor disorders or disturbances of emotional behavior. A cortical tumor can cause a specific impairment that depends on its location. In addition, cortical tumors frequently serve as an irritative stimulus to brain tissue, resulting in focal epilepsy. Penetrating injuries to the brain by a blow from a sharp object that penetrates the skull will cause localized damage, with effects similar to a tumor, and may cause focal epilepsy.

More diffuse and widespread damage to the brain is caused by blows to the head that slam the brain against the skull despite its surrounding liquid cushion. Frequent blows to the head that occur in body contact sports such as boxing, football, or ice hockey often kill widespread brain cells by mechanical damage or bursting small blood vessels to cause hemorrhage. An event of this kind is called a **concussion.** Enough concussions result in symptoms that are commonly described as "punch drunk"—

sensory impairment, motor incoordination, loss of intelligence, and psychotic irrationality—the symptoms of extreme drunkenness. Brain hemorrhages result from bursting blood vessels in the brain, a so-called "stroke." Strokes can result from high blood pressure in the small capillaries in the brain. They burst from the pressure, and the cells that they nurture die. The damage is most likely to be cumulative and widespread, with the resulting symptoms increasing over a period of time, but focal damage can occur. Sometimes many little strokes occur over weeks and months, but a recognizable stroke means more massive damage. Sometimes the damage is confined to one hemisphere of the brain, resulting in paralysis to one side of the body. The symptoms of brain damage that result from anoxia differ from those just described because the cells of the cortex succumb first, and the damage is total and extensive. If anoxia is severe enough, the individual never recovers from coma. The cortical cells are largely destroyed, whereas the lower centers survive to maintain the automatic (homeostatic) activities of the body. Alcoholism of long standing diffusely impairs the brain, although some symptoms can be reversed after withdrawal and improved diet. Korsakoff's syndrome includes amnesia, irresponsibility, impaired intellect, delusions, and euphoria.

Disease

Certain disease organisms attack the brain directly, whereas others impair its circulatory and protective structures. In either case the effects on behavior can be profound. For example, syphilis begins to attack brain tissue within about 5 years of the original primary infection. It seems to impair frontal lobe function more than other parts of the brain. The symptoms therefore include listlessness, irritability, lack of social concern, indifference to consequences, and, eventually, delusions.

Cerebrospinal meningitis, as the name implies, attacks the meninges or covering tissue of the brain and spinal cord. Unless arrested, neurological symptoms follow. Cord damage results, of course, in crippling, and in somesthetic sensory impairment. The damage to higher centers shows up in impairment to memory, concentration, and emotional stability.

Encephalitis often has more focal effects. This disorder was discussed in Chapter 15 because one form of the disorder damages brain centers that seem to control activation of other parts of the brain. Encephalitis, literally speaking, means only "brain irritation." But encephalitis lethargica, or "sleeping sickness," results from an organism carried by flies and was common at one time in Africa. This form of the disease attacks centers in the diencephalon that form part of the ARAS, and the victim sleeps much of the time. Irritation of the hypothalamus in another form of the disorder results in emotionality, restlessness, irritability, and sometimes seizures. The victim is subject to extreme mood changes from euphoria to depression and some indifference to the consequences of his behavior. There are also occasional movement disorders. Children seem especially susceptible to various kinds of encephalitis. **Rheumatic fever,** a variety of the disorder, is more common among children than adults and can leave behind the symptoms noted above.

Senile psychosis

Degenerative changes in the brain seem, sooner or later, to occur with old age in the majority of the population. Whether or not these changes result in personality disorders seems to depend on how extensive they are and whether or not circulatory disorders (principally arteriosclerosis) are a complicating factor. Losses in brain weight and volume that are not accompanied by arteriosclerosis are common findings in postmortem examinations of the elderly. These changes are related to varied and diffuse symptoms, the most common being disturbances of recent memory (RA), emotional apathy, and lapses of attention. (The symptoms are difficult to distinguish from changes in morale and motivation that are often seen in the elderly, as they react to their diminishing physical ability to cope with the world around them.) Mild incoordination and tremors are usual. Arteriosclerosis and the strokes that result give more specific symptoms as more specific brain areas are damaged.

MENTAL DEFICIENCY

Severe mental deficiency can often be detected at birth or in early childhood, suggesting that prenatal (before birth) or hereditary factors are involved in various kinds of feeblemindedness. In some cases the factors responsible are known, and in other cases sets of well-known symptoms have been classified. Many mentally deficient children are born, however, to normal parents after apparently normal prenatal development.

Prenatal factors

Any of a number of factors may cause failure of the brain to develop normally and result in a mentally deficient child. Although the nervous system seems less susceptible to damage before birth than later, it is subject to trauma in spite of its protected environment and early stage of development. Food and waste material are exchanged between the blood of the mother and the embryo in the placenta; extreme malnutrition of the mother or toxins (poisons) in the mother's blood may therefore affect the developing nervous system of the embyro. Disease organisms may reach the embryo by the same route if not effectively neutralized by the leukocytes of the mother. Measles is one common example. Excessive use of x-rays may cause genetic changes in the cell nuclei of the infant (mutations), resulting in abnormalities of nervous system development.

Mechanical damage

Mechanical damage to the brain of the fetus usually occurs at birth, although the mother may suffer internal injuries caused by accidents that can damage the unborn child's brain. When instruments are required to help the mother expel the fetus at birth, they may damage the brain of the infant because the physician cannot always see to place them accurately or may have to apply too much pressure to the soft skull of the infant. Hemorrhage or mechanical damage to the brain may result. During a long and difficult delivery, the umbilical cord may be twisted, or the infant may not begin to breathe soon enough after birth, depriving the brain of oxygen for a period long enough to asphyxiate brain cells. All these factors affect the brain more than other tissue, and brain cells cannot replace themselves to restore the effects of impairment.

Hereditary factors

Hereditary factors certainly underlie much mental deficiency. **Mongolism,** a type of feeblemindedness named for the mongoloid racial features of these children, is caused by an excess chromosome in the germ tissue of one parent, a chromosome that has been identified. Less specifically classified mental deficiency can also be caused by hereditary factors. Many studies show that mentally deficient parents produce mentally deficient children at a high rate of probability.

Specific disorders

Mongolism has already been identified. **Phenylpyruvic oligophrenia** is a metabolic disorder that impairs brain development and often results in feeblemindedness. It is caused by the individual's inability to metabolize a specific amino acid (phenylpyruvic acid).

A **microcephalic** child, as the name implies, is born with an undersized brain and head and is usually mentally deficient.

Hydrocephalus (water on the brain) is caused by an imbalance in the production and drainage of cerebrospinal fluid. Excess cerebrospinal fluid collects in the ventricles and beneath the meninges of the brain. The resulting fluid pressure can cause mechanical damage to the brain, which results in mental deficiency if not relieved in time. Since the sutures, or "joints," between the cranial bones of the infant have not yet hardened, the skull becomes large and domelike as it expands under this pressure. On the other hand, premature hardening of the cranial sutures can cause pressure on the developing brain of the infant that can retard his development and cause mental retardation.

Finally, **cretinism** should be mentioned here as it was in Chapter 3. Cretinism results from thyroid deficiency or lack of stimulation of the thyroid gland by the anterior pituitary. Unless diagnosed early and treated with thyroxin or some other drug to raise the metabolic rate, mental deficiency follows.

CONCLUSION

This chapter has concerned, in a general way, the relationships encountered by man between the stresses of life, his mental state, and his physical well-being. This chapter also concludes the book. It might therefore be permissible to draw a few conclusions about how knowledge of psychosomatic relationships might be useful in everyday life. It has been seen, for example, that rather severe stress can affect behavior and reduce effectiveness without the individual being aware of its presence, although the effect of the stress is obvious to others. Thus it seems useful to accept the opinions of others on occasion, rather than trusting one's own introspection, regarding the effects our rather complex civilization is having upon our physical well-being. Tolerance for stress differs widely among individuals, and individuals may be less able to tolerate one kind of stress than another. An accurate knowledge of one's limitations in this regard is not easily acquired, but it seems well worth the effort to acquire, judging by the severe physical debilities that can ensue. On the other hand, resistance to physical stress and psychological stress can be improved by physical conditioning and development of more effective modes of behavior. Such physical and psychological conditioning requires exposure to stress that is within individual limits of coping with the stress situation. Useful conclusions are equally obvious from the facts surveyed on the effects of diet, endocrine imbalance, sleep, isolation, drugs (including alcohol and tobacco), neurosis, psychosis, disease, and prenatal, dietary, and hereditary factors in mental deficiency. Simple self-interest rather than moralistic considerations seems to compel moderation in all things, including moderation itself!

SUMMARY

Since one can be under stress without being aware of it, and since the level of awareness can be objectively measured using the EEG, it appears that stress, rather than conscious events such as anxiety, should be investigated as the origin of psychosomatic disorders. Any stimulus can upset homeostasis and therefore any stimulus can be a stressor, but only to the degree and for the time that it creates internal imbalance. Individuals differ in their tolerance for various kinds of physical and psychological stress; their tolerance may be improved by physical and psychological exposure to stress within tolerance limits. Exposure beyond those limits leads to the stress syndrome, which includes a period of adjustment with glandular and other changes, a stage of exhaustion, and death. Neither quantitative nor qualitative excesses in diet seem to affect the brain unduly, nor does starvation if certain dietary essentials are provided. Deprivation of vitamin B_1 in infancy or certain amino acids, calcium, or magnesium impairs brain function. Glandular abnormalities impair vigor, sex behavior, growth, and body development; individual reactions to abnormality are stressful. Exercise within tolerance limits improves tolerance for exercise; beyond these limits physical impairment results. Physiological fatigue results from an oxygen debt in the muscles, but a work decrement can follow motivational changes as well. Anoxia can result from impairment to the lungs, heart, circulatory system (including anemia), or reduced air pressure at high altitudes, when the partial pressure of oxygen is insufficient for diffusion from the lungs to blood in the capillaries. In the near-vacuum of space the blood boils as the gases of air come out of solution. The increased air pressure required for diving can put enough nitrogen from the air into the blood to cause nitrogen narcosis. Decompression must be slow or the nitrogen will form bubbles in the blood.

Sleep seems to be a necessity for CNS functioning. Sleep results from a level of arousal that follows the day-night cycle in man and some adult animals, but not in infants. If a hyponotoxin accumulates from the metabolism of the waking brain to drug the brain to sleep, it has not been found.

Functional disorders of the nervous system cause no observable damage to the brain, but they may cause psychosomatic damage to many organs of the body that malfunction as a result. The sensory deprivation resulting from isolation disorganizes brain function, as shown by the hallucinations that follow this treatment. The CNS is susceptible to stimulating, depressing, and disorganizing drugs. Caffeine is a mild and nonaddicting stimulant. The drugs in tobacco are addicting and some of them can irritate tissue enough for cancer to result. Benzedrine is an addicting cortical stimulant used for wakefulness and to raise the metabolic rate. Ethyl alcohol is a depressant, measured in proof or in percent-

age, whose effects depend on intake rate, body size, and elimination rate via exercise. It is not addicting unless it is used regularly for a long time, but alcoholics are psychologically dependent on its effects. Marijuana is intoxicating but not addicting. Opium and its derivatives (heroin and morphine) are addicting narcotics. Analgesics such as aspirin relieve pain without causing sleep. Tranquilizers such as chlorpromazine or reserpine affect ARAS or SNS activity more selectively, to relieve anxiety and reduce muscle tension. Hallucinogens, psychotomimetic, or psychodelic drugs such as LSD, peyote, and mescaline, cause distorted perceptions and hallucinations in small doses.

Epilepsy is caused by a focal tumor or injury or by widespread brain excitability, is detectable by the EEG, and results in seizures like those produced by stimulant drugs or ECS. The seizures are too infrequent to cause brain damage and can be controlled with anticonvulsant drugs.

Neurosis is a vague term that refers to anxiety and persistent maladaptive behavior. Hysterical neurotics develop functional anesthesias and paralyses. Neuroses seem to be functional disorders resulting from stresses that have no known organic causes and are relieved by psychotherapy or spontaneous remission. Psychoses may be functional or organic, are marked by delusions and hallucinations, and usually require institutional care. Schizophrenia and manic-depressive psychosis have hereditary components.

Neurosis and the psychoses have been treated by various therapies. The evidence favors behavior therapy for neurosis and physical therapies for psychosis, particularly drug therapy. The tranquilizers seem particularly effective in calming agitated psychotics. The antidepressant drugs may act by controlling the level of brain catecholamines. Other physical therapies include prefrontal lobotomy or topectomy, shock therapies, and carbon dioxide therapy, with little systematic evaluation of treatment effects.

Brain injury can cause sensory or motor disorders and disturbances of emotion, memory, or even psychosis, depending on the site of the injury or how widespread it is. Focal tumors and penetrating injuries often cause epilepsy. Repeated concussions can result in a "punch-drunk" syndrome that includes mild psychosis. Strokes (hemorrhage) can be focal or widespread in effect. Long-standing alcoholism damages the brain, and psychosis results.

Disease organisms cause syphilis and cerebrospinal meningitis by attacking the brain; psychotic symptoms often follow. One form of encephalitis attacks the ARAS to cause stupor and another the hypothalamus for emotional symptoms. Senile psychosis results from changes in the brain with age, including shrinkage and, sometimes, arteriosclerosis. Recent memory, apathy, and attention defects follow.

Mental deficiency can result from hereditary, prenatal or traumatic causes. Prenatal malnutrition, toxins, and disease are included. The use of instruments at birth can cause mechanical damage to the brain. Anoxia during birth can damage the brain. Mongolism, caused by an abnormal chromosome, is hereditary. Less specific mental deficiency can also be hereditary. Phenylpyruvic oligophrenia is the result of a metabolic disorder. The causes of microcephaly are not known, but hydrocephalus results from excess cerebrospinal fluid. Cretinism is caused by subnormal thyroid output.

READINGS

Barron, F., Jarvik, M. E., and Bunnell, S.: The hallucinogenic drugs, Sci. Amer. **210**:38-49, April, 1964. (W. H. Freeman Co. Reprint No. 483.)

Brady, J. V.: Ulcers in "executive" monkeys, Sci. Amer. **199**:95-100, Oct., 1958. (W. H. Freeman Co. Reprint No. 425.)

Chapman, C. B., and Mitchell, J. H.: The physiology of exercise, Sci. Amer. **212**:88-96, May, 1965. (W. H. Freeman Co. Reprint No. 1011.)

Collier, H. O.: Aspirin, Sci. Amer. **209**:96-108, Nov., 1963. (W. H. Freeman Co. Reprint No. 169.)

Constantinades, P. C., and Carey, N.: The alarm reaction, Sci. Amer. **180**:20-23, March, 1949. (W. H. Freeman Co. Reprint No. 4.)

Eysenck, H. J.: New ways in psychotherapy, Psychology Today **1**:39-47, June, 1967.

Gates, M.: Analgesic drugs, Sci. Amer. **215**:131-136, Nov., 1966.

Goldstein, K.: Prefrontal lobotomy: analysis and warning, Sci. Amer. **182**:44-47, Feb., 1950. (W. H. Freeman Co. Reprint No. 445.)

Gray, G. W.: Cortisone and ACTH, Sci. Amer. **182**:30-36, March, 1950. (W. H. Freeman Co. Reprint No. 14.)

Hammond, E. C.: The effects of smoking, Sci. Amer. **207**:39-51, July, 1962. (W. H. Freeman Co. Reprint No. 126.)

Harlow, H. F.: Love in infant monkeys, Sci. Amer. **200**:68-74, June, 1959. (W. H. Freeman Co. Reprint No. 429.)

Harlow, H. F., and Harlow, M. K.: Social deprivation in monkeys, Sci. Amer. **207**:137-146, Nov., 1962. (W. H. Freeman Co. Reprint No. 473.)

Himvich, H. E.: The new psychiatric drugs, Sci. Amer. **193**:80-86, Oct., 1955. (W. H. Freeman Co. Reprint No. 446.)

Jackson, D. D.: Schizophrenia, Sci. Amer. **207**:65-74, Aug., 1962. (W. H. Freeman Co. Reprint No. 468.)

Jarvik, M. E.: The psychopharmacological revolution, Psychology Today **1**:51-59, May, 1967.

Levine, S.: Stimulation in infancy, Sci. Amer. **202**:80-86, May, 1960. (W. H. Freeman Co. Reprint No. 436.)

Masserman, J. H.: Experimental neuroses, Sci. Amer. **182**:38-43, March, 1950. (W. H. Freeman Co. Reprint No. 443.)

Melzack, R., and Thompson, W. R.: Early environment, Sci. Amer. **194**:38-42, Jan., 1956. (W. H. Freeman Co. Reprint No. 469.)

Nichols, J. R.: How opiates change behavior, Sci. Amer. **212**:80-88, Feb., 1965. (W. H. Freeman Co. Reprint No. 491.)

Selye, H.: The stress of life, New York, 1956, McGraw-Hill Book Co.

Weeks, J. R.: Experimental narcotic addiction, Sci. Amer. **210**:46-52, March, 1964. (W. H. Freeman Co. Reprint No. 178.)

References

Some references cover large areas of physiological psychology and were written by a single author or by multiple authors. These are listed initially as general references; their appropriateness to areas within physiological psychology will be evident from their titles. Following this list, by chapter heading, appear secondary sources in which references to the original literature may be found. Such references include review articles, individually authored chapters in edited books, and books useful in only narrow areas of physiological psychology. Occasional original articles appear when they are of particular importance or are not mentioned in secondary sources.

GENERAL REFERENCES

Altman, J.: Organic foundations of animal behavior, New York, 1966, Holt, Rinehart & Winston, Inc.

Deutsch, J. A., and Deutsch, D.: Physiological psychology, Homewood, Ill., 1966, The Dorsey Press, Inc.

Geldard, F. A.: The human senses, New York, 1953, John Wiley & Sons, Inc.

Grossman, S. P.: A textbook of physiological psychology, New York, 1967, John Wiley & Sons, Inc.

Morgan, C. T.: Physiological psychology, ed. 3, New York, 1965, McGraw-Hill Book Co.

Thompson, R. F.: Foundations of physiological psychology, New York, 1967, Harper & Row, Publishers.

Wenger, M. A., Jones, F. N., and Jones, M. H.: Physiological psychology, New York, 1956, Henry Holt & Co.

Wyburn, G. M.: The nervous system: An outline of the structure and function of the human nervous system and sense organs, New York, 1960, Academic Press, Inc.

CHAPTER REFERENCES

Chapter 3

Feder, H. H., and Whalen, R. E.: Feminine behavior in neonatally castrated and estrogen-treated male rats, Science 147:306-307, 1965.

Gittes, R. F., and Irvin, G. L.: Thyroid and parathyroid roles in hypercalcemia: Evidence for a thyrocalcitron-releasing factor, Science 148:1737-1739, 1965.

Hoffman, R. A., and Ritter, R. J.: Pineal gland: influence on gonads of male hamsters, Science 148:1609-1611, 1965.

Lee, J., and Knowles, F. G. W.: Animal hormones, London, 1965, Hutchinson & Co.

Moore, W. W.: General endocrinology: hypophysis; endocrine functions of the pancreas; functions of the parathyroid glands; thyroidal physiology; the adrenal cortex; the endocrinology or reproduction. In Selkurt, E. E., editor: Physiology, Boston, 1963, Little, Brown & Co.

Tepperman, J.: Metabolic and endocrine physiology, Chicago, 1962, Year Book Medical Publishers, Inc.

Chapter 4

Brazier, M. A. B.: The electrical activity of the nervous system, ed. 2, London, 1960, Pitman Medical Publishing Co., Ltd.

Eccles, J. C.: Ionic mechanism of post-synaptic inhibition, Science 145:1148-1154, 1964.

Eccles, J. C.: Neuron physiology: introduction. In Field, J., editor: Handbook of physiology, vol. 1, Baltimore, 1960, The Williams & Wilkins Co.

Eccles, J. C.: The physiology of synapses, New York, 1964, Academic Press, Inc.

Hodgkin, A. L.: The conduction of the nervous impulse, Springfield, Ill., 1964, Charles C Thomas, Publisher.

Hodgkin, A. L.: The ionic basis of nerve conduction, Science **145**:1154-1159, 1964.

Huxley, A. F.: Excitation and conduction in nerve: quantitative analysis, Science **145**:1154-1159, 1964.

Lorenti de' No', R.: Continuous conduction of action potentials by peripheral mylenated fibers, Science **140**:383, 1963.

McLennan, H.: Synaptic transmission, Philadelphia, 1963, W. B. Saunders Co.

Patton, H. D.: Spinal reflexes and synaptic transmission. In Ruch, T. C., Patton, H. D., Woodbury, J. W., and Towe, A. L.: Neurophysiology, ed. 2, Philadelphia, 1965, W. B. Saunders Co.

Stevens, C. F.: Neurophysiology: a primer, New York, 1966, John Wiley & Sons, Inc.

Suckling, E. E.: Bioelectricity, New York, 1961, McGraw-Hill Book Co.

Chapter 5

Bajuez, E.: "Red" skeletonal muscle fibers: relative independence of neural control, Science **145**:938-939, 1964.

McLennan, H.: Synaptic transmission, Philadelphia, 1961, W. B. Saunders Co. (Chapter 2).

Woodbury, W. J., and Ruch, T. C.: Muscle. In Ruch, T. C., Patton, H. D., Woodbury, J. W., and Towe, A. L., editors: Neurophysiology, ed. 2, Philadelphia, 1965, W. B. Saunders Co.

Chapter 6

Kreig, W. J. S.: Functional neuroanatomy, ed. 2, Evanston, Ill., Brain Books.

Ranson, S. W., and Clark, S. L.: The anatomy of the nervous system: its development and function, ed. 10, Philadelphia, 1959, W. B. Saunders Co.

Truex, R. C.: Strong and Elwyns' human neuroanatomy, ed. 4, Baltimore, 1959, The Williams & Wilkins Co.

Chapter 7

Stevens, S. S.: Mathematics, measurement, and psychophysics. In Stevens, S. S., editor: Handbook of experimental psychology, New York, 1951, John Wiley & Sons, Inc.

Woodworth, R. S., and Schlosberg, H.: Experimental psychology, rev. ed., New York, 1954, Henry Holt & Co., Inc.

Chapter 8

Barber, T. H.: Toward a theory of pain, psychol. Bull. **56**:430-460, 1959.

Geldard, F. A.: Cutaneous channels of communication. In Rosenblith, W. A., editor: Symposium on principles of sensory communication, Cambridge, Mass., 1961, The M.I.T. Press.

Melzack, R., and Wall, P.: Pain mechanisms: a new theory, Science **150**:971-979, 1965.

Rose, J. E., and Montcastle, V. B.: Touch and kinaesthesis. In Field, J., editor: Handbook of physiology, vol. 1, Baltimore, 1960, The Williams & Wilkins Co.

Ruch, T. C.: Neural basis of somatic sensation. In Ruch, T. C., Patton, H. D., Woodbury, J. W., and Towe, A. L., editors: Neurophysiology, ed. 2, Philadelphia, 1965, W. B. Saunders Co.

Sweet, W. H.: Pain. In Field, J., editor: Handbook of physiology, vol. 1, Baltimore, 1960, The Williams & Wilkins Co.

Zotterman, Y.: Thermal sensations. In Field, J., editor: Handbook of physiology, vol. 1, Baltimore, 1960, The Williams & Wilkins Co.

Chapter 9

Bridgeman, C. F., and Eldred, E.: Hypothesis for a pressure-sensitive mechanism in muscle spindles, Science **143**:481-482, 1964.

Gernandt, B. E.: Vestibular mechanisms. In Field, J., editor: Handbook of physiology, vol. 1, Baltimore, 1960, The Williams & Wilkins Co.

Guedry, F. E.: Psychophysiological studies of vestibular function. In Neff, W. D.: Contributions to sensory physiology, vol. 1, New York, 1965, Academic Press, Inc.

Ruch, T. C.: Pontobulbar control of posture and orientation in space. In Ruch, T. C., Patton, H. D., Woodbury, J. W., and Towe, A. L., editors: Neurophysiology, Philadelphia, 1965, W. B. Saunders Co.

Wersall, J., and Flock, A.: Functional anatomy of the vestibular and lateral line organs. In Neff, W. D.: Contributions to sensory physiology, vol. 1, New York, 1965, Academic Press, Inc.

Chapter 10

Adey, W. R.: The sense of smell. In Field, J., editor: Handbook of physiology, vol. 1, Baltimore, 1960, The Williams & Wilkins Co.

Amoore, J. E.: Current status of the steric theory of odor, Ann. N. Y. Acad. Sci., **116**:457-476, 1964.

Gorman, W.: Flavor, taste, and the psychology of smell, Springfield, Ill., 1964, Charles C Thomas, Publisher.

Kalmus, H., and Hubbard, S. J.: The chemical senses in health and disease, Springfield, Ill., 1960, Charles C Thomas, Publisher.

Patton, H. D.: Taste, olfaction and visceral sensation. In Ruch, T. C., Patton, H. D., Woodbury, J. W., and Towe, A. L., editors: Neurophysiology, ed. 2, Philadelphia, 1965, W. B. Saunders Co.

Pfaffman, C.: The sense of taste. In Field, J., editor: Handbook of physiology, vol. 1, Baltimore, 1960, The Williams & Wilkins Co.

Pfaffman, C.: De gustibus, Amer. Psychol. **20**:21-33, 1965.

Pfaffman, C.: Taste: its sensory and motivating properties, Amer. Sci. **52**:187-206, 1964.

von Békésy, G.: Duplexity theory of taste, Science **145**:834-835, 1964.

Chapter 11

Ades, H. W.: Central auditory mechanisms. In Field, J., editor: Handbook of physiology, vol. 1, Baltimore, 1960, The Williams & Wilkins Co.

Davis, H.: Excitation of auditory receptors. In Field, J., editor: Handbook of physiology, vol. 1, Baltimore, 1960, The Williams & Wilkins Co.

Davis, H., and Silverman, S. R., editors: Hearing and deafness, rev. ed., New York, 1962, Holt, Rinehart & Winston, Inc.

Towe, A. L.: Audition and the auditory receptors. In Ruch, T. C., Patton, H. D., Woodbury, J. W., and Towe, A. L., editors: Neurophysiology, ed. 2, Philadelphia, 1965, W. B. Saunders Co.

Chapter 12

Chapanis, A.: Color names for color space, Amer. Sci. **53**:327-346, 1965.

Bartley, S. H.: Central mechanisms of vision. In Field, J., editor: Handbook of physiology, vol. 1, Baltimore, 1960, The Williams & Wilkins Co.

Brown, P. K., and Wald, G.: Visual pigments in single rods and cones of the human retina, Science **155**:273-279, 1967.

DeValois, R. L.: Behavioral and electrophysiological studies of primate vision. In Neff, W. D.: Contributions to sensory physiology, vol. 1, New York, 1965, Academic Press, Inc.

Dowling, J. E.: The site of visual adaptation, Science **155**:273-279, 1967.

Fatchchand, R., Laufer, M., and Svaetichin, G.: Retinal receptor potentials and their linear relationship to light intensity, Science **137**:666-667, 1962.

Granit, R.: Neural activity in the retina. In Field, J., editor: Handbook of physiology, vol. 1, Baltimore, 1960, The Williams & Wilkins Co.

Hartline, H. K.: Vision-introduction. In Field, J., editor: Handbook of physiology, vol. 1, Baltimore, 1960, The Williams & Wilkins Co.

Marks, W. B., Dobelle, W. H., and MacNichol, E. F.: Visual pigments in single primate cones, Science **143**:1181-1183, 1964.

Ruch, T. C.: Vision. In Ruch, T. C., Patton, H. D., Woodbury, J. W., and Towe, A. L., editors: Neurophysiology, ed. 2, Philadelphia, 1965, W. B. Saunders Co.

Svaetichin, G., and MacNichol, E. F.: Retinal mechanisms for chromatic and achromatic vision, Ann. N. Y. Acad. Sci. **74**:385-404, 1958.

Svaetichin, G., Negishi, K., Fatechand, R., Drujan, B. D., and DeTesta, A. S.: Nervous function based on interaction between neuronal and non-neuronal elements. In DeRobertis, E. D. P., and Carrea, R.: Progress in brain research, vol. 15, New York, 1965, American Elsevier Publishing Co.

Wald, G.: The photoreceptor process. In Field, J., editor: Handbook of physiology, vol. 1, Baltimore, 1960, The Williams & Wilkins Co.

Wald, G.: The receptors of human color vision, Science **144**:1007-1016, 1964.

Weymouth, F. W.: The eye as an optical instrument. In Ruch, T. C., Patton, H. D., Woodbury, J. W., and Towe, A. L., editors: Neurophysiology, ed. 2, Philadelphia, 1965, W. B. Saunders Co.

Chapter 13

Krieg, W. J. S.: Functional neuroanatomy, ed. 2, Evanston, Ill., Brain Books, chap. 18.

Patton, H. D.: Reflex regulation of movement and posture. In Ruch, T. C., Patton, H. D., Woodbury, J. W., and Towe, A. L., editors: Neurophysiology, ed. 2, Philadelphia, 1965, W. B. Saunders Co.

Ruch, T. C.: Basal ganglia and cerebellum. In Ruch, T. C., Patton, H. D., Woodbury, J. W., and Towe, A. L., editors: Neurophysiology, ed. 2, Philadelphia, 1965, W. B. Saunders Co.

Ruch, T. C.: The cerebral cortex: its structure and motor functions. In Ruch, T. C., Patton, H. D., Woodbury, J. W., and Towe, A. L., editors: Neurophysiology, ed. 2, Philadelphia, 1965, W. B. Saunders Co.

Ruch, T. C.: Pontobublar control of posture and orientation in space. In Ruch T. C., Patton, H. D., Woodbury, J. W., and Towe, A. L., editors: Neurophysiology, ed. 2, Philadelphia, 1965, W. B. Saunders Co.

Chapter 14

Bonin, G. von: Essay on the cerebral cortex, Springfield, Ill., 1950, Charles C Thomas, Publisher.

Lindsley, D. B.: Attention, consciousness, sleep and wakefulness. In Field, J., editor: Handbook of physiology, vol. 3, Baltimore, 1960, The Williams & Wilkins Co.

Magoun, H. W.: The waking brain, ed. 2, Springfield, Ill., 1963, Charles C Thomas, Publisher.

McCleary, R. A., and Moore, R. Y.: Subcortical mechanisms of behavior, New York, 1965, Basic Books, Inc.

Patton, H. D.: Reflex Regulation of Movement and Posture. In Ruch, T. C., Patton, H. D., Woodbury, J. W., and Towe, A. L., editors: Neurophysiology, ed. 2, Philadelphia, 1965, W. B. Saunders Co.

Pribram, K. H., and Kruger, L.: Functions of the "olfactory brain." In Isaacson, R. L., editor: Basic readings in neuropsychology, New York, 1964, Harper & Row, Publishers.

Ruch, T. C.: The basal ganglia and cerebellum. In Ruch, T. C., Patton, H. D., Woodbury, J. W., and Towe, A. L., editors: Neurophysiology, ed. 2, Philadelphia, 1965, W. B. Saunders Co.

Ruch, T. C.: The cerebral cortex: it's structure and motor function. In Ruch, T. C., Patton, H. D., Woodbury, J. W., and Towe, A. L., editors: Neurophysiology, ed. 2, Philadelphia, 1965, W. B. Saunders Co.

Ruch, T. C.: Pontobulbar control of posture and orientation in space. In Ruch, T. C., Patton, H. D., Woodbury, J. W., and Towe, A. L., editors: Neurophysiology, ed. 2, Philadelphia, 1965, W. B. Saunders Co.

Smythies, J. R.: The neurological foundations of psychiatry, New York, 1966, Academic Press, Inc.

Warren, J. M., and Alsert, K., editors: The frontal granular cortex and behavior, New York, 1964, McGraw-Hill Book Co.

Chapter 15

Beh, H. C., and Barratt, P. E. H.: Discrimination and conditioning during sleep as indicated by the electroencephalograph, Science **147**:1470-1471, 1965.

Heath, R. G.: Electrical self-stimulation of the brain in man, Amer. J. Psychiatr. **120**:571-577, 1963.

Hetherington, A. W., and Ranson, S. W.: Hypothalamuc lesions and adiposity in the rat. In Isaacson, R. L., editor: Basic readings in neuropsychology, New York, 1964, Harper & Row, Publishers.

Kleitman, N.: Sleep and wakefulness, rev. ed., Chicago, 1963, University of Chicago Press.

Miller, N. E.: Chemical coding of behavior in the brain, Science **148**:328-338, 1965.

Murray, E. J.: Sleep, dreams and arousal, New York, 1965, Appleton-Century-Crofts.

Olds, J., and Milner, P.: Positive reinforcement produced by electrical stimulation of septal area and other regions of rat brain. In Isaacson, R. L.: Neuropsychology, New York, 1964, Harper & Row, Publishers.

Olds, J., Travis, R. P., and Schwing, R. C.: Topographical organization of self-stimulation functions, J. Comp. Physiol. Psychol. **53**:23-32, 1960.

Reynolds, R. W.: Hypothalamic lesions and disinhibition of feeding, Science **150**:1322, 1965.

Roffwarg, H. P., Muzio, J. N, and Dement, W. C.: Ontogenetic development of the human sleep-dream cycle, Science **152**:604-619, 1966.

Samuels, I.: Reticular mechanisms and behavior, Psychol. Bull. **56**:1-25, 1959.

Smith, O. A.: The physiologic basis of motivation. In Ruch, T. C., Patton, H. D., Woodbury, J. W., and Towe, A. L., editors: Neurophysiology, ed. 2, Philadelphia, 1965, W. B. Saunders Co.

Stellar, E.: Drive and motivation. In Field, J., editor: Handbook of physiology, vol. 3, Baltimore, 1960, The Williams & Wilkins Co.

Stellar, E.: The physiology of motivation. In Isaacson, R. L., editor: Neuropsychology, New York, 1964, Harper & Row, Publishers.

Teitelbaum, P., and Epstein, A.: The lateral hypothalamic syndrome, Psychol. Rev. **69**:74-90, 1962.

Chapter 16

Bard, P., and Mountcastle, V. B.: Some forebrain mechanisms involved in expression of rage with special reference to suppression of angry behavior. In Isaacson, R. L., editor: Neuropsychology, New York, 1964, Harper & Row, Publishers.

Brady, J. V.: Emotional Behavior. In Field, J., editor: Handbook of psychology, vol. 3, Baltimore, 1960, The Williams & Wilkins Co.

Gellhorn, E.: Motion and emotion: the role of perception in the physiology and pathology of the emotions. Psychol. Rev. **71**:457-472, 1964.

Gellhorn, E.: The neurophysiological basis of anxiety: a hypothesis, Perspect. Biol. Med. **8**:488-515, 1965.

Gellhorn, E.: Prolegoma to a theory of the emotions, Perspect. Biol. Med. **4**:403-436, 1961.

Goddard, G. V.: Functions of the amygdala, Psychol. Bull. **62**:89-109, 1964.

Lindsley, D. B.: Emotion. In Stevens, S. S.: Handbook of experimental psychology, New York, 1951, John Wiley & Sons, Inc.

MacLean, P. D.: Psychosomatic disease and the visceral brain: recent developments bearing on the Papez theory of emotion. In Isaacson, R. L.: Neuropsychology, New York, 1964, Harper & Row, Publishers.

Papez, J. W.: A proposed mechanism of emotion. In Isaacson, R. L.: Neuropsychology, New York, 1964, Harper & Row, Publishers.

Pribram, K. H., and Kruger, L.: Functions of the olfactory brain. In Isaacson, R. L.: Neuropsycology, New York, 1964, Harper & Row, Publishers.

Ruch, T. C.: Neurophysiology of emotion. In Ruch, T. C., Patton, H. D., Woodbury, J. W., and Towe, A. L., editors: Neurophysiology, ed. 2, Philadelphia, 1965, W. B. Saunders Co.

Schlosberg, H.: Three dimensions of emotion, Psychol. Bull. **62**:89-109, 1964.

Schreiner, L., and Kling, A.: Behavioral changes following rhinencephalic injury in the cat. In Isaacson, R. L.: Neuropsychology, New York, 1964, Harper & Row, Publishers.

Simon, A., Herbert, C. C., and Strauss, R., editors: The physiology of emotions, Springfield, Ill., 1961, Charles C Thomas, Publisher.

Chapter 17

Asrantian, E. A.: Compensatory adaptations, reflex activity, and the brain, New York, 1965, Pergammon Press, Inc.

Bennett, E. L., Diamond, M. C., Krech, D., and Rosensweig, M. R.: Chemical and anatomical plasticity of brain, Science **146**:610-619, 1964.

Briggs, M. H., and Kitto, G. B.: The molecular basis of learning and memory, Psychol. Rev. **69**:537-541, 1962.

Deutsch, J. A., Hamburg, M. D., and Dahl, H.: Acetylcholinesterase-induced amnesia and its temporal aspects, Science **151**:221-223, 1966.

Gaito, J.: A biochemical approach to learning and memory, Psychol. Rev. **68**:285-292, 1961.

Gaito, J.: DNA and RNA as memory molecules, Psychol. Rev. **70**:471-480, 1963.

Gaito, J. and Zavala, A.: Neurochemistry and learning, Psychol. Bull. **61**:45-61, 1964.

Galambos, R. and Morgan, C. T.: The neural basis of learning. In Field, J., editor: Handbook of physiology, vol. 3, Baltimore, 1960, The Williams & Wilkins Co.

Glickman, S. E.: Perseverative neural processes and consolidation of the memory trace, Psychol. Bull. **58**:218-233, 1961.

Glickstein, M.: Neurophysiology of learning and memory. In Ruch, T. C., Patton, H. D., Woodbury, J. W., and Towe, A. L., editors: Neurophysiology, Ed. 2, Philadelphia, 1965, W. B. Saunders Co.

Hudspeth, W. J., and Gerbrandt, L. K.: Electroconvulsive shock: conflict, consolidation, and neuroanatomical functions, Psychol. Bull. **63**:377-383, 1965.

John, E. R.: Mechanisms of memory, New York, 1967, Academic Press, Inc.

Kimble, D. P.: The anatomy of memory, Palo Alto, Calif., 1965, Science & Behavior Books, Inc.

Landauer, T. K.: Two hypotheses concerning the biochemical basis of memory, Psychol. Rev. **71**:167-179, 1964.

Lewis, D. J., and Maher, B. A.: Neural consolidation and electroconvulsive shock, Psychol. Rev. **72**:225-239, 1965.

Luttges, M., Johnson, T., Buck, C., Holland, J., and McGaugh, J.: An examination of "transfer of learning" by nucleic acid, Science **151**:834-837, 1966.

McGaugh, J. L.: Time-dependent processes in memory storage, Science **153**:1351-1358, 1966.

Miller, G. A., Galanter, E., and Pribram, K. H.: Plans and the structure of behavior, New York, 1960, Henry Holt & Co.

Rimland, B.: Infantile autism, New York, 1964, Appleton-Century-Crofts.

Rosensweig, M. R.: Environmental complexity, cerebral change and behavior, Amer. Psychol. **21**:321-332, 1966.

Rosensweig, M. R., Krech, D., and Bennett, E. L.: A search for relations between brain chemistry and behavior, Psychol. Bull. **57**:476-492, 1960.

Russell, W. R.: Brain, memory, learning, Oxford, England, 1959, The Clarendon Press.

Schmitt, F. O.: Molecules and memory, New Scientist **23**:643-645, 1965.

Smith, D. D.: Mammalian learning and behavior, Philadelphia, 1965, W. B. Saunders Co.

Sperry, R. W.: Cerebral organization and behavior, Science **133**:1749-1757, 1961.

Walker, E. L.: Action decrement and its relation to learning, Psychol. Rev. **65**:129-142, 1958.

Chapter 18

Eiduson, S., Geller, E., Yuliviler, A., and Eiduson, B. T.: Biochemistry and behavior, Princeton, N. J., 1964, D. Van Nostrand Co.

Humphrey, G., and Coxon, R. V.: The chemistry of thinking, Springfield, Ill., 1963, Charles C Thomas, Publisher.

Selye, H.: The physiology and pathology of exposure to stress, Montreal, 1960, Acta, Inc.

Zigler, E.: Familial mental retardation: a continuing dilemma, Science **155**:292-298, 1967.

Glossary*

ablation Removal of part of the brain or part of the body by surgical means.

absolute refractory period The period accompanying the *spike potential;* during this period the nerve cell cannot be excited.

absolute threshold Minimum physical energy that stimulates a receptor 50% of the time; a statistical average of receptor sensitivity.

absorb To take up, as light absorbed by a surface or by a color filter.

accommodation Process of thickening the lens of the eye to focus diverging rays of light from nearby objects on the *fovea* of the retina; visual focussing on nearby objects.

acetylcholine (ACh) A chemical transmitter substance released at *synapses* by the *synaptic knobs* of one neuron to excite other neurons.

acetylcholine esterase (AChE) An *enzyme* that speeds the destruction of *acetylcholine (ACh)* after ACh release at the *synapse*. The presence of acetylcholine esterase limits the response of a neuron to the chemical transmitter released at synapses.

ACh See *acetylcholine.*

AChE See *acetylcholine esterase.*

achromatic Without *hue,* as grays, blacks and whites.

acoustic Rapid variations in air pressure (sound), especially as they result in hearing.

acromegaly A misproportioned body caused by hypersecretion of *somatotropic hormone* by the *adenohypophysis* after normal growth has ceased. Lengthwise growth in the bones is no longer possible, and the body and features become misshapen.

ACTH Adrenocorticotropic hormone; a hormone

*Italicized words in definitions are included in the glossary.

of the anterior pituitary gland that stimulates secretion of *corticoids* by the *adrenal cortex* and controls the hormone output of the adrenal cortex.

action potential Complete sequence of electrical events accompanying and following the nerve impulse; changes in the potential of the nerve cell membrane that result from conduction.

active avoidance A learning situation in which the subject must perform a specific act to avoid punishment.

actomysin The chemical making up *myofibrils,* threadlike particles that are the contraction mechanism of muscle cells.

acute Immediate, as an animal operated upon and kept alive and anesthetized only for the duration of a physiological experiment.

acute preparation See *acute.*

adaptation Decrease in the response of a receptor and in the perceived intensity of a stimulus resulting from a constant rate of stimulation; loss of receptor sensitivity caused by stimulation.

addiction Physiological dependence on a drug.

adenohypophysis Anterior part of the *hypophysis* (pituitary gland) that secretes the *somatotropic, thyrotropic, adrenocorticotropic* and *gonadotropic hormones.*

adenosine diphosphate (ADP) A compound involved in the energy-releasing and energy-storing reactions of the cell that has one energy-rich phosphate bond.

adenosine triphosphate (ATP) A compound involved in the energy-releasing and enegy-storing reactions of the cell that has two energy-rich phosphate bonds.

adenylic acid (AA) The compound attached to others in the cell in energy-storing or energy-releasing reactions via energy-rich phosphate bonds.

adequate stimulus An energy change that activates a receptor and is the form of energy to which the receptor is most sensitive, e.g., light for the eye or sound for the ear.

ADH See *antidiuretic hormone.*

adipsia Lack of a thirst *drive;* absence of drinking behavior when the body water supply is low.

adrenal cortex Covering or outer cells of the adrenal glands that produce *corticoids.*

adrenal medulla The core, or central portion, of the adrenal glands that produces the hormones *epinephrine* and *norepinephrine.*

adrenaline See *epinephrine.*

adrenergic Pertaining to *epinephrine (adrenaline)* as a nerve cell transmitter. A nerve cell that stimulates other nerve cells by release of epinephrine is an adrenergic cell.

adrenocorticotropic hormones (**ACTH**) The hormone of the *adenohypophysis* (anterior pituitary gland) that stimulates the *adrenal cortex* to produce *corticoids;* secreted by the anterior pituitary gland to control the hormone output of the adrenal cortex.

aerial perspective A *monocular cue* to distance. Lack of perfect transparency of the air results in blurred outlines of distant objects.

afferent Carrying impulses toward a *center,* as when sensory nerves carry nerve impulses toward the brain or spinal cord.

afterdischarge Firing of the motoneurons of a reflex after the reflex stimulus has ceased to act. As a result of afterdischarge, the reflex response continues for a time after the reflex stimulus ends.

afterimages Sensations that follow after stimulation has ended. The sensation to the stimulus may continue or change.

ageusia Lack of taste sensitivity—taste blindness.

agnosia Inability to recognize objects presented via a given sensory modality; for example, a subject may recognize an object by seeing it but not by feeling its outlines.

agonist muscles Muscles that perform a given movement.

alcohol A nonaddicting depressing drug contained in wine, beer, and whiskey.

allocortex In evolutionary terms, the oldest areas of the cerebral cortex, originally devoted to smell.

all-or-none law The statement that the nerve cell responds with the maximum polarization change its electrical and chemical condition permits, if it responds at all.

alpha block Desynchronization of *alpha rhythm* of the *EEG* (brain waves) caused by a flashing light, concentration, or arousal. Low-voltage desynchronized brain waves replace the regular 10-per-second alpha waves.

alpha block conditioning Conditioning the *alpha block* to a stimulus that does not ordinarily produce the alpha block response. As a result, alpha block will result from presenting the stimulus.

alpha cells Endocrine cells of the *pancreas* that secrete the hormone *glucagon,* a hormone that stimulates the storage of blood sugar in the liver and muscles.

alpha rhythm A 10 to 14 cps rhythm often seen in the EEG of a resting but awake subject.

alpha wave driving Changing the frequency of *EEG* alpha waves by using a dim flashing light of desired frequency; the alpha waves follow the frequency of the flashing light.

amacrine cells Cells of the *retina* that interconnect retinal *bipolar* neurons with one another.

amblyopia Impaired vision that does not result from detectable defects in the eye; often caused by suppression of the input from one eye by the brain to avoid double vision caused by conflicting images from the two eyes.

amino acid Type of organic acid that is the major ingredient of protein molecules, which are an essential part of the structure of the cell.

amnesia Partial or complete loss of memory.

amphetamine A nonaddicting type of drug that stimulates the SNS, causes peripheral vasoconstriction, and promotes wakefulness and arousal.

amplitude In physics, difference between extreme limits of an oscillation or vibration, e.g., limits of the air pressure change in a sound wave.

ampulla A bulblike swelling on the end of each *semicircular canal,* where it contacts the *utriculus.* Contains the *crista,* a receptor responding to head movements.

amygdala A nuclear complex buried in the temporal lobe; important in the organization of emotion by the *limbic system.*

anabolism A metabolic reaction that requires energy input to proceed.

analgesic Any drug that relieves pain without causing unconsciousness; also, an area of the body that does not respond to pain stimuli.

anastomosis In neurology, a network of interlaced nerves and nerve fibers.

anatomist One who studies anatomy.

anatomy Structural relationship of parts of the body.

androgens Male sex hormones, produced by the *testes* (testicles) of the male.

anelectrotonus Increase in the polarized condition of the cell membrane without excitation of the nerve impulse.

anemia Lack of red blood corpuscles.

annulospiral endings Sensory endings in specialized *muscle spindle* cells that initiate the *stretch reflex.*

anode A positively charged electrode, i.e., one that lacks *electrons.*

anosmia Lack of smell sensitivity—smell-blindness.

anoxia Condition in which the tissues are not receiving enough oxygen from the lungs via the circulatory system to sustain their metabolic activity.

ANS See *autonomic nervous system.*

antagonist muscles Muscles that would oppose a given movement if ' ot relaxed; for example, the *extensor muscles* of the arm are the antagonist muscles for arm flexion.

anterior Toward the head end of the four-legged animal or the embryo; toward the front in man (standing erect).

anterior chamber The cavity of the eyeball that lies between the *cornea* and the *iris.*

anterior lobe of cerebellum See *paleocerebellum.*

anterior pituitary gland See *adenolypophysis.*

anterior vertical canal The anterior vertical one of the three *semicircular canals* of the *inner ear.* (The semicircular canals are part of the receptor mechanism that responds to head movement.)

antidiuretic Any influence that reduces the loss of body water that results from the formation of urine in the kidney.

antidiuretic hormone A hormone of the *posterior pituitary gland* that has an *antidiuretic* effect.

antienzyme See *enzyme inhibitor.*

aperiodic A change that does not repeat itself, such as the aperiodic air pressure changes of *noise.*

aphagia Lack of a hunger *drive;* absence of eating behavior sufficient to the needs of the body.

aphasia Impairment in language skills, usually caused by brain damage. Inability to recognize words by sight (word-blindness) or by sound (word-deafness), for example.

apoenzyme The larger protein molecule that, together with the coenzyme, makes up an enzyme system, which speeds chemical reactions without being consumed in the reaction.

aqueous humor Fluid that fills the *anterior* and *posterior chambers* of the eyeball.

arachnoid layer *Vascular* middle layer of the *meninges* that cover the brain and spinal cord.

ARAS See *ascending reticular activating system.*

archicerebellum In terms of evolution, the oldest part of the cerebellum. See *flocculonodular lobe.*

arcuate nucleus That part of the *ventrolateral nucleus* of the *thalamus,* where *second-order neurons* excited by sensory nerves from the tongue and face terminate; a part of the nerve pathways serving taste and *somesthesis.*

arteries Blood vessels running from the heart to the tissues.

ascending reticular activating system (ARAS) A system of many short fibers of the central gray of the brainstem that is excited by collaterals of the afferent *spinothalamic system* and activates or arouses activity in the whole brain, particularly the cortex.

association areas Those parts of the *cerebral cortex* that are neither *sensory projection areas* nor *motor projection areas.* Originally presumed to be parts of the cortex that associated sensory input with motor output.

association neuron A nerve cell of the *CNS* that is neither sensory nor motor in function.

astigmatism An eye condition in which the lens or cornea has an uneven curvature.

attentional adaptation A decrease in the perceived intensity of a stimulus caused by inattention.

audiogram A graph of the results of *audiometry,* or testing the sensitivity of the ear to various frequencies (pitches) of sound.

audiometry measurement of the *absolute threshold* of the ear for loudness over a range of frequencies.

audition Hearing.

auditory projection area Area 41 of the *temporal lobe* of the *cerebrum,* where filters of the classical auditory pathway terminate; the sensory projection area of the cortex for audition.

aural harmonics Overtones added to a sound by resonant vibrations of the *cochlea.*

autonomic balance ($\overline{A}$) Relative amount of *SNS* activity compared to *PNS* activity; degree of sympathetic versus parasympathetic control of visceral activity.

autonomic nervous system (ANS) Motor nerve supply to the viscera; the efferent fibers of the peripheral nervous system that supply the viscera with a dual innervation of two divisions, the *sympathetic* and *parasympathetic.*

axoaxonic synapses Synapses between the axon terminals *(end feet)* of one axon and the *axon filaments* of another.

axodendritic synapses Synapses between the axon terminals *(end feet)* of one axon and the *dendrites* and *cell body* of another.

axon An extension from the cell body of the neuron that carries nerve impulses away from the cell body and to other neurons.

axon filaments Fine threadlike extensions of the end of an *axon.*

axon hillock Area of the cell body from which the *axon* arises.

basal ganglia Certain subcortical nuclei of the *endbrain,* including the putamen, caudate nucleus, and globus pallidus.

basal metabolic rate (BMR) A measure of the metabolic rate taken with the subject fasting and at rest. The oxygen consumed in breathing under these conditions indicates the minimum rate of chemical reactions in the body.

basilar membrane The membrane forming part of the division between the *scala metdia* and *scala tympani of the cochlea.* The *organ of Corti* rests on the basilar membrane, part of the auditory apparatus.

basket endings *Afferent* nerve endings that surround roots of body hair and respond to touch (pressure) on the hair.

beats Variations in loudness that occur when the *fundamental* frequencies of two tones come in and out of *phase.* Beats occur at the same rate as the difference in frequency of the two tones.

behavior Any observable act of a living organism.

bel Unit on a logarithmic scale of sound intensity. The number of bels form the exponent of 10; the resulting number is multiplied by 0.0002 dyne/cm.², a zero point approximating the human hearing threshold.

Benzedrine See *amphetamine.*

beta cells Endocrine cells of the pancreas secreting the hormone *insulin,* that stimulates the utilization of blood sugar by the cells.

bilaterally symmetrical The same on either side.

binocular cue Any cue to depth or distance that depends on sensations from *both* eyes.

binocular parallax Difference in the angle of regard for the two eyes viewing nearby objects. Parallax results from the position of the eyes in the head.

biochemistry The study of chemical reactions in living organisms.

bipolar cell layer A layer of cells of the *retina* that transfer excitation from the *rods* and *cones* to the *ganglion cells* of the *optic nerve.*

bipolar neuron A neuron with a single *axon* and a single *dendrite,* arising at different points from the *cell body.*

blast olfactometer A device for releasing a known amount of odorous gas under pressure up the nostril; used in measuring smell thresholds.

blastula That early stage of development in the embryo when cell multiplication has produced a hollow ball of cells.

blood-brain barrier A physiological mechanism that filters the *extracellular fluid* of the brain from blood in a manner that makes it chemically different from other extracellular fluids of the body.

brain (encephalon) A large soft mass of nervous and supporting tissue contained within the skull.

brainstem All of the *brain* except the *cerebral* and *cerebellar hemispheres.*

brainstem reticular formation (BSRF) Mass of gray matter of the *brainstem* made up chiefly of short, branching *Golgi type II* cells. The BSRF arouses the brain to activity and stimulates or inhibits extensor motoneurons.

brightness Visual sensation that results from light intensity.

brightness constancy An assumption that objects remain constant in brightness and that changes in apparent brightness result from changes in the amount of light falling on the object.

Brodman system A system for identifying different areas of the *cerebral cortex* by the relative thickness of the six cortical layers, assigning each such area an arbitrary number.

buffer A chemical compound that reacts with either hydrogen or hydroxyl ions to bind them so as to neutralize either an acid or basic solution.

caffeine A mild and nonaddicting cortical stimulant present in coffee, tea, and some soft drinks.

calorie A unit of heat. As commonly used in diets, the unit is 1,000 times the amount of heat necessary to raise the temperature of 1 gram of water by 1° C.

camphoraceous One of the seven primary qualities of *stereochemical* smell *theory* whose receptor site is shaped like a hemispherical basin.

cancer An abnormal tissue growth (tumor) caused by uncontrolled cell multiplication.

candle A standard measure of the brightness of a light source. One candle emits 4π *lumens* of luminous *flux.*

capillaries Thin-walled tiny blood vessels, through whose walls oxygen, carbon dioxide, and waste are exchanged with the *extracellular fluid.*

CAR See *conditioned avoidance response.*

carbohydrates Sugars and starches of various kinds from which the body derives glucose, the essential food of specialized cells.

carcinogen An agent that can cause *cancer* (malignant tumors).

cardiac muscle The muscle that forms the heart; intermediate in structural and functional characteristics between *striate* and *smooth muscle.*

cardioaccelerator center A center in the *medulla* that excites the heart to beat faster.

cardioinhibitory center A center in the medulla that acts to slow the heart rate.

carotid sinus A dilated area in either of the two carotid arteries supplying the brain that is sensitive to blood pressure and stimulates a reflex regulating heart rate.

carrier In genetics, an individual whose germ tissue contains genes for a given physical characteristic, whether or not that individual has the characteristic.

catabolism A metabolic reaction that releases energy.

catalyst A chemical that speeds the rate of a chemical reaction without being used up by the reaction.

cataracts Clouding of the *cornea* of the eye that results in partial or complete blindness.

catelectrotonus Reduction in the polarized condition of the cell membrane without excitation of an impulse.

cathode A negatively charged electrode, i.e, one that has surplus electrons.

cathode-ray oscilloscope A device for measuring rapid voltage changes using a glowing trace left on the face of an evacuated tube by the rapid elevation of a stream of electrons that sweeps across the tube face at a known rate.

causalgia A severe and burning pain sensation that spreads from a focal point (often uninjured) to surrounding areas.

cell A protoplasmic body that is the unit of life. A cell can be an independent living organism or a specialized unit of a complex many-celled organism.

cell assemblies Groups of interconnected cortical cells supposed to excite one another over and over again. Cell assemblies are involved in *phase sequence* hypothesis of perceptual learning.

cell body The part of the nerve cell containing its *nucleus*.

cell colony A cluster of otherwise independent cells.

cell membrane The membrane that separates the cytoplasm of a cell from the environment of the cell.

cell metabolism Chemical reactions of a cell that are required for life.

center A group of nerve cell bodies where many *synapses* are found. See also *nucleus*.

central nervous system (CNS) The brain and spinal cord.

central sulcus The *sulcus* that divides each *cerebral hemisphere* into an anterior one third and posterior two thirds; it separates the *somesthetic* sensory and *motor projection areas*.

CER See *conditioned emotional response*.

cerebellar hemispheres See *cerebellum*.

cerebellar system All proprioceptive and cortical input to the cerebellum and all cerebellar output to cortical and subcortical centers involved in movement.

cerebellum A large paired suprasegmental structure of the hindbrain, consisting of two hemispheres connected by a central vermis and mediating postural responses to input from the *vestibular senses*, *muscle spindles*, and *cerebral cortex*.

cerebral aqueduct The tubular passage inside the midbrain that connects the *third* and *fourth ventricles*.

cerebral cortex Gray matter covering the *cerebral hemispheres*.

cerebral hemispheres Large twin *suprasegmental* masses of the brain of higher mammals that develop embryologically from the *endbrain* and overlie most lower parts of the brain.

cerebral peduncles Ropelike enlargements on the base of the brain formed by tracts that run between the *cerebral hemispheres* and lower centers.

cerebrospinal fluid The tissue fluid surrounding the brain and spinal cord and filling the *ventricles*.

cerebrospinal meningitis A disease that attacks the *meninges* (coverings) of the brain tissue and causes brain damage.

cerebrum See *cerebral hemispheres*.

cervical Pertaining to the neck.

cervix Opening between the *uterus* and the *vagina*.

CFF See *critical flicker fusion frequency*.

chemical The atomic or molecular structure of matter.

chemoreceptor A receptor that responds to chemical change, such as those of the carotid sinus that react to blood acidity caused by high carbon dioxide content.

chlorine (Cl⁻) An element that moves freely across the nerve cell membranes, as an *ion*.

cholinergic Refers to nerve fibers that release *acetylcholine (ACh)* as a transmitter substance at their synapses with other nerve cells.

chorionic hormone A hormone of the placenta that inhibits the *estrus cycle* during pregnancy.

choroid coat The vascular pigmented middle layer of eye tissue that lies beneath the *sclerotic coat*.

choroid plexus Vascular structures that secrete the *cerebrospinal* fluid in the brain.

chromatic Having the characteristic of *hue*, such as reds, greens, yellows, and blues.

chromosomes Microscopic rod-shaped bodies in the cell nucleus. Chromosomes contain the DNA molecules that govern hereditary characteristics, cell specialization, and cell function.

chronic Of long standing, as an animal kept alive for a period of weeks after an experimental operation, or a chronic disease.

ciliary body A ring of muscle tissue that surrounds the lens of the eye, is attached to the lens by the *suspensory ligament*, and contracts in *accommodation* to thicken the lens for focus on nearby objects.

ciliary ring See *ciliary body*.

cingulate gyrus The *gyrus* just dorsal to the *corpus callosum* on the medial surface of the *cerebral hemispheres* in the *longitudinal fissure*.

circular fibers Smooth muscle fibers that circle a visceral tube or the pupil to constrict either when contracted.

circulatory system The system of heart, arteries, capillaries, and veins that carries blood to all parts of the body.

classical conditioning See *type I CR*.

clonus A series of muscle contractions interrupted

by partial relaxation to give a jerky contraction.

closed chain See *reverberatory circuit.*

CNS See *central nervous system.*

CO₂ Carbon dioxide.

cocaine A powerful stimulant drug usually absorbed through the mucous membranes.

coccygeal Pertaining to the fused *vertebrae* that form the rudiment of a tail in man.

cochlea The coiled, fluid-filled structure of the *inner ear.* The cochlea contains the structures that transduce sound vibrations into nerve impulses in hearing.

cochlear duct See *scala media.*

cochlear microphonic An electrical response of the *organ of Corti* to sound that follows the form of the sound wave as a microphone does.

coenzyme A smaller prosthetic group that, together with the *apoenzyme,* makes up an *enzyme system.*

COEPS See *cortically originating extra pyramidal system.*

cold A decrease in temperature (molecular motion), especially as it stimulates the cold receptors to result in cold sensations.

collateral ganglia *Ganglia* of the *SNS* found in the body cavity and neck; formed by *cell bodies* and *synapses* of *postganglionic* sympathetic neurons.

colliculi Four visual and auditory reflex centers that form four pea-shaped enlargements on the roof of the *midbrain.*

color Any visible mixture of wavelengths of light.

color formula The formula regulating the way that the seven *primary qualities* of vision mix to form *secondary qualities:* C = (R or G) + (B or Y) + (Wh or Bl) + Gr.

color pyramid A geometric figure that describes the response of the eye to *hue, saturation,* and *brightness* in terms of the *color formula.*

color wheel A device for color mixing by rapidly rotating a wheel, segments of which differ in *hue.*

commissural fibers Refers to fibers connecting the *cerebral hemispheres,* such as those of the *corpus callosum* and anterior and posterior commissures.

common chemical sense Pain sensitivity of the mucous membranes, particularly of the eyes, nose, and mouth, when stimulated by substances in solution.

compensation Lack of sensation caused by the simultaneous stimulation of different (opposed) qualities.

complex periodic wave Graph of a complex change that repeats itself, such as the pressure changes of a *complex tone.*

complex tone A tone made up of several *simple tones* produced by a complex vibrating body.

concentration gradient Difference in concentration of an element or molecule in a solution, taken between two points in the solution or on either side of a membrane dividing the solution.

concussion A blow on the head that damages brain cells or impairs their function.

conditioned avoidance response (CAR) Any learned response performed to avoid punishment.

conditioned emotional response (CER) Fear-induced behavior such as "freezing" or crouching to a signal that precedes unavoidable punishment (shock).

conditioned response (CR) A response that results from repeated presentation of a *conditioned stimulus* followed by an *unconditioned stimulus (reinforcement).* A simple learned response to a stimulus.

conditioned stimulus (CS) A stimulus that results in a *conditioned response* only after being paired with an *unconditioned stimulus.*

conduction The property of a cell membrane that carries excitation from one part of the cell to another.

conduction time Time required for excitation to be transmitted from one part of the nervous system to another.

conductor A material in which ion or electron movement is relatively unimpeded. A good conductor offers little resistance to the flow of electrical *current.*

cones High-threshold *chromatic* visual receptors containing *iodopsin* found in the central area of the *retina;* most active in daylight

consolidation According to the *two-phase hypothesis,* the process of laying down a permanent memory trace that is caused by *perseveration* of neural activity following practice.

consonance Degree to which two or more sound stimuli have *consonant frequencies.*

consonant frequencies Frequencies whose pitches fuse or blend well together.

constancy An unconscious assumption that objects remain constant in size, shape, and brightness, despite changes in their location and brightness.

contraction Ability of a cell to change shape. A property especially developed in muscle cells.

contraction time Time required for a muscle to reach full contraction after it has begun to shorten.

contralateral Opposite side.

contrast In sensory psychology, when stimulation by one sensory quality enhances sensitivity to another sensory quality.

convergence In vision, extent to which the two

eyes are crossed so as to focus a nearby object on the *fovea* of each eye.

coordination Divergence of many (motor) outputs from a single *center* or group of centers in the nervous system.

cornea The transparent outer tissue in the front of the eyeball that light first encounters in entering the eye.

corpus callosum Sickle-shaped band of crossing nerve fibers connecting the *cerebral hemispheres.*

corpus luteum Endocrine structure that develops from the *follicle* after *ovulation* in the female and secretes *progesterone* to maintain pregnancy.

corpus striatum Striped bodies; subcortical *centers* within the *cerebral hemispheres,* consisting of alternating layers of *gray* and *white matter.*

correlation Convergence of many inputs on a single area of the nervous system.

cortex The surface gray matter of either the *cerebral* or *cerebellar hemispheres,* usually the former.

cortically originating extrapyramidal system Neurons of the *extrapyramidal system* that originate in the cortex and descend the *brainstem* and *spinal cord* to the *motor neurons.*

corticobulbar tract Fibers that run from the *motor projection area* to excite the cranial *motoneurons.*

corticoids Hormones of the adrenal cortex that govern the sodium and potassium balance of the body.

corticopontocerebellar tract A tract running from the *premotor cortex* to the pons and thence to the cerebellar hemispheres *(neocerebellum).*

coupled receptor A *receptor* that shares an *afferent* (sensory) neuron with another receptor, particularly in vision. Either receptor can excite the sensory neuron.

CR See *conditioned response.*

cranial nerves The twelve pairs (in man) of *nerves* that connect the brain directly with *receptors* and *effectors* of the head.

creatine phosphate (CP) The form in which *adenosine triphosphate* is stored in the cell as a source of energy for chemical reactions in the cell.

cretinism A variety of mental deficiency caused by hypothyroidism (insufficient thyroid secretion) in childhood.

cribriform plate The bone that forms the roof of the nasal passages and part of the floor of the brain case and contains holes through which the fibers of the olfactory neurons pass en route to the *olfactory bulb.*

crista A ridge of sensory cells inside the *ampula*

that thrust hair endings into the *cupula.* The cells respond to rotary acceleration and deceleration of the head.

critical flicker fusion frequency (CFF) The rate at which a light is flashing when a subject just begins to perceive it as a steady light; a temporal visual *threshold.*

cross-adaptation When *adaptation* to the stimulus for one sensory *quality* raises the *threshold* for sensing another quality.

crossed-extension reflex Extension of a limb caused by pain stimulation of the *contralateral* (opposite) limb.

crossovers Refers to the twisting of pairs of chromosomes. As a result the final cell division producing reproductive cells may contain genes from both chromosome of a pair.

CS See *conditioned stimulus.*

cuneate nucleus A nucleus of the *medulla* containing synapses between *first-* and *second-order neurons* serving *kinesthesis* and pressure impulses ascending from the *spinal cord* (see *gracile nucleus*).

cupula The gelatinous mass that crowns the *crista;* a part of the receptor mechanism for head movement.

current Movement of *electrons* or *ions* in a *conductor* that constitutes electricity.

cutaneous Pertaining to the skin.

cutaneous senses Receptors located just beneath the surface of the skin, serving sensations of pressure, warmth, cold, and pain.

cytoplasm The protoplasm of the cell external to the nucleus.

decerebrate rigidity A posture of rigid extension of the limbs (in a four-legged animal), caused by release of the BSRF and *vestibular nuclei* from cortical inhibition by removal of *cortex* or *cerebrum.*

decibel scale A physical scale of sound intensity, designed to match the response characteristics of the human ear. The zero point is a pressure energy of 0.0002 dyne/cm.^{2}. Each unit is an exponent to the base ten, multiplied by the zero point, thus 15 decibels would be $10^{1.5} \times 0.0002$ dyne/cm.^{2}, and so on.

delayed reaction A learning task in which the subject sees where a reward is concealed, but is prevented from approaching it for a measured period of time so that it must react to the memory of the reward's location.

delta waves Large 3 to 5 cps waves often seen in the *EEG* of sleeping subjects.

delusions False beliefs.

dendrites Extensions of the cell body of a nerve cell that receive excitation or inhibition from other nerve cells.

density The psychologically scaled hardness of a tone, as a function of *pitch* and *loudness.*

dentate nucleus Output nucleus of the cerebellar hemispheres *(neocerebellum).*

dentatorubrothalamic tract A tract from the dentate nucleus of the cerebellar hemispheres to the red nucleus, *thalamus,* and *motor projection area.*

dermatone An area, especially on the skin, sending somesthetic input to a single dorsal spinal root.

dermis Inner layer of the skin that lies beneath the *epidermis.*

descending reticular activating system The outflow from the BSRF that increases muscle tone and therefore increases the sensory feedback that mobilizes the brain in an aroused state.

deuteranomaly Red-green hue weakness with a shift of the maximum brightness from 555 to 560 mμ.

deuteranopia Red-green hue blindness in which reds and greens are confused with bluish and yellowish grays.

diabetes insipidus Water loss and excess urination caused by a lack of *antidiuretic hormone* from the posterior pituitary gland *(neurohypophysis).*

diabetes mellitus Failure of the *beta cells* of the *pancreas* to produce enough *insulin.* Insulin is necessary to blood sugar utilization by the cells of the body.

diabetic coma A coma that results from *diabetes mellitis;* lack of *insulin* from the pancreas results in an oversupply of sugar to the brain cells.

dichromatism Inability to distinguish between either red and green or blue and yellow.

diencephalon Posterior part of the *forebrain* from which the *thalamus* and *hypothalamus* develop.

difference limen See *difference threshold.*

difference threshold Minimum difference between two stimuli that can be detected 75% of the time (halfway between chance and perfection).

difference tone A perceived tone, created by *aural harmonics* (resonant vibrations in the *cochlea*) when two *sine wave* tones are sounded. The frequency of the difference tone is the difference between the frequencies of the sine wave tones.

diffuse thalamic projection system (DTPS) Sensory projection to the cortex via the nonspecific association nuclei of the thalamus, excited by collaterals of the sensory pathways (STPS).

diffusion The process by which gasses such as oxygen and carbon dioxide are exchanged between lungs and blood and tissue fluid as a function of their relative partial pressures (concentrations).

diplacusis An imbalance in pitch perception that results when input from the two ears differs in apparent pitch for the same tone.

direct inhibition Inhibition caused by hyperpolarization of *neurons* or by blocking excitation to neurons.

dissonant frequencies Frequencies whose *pitches* sound harsh or discordant when sounded together.

DL (difference limen) See *difference threshold.*

DNA (desoxyribronucleic acid) Complex helical molecule found in the *chromosomes* of all cells; the sequence of *amino acids* in these molecules determines the inherited characteristics *(genes)* of the individual and regulates the *metabolism* of each cell.

dominant In heredity, a *gene* that determines a physical characteristic of the individual, whether or not a paired *recessive* gene is present.

dominator curve A graph of the threshold of individual *ganglion cell* response to light of a range of wavelengths stimulating the *retina.*

dorsal Toward the back.

dorsal cochlear nucleus One of the two sensory nuclei of the *acoustic* branch of the *statoacoustic nerve* (see *ventral cochlear nucleus*).

dorsal columns The *dorsal funiculus* of either side of the cord that carries kinesthetic and pressure input from the spinal cord to the brain.

dorsal funiculus The part of the peripheral *white matter* of the *spinal cord* that lies between the *dorsal roots* and the midline on either side of the cord.

dorsal horns See *dorsal columns.*

dorsal ramus In the *spinal cord,* the *dorsal* branch of the paired *spinal nerves* that arises from the junction of the *dorsal* and *ventral roots* and carries sensory and motor fibers to the back.

dorsal root In the spinal cord, the *dorsal* termination of the paired *spinal nerves* at the *spinal cord.*

dorsal root ganglion The *ganglion* (collection of *cell bodies*) formed on each *dorsal root* of the *spinal cord* by the cell bodies of the *unipolar* sensory *neurons.*

DRAS See *descending reticular activating system.*

drive A CNS mechanism for arousing and sustaining behavior in the presence of a *need state.*

DTPS See *diffuse thalamic projection system.*

duct glands Glands that have ducts or pipelines to carry their secretion to its site of action.

ductless glands See *endocrine glands.*

duplex color A color containing two elements of the *color formula.*

dura mater The tough, fibrous outermost layer of the *meninges* (connective tissue layers covering the *brain* and *spinal cord*).

dural sinuses Reservoirs beneath the *dura mater* covering the dorsal *cerebrum* into which the venous circulation of the brain empties.

ECG See *electrocorticogram.*

ECS See *electroconvulsive shock.*

ectoderm The outermost layer of cells in the *gastrula* stage of the *embryo* from which the skin, hair, teeth, and nervous system develop.

EEG See *electroencephalogram.*

effector A muscle or a gland. Any organ of response.

efferent Carrying impulses away from a *center,* as when motor nerves carry nerve impulses from the brain and spinal cord to an *effector.*

electroconvulsive shock An electrical current stimulus to the brain that results in massive stimulation and an epileptiform convulsion.

electrocorticogram A recording of the electrical activity of the *cerebral cortex,* taken from electrodes placed directly on the cortex.

electroencephalogram (**EEG**) A recording of the electrical activity of the brain, particularly the *cortex,* taken with electrodes placed on the scalp.

electromagnetic spectrum The energy spectrum that includes light, radio waves, x-rays, etc.

electron A negative particle in an atom of matter.

electron microscope A device for magnifying the image of submicroscopic structures by passing electrons through them and focusing the electrons with electromagnets.

electroretinogram (**ERG**) A gross electrical record of the response of the eye to light; usually one electrode is placed on or near the cornea and the other near the back of the eye.

electrotonus A change in the *polarized condition* of the cell membrane that is insufficient to excite an impulse in the cell.

elimination The process by which cells and multicellular organisms rid themselves of waste material.

embryo The immature organism from conception to three months of prenatal (before birth) development.

embryological A term that refers to study of the development of the individual from a single fertilized cell to birth.

encapsulated Surrounded by a specialized-looking capsule structure, as in *specialized nerve cells.*

encephalitis Literally, brain inflammation; usually refers to encephalitis lethargica (sleeping sickness), an infectious disease that destroys the arousal centers of the brain; the patient sleeps much of the time unless outside stimuli arouse him.

encephalization The concept that phylogenetically newer and more complex parts of the brain take over, or dominate, functioning of older parts of the brain.

end feet Small bulblike endings of the *axon filaments.*

endbrain The anterior part of the forebrain from which the *cerebral hemispheres* and *corpus striatum* develop.

endocrine glands Glands that deposit their secretions into the bloodstream via the extracellular fluid and capillaries.

endoderm The innermost layer of cells in the *gastrula* of the *embryo;* the *gut* and other viscera develop from this layer of cells.

endolymph The fluid contained in part of the membranous labyrinth of the inner ear; fluid of the *semicircular canals* and *sacs* and the *scala media* of the *cochlea.*

end-plate The thickened indentations of muscle *sarcolemma* that form part of the *myoneural junction;* the site of transfer of excitation from nerve cells to muscle cells.

end-plate potential (**EPP**) Electrotonic potential induced at the *myoneural junction* by motoneurons. The EPP results in the muscle action potential that stimulates contraction of the muscle cell.

energy Light, sound, temperature, mechanical deformation, and other physical events, especially as they affect the senses.

energy-rich phosphate bond A chemical bond between compounds made up of a phosphate; in a cell, breaking the bond releases energy and making the bond stores energy for chemical reactions.

engram Physical changes in the brain that are presumed to result from learning—the memory trace.

entorhinal area The cortical area posterior and ventral to the *corpus callosum* in the *longitudinal fissure.*

entorhinal cortex See *entorhinal area.*

enzyme An organic *catalyst* that increases the rate of specific chemical reactions in the cell.

enzyme inhibitor An enzymelike compound that slows rather than speeds a chemical reaction.

enzyme system An *enzyme* made up of an *apoenzyme* and a *coenzyme.*

epidermis The outermost layer of the skin, consisting of an outer layer of dead cells and an inner layer of living cells to replace them.

epilepsy Seizures caused by an abnormal amount of activity in brain cells.

epinephrine A hormone secreted by the *adrenal medulla* whose effects mimic *sympathetic nervous system* arousal, including an increase in heart rate. Also a transmitter at the nerve endings of the SNS (see also *noreprinephrine*),

EPSP See *excitatory postsynaptic potential.*

equipotentiality The principle asserting that any part of the cortex can serve as well as any other part in learning. See *mass action.*

ERG See *electroretinogram.*

ergotropic Having to do with drive or arousal,

such as the centers controlling the *sympathetic nervous system* in the *hypothalamus.*

essential amino acid One of the ten *amino acids* required by the body that the body cannot manufacture.

essential fatty acid One of the three *fatty acids* required by the body that the body cannot manufacture.

estrogens Female sex *hormones* produced by the *follicles* of the *ovary.*

estrus cycle In female mammals, the periodic cycle of *hormone* changes and their effect on the reproductive apparatus, culminating in estrus, the period of greatest sexual receptivity in the female.

ethereal One of the seven primary smell qualities of *stereochemical* smell *theory* that appears to have a slot-shaped receptor site.

eustachian tube The tube that connects the *middle ear* with the throat.

evolution The process by which new species arise in nature over long periods of time, according to the principles of random variation and natural selection.

excitatory postsynaptic potential (EPSP) Partial depolarization of cell bodies and dendrites in response to release of excitatory transmitter substance by *synaptic knobs.*

expiratory center A reflex center in the medulla that excites forced exhalation during hard breathing.

exposure deafness An auditory defect for certain frequency ranges that is caused by overstimulation of the auditory mechanism by loud sounds at those frequencies.

extensor muscles Muscles that extend the limbs or body.

extensor thrust reflex Reflex extension of a limb in response to either pressure on the sole of the foot or spreading the digits.

extent The sensed size of a sensation caused by the extent of the perceptual field for that sensation aroused by the stimulus.

external auditory meatus The opening leading from the *pinna* to the *tympanum* (eardrum) in the ear. The pressure waves of sound reach the eardrum via this passage.

exteroceptors Receptors located at or near the surface of the body that respond to physical events in the environment.

extinguish To eliminate a *CR* by repeated *CS* presentations without *US reinforcement;* loss of a simple learned response caused by lack of punishment or reward.

extracellular fluid The fluid (plasma) inside the body that surrounds all cells.

extrapyramidal system A system of many short branching cells connecting the *premotor area* of the cortex with subcortical nuclei and with the motoneurons.

extrinsic Outside of, particularly with reference to the muscles attached to the eye that move the eyeball.

facilitation When two stimuli to a reflex cause a response greater than the sum of the reflex contractions to each stimulus alone.

fallopian tubes (oviducts) The ducts leading from the *ovaries* to the *uterus.* The ova (egg cells) produced by the ovaries reach the uterus via these tubes.

fast component The more rapid of the back and forth eye movements of *rotational* or *postrational nystagmus* (reflex eye movements).

fat A compound made up of a glycerol and a *fatty acid.* Fats, along with *proteins* and *carbohydrates,* are an essential for life.

fatty acid An acid compound that forms the basis for *fats.*

feeding center Centers in the *hypothalamus* whose stimulation by internal changes of hunger arouse the *CNS* in a hunger *drive.*

fetus The immature organism from three months after conception until birth.

fibrils See *myofibrils* or *neurofibrils.*

final common path Motoneurons to a given reflex response whatever stimulus is used to elicit the response.

first harmonic See *fundamental.*

first overtone The *sine wave* component of a *complex tone* that is twice the *frequency* of the *fundamental.*

first-order neuron A sensory neuron that runs from *receptors* to the *CNS.*

fissure A large *sulcus.*

flaccid paralysis Lack of motor control accompanied by muscle relaxation; usually caused by damage in the *pyramidal system.*

flexion reflex The reflex flexion of a limb in response to pain stimulation of that limb.

flexor muscles Muscles that flex the limbs or body.

flocculonodular lobe The two flocculi (sing., *flocculus*) and the *nodule* of the cerebellum. These structures receive input from the *vestibular senses.*

flocculus A paired cerebellar structure that receives input from the *vestibular senses.*

floral One of the seven primary qualities of *stereochemical* smell *theory* whose receptor site is probably shaped like a keyhole.

flower-spray endings Sensory endings in the *muscle spindle* that inhibit muscle contraction, probably in response to pressure from the contraction of surrounding muscle fibers.

flux Rate of flow.

follicles Tissue formations in the *ovaries* that produce *ova* (egg cells) and secrete *estrogens* (female sex hormones).

follicle-stimulating hormone (FSH) A hormone of the *adrenohypophysis* (anterior pituitary gland) that stimulates the *gonads* to produce reproductive cells *(sperm or ova)*.

footcandle The amount of light reaching a one square foot surface placed one foot from a standard candle. A measure of *illuminance,* or the light falling on a surface.

forebrain The anterior one of the three primitive enlargements of the developing brain in the *embryo.*

fornix A tract that leads from the *hippocampus* in each hemisphere to the *mammillary bodies* of the *hypothalamus.*

Fourier's law In any *complex tone* with a *fundamental* frequency n, the *overtone* frequencies are 2 n, 3 n, and so on.

fourth ventricle The *ventricle* (central cavity) of the *hindbrain.*

fovea Point of clearest vision of the *retina,* formed by a depression that is in line with the pupil of the eye when vision is directed toward an object.

free nerve ends Unspecialized looking sensory nerve endings profusely distributed in skin and muscles and present in viscera.

frequency The number of times an event happens per second, such as the number of air pressure variations per second in a tone of a given frequency.

frontal lobe That part of each *cerebral hemisphere* anterior to the *central sulcus.*

functional disorders Disturbances in the functioning of the *CNS* resulting from *stress* that cause physical symptoms and behavior abnormalities.

functional integrity The ability of any living cell to carry out the internal changes required by the cell to survive.

fundamental The lowest *frequency* of the *sine wave* components of a *complex tone;* the component having greatest *amplitude* that determines the *pitch* of a complex tone.

fundus The large interior cavity of the eyeball that extends from the *lens* and *ciliary ring* to the *retina.*

funiculus A bundle of nerve fibers in the *spinal cord* or *brainstem.*

fusion The sensation that results when two different sensory qualities fuse to give a third quality, such as the fusion of red and yellow into orange.

galvanic skin response (GSR) Change in the resistance of the skin to a minute flow of current; a measure of sweat gland response to *SNS* activity.

gamma efferents Motor nerve fibers of a small size classification, particularly the *motoneurons* to the *muscle spindle* fibers.

ganglia Pleural of ganglion; a collection of nerve cell bodies that lie outside the brain and spinal cord (whether or not synapses occur).

ganglion cell Type of cell making up the optic nerve.

ganglion cell layer The layer of cells in the *retina* that receive excitation from the *bipolar* neurons and whose axons make up the *optic nerve.*

gastrula The stage in embryonic development when the *embryo* develops two layers.

gene A complex chemical structure in the cell *nucleus* that determines a unitary hereditary characteristic such as eye color.

gene linkage Refers to the fact that all the genes *(DNA* molecules) of a given chromosome are inherited together.

general senses Sensory *receptors* found at locations over the entire body.

generator potential The partially depolarized state of a *receptor* that results from receptor excitation and fires sensory *nerve impulses.*

germ cells Sperm or *ova.*

germ tissue See *germ cells.*

GI tract Gastrointestinal tract; the esophagus, stomach, intestines, etc.

gland A secretory organ or structure that manufactures and discharges a secretion that affects some other part of the body.

glial cells Supporting cells of the central nervous system that may also have a nutritive function.

glomeruli Complex synapses in the *olfactory bulbs* where the sensory nerve fibers from olfactory receptors end.

glucagon The hormone of the *alpha cells* of the *pancreas* that stimulates the liver and muscles to release stored blood sugar to body cells.

glucose Blood sugar, the form of foodstuff best utilized by the specialized cells of the body.

glucostatic theory The theory that the level of blood sugar affects hypothalamic cells to arouse eating behavior when the blood sugar level is low.

glycogen The compound into which blood *glucose* is transformed for storage in the liver and muscles.

goiter Swelling in the neck region caused by hypertrophy (increase in size) of the *thyroid gland.*

Golgi tendon organ A high-threshold receptor that responds to a pull on a muscle tendon by reflexly inhibiting the muscle. The pull may be externally applied, initiated by the muscle, or both.

Golgi type I neuron A *multipolar neuron* with a long axon that carries excitation from one part of the CNS to another.

Golgi type II neuron A *multipolar neuron* with a short branching *axon* that spreads excitation to other nearby neurons.

gonadotrophic hormones (GTH) The *follicle-stimulating (FSH)*, *luteinizing (LH)*, and *lactogenic (prolactin)* hormones of the *adenohypophysis* (anterior pituitary gland) that stimulate the *gonads* to produce hormones and reproductive cells and regulate the female *estrus cycle*.

gonads Male and female; structures containing endocrine cells and reproductive tissue that produce sex hormones and cells *(sperm* or *ova)* necessary for reproduction.

gracile nucleus A nucleus of the *medulla* containing synapses between *first-* and *second-order neurons* serving *kinesthesis* and pressure impulses ascending from the spinal cord (see *cuneate nucleus).*

graded potential A partly depolarized state, as in a *receptor* or a nerve *cell body* and *dendrites,* that fires nerve impulses in the *axon.*

gray commissure In the *spinal cord,* the gray matter connecting the *dorsal* and *ventral* columns of either side of the cord across the midline.

gray matter Parts of the CNS containing many *cell bodies* and *synapses.*

gray ramus The branch carrying *postganglionic* neurons of the SNS from a sympathetic chain ganglion to the spinal nerves in the *thoracic* and *lumbar* cord.

growth Increase in size of a single-celled organism or increase in the number of cells (therefore the size) of a many-celled organism.

GSR See *galvanic skin response.*

gustation Taste sensitivity of the tongue to sweet, sour, salt, and bitter.

gut Gastrointestinal tract (see *GI tract).*

gyrus The surface area between two sulci (sing., *sulcus)* in the *cerebral cortex.*

habit A learned pattern of behavior.

habituation Loss of attention to a stimulus caused by repetition or lack of novelty.

hair cells Receptor cells ending in hairlike processes, such as those of the *organ of Corti, vestibular senses,* or *olfactory epithelium.*

hallucination A bizarre or self-induced *perception* without a known objective cause. "Seeing things" or "hearing things."

helicotrema The opening at the apex of the *cochlea* that connects the *scala vestibuli* with the *scala tympani.*

heterogenous Containing varied components.

hindbrain The posterior one of the three primitive enlargements in the developing brain of the *embryo.*

HIOMT An enzyme, blocked by SNS response to

light, necessary for manufacture of the hormone *melatonin* by the *pineal gland.*

hippocampus *Allocortex* that was "rolled into" the center of the cerebral hemispheres in phylogenetic development; phylogenetically older cortical tissue that is "buried" in the *cerebral hemispheres.*

homeostasis Reactions that maintain a dynamic equilibrium (changing balance) of the internal environment of the body, keeping the environment of the cells within the physical and chemical limits that support life.

homeostats Centers of the hypothalamus sensitive to conditions in the *internal environment* and involved in *drives;* abnormal internal conditions stimulate these centers and arouse behavior.

homogeneous Containing only one type of component.

hopping reflex A series of hopping responses to being shoved off balance.

horizontal canal The horizontal one of the three *semicircular canals* of the *inner ear* that react to rotary head movements.

horizontal cells In the *cerebral cortex,* cells of the most superficial layer. In the *retina,* cells that interconnect the visual receptors.

hormones Secretions of the ductless or *endocrine glands* carried by the circulation to affect metabolic reactions in selected *target tissue* over the entire body.

hue Response of the eye to the wavelength of light.

hyperalgesic pain A very painful burning sensation that results from pressure stimulation near an injured area.

hyperglycemia Abnormally high blood sugar.

hyperopic An eye condition in which the lens is too thin or the eyeball too "short" (in an anterior to posterior dimension). The patient cannot focus distant objects on the retina without *accommodation.*

hypersecretion Oversecretion.

hyperthyroidism Overproduction of *thyroxin* by the *thyroid gland.* The condition results in an abnormally high metabolic rate.

hypnotoxin A hypothetical fatigue by-product of nervous activity that accumulates in the brain during waking hours and causes sleep until disposed of by *metabolism.*

hypoglycemia Abnormally low blood sugar.

hypophysis The pituitary gland, which hangs from the base of the brain. See *adenohypophysis* and *neurohypophysis.*

hypothalamic hyperphagia A syndrome of overeating, obesity, and ferocity that results from destruction of the *ventromedial nucleus* of the *hypothalamus.*

hypothalamus An area of the brain in the walls

and floor of the *third ventricle* that controls reactions of the *hypophysis* and *ANS* and is sensitive to internal changes in the body *(need state).*

hypothyroidism Undersecretion of *thyroxin* by the *thyroid gland.* Causes *cretinism* and *myxedema.*

hysteria A neurosis in which the individual becomes functionally paralyzed in one or more limbs or shows sensory anesthesias. No damage to the nervous system can be found and the symptoms often disappear under hypnosis.

illuminance The amount of light falling on a surface.

impairment Impaired function of a tissue, usually caused by *oxygen debt* that accompanies fatigue.

inadequate stimulus An energy change that activates a *receptor* but is not the form of energy for which the receptor is specialized to respond.

incentive A reward. More technically, the external stimulus that changes the *need condition* and therefore reduces the *need state, drive,* and *sensitizing stimulus* in motivated behavior.

inclusions An approximate and inclusive term for the many specialized structures found in the cell's *cytoplasm.*

incus The *ossicle* that conducts sound vibrations from the *malleus* to the *stapes* in the middle ear.

indirect inhibition When excitation of a neuron is reduced because pathways to the neuron become involved in other responses.

inferior colliculi (sing., **colliculus**) A pair of auditory reflex centers found in the tectum (roof) of the midbrain.

inhibition Reduction in response caused by stimulation of an incompatible response. Also, increase in *threshold* of a receptor or nerve cell.

inhibitory postsynaptic potential (**IPSP**) The increase in polarization (and increased threshold) of *cell body* and *dendrites* that follows release of an inhibitory transmitter substance at *synapes.*

inner ear *Cochlea* and the *vestibular senses.*

innervated To receive nerve fibers or to receive excitation via those nerve fibers.

innervation ratio Ratio between the number of nerve cells in the nerve to a muscle and the number of muscle cells in that muscle, expressed as 1:N or 1/N.

inspiratory center A reflex center in the *medulla* that causes inhalation.

instinct A *drive* plus inherited patterns in the *CNS* that arouse behavior appropriate to that drive, e.g., nest-building behavior in the rat as a response to low temperatures.

instinctive reactions Responses governed by inherited patterns of activity in the nervous system.

instrumental conditioning Learning a response (CR) to a stimulus (CS) when the response is followed by reward or punishment avoidance (CAR) and when the subject must respond before such *reinforcement* can occur (i.e., the response is instrumental in obtaining reward or avoiding punishment).

insulin The hormone of the *beta cells* of the *pancreas* that inhibits blood sugar release by the liver and muscles and stimulates blood sugar utilization by the cells of the body.

insulin shock Convulsions resulting from an oversupply of *insulin* due to the consequent low blood sugar that excites the *CNS.*

intensity Change in sensation that results from an increase in stimulation.

intention tremor Trembling of a limb that occurs only when movement is attempted.

intermediary metabolism Chemical reactions that go on outside the cells, supply the cells with glucose and oxygen, and eliminate carbon dioxide and waste.

internal environment Chemical, physical, and other conditions inside the body, surrounding the individual cells.

interneuron See *association neuron.*

interoceptors Receptors located in the *viscera* that respond to physical events inside the body.

interposition A *monocular cue* to distance that is produced when a nearby object partly cuts off the view of a more distant object.

interstitial tissue The tissue of the testes that produces *androgens,* or male sex hormones.

interval scale A scale with equal intervals between the units but an arbitrary zero.

intracellular fluid The fluid inside the cells.

intrinsic Included wholly within an organ.

introspection Observation of conscious events and reporting on them.

iodopsin The photochemical visual pigment of the *cones.*

ion An element or molecule that lacks *electrons* or has surplus electrons and therefore carries a charge; bioelectricity is caused by the movement of ions.

ipsilateral Same side.

IPSP See *inhibitory postsynaptic potential.*

iris A smooth muscle structure whose contractions open or close the *pupil* to regulate the amount of light entering the eye; its pigment determines the color of the eyes.

irritability Excitability; see *stimulus.*

Ishihara's test A test for defects in *hue* sensitivity (color blindness) that depends on numerals that are perceived by the subject as outlined by an array of colored dots that differ in hue and brightness.

isometric Without change in length, as when a muscle contracts without shortening.

isotonic Without change in tension, as when a muscle shortens as it contracts.

juxtallocortex See *transitional cortex.*

kinesthesis Sensations of position and movement from the limbs, neck, and body trunk.

kinesthetic senses Receptors in the joints, tendons, and muscles that give rise to sensations of limb and body position and movement.

Klüver-Budy syndrome Docile, oral, undiscriminative, and hypersexed behavior in monkeys that results from bilateral removal of the *temporal lobes* of the brain.

Krause end bulbs *Encapsulated* endings of afferent neurons in the skin found in cold-sensitive areas.

kymograph A paper-covered drum that rotates at a controlled speed. A pen, connected to a physiological instrument, records physiological events on the kymograph as a moving line.

labyrinth Membranous sensory structures, of both *audition* and *proprioception,* in the *inner ear.*

lactogenic hormone A hormone of the *adenohypophysis* (anterior pituitary gland) that brings the *corpus luteum* to maturity, stimulates *progesterone* output by the *ovaries,* and stimulates the mammary glands.

lambert A measure of *luminance* (emitted or reflected brightness) in terms of *lumens* per square centimeter of area.

latent period The time elapsing between the stimulus to a response and response initiation, especially in a *muscle twitch* or a *reflex.*

lateral corticospinal tract A crossed motor tract of the *lateral funiculus* of spinal cord. The tract originates in the *motor projection area* and the axons terminate near the *motoneurons* of the cord.

lateral fissure The fissure between the *temporal* and *parietal lobes* of each *cerebral hemisphere.*

lateral funiculus The part of the peripheral *white matter* of the *spinal cord* that lies between the *dorsal roots* and *ventral roots* on either side of the cord.

lateral geniculate body The terminus of *ganglion cell* axons from the eye and the origin of fibers going to the *visual projection area* of the *cerebral cortex.*

lateral hypothalamic nuclei Paired nuclei in the *hypothalamus* that appear to act as a *feeding center.*

lateral hypothalamic syndrome Four stages of recovery from the *aphagia* (absence of feeding behavior) and *adipsia* (absence of drinking behavior) that follow ablation of the *lateral hypothalamic nuclei.*

lateral hypothalamic zone A part of the *hypothalamus* located in the walls of the *third ventricle* lateral to the *medial hypothalamic area.*

lateral lemniscus The auditory pathway that ascends the brainstem to the *medial geniculate body.*

lateral spinothalamic tract Fibers that originate from synapses with neurons carrying pain and temperature input to the cord; they ascend the *lateral funiculus* of the cord and join the *medial lemniscus* to end in the *thalamus.*

lateral ventricles *Ventricles* of the *cerebral hemispheres.*

law of complements For each *hue* there is another hue that will mix with it to give a gray, white, or black.

law of resultants Mixed *hues* that match will mix without changing hue, irrespective of their components.

law of specific nerve energies The generalization stating that the chemical and electrical characteristics of the nerve impulse do not depend on the receptor or nerve stimulated; all nerve impulses have the same general characteristics.

law of supplements Noncomplementary hues mix to give an intermediate hue.

learned reactions Responses that have been changed as a result of practice or experience.

lengthening reaction The sudden relaxation of an extensor muscles that occurs whenever the *Golgi tendon organ* is stimulated by external pressure to bend a limb, bending that is resisted by the *stretch reflex.*

lens The crystalline structure behind the *pupil* of the eye that focusses light rays on the *retina.*

LGN See *lateral geniculate body.*

light and shade A *monocular cue* to depth resulting from adaptation to overhead light (e.g., from the sun). The lower parts of protuberances are shaded but the upper parts of cavities are shaded.

limbic system The "ring" of interconnecting pathways and centers that includes the *septum, cingulate gyrus, hippocampus, entorhinal area, amygdala,* and anterior *thalamus.*

linear perspective A *monocular cue* to distance produced by the diminishing apparent size and spacing of evenly spaced and similar objects, as their distance from the observer increases.

local excitatory state The catelectrotonic change that precedes the *spike potential;* a partial depolarization of the nerve cell membrane that occurs just prior to the nerve impulse.

long spinal reflex A *reflex* involving several segments of the *spinal cord.*

longitudinal fissure The *fissure* that divides the right and left *cerebral hemispheres.*

loop circuit See *reverberatory circuit.*

loudness The sensation that results from changes in the intensity of sound.

LSD Lysergic acid diethylamide, a *psychomimetic drug.*

lumbar Pertaining to the unsupported vertebrae between the ribs and pelvis (hips).

lumen A standard measure of density of light; one *candle* radiates 4 π lumens.

luminance *Brightness* of a surface that is reflecting or radiating light.

luteinizing hormone A hormone of the *adenohypophysis* (anterior pituitary gland) that stimulates the gonads to produce sex hormones *(androgens* or *estrogens).*

lymph vessels Auxiliary circulatory vessels that return excess tissue fluid to the heart to be added to the blood. The lymph the vessels contain is more dilute than the blood and contains no *red blood cells.*

lymphocyte A representative type of white blood cell (erythrocyte) that combats disease organisms and other foreign proteins in the body.

macula The patch of sensory tissue, including *otoliths, hair cells,* and gelatinous mass inside the *sacs* of the *inner ear.* The cells respond to linear acceleration and deceleration and to head position.

macula sacculi *Macula* of the *saccule.* The sacculus is one of the two structures containing a macula.

macula utriculi *Macula* of the *utriculus,* which is one of the two sensory structures containing a macula.

main sensory nucleus fifth nerve The nucleus of termination for the sensory fibers of cranial nerves serving pressure.

malleus One of a chain of three bones conducting sound vibrations from the eardrum to the cochlea. The bony *ossicle* connected to the *tympanum,* which conducts sound vibrations to the *incus.*

mammillary bodies Paired nuclei that protrude on the ventral side of the brainstem in the posterior *hypothalamus.*

marijuana A nonaddicting depressant drug from the leaves of a common plant that is usually smoked like tobacco.

masking When a tone of higher intensity makes a low-intensity tone inaudible.

mass action A principle that asserts that all parts of the cortex act as a whole in learning. See *equipotentiality.*

mechanical Forms of physical energy that deform tissue to stimulate, such as pressure stimulation on the skin.

medial forebrain bundle (MFB) A tract running through each *lateral hypothalamic zone* to interconnect it with the *septum, ARAS,* and *rhinencephalon.*

medial geniculate body A nucleus of the auditory nervous pathways; the terminus of the auditory fibers of the *lateral lemniscus* that relays excitation to the cortex.

medial hypothalamic area Densely packed cells closely surrounding the walls and floor of the *third ventricle.*

medial lemniscal system The afferent system of tracts that serve *kinesthesis* and the more sensitive pressure receptors.

medial lemniscus A tract of the *brainstem* serving the somesthetic senses of pressure, pain, and temperature, which terminates in the *posteroventral nucleus* of the *thalamus* that relays excitation to the *cerebral cortex.*

medial longitudinal fasciculus A tract of the brainstem that interconnects the *vestibular nuclei* with the cranial nerve nuclei controlling eye and head movements.

mediolus A bony shelf in the *cochlea* of the inner ear that forms part of the division between the *scala media* and *scala tympani.*

medulla The posterior part of the *hindbrain.*

Meissner's corpuscles *Encapsulated* sensory endings of nerve cells in touch-sensitive hairless skin areas; these endings seem to be pressure receptors.

melatonin A hormone of the *pineal gland* that inhibits output of sex hormones by the *gonads.*

meninges The three layers of connective tissue covering the *brain* and *spinal cord.*

mesencephalic nucleus of fifth nerve The nucleus of termination for the sensory fibers of cranial nerves serving *kinesthesis.*

mesoderm The middle layer of cells in the *gastrula* of the *embryo* from which the *striate muscles* develop.

messenger RNA The ribonucleic acid molecule that is assembled on the *DNA* molecules in the nucleus of the cell, migrates to the *ribosomes* of the cell cytoplasm, and forms a pattern for *transfer RNA.*

metabolism Chemical reactions of life that change foodstuff into energy and waste.

MFB see *medial forebrain bundle.*

microcephalic A feebleminded child born with an abnormally small head and brain.

microelectrode An electrode of 0.5 to 5 microns diameter, usually made by stretching a heated glass tube until it breaks with a fine point and filling it with a potassium chloride solution.

micron (μ) A millionth of a meter.

microscope A device for optically magnifying the image of thin slices of tissue. Light is passed through the tissue, and the resulting image is magnified by a system of lenses.

microtome A precision instrument for cutting tissue into thin transparent slices for attachment to a glass slide and observation with the *microscope.*

midbrain The middle of the three primitive enlargements of the developing brain in the *embryo*.

middle ear The cavity in the skull bounded by the *tympanum* on one side and the *inner ear* on the other and connected to the oral cavity by the *eustachian tube*.

millimicron (mμ) A thousanth of a millionth of a meter or one millionth of one millimeter.

mineral A nonorganic element or compound of a type that results from inorganic reactions; some minerals such as sodium, potassium, calcium, and phosphorous are essential to life.

minimum separable angle The minimum *visual angle* sensed between two objects; a test of visual acuity.

minimum visible angle The minimum *visual angle* of an object that can be sensed; a test of visual acuity.

minty One of the seven primary qualities of *stereochemical* smell *theory* whose receptor site seems to be wedge-shaped.

miotic division The final cell division in reproductive tissue that produces the sperm or ova.

mitosis Cell division, a form of cell reproduction.

mitotic division Normal cell reproduction by cell division or *mitosis*.

mixing olfactometer A device for mixing odorous vapors of known concentrations for tests of the sensations that result.

modulator curve A graph of the threshold of individual *ganglion cell* response to light of certain wavelengths; the measures are taken after adapting some of the *rods* and *cones* with other wavelengths.

mongolism A type of hereditary feeblemindedness caused by an excess *chromosome* in the germinal material.

monochromatism Complete *hue*-blindness.

monocular cue Any cue to depth or distance that depends on sensations from only one eye.

monophasic Having only one change of condition. In sleep, a cycle consisting of a single waking period and a single sleeping period each 24-hour day.

monosynaptic A reflex pathway having only one set of synapses between *afferent* (sensory) neurons and *efferent* (motor) neurons, no *interneurons* being involved.

morphine A powerful, addicting, narcotic drug.

motive A *drive* plus a *habit* appropriate to that drive, e.g., hunger accompanied by learned behavior leading to satiation.

motoneuron See *motor neuron*.

motoneuron pool Group of motoneurons participating in a response.

motor nerve A bundle of independently conducting nerve fibers connecting the *central nervous system* with the *effectors* (muscles and glands).

motor neuron A single nerve cell connecting the *CNS* with an *effector*.

motor projection areas Those parts of the *cerebral cortex* where nerve pathways to the *striate muscles* originate.

motor unit A single motor or *efferent* neuron and the several *striate muscle* cells it *innervates* (excites to contraction).

mμ See *millimicron*.

multicellular organism Any living organism that is made up of many specialized cells.

multinuclear cell Any cell with more than one nucleus such as *striate muscle* cells or *neurolemma* (Schwann) cells.

multipolar neuron A nerve cell with several *dendrites* and an *axon* arising from the *cell body*.

muscle action potential Polarization reversal of the muscle cell *sarcolemma* (membrane) that excites contraction of the cell.

muscle spindle A specialized muscle cell containing sensory structures (*annulospiral* and *flower-spray endings*) that participates in the *stretch reflex* (contraction in response to stretch of the muscle).

muscle tone Continuous contraction of some motor units in relaxed healthy muscle caused by the *stretch reflex*.

muscle twitch In a nerve-muscle preparation, a single contraction of the muscle caused by electrical stimulation of the *motor nerve* to the muscle.

muscular Pertaining to the *striate muscles*.

musky One of the seven primary qualities of *stereochemical* smell *theory* whose receptor site is probably like an eliptical flat-bottomed pan.

mutation Change in the physical characteristics of an individual caused by the effects of radiation or other agents on the genetic material from which he developed.

myelin sheath A fatty covering of *axons* thought to be secreted by the *neurolemma* in the *peripheral nervous system* and by the *glial cells* in the *CNS*.

myofibrils Threadlike structures that run the length of the interior of the muscle cell and are the contractile mechanism of the cell.

myoneural junction Junction between each ending of a motor nerve cell and each striate muscle cell.

myopic An eye condition in which the lens is too thick or the eyeball too "long" in an anterior to posterior dimension. The patient cannot focus the image of distant objects on the retina.

myotatic reflex See *stretch reflex*.

myxedema Adult *hypothyroidism* that results in lowered metabolic rate, sluggishness, and increased sleep.

nasal septum The cartilage, covered with mucous membrane, that divides the two nostrils and nasal passages from one another.

nasopharynx Nasal passages, mouth, and upper throat.

natural selection The process by which members of a species with physical characteristics that increase their chance of survival and breeding perpetuate these characteristics until they dominate the species.

need A change in the *internal environment* that disturbs *homeostasis,* the internal balance of conditions necessary for survival.

need condition Any state of affairs in the external environment that disturbs equilibrium in the *internal environment.*

need state The disturbance in the equilibrium of the *internal environment* caused by a *need condition.*

negative afterimage A visual sensation of opposite *hue* or *brightness* that follows prolonged visual sensation of a given hue or brightness.

negative afterpotential The partly depolarized state of the *neuron* during recovery from the *spike potential* (nerve impulse).

negative aftersensation Appearance of an opposite sensation after a continuous stimulus ceases to act. See *negative afterimage.*

neocerebellum In evolutionary terms, the newest part of the cerebellum, the cerebellar hemispheres, which is in two-way communication with the cerebral cortex.

neocortex The phylogenetically newest part of the *cerebral cortex,* including all but the cortex lining the fissure between the hemispheres, the cortex covering ventral parts of the hemispheres, and the *hippocampus.*

nerve deafness Auditory defects resulting from damage to the hair cells or the sensory nerve cells that *innervate* them.

nerve impulse see *action potential.*

nerve membrane Membrane of the *neuron* or nerve cell.

nerves Bundles of independently conducting nerve fibers that make up the *peripheral nerovus system.*

nervous system The system of microscopic cells that are specialized for conduction and contained in the *brain* and *spinal cord (central nervous system)* and *peripheral nerves (peripheral nervous system).*

neural groove The groove along the middorsal line of the *embryo* from which the *neural tube* develops.

neural tube The tube that develops from the dorsally placed *neural groove* of the *embryo* to form the *brain* and *spinal cord.*

neurofibrils Fine hairlike structures that extend the length of the *axon* inside a nerve cell.

neuroglia See *glial cells.*

neurohumors Transmitter chemicals, secreted by nerve cell endings, that excite or inhibit nerve, gland, and muscle cells.

neurohypophysis The posterior portion of the *hypophysis* (pituitary gland) that is supplied with nerve cells from the hypothalamus and that secretes *oxytocin, vasopressin,* and *antidiuretic hormone.*

neurolemma (Schwann cell) A multinuclear supporting cell covering axons of the *peripheral nervous system,* which sometimes secretes a *myelin sheath* that covers the axon.

neuromyal junction See *myoneural junction.*

neuron A nerve cell.

neurosecretion A transmitter substance released by *neurons* at *synapses* and at junctions with muscle and gland cells.

neurosis Persistant maladaptive behavior accompanied by reports of anxiety and *psychosomatic* symptoms.

nicotine A drug found in tobacco that is an *SNS* stimulant.

nociceptors Pain receptors.

nodes of Ranvier Regular interruptions in the *myelin sheath* covering an *axon.*

nodule A centrally located cerebellar structure that receives input from the *vestibular senses.* See *flocculus.*

noise Sounds made up of *aperiodic* air pressure changes with many high-frequency components.

nominal scale Measurement that involves only discrimination and sorting; magnitude is not involved.

noradrenaline See *norepinephrine.*

norepinephrine A hormone secreted by the *adrenal medulla,* whose effects mimic *sympathic nervous system* arousal and cause peripheral vasconstriction; also a transmitter substance at *postganglionic* endings of the SNS (see *epinephrine*).

nucleus The central body within a cell that contains the basic mechanisms for cell growth, repair, and reproduction. Also a collection of nerve cells where many *synapses* are made.

O$_2$ Oxygen.

occipital lobe That part of each *cerebral hemisphere* posterior to the *parietal lobe;* the most posterior lobe of the cerebral hemisphere.

occlusion When two sitmuli to a reflex cause a response that is less than the sum of the reflex contractions to each stimulus alone.

ogive A graph of the accumulated frequency or percent of events or individuals included with increases in a quantitative measure.

olfaction The sense of smell.

olfactometer A crude device for measuring smell threshold by sliding an odorous hard-rubber tube over a graduated glass cylinder, whose other end is inserted in the nostril.

olfactorium A small room whose atomspheric content of odorous gases can be controlled for testing odor thresholds.

olfactory bulbs Enlargements of the ends of the *olfactory tracts* on the base of the brain, where the olfactory neurons terminate.

olfactory cleft See *olfactory epithelium.*

olfactory epithelium Smell-sensitive area of the roof of the nasal passages to either side of the *nasal septum.*

olfactory tracts Extensions on the base of the brain formed by tracts that run between the *olfactory bulbs* and *prepyriform area.*

olive An important nucleus of the auditory pathway in the *medulla* and an accessory nucleus to the *cerebellum.*

opium A variety of *morphine* that is smoked by addicts; an addicting drug.

optic chiasma The hemidecussation (half-crossing) of the *ganglion cells* from the *retina* of the eye in the *diencephalon.*

optic nerve The visual *ganglion cell* axons that run from the eyeball to the *optic chiasma.*

optic tract *Ganglion cell* axons that run between the *optic chiasma* and the *lateral geniculate bodies.*

optomotor neuclei Nuclei of the third, fourth, and sixth cranial nerves that regulate eye movements.

ordinal scale A rank order scale; the intervals between units need not be equal.

organ An organization of differently specialized cells *(tissues)* that are arranged in a cooperative way to perform a function, e.g., the stomach is an organ of muscular, connective, glandular, and other tissue for digesting food.

organ of Corti Auditory receptor structure of the *inner ear* that rests on the *basilar membrane* and transduces fluid movements in the *cochlea* of the *inner ear* into nerve impulses.

organic compounds A class of compounds made up of carbon atoms to which oxygen, hydrogen, nitrogen, or sulfur are chemically linked. Living organisms are made of organic compounds.

organic pain receptors Pain receptors in the *viscera.*

organic senses Receptors in the *viscera* for pressure, cold, warmth, and pain.

organism Any form of life, from a virus or a single cell to a complex many-celled animal such as man.

orienting reflex Responses made by an animal to a novel stimulus, such as pricking up the ears, sniffing, etc.

ossicles The three bony levers in the middle ear that connect the *tympanum* with the *oval window* of the *inner ear;* the ossicles conduct sound vibrations from the tympanum to the oval window.

otoliths Particles of calicum carbonate that are embedded in the gelatinous material of the *macula.*

outer ear *Pinna, tympanum,* and *external auditory meatus.*

ova Female reproductive cells.

oval window The membrane-covered opening to the fluid-filled *inner ear;* sound vibrations are carried by the *ossicles* to the oval window, which communicates with the *scala vestibuli.*

ovaries Female *gonads,* or reproductive organs.

overtone In a *complex tone,* frequencies showing *resonance* of parts of the vibrating body to simple multiples of the fundamental frequency; see *Fourier's law.*

ovulation Release of an *ovum* by the *follicles* of the *ovaries.*

ovum Female egg cell.

oxidation A class of chemical reactions that includes reaction of a chemical substance (e.g., a food) with oxygen to give off heat and energy.

oxidize See *oxidation.*

oxygen debt The amount of oxygen necessary to restore a tissue to equilibrium after its metabolic need for oxygen has exceeded the available supply.

oxytocin A presumed hormone of the neurohypophysis (posterior pituitary gland) with the same effects as *vasopressin.* Both hormones appear to contract smooth muscle and stimulate the mammary glands to produce milk.

pacinian corpuscles Large encapsulated pressure receptors found in the subcutaneous fat, joints, and in the mesentaries that support the viscera.

pain Any stimulation of free nerve endings that gives rise to pain sensations.

paleocerebellum A phylogenetically older part of the cerebellum that consists of the *anterior* and *posterior lobe,* receives input from muscle spindles, and regulates postural extensor tone.

paleocortex See *allocortex.*

pancreas A gland that lies between the stomach and small intestine (duodenum) and contains the endocrine *alpha* and *beta cells* that secrete *glucagon* and *insulin.*

parabiotic Sharing of a common organ or system between two animals; e.g., interconnected circulatory systems.

paradoxical cold *Inadequate stimulation* of cold receptors by an intense warm stimulus.

paradoxical warmth *Inadequate stimulation* of warm receptors by an intense cold stimulus.

parallel circuit Several nervous pathways, usually of different length, beginning and ending at the same points in the nervous system.

paraplegic An individual whose spinal cord has been severed. Parts of the body below the secretion are paralyzed and anesthetic as a result.

parasympathetic division A division of the *autonomic nervous system (ANS)*; an efferent nerve supply that innervates the *viscera* and discretely stimulates digestive functions as well as forming part of certain reflexes of the smooth muscles.

parasympathetic ganglia Collections of cell bodies of the *postganglionic PNS* nerve fibers; the ganglia lie near the smooth muscles and glands, which the postganglionic fibers *innervate*.

parasympathetic nervous system (PNS) See *parasympathetic division*.

parasympathetic overcompensation When the *PNS* is aroused by *SNS* activity and becomes dominant over some phase of *SNS* activity so that *PNS* responses occur.

parathormone The hormone of the *parathyroid glands* that governs calcium and phosphate levels of the body.

parathyroid gland Four small *endocrine glands* embedded in the *thyroid glands* of the neck, which produce *parathormone* to control the calcium and phosphorus levels in the body.

parietal lobe That part of each *cerebral hemisphere* that lies between the *occipital lobe* and the *central sulcus*.

Parkinson's disease A disorder characterized by tremors at rest, muscle rigidity, and lack of facial expression, all caused by damage of the *basal ganglia*.

passive avoidance response A learned response of immobility or stopping some kind of ongoing behavior to avoid punishment.

penis external genitals of the male, exclusive of the *gonads* and *scrotum*.

perception A conscious event, initiated by *sensation*, but including memory, classification, and integration of the input from several sense organs.

perilymph The fluid of the *labyrinth* that surrounds it and is also contained in the *scala vestibuli* and *scala tympani* of the *cochlea*.

period of adjustment The period during which an organism successfully copes with an abnormal stress. See *stress syndrome*.

period of latent addition In a nerve cell, the period of lowered threshold to excitation that accompanies the *local excitatory state* preceding a *nerve impulse* or results from subthreshold excitation.

periodic Repeated regularly.

peripheral nervous system *Nerves* that lie outside the *brain* and *spinal cord* and connect the latter with *receptors* and *effectors*.

peripheral somatic nervous system (PSNS) The *peripheral nervous system*, exclusive of the *autonomic nervous system*, that connects the *CNS* with *receptors* and *striate muscles*.

peristalsis Regular contractions of the intestine that aid in digestion.

perseveration Brain activity that follows practice, is the basis for immediate memory, and lays down the permanent memory trace *(consolidation)* in the *two-phase hypothesis* of learning and memory.

phase Each cycle of a periodic event is divided into 360 degrees. A phase is the point the periodic event has reached in this cycle at any instant in time.

phase sequence A number of *cell assemblies*, repeatedly excited in order by a perceptual act, such as successively viewing the corners of a triangle.

phenylpyruvic oligophrenia An inability to metabolize an essential amino acid that causes feeble-mindedness.

phi phenomenon Perceived motion as a result of successively presenting two similar stimuli, displaced in space, at critical intervals and durations. (Basis of animated signs and of motion pictures.)

photic Electromagnetic energy in the 400 to 750 mμ wavelengths range that stimulates the eye.

photopic See *chromatic*.

physiological fatigue The *oxygen debt* incurred by muscles, exercised beyond the capacity of the body to supply them with oxygen.

physiological psychology Study of the relationships between physiology and behavior.

physiological zero That range of skin temperatures at which neither warmth nor cold is sensed.

physiologist One who studies the function of the tissues, organs, and systems of the body.

physiology Study of the functioning of tissues, organs, and systems of the body.

pia mater The fragile inner-most layer of the *meninges* that cover the *CNS*.

piloerector muscles Muscles that erect the body hair; aroused by *SNS* excitation in emotional states or cold environments.

pineal gland An *endocrine gland* atop the posterior third ventricle that secretes *melatonin* to inhibit sex hormone output by the *gonads*.

pinna The "ear"—the convoluted structure on either

side of the head that channels the pressure waves of sound to the *external auditory meatus*.

pitch The single quality of hearing; the sensation that changes with changes in the *frequency* of a tone, e.g., to form the musical scale.

pituitary dwarf An individual that is dwarfed by undersecretion of *somatotropic hormone* from the *adenohypophysis* (anterior pituitary gland).

pituitary giant Giantism resulting from oversecretion of *somatotropic hormone* by the *adrenohypophysis* in childhood.

placenta Site of interchange of carbon dioxide, oxygen, food, and waste, between the embryo or fetus and the pregnant mother's circulation.

placing reflex When the paw of an animal is pressed against the edge of a surface, it is reflexly placed on the surface.

planaria Small primitive invertebrates with a nerve-net nervous system and the ability to regenerate missing parts; used in experiments on the role of DNA and RNA in learning.

plexus A network of *nerves*.

pneumograph An instrument for measuring and recording the rate and depth of breathing as a record on a moving paper tape.

pneumotaxic center A reflex center in the pons involved in control of the *inspiratory center* and *expiratory center* during hard breathing.

PNS See *parasympathetic division*.

PNS compensation An increase in PNS activity caused by an increase in SNS activity.

polarized condition A difference in voltage across a poor conductor; as the difference in charge, positive to negative, on the outside and inside of the cell membrane.

polygraph An instrument that measures several responses controlled by the *ANS*, such as the *GSR*, *pneumograph*, and *sphygmomanometer*; results are recorded as line movements on a paper tape.

polyphasic Many alterations between two states; usually refers to a sleep cycle consisting of several periods of sleep and several periods of wakefulness each day.

pons The ventral surface enlargement on the anterior part of the *hindbrain* formed by crossing tracts from higher parts of the brain en route to the *cerebellum*.

portal system A system of blood vessels that carries a secretion from a limited site of production directly to a limited site of action.

positive afterimage A visual sensation that continues after the stimulus initiating it ceases to act.

positive afterpotential The overpolarized condition of the *axon* that follows the *negative afterpotential* of the *nerve impulse*.

positive aftersensation Continuance of a sensation after the stimulus initiating it ceases to act. See *positive afterimage*.

postcentral gyrus The *gyrus* of the cerebral cortex just posterior to the *central sulcus*.

posterior Toward the tail end of a four-legged animal or an *embryo;* toward the back in man (standing erect).

posterior chamber The cavity of the eyeball that lies between the *iris* and the *lens*.

posterior lobe of cerebellum See *paleocerebellum*.

posterior pituitary gland See *neurohypophysis*.

posterior vertical canal The posterior vertical one of the three *semicircular canals* of the *inner ear*.

posteroventral nucleus A *nucleus* of the *thalamus* that receives input from *somesthesis* and projects this input to the cerebral cortex.

postganglionic Refers to neurons of the *ANS* that run from ganglia (see *ganglion*) outside the *CNS* to *effectors*.

postrotational nystagmus Reflex eye movements that result from rotational deceleration and are seen after rotation ceases.

postsynaptic inhibition *Direct inhibition* such as occurs when *Renshaw cells* hyperpolarize a neuron.

potassium (K⁺) An element found inside nerve cells as an *ion*.

precentral gyrus The gyrus of the cerebral cortex that lies just anterior to the *central sulcus*.

prefrontal lobe Area of the cerebral hemispheres that is anterior to the *premotor area*.

prefrontal lobectomy Removal of the *prefrontal lobes* of the *cerebral cortex* (anterior to area 6).

prefrontal lobotomy Severing the fibers connecting the thalamus with the prefrontal areas of the cerebral cortex.

prefrontal topectomy Removal of selected areas of the *prefrontal lobes* of the cerebral cortex.

preganglionic Refers to neurons of the *ANS* that run from the *CNS* to ganglia (see *ganglion*), where they synapse with *postganglionic* neurons going to the effectors.

premotor area Area 6 of the cerebral cortex in the Brodman system; the origin of most cortical fibers participating in the *extrapyramidal system* regulation of background movements and the origin of fibers going to the *cerebellum*.

premotor cortex See *premotor area*.

prepyriform area The projection area for smell on the base of the brain; terminus of the *olfactory tracts*.

presbyopia Restricted *accommodation* of the lens that occurs in the elderly. It results in diminished acuity and increases distance to the nearest point at which the eyes can be focused.

pressure Mechanical deformation of the skin, muscles, or viscera, especially as it results in sensations.

presubiculum The cortical area medial to the temporal lobes.

presynaptic inhibition *Direct inhibition* by *axoaxonic synapses* that blocks effective excitation of presynaptic endings.

pretectal nuclei Visual reflex centers of the *diencephalon* that regulate the *iris* and *ciliary body.*

primary endings See *annulospiral endings.*

primary hues See *unique hues.*

primary qualities Irreducible attributes of a sensory modality such as primary hues in vision or primary tastes; sensory qualities whose component sensations cannot be detected.

progesterone A hormone of the *corpus luteum* of the *ovary* that inhibits production of *folliclestimulating hormone* by the *adenohypophysis.* Progesterone prepares the female organs for pregnancy.

projection fibers Nerve fibers reaching or leaving a *center* of the brain, especially the *cerebral cortex.*

prolactin See *lactogenic hormone.*

proprioception Sensations of position and movement, including *kinaesthesis* and the *vestibular senses.*

proprioceptors The general *kinesthetic* receptors of the joints and muscles and the special *vestibular senses* of the inner ear, both of which give rise to sensations of position and movement.

prostate gland A gland of the urogenital system of the male that contributes secretions to the *semen.*

protanomoly Red-green hue weakness with a shift of maximum brightness from 555 to 540 mμ.

protanopia Red-green hue blindness with a shortened visible spectrum at the red end.

protein A large organic compound made primarily of amino acids that is both an essential food and an essential part of the structure of cells.

protoplasm The primitive organic material of which cells are made.

pseudoconditioning A reaction to a *CS* caused by *stimulus sensitization* rather than conditioning.

pseudopod False foot; an extension of the cell caused by protoplasm flow that thrusts out a process for cell movement.

PSNS See *peripheral somatic nervous system.*

psychodelic drugs See *psychotomimetic drugs.*

psychophysics Measurable relationships between changes in physical energy and changes in the attributes of sensation.

psychosis See *psychotic.*

psychosomatic *Stress*-induced malfunction of the organs of the body.

psychotic An individual suffering from a psychosis with unrealistic and illogical *delusions,* bizarre *hallucinations,* and disorganized behavior.

psychotomimetic drugs Drugs that mimic the effect of *psychosis* by producing *hallucinations* and bizarre sensations.

PTC Phenylthiocarbamide, a substance to which some individuals inherit a high taste threshold; used in studies of taste and heredity.

pulmonary circulation The system of blood vessels that carry blood from the heart to the lungs and back for gas exchange with the air in the lungs.

pungent One of the seven primary qualities of smell, according to the *stereochemical* smell *theory;* a quality determined by a positive charge of the substance smelled.

pupil Opening in the *iris* of the eye through which light enters the eye.

Purkinje shift The change in apparent brightness of various wavelengths with the change from daylight *(cone)* to night *(rod)* vision or the reverse.

putrid One of the seven primary qualities of smell according to the *stereochemical* smell *theory;* a quality determined by a negative charge on the molecule smelled.

pyramidal system Fibers that run from the *motor projection area* to the level of the motoneurons and are carried in the pyramids of the brain and pyramidal tracts of the spinal cord.

pyramidal tract See *pyramidal system.*

pyriform lobe Projection area for smell on the ventral surface of the *temporal lobe* of the cerebral cortex.

quadruplex color A *color* containing four elements of the *color formula.*

quality The attribute that distinguishes one sensory modality from another and that distinguishes sensation differences within a modality that are not caused by *intensity, extent,* or duration.

RA See *retroactive amnesia.*

radial fibers Smooth muscle fibers that radiate from an opening such as the *pupil;* their contraction increases the size of the opening.

radiate To give off or emit, as light is radiated by a *luminous* source.

random variation Variation in the characteristics of individual members of a species that occurs by chance or as a result of *mutation.*

rapid eye movements (REM) Eye movements that accompany dreaming during stage 1 sleep, recorded as muscle activity from electrodes placed near the *extrinsic* eye muscles.

ratio scale A scale that has both equal intervals between units and a true zero because the units can be used to form ratios.

receptors Structures specialized for irritability in response to various forms of energy, e.g., light, heat, cold, sound, or mechanical deformation.

recessive In heredity, a *gene* that will not determine a physical characteristic of the individual unless paired with another recessive gene for the same characteristic.

reciprocal innervation Excitation arrangements in the *CNS* that inhibit an *antagonist muscle* when the paired *agonist muscle* contracts.

recruitment The addition of active motoneurons to a response, a few at a time.

recurrent collateral A branch of a nerve fiber that turns back toward the origin of the fiber.

red blood cells The cells that, through chemical reaction, bind oxygen or carbon dioxide for gas exchange between the lungs, blood, and tissue fluid.

red muscles *Extensor muscles* specialized for long sustained contractions, such as the thigh muscles of birds or rodents.

reflect To bounce off, as light reflected from a surface.

reflex An automatic and predetermined response to a stimulus, determined by interneuron *synapses* in the CNS and including *receptor, afferent* neuron, *association neuron, efferent* neuron, and *effector* elements.

reflex figure Opposite positions of the forelimbs and hindlimbs that result from a *flexion* and *crossed-extension reflex* in one pair of limbs.

refract To bend, as light is refracted by a lens or prism.

reinforcement Reward or punishment.

Reissner's membrane The membrane between the *scala vestibuli* and the *scala media* in the *cochlea* of the *inner ear*.

relative movement A *monocular cue* to distance produced by the apparently faster relative motion of nearby objects compared to distant objects.

relative refractory period The period during the early part of the *negative afterpotential* when the *axon* is harder to stimulate than it normally is.

relaxation time The time required for a muscle to reach its original length after full contraction has been attained.

releasing stimulus An *incentive*, or a cue to an incentive, that releases behavior appropriate to an active drive such as hunger or thirst.

REM See *rapid eye movements*.

Renshaw cells Short *Golgi type II neurons* that release GABA at synapses to hyperpolarize and therefore inhibit other neurons.

reproduction Refers to the production of two cells from one in cell *mitosis*, or to the production of a new cell by joining egg and sperm cells in a multicellular organism.

resonance The tendency of an object to vibrate at a characteristic frequency. In a complex instrument of several parts, this produces *overtones* as well as a *fundamental* frequency.

resonate See *resonance*.

respiratory quotient (RQ) Ratio between the carbon dioxide given off by the body and the oxygen intake, CO_2/O_2; a measure of *metabolism*.

resting discharge The firing of a neuron that goes on in the absence of stimulation.

resting potential The difference in charge, positive to negative, across the membrane of cells when they are not stimulated.

reticulospinal tract A *tract* of the spinal cord that originates in the *brainstem reticular formation* and terminates on spinal *motoneurons*.

retina An extension of the brain that contains the visual receptors; found in the posterior part of the *fundus* of the eyeball.

retinal disparity The difference between the images produced on the *retinas* of the two eyes by a nearby object.

retroactive amnesia Loss of memory for recent events when older memories remain unimpaired.

retroactive inhibition Forgetting of an event because of the occurrence of an intervening event.

reverberatory circuit A circular nervous pathway that can reexcite itself over and over.

rheumatic fever Inflammation of joints caused by bacteria that sometimes destroy tissue in the brain and spinal cord.

rhinencephalon Hippocampus, amygdala, cingulate gyrus, and pyriform area; brain structures once thought to be integrating centers for smell.

rhodopsin Photochemical visual pigment of the *rods* chemically changed by light to stimulate optic nerve impulses.

ribosome A type of inclusion in the cell in which *enzymes* are assembled that determine the metabolic reactions of the cell.

righting reflexes A series of reflexes that stimulate one another to right the animal's position, beginning with vestibular stimulation and continuing with reflexes that twist the body into an upright position.

rods Low-threshold *achromatic* visual receptors containing *rhodopsin,* found in the periphery of the *retina;* night vision receptors.

rotational nystagmus Reflex eye movements that result from rotational acceleration of the head.

round window The membrane-covered window that relieves the pressure changes of cochlear fluid caused by sound vibrations.

Ruffini endings *Encapsulated* endings of *afferent* neurons found in the skin of warmth-sensitive areas.

sacculus A sensory apparatus of the *inner ear* that responds to head position and linear acceleration; see *utriculus*.

sacral Pertaining to the vertebrae (sing., *vertebra*) of the pelvis (hips).

sacs See *sacculus* and *utriculus.*

sarcolemma The muscle cell membrane that is the excitation mechanism for the cell.

sarcoplasm *Cytoplasm* of the muscle cell.

satiation center See *satiety center.*

satiety center A center in the *hypothalamus,* probably the *ventromedial nucleus* whose stimulation by internal changes that result from feeding stops eating behavior.

saturated Colors that contain maximum *hue* (contain little gray).

saturation Degree of *hue* response of the eye to a color; lack of gray in a color.

scala media The middle chamber of the *cochlea* that lies between the *scala vestibuli* and *scala tympani* and contains *the organ of Corti.*

scala tympani The fluid-filled lower chamber of the *cochlea* that receives sound vibration from the *scala media* via the *basilar membrane;* pressure changes are relieved by the *round window.*

scala vestibuli The fluid-filled upper chamber of the *cochlea* that receives vibrations from the *oval window* via the *ossicles.*

sclera See *sclerotic coat.*

sclerotic coat The tough opaque white, outer fibrous tissue that forms the white of the eyeball.

scotopic See *achromatic.*

scratch reflex Alternate flexion and extension of a hindlimb in scratching movements, stimulated by tickling the flank of an animal.

scrotum The sac that contains the testes or *gonads* in the male.

second harmonic See *first overtone.*

second motor area A topographically organized cortical motor area on the lateral surface of the precentral gyrus of the cerebral cortex.

second signalling system A hypothesis that language representation in the CNS is a mediating symbolic system that enables man to learn much more rapidly than lower animals, especially in the *conditioned response.*

secondary endings See *flower-spray endings.*

secondary qualities Mixtures of *primary qualities* within a sensory modality to produce a different sensation; e.g., in vision, the mixture of red and yellow for an orange sensation.

second-order neuron The neuron that runs from the *first-order (sensory) neuron* to a subcortical center such as the *thalamus.*

secretion The ability of a cell to manufacture a needed substance and supply it to the cell itself or to other cells; especially developed in *endocrine* and exocrine *glands.*

segment One section of any serially repeated structure.

selective permeability A property of the cell membrane that permits passage of some types of *ions* and molecules (chemicals) but not others because of their properties of size, charge, and so on.

semen Fluid output of the male sexual apparatus, containing *sperm* and glandular secretions.

semicircular canals The three semicircular membranous structures of the nonauditory *labyrinth* of each *inner ear;* a sensory apparatus for detecting rotary movements of the head.

seminal duct Carries sperm from the *seminiferous tubules* to the *prostate gland* in the male sexual apparatus.

seminal vesicle A tube carrying *semen* to the *urethra* of the male *penis.*

seminiferous tubules Tubes in which *sperm* develop.

sensation The immediate impression senses make on the brain as detected by the method of *introspection.*

sense organs *Organs* that are specialized to be irritable to a specific form of physical energy.

sensitizing stimulus Any aspect of a *need state* that arouses a *drive* in the CNS.

sensory appropriation Alteration of a cell into a *specialized receptor* because of its invasion by a sensory nerve fiber.

sensory deprivation Severe reduction in sensory input by experimental techniques.

sensory gating *Efferent* control of *afferent* sensory input.

sensory nerve A bundle of independently conducting nerve fibers connecting *receptors* with the *central nervous system.*

sensory neuron A single nerve cell connecting a *receptor* with the *CNS.*

sensory projection area Those parts of the *cerebral cortex* where pathways from the *receptors* terminate.

septal area See *septum.*

septum The anterior part of the *cingulate gyrus* that lies on the medial surface of each cerebral hemisphere in the longitudinal fissure.

sex linkage Refers to *genes* contained in the *chromosomes* determining sex; when physical characteristics of the individual and the genes he carries will be determined by the same chromosomes that determine his sex.

sham rage Violent but brief attack responses in decorticate animals that are caused by release of hypothalamic rage centers from cortical inhibition.

shape constancy The assumption that objects remain constant in shape and that apparent changes in shape are caused by a changed angle of regard.

shortening reaction The sudden contraction that

follows relaxation of resistance to flexing a limb *(lengthening reaction);* it is caused by the lack of stimulation of the *Golgi tendon organ* and renewed stimulation of the *annulospiral endings* that accompanies relaxation and stretch.

silent period The brief period of muscle relaxation that follows the *tendon jerk* reflex.

simple tone A tone whose pressure variations can be graphed as a *sine wave.*

simultaneous contrast Increase in the perceived intensity of a sensation of one *quality* caused by the simultaneous stimulation of another quality.

simultaneous induction Mutual enhancement of sensitivity to two sensory *qualities* that are stimulated simultaneously.

sine wave A function, similar to a horizontal **S**, that describes *periodic* phenomena such as the air pressure changes produced by a *simple tone.*

size constancy The assumption that objects remain constant in size and that any apparent size changes are caused by changes in distance of the object from the observer.

slow component The slower of the back and forth eye movements of *rotational* or *postrotational nystagmus.*

smooth muscle The muscle that lines the walls of all hollow viscera but the heart—the arteries, intestines, stomach, etc.

Snellen's test A test of visual acuity that determines the subject's ability to read letters of diminishing sizes at a distance of 20 feet.

SNS See *sympathetic division.*

SNS reactivity How readily the SNS is aroused by environmental stimuli; a measure of mobilization or general activation.

sodium (Na⁺) An element excluded from nerve cells as an *ion.*

somatic muscle See *striate muscle.*

somatotropic hormone (STH) A hormone of the *adenohypophysis* (anterior pituitary gland) that controls body growth.

somesthesis Sensations from the skin and viscera of pressure, warmth, cold, and pain.

somesthetic projection area Area of the *cerebral cortex* that is the terminus of the nerve pathways for skin sensations.

spastic See *spastic paralysis.*

spastic paralysis Loss of motor control accompanied by exaggerated extensor tone; usually caused by damage to the *extrapyramidal system.*

special senses Receptors found only in the head.

specialized nerve cell A sensory neuron whose endings form a specialized sensory structure.

specialized receptor cell A cell, specialized for irritability to a particular form of physical energy, that stimulates a separate *sensory neuron.*

specific hunger Avidity for a specific substance needed by the body.

specific thalamic projection system (STPS) Classical and anatomically distinct sensory pathways for vision, hearing, and somesthesis.

sperm Male reproductive cells.

sphincters Muscles that close off segments of the tubular viscera, as at the lower ends of the stomach, rectum, and bladder.

sphygmomanometer An instrument for measuring heart rate and blood pressure.

spike potential Explosive polarization reversal that carries the nerve impulse down the *axon* of the nerve cell.

spinal cord Ovoid mass of soft nervous and supporting tissue contained within the vertebral canal.

spinal nerves *Nerves* that originate in the *spinal cord.*

spinal nucleus of fifth nerve The nucleus of termination for sensory fibers of the *cranial nerves* serving temperature and pain.

spinal reflex A *reflex* mediated by the *spinal cord.*

spinal shock A syndrome (set of symptoms) that ensues when the *spinal cord* is severed; e.g., all muscles receiving innervation from below the lesion lose tone and become flaccid because of lack of excitation from higher centers.

spinal tract of fifth nerve Tract of decending pain and temperature fibers from *cranial nerves* that terminates in the *spinal nucleus of fifth nerve.*

spinocerebellar tracts Tracts that run from the *spinal cord* to the *cerebellum.*

spinothalamic system The afferent system of spinal *tracts* that serve pain, temperature, and crude pressure sensitivity.

spiral ganglion The *ganglion* near the cochlea that contains the cell bodies of *bipolar neurons,* which form the acoustic branch of the *statoacoustic nerve* (nerve VIII).

stage of exhaustion That period of the *stress syndrome* during which the animal's adjustment to the stress fails.

stapedius A muscle that pulls on the *stapes,* limiting the response of the middle ear bones to loud sounds in a *reflex* that prevents damage to the auditory apparatus.

stapes The *ossicle* of the chain of middle ear bones that conducts sound vibrations from the *incus* to the *oval window.*

statoacoustic nerve The *cranial nerve* serving the *organ of Corti* and the *vestibular senses* for hearing and balance, respectively.

stereochemical theory A theory about the effects of molecular shape; in olfaction, the theory that *primary* odor *qualities* depend on the shape or charge of the odorous molecules.

stereoscope A device for simulating a three-dimensional view by presenting pictures taken from different angles to the two eyes.

stereotaxic apparatus An instrument for stereotaxically placing the tip of an electrode in a known position in an animal's brain. The electrode is positioned by a three-dimensional atlas of the brain.

stimulation Activation of *sense organs* or nervous tissue by any form of physical energy—mechanical, chemical, acoustic, photic, or electrical.

stimulus Any physical energy change that activates a *receptor.*

stimulus sensitization An increase in the probability of giving a *UR* to any stimulus after the subject has been sensitized by a punishing *US;* leads to *pseudoconditioning.*

STPS See *specific thalamuc projection system.*

stress Any stimulus, internal or external, that disturbs the dynamic equilibrium of the systems of the body.

stress syndrome Sequence of events that follows application of severe *stress* to an organism.

stress tolerance Individual ability to withstand *stress* without disability.

stressor A stimulus causing *stress.*

stretch reflex Reflex contraction of a muscle to stretch of that muscle; a *monosynaptic* reflex induced by the *annulospiral endings* of the *muscle spindle.*

striate cortex See *visual projection area.*

striate muscle Muscles that move the body and limbs.

subcutaneous fat A layer of fat that lies just beneath the skin in mammals.

subnormal period The period of decreased sensitivity of the *axon* to stimulation that accompanies the *positive afterpotential* following the nerve impulse.

substrate Element(s) or molecule(s) that an *enzyme* interacts with in a chemical reaction.

successive contrast Increase in the perceived intensity of a *quality* caused by the prior stimulation of an opposite quality; e.g., increased sensitivity to a red hue following prolonged exposure to green.

successive induction When stimulation of one quality enhances sensitivity to a second quality, presented after the first stimulus is removed; see *successive contrast.*

sulcus Surface folds that are found in the *cerebral cortex.*

summation When two stimuli produce a greater response than one, or when two or more stimuli give rise to an effective response in a receptor or nerve cell when one will not.

summation tone A perceived tone, created by *aural harmonics* when two *sine wave* tones are

sounded. The frequency of the summation tone is the sum of the frequencies of the two sine wave tones.

superior colliculi (sing., **colliculus**) A pair of visual reflex centers found in the tectum (roof) of the midbrain.

supernormal period The period during the last part of the *negative afterpotential,* when the threshold of the *axon* is lower than normal.

supplementary motor area A topographically organized motor area of the *cerebral cortex* buried in the *longitudinal fissure.*

suprasegmental Above the segmented portion of the *CNS.*

suspensory ligament The structure that attaches the *ciliary body* to the *lens* in the eye.

sympathetic chain ganglia Interconnected *ganglia* that lie on the bony vertebral column receive excitation from the *spinal nerves,* send excitation to the *viscera,* and form part of the *sympathetic division* of the ANS.

sympathetic division (**SNS**) A division of the *autonomic nervous system (ANS)* that innervates the *viscera* and diffusely prepares it for vigorous body arousal in emotional states.

sympathetic nervous system (**SNS**) See *sympathetic division.*

sympatheticoadrenal Involving the *SNS* and *adrenal glands.*

synapse Where the *terminal arborization* of one *neuron* meets the *dendrites* and *cell body* of another to transfer excitation from one nerve cell to another.

synaptic delay The time required for one neuron to stimulate another at a *synapse.*

synaptic knob The terminal knob on an *axon filament* that comes close to a *cell body* or *dendrite* to form a *synapse.*

synaptic vesicles Small globules in the *synaptic knobs* of *axon filaments* at *synapses* that are believed to release a chemical transmitter in synaptic conduction of excitation between nerve cells.

system A number of *organs,* anatomically and functionally arranged for the performance of a generalized function; e.g., the organs of the digestive system—stomach, intestines, and so on.

systemic circulation The system of blood vessels that carry blood to and from the heart and all tissues of the body except the lungs.

tactile disks Disk-shaped endings on sensory nerve filaments in the skin that seem to serve touch (light pressure).

target tissue Similarly specialized cells that are affected in a specific way by *hormones* of the *endocrine glands.*

taste bud A moat- and islandlike structure on the tongue containing receptor cells for taste.

tectoral membrane The overlying membrane in which the *hair cell* endings of the *organ of Corti* are embedded.

temperature Change in the molecular activity of matter sensed as warmth or cold.

temporal lobe The part of each *cerebral hemisphere* that lies below the *lateral fissure.*

tendon jerk A rapid muscle contraction (caused by the *stretch reflex* response) to striking the muscle's tendon.

tensor tympani A muscle that pulls on the *malleus* to tighten the *tympanum* in a protective reflex to limit the response of the middle ear bones to loud sounds.

terminal arborization Endings on the *axon* of a nerve cell.

terminal threshold That intensity of receptor stimulation where stimulus intensity increase results in a change in sensation only 50% of the time; a statistical measure of the maximum response of a *receptor* or *sense organ.*

testes Male *gonads* that produce reproductive cells and sex *hormones.*

tetanus A smooth, maintained, maximum muscle contraction.

tetany Muscle spasm.

texture A *monocular cue* to distance produced by the increasing apparent "smoothness" of a rough surface with distance.

thalamus Paired egg-shaped masses of *nuclei* of the walls of the *diencephalon;* an intergating center that relays excitation to the sensory projection areas of the cerebral cortex.

thermal A change in heat or rate of molecular motion, especially as it affects temperature receptors to produce warmth and cold sensations.

third ventricle *Ventricle* of the *diencephalon.*

third-order neuron Any neuron that runs from subcortical centers such as the *thalamus* to a *sensory projection area,* usually in the cortex.

thoracic Pertaining to the area of the chest, thorax, or ribs.

threshold The least change in physical energy that will, on the average, affect the response of a receptor. Without a modifier, it usually refers to the *absolute threshold.*

thymus gland An organ behind the sternum whose function is the manufacturing of *lymphocytes* (white blood cells).

thyroid gland A paired endocrine gland in the neck, whose hormone, *thyroxin,* governs the metabolic rate of the body.

thyrotropic hormone (**TTH**) The hormone of the *adenohypophysis* (anterior pituitary gland) that stimulates the *thyroid gland* to produce *thyroxin.*

thyroxin The hormone of the *thyroid gland* that determines the metabolic rate of all cells of the body.

timbre Complex of *overtones* in a *complex tone* that enables the listener to recognize the source; e.g., the difference between a trumpet and violin playing the same *fundamental* tone.

tinnitus A continuous ringing, tinkling, or buzzing sound in the ear caused by infections or other disorders of the auditory mechanism; not caused by an external stimulus.

tissue A collection of cells, specialized for a common function; e.g., nervous tissue, muscle tissue, etc.

tonal gap An auditory defect restricted to a certain *frequency* range.

tonal island A *frequency* range of relatively normal hearing surrounded by *tonal gaps.*

tonotopic See *tonotopic organization.*

tonotopic organization The organization of various nuclei of the auditory pathway so that points along the length of the *organ of Corti* that respond to tones of different *pitch* are spatially represented in an organized way.

topographical organization In neuroanatomy, an arrangement whereby stimulus imputs from different parts of the body arrive at corresponding points in brain centers, such as the *cerebral cortex.*

TOTE Test, operate, test, exit; a theory of the sequence of events in recognition, where sensory input is compared to memory content and response (exit) follows recognition.

tract A bundle of axons carrying excitation from one part of the *CNS* to another.

tractus solitarious A *tract* of the brainstem, carrying *first-order* neurons from the receptors serving taste.

tranquilizer Any drug that reduces arousal (anxiety) without a major anesthetic effect.

transcortical association The concept that areas of the *cerebral cortex* are interconnected in learning without involving subcortical nuclei.

transducer A structure, living or nonliving, that transforms one form of energy into another; *receptors* are transducers because they transform physical energy into nerve impulses.

transected Cut completely through.

transfer RNA Ribonucleic acid, patterned by messenger RNA in the ribosomes, that assembles amino acids into the enzymes necessary for cell specialization and repair.

transitional cortex Areas of the cerebral cortex in the *longitudinal fissure* and elsewhere that are phylogenetically younger than *allocortex* but older than *neocortex.*

transmission deafness Defects in hearing caused by failure of the middle ear bones to conduct accurately the vibrations of the eardrum in response to sound to the *cochlea.*

transmit To pass through, as light is transmitted by a color filter.

trichromatism Normal or near-normal hue vision.

triplex color A color containing three elements of the *color formula*.

tritanomoly A weakness in the perception of yellow and green hues.

trophotropic Functions having to do with digestion, satiation, cell maintenance, and so on, controlled largely by the PNS centers of the *hypothalamus*.

tumor A mass of tissue formed by overproduction of cells in a specific location. Brain tumors are masses of tissue in the brain formed by overproduction of *glial cells*.

tuning fork A device, shaped like a two-tined fork, that produces a *simple tone* when struck.

turbinate bones Baffle-shaped formations in the nasal passages that cause eddy currents in inspired air.

two-phase hypothesis The hypothesis that learning occurs in two stages, immediate memory depending on *perseveration* of neural activity that lays down a permanent *engram (consolidation)*.

two-point threshold The closest together two points may be placed on the skin and still be distinguished as separate; used as an indicator of receptor density in the skin in testing sensitivity to pressure.

tympanum The eardrum; the membrane that closes off the inner end of the *external auditory meatus* and vibrates in response to the air pressure variations of sound.

type I CR Classical conditioning. The *CR* is similar to the *UR*, and training follows a procedure where the *US* always follows the *CS*, whether or not the *CR* occurs; e.g., training a dog to salivate to a bell (CS) by feeding him (US) each time the bell is rung.

type II CR Instrumental conditioning. The CR differs from the UR and is necessary to occurrence of the US; e.g., a rat learns to press a lever (CR) to obtain food (US).

unconditioned response (UR) A response reliably produced by an *unconditioned stimulus*.

unconditioned stimulus (US) A stimulus that reliably results in an *unconditioned response*.

unipolar neuron A nerve cell with both *axon* and *dendrite* arising from a single process of the *cell body*.

unique color One whose components cannot be visually detected (red, green, yellow, blue, black, white, and gray).

unique hues The four *chromatic primary qualities* of vision (red, green, yellow, and blue).

unspecialized nerve cell A sensory neuron whose receptor endings are an *anastomosis* of *free nerve ends*.

UR See *unconditioned response*.

urethra The output tube leading from the bladder to the *vagina* (female) or *penis* (male).

US See *unconditioned stimulus*.

uterus That part of the female reproductive apparatus in which the *embryo* develops.

utriculus A sensory apparatus of the *inner ear* that responds to head position and linear acceleration; see *sacculus*.

vacuum-tube amplifier An electronic device for amplifying voltage changes, including those detected in living tissue.

vagina Muscular tube that is penetrated in sexual intercourse and forms a passage between both the *uterus* and bladder and the external orifice.

vago-insulin Involving stimulation of *insulin* output from the pancreas by the *vagus nerve;* used in referring to the *PNS*.

vagus nerve Tenth *cranial nerve* that contains many fibers of the *autonomic nervous system*.

vascular Containing many blood vessels.

vasoconstrictor center A center in the *medulla* that excites constriction of arteries to raise blood pressure.

vasodilator center A center in the *medulla* that stimulates dilation of arteries to lower the blood pressure.

vasopressin A presumed hormone of the *neurohypophysis* (posterior pituitary gland) that raises the blood pressure by causing peripheral vasoconstriction.

veins Blood vessels that return blood from the tissues to the heart.

ventral Toward the front or "belly" side.

ventral cochlear nucleus One of two sensory nuclei of the acoustic branch of the *statoacoustic nerve* (see *dorsal cochlear nucleus*).

ventral columns The *ventral* extension of the central *gray matter* of the *spinal cord* on either side of the midline.

ventral corticospinal tract A tract of the *ventral funiculus* of the spinal cord that originates in the *motor projection area* and terminates near the *motor neurons* of the cord.

ventral funiculus The part of the peripheral *white matter* of the *spinal cord* that lies between the *ventral roots* and the midline on either side of the cord.

ventral horns See *ventral columns*.

ventral ramus In the spinal cord, the ventral branch of the paired spinal nerves that arises from the junction of the *dorsal* and *ventral roots* and carries sensory and motor fibers to the front, ventral, or anterior (in man) part of the body.

ventral root In the spinal cord, the *ventral* termination of the paired *spinal nerves* at the spinal cord.

ventral spinothalamic tract Fibers that originate

in the *spinal cord* form synapses with sensory fibers serving pressure, ascend the cord in the *ventral funiculus*, and join the *medial lemniscus* to end in the *thalamus*.

ventricle A larger hollow area inside the brain.

ventrolateral nucleus A nucleus of the *thalamus* that integrates somesthetic input and distributes it to the somesthetic projection area of the cerebral cortex.

ventromedial nucleus Paired *nuclei* of the hypothalamus that act as *satiation centers* to reduce eating behavior; destruction of these nuclei results in *hypothalamic hyperphagia*.

vertebra One of the individual jointed bones of the *vertebral column*.

vertebral column Jointed bony vertebrae (sing., *vertebra*) extending down the middorsal line of vertebrate animals, including man; the backbone.

vesicles Small globular inclusions, especially those in nerve endings at the *synapse* and *myoneural junction*, that are believed to contain a transmitter substance for exciting or inhibiting nerve and muscle cells.

vestibular nuclei Nuclei of the *vestibular* branch of the *statoacoustic nerve* (VIII), which excite extensor motoneurons and are inhibited by higher centers.

vestibular senses Sensory structures in the *labyrinth* of the *inner ear* that respond to head position and movement.

vestibular sensitivity Sensitivity to the balance, position, and movement receptors of the *inner ear*.

vestibulospinal tract A tract of the spinal cord that originates in the *vestibular nuclei* and ends on the extensor *motoneurons* of the cord.

vigilance A state of arousal.

villi Tufts of tissue in the *arachnoid layer* of the *meninges* extending into *dural sinuses* of the brain to reabsorb *cerebrospinal fluid* into the blood.

viscera Stomach, intestines, heart, bladder, arteries, and so on—the internal organs.

visceral Pertaining to the *viscera*.

visceral muscles Muscles that line the walls of the *viscera;* the arteries, stomach, intestines, heart, etc.

visible spectrum Light, the visible part of the *electromagnetic spectrum*.

vision Stimulation of the eye by light.

visual angle The angle subtended at the eye by light rays coming from an object.

visual projection area Area of the *cerebral cortex* that is the terminus of the nerve pathways for vision.

vitamin Any of a group of organic compounds whose accessory actions are necessary to the chemical reactions that support life.

vitamin D A *vitamin* that regulates calcium and phosphorus levels of the body.

vitreous humor The jellylike substance that fills the *fundus* of the eyeball.

volley theory A statement that the frequency of auditory nerve impulses follows the frequency of sound waves by means of nerve cells firing in alternation.

volt Amount of electrical charge (potential difference) that will result in a current of one ampere passing through a conductor with a resistance of one ohm.

volume The perceived size of a tone as a function of *pitch* and *loudness;* a measure of auditory *extent*.

wakefulness of choice The wakefulness of a *monophasic* sleep cycle that results from conditioning; a single waking period each day.

wakefulness of necessity Wakefulness resulting from bodily need or discomfort.

warmth An increase in temperature (molecular motion), especially as it stimulates the warm receptors to result in warm sensations.

wavelength The measured length of a complete cycle of change in a periodic (repeated) phenomenon, e.g., the wavelength of the pressure variation of a tone or of the *electromagnetic* spectrum of a given light *frequency*.

Weber's law The generalization that there is a constant relation between the increase in stimulus intensity required to reach the *difference threshold* and the stimulus intensity from which the increase originates ($\triangle I/I = C$).

white matter Parts of the CNS containing nerve *tracts* with many myelinated *axons* (see *myelin sheath*). The fatty myelin sheath covering on axons gives a whitish appearance to the tissue.

white muscles *Flexor muscles* specialized for rapid contraction, such as the breast muscles of birds.

white ramus The branch via which *preganglionic* axons of the SNS leave the *spinal nerves*.

work decrement Reduction in work output.

z line Krause's lines, connective tissue that invades *striate muscle* cells to divide each cell in segments.

Index

445